McDougal Littell

Teacher's Edition

MIDDLE GRADES

MATH*Thematics*®

SENIOR AUTHORS **Rick Billstein**
Jim Williamson

About the Teacher's Edition

This annotated Teacher's Edition provides Warm-Up Exercises
and Closure Questions for each section in the Student Edition—
all conveniently annotated at point of use. Answers to questions
within lessons and to Practice & Application Exercises are
annotated directly on the student pages. Answers that do not fit
on these pages appear in an Additional Answers section
beginning on page A1.

SUCCESS THROUGH EXPLORING MATHEMATICS
The
STEM
Project

BOOK

2

McDougal Littell

Evanston, Illinois • Boston • Dallas

AUTHORS

SENIOR AUTHORS

▶ **Rick Billstein**   Department of Mathematical Sciences, University of Montana, Missoula, Montana

▶ **Jim Williamson**   Department of Mathematical Sciences, University of Montana, Missoula, Montana

CONSULTING AUTHORS

▶ **Perry Montoya**   Teacher, Mesa Public Schools, Mesa, Arizona

▶ **Jacqueline Lowery**   Teacher, Indian Queen Elementary School, Fort Washington, Maryland

▶ **Dianne Williams**   Teacher, Booker T. Washington Middle School for International Studies, Tampa, Florida

THE STEM PROJECT   *Middle Grades Math Thematics®* is based on the field-test versions of The STEM Project curriculum. The STEM Project was supported in part by the

 NATIONAL SCIENCE FOUNDATION

under Grant No. ESI-9150114. Opinions expressed in *Middle Grades Math Thematics®* are those of the authors and not necessarily those of the National Science Foundation.

STEM WRITERS

Mary Buck, Clay Burkett, Lynn Churchill, Chris Clouse, Roslyn Denny, William Derrick, Sue Dolezal, Doug Galarus, Paul Kennedy, Pat Lamphere, Nancy Merrill, Perry Montoya, Sallie Morse, Marjorie Petit, Patrick Runkel, Thomas Sanders-Garrett, Richard T. Seitz, Bonnie Spence, Becky Sowders, Chris Tuckerman, Ken Wenger, Joanne Wilkie, Cheryl Wilson, Bente Winston

STEM TEACHER CONSULTANTS

Polly Fite, Jean Howard, Paul Sowden, Linda Tetley, Patricia Zepp

ABOUT THE COVER

The students shown on the back cover are from John Glenn Middle School in Maplewood, Minnesota.

ISBN 0-618-50170-3   X23456789–VH– 08 07 06 05 04   Teacher's Edition: ISBN 0-618-50168-1

MIDDLE GRADES
MATH Thematics

WELCOME

COURSE GOALS

This course will help you:

▶ Learn all the important middle grades mathematics concepts and skills that prepare you for high school and beyond.

▶ Develop the reasoning, problem solving, and communication skills that enable you to apply mathematics to real-life activities.

▶ Value mathematics and become confident in using it to make decisions in daily life.

SUCCESS THROUGH EXPLORING MATHEMATICS

Theme Approach
You will be learning through thematic modules that connect mathematical concepts to real-world applications.

Active Learning
The lessons in this course will get you actively involved in exploring, modeling, and communicating mathematics using a variety of tools, including technology when appropriate.

Varied Practice and Assessment
The variety of types of practice and assessment will help reinforce and extend your understanding. You will learn to assess your own progress as you go along.

MAKING CHOICES

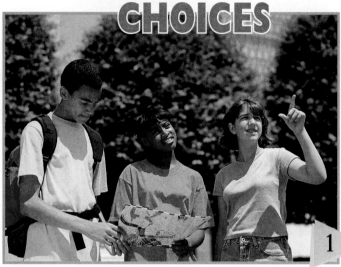

1

Connecting the Theme *Many real-world situations require people to make choices and decisions. You'll see how mathematics can help you analyze situations in your daily life and make wise decisions.*

SEARCH and RESCUE

MODULE 2

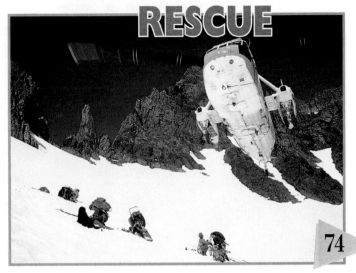

74

Connecting the Theme *When a hiker is lost, a plane goes down, or a boat is missing, a Search and Rescue team is called in to find them. You'll investigate some of the mathematics related to search and rescue operations.*

Module Features

Assessment Options

A UNIVERSAL LANGUAGE

146

Connecting the Theme *By exploring how mathematics has been used in other countries and in other times, you'll see why it is called "a universal language."*

MODULE **4**

The **ART** of **MOTION**

230

Connecting the Theme *One way that artists make their work look lifelike is to create a sense of motion. You'll see how mathematics can be used to add motion to art.*

MODULE 5

RECREATION

310

Connecting the Theme *People relax in many different ways, such as running, attending movies, and playing sports. You'll investigate some of the mathematics related to recreational activities.*

FLIGHTS of FANCY

MODULE 6

376 ▶

Connecting the Theme *In this module, you will explore the flight of humans, birds, kites, and even a whale! You'll construct models to interpret and solve problems.*

Module Features

MODULE PROJECT
Wild Wings, pp. 377, 408, 433, and 451

CAREER CONNECTION
Artist, p. 420

EXTENSION
The Sum of the Measures of the Angles of Any Polygon, p. 432
Traversable Networks, p. 449

Assessment Options

PORTFOLIO ASSESSMENT
  EXTENDED EXPLORATION (E²):
  Locating the Hub, p. 435
  REFLECTING ON THE SECTION:
  pp. 392, 407, 419, 431, and 448

ONGOING ASSESSMENT
  CHECKPOINTS: pp. 381, 384, 387, 396, 397, 398, 400, 403, 413, 416, 425, 428, 438, 440, 441, 443, and 444
  KEY CONCEPTS QUESTIONS:
  pp. 388, 389, 404, 405, 417, 429, 445, and 446
  STANDARDIZED TESTING:
  pp. 409, 421, 434, and 450

MODULE ASSESSMENT
  REVIEW AND ASSESSMENT:
  pp. 452 and 453
  REFLECTING ON THE MODULE:
  p. 453

MODULE 7

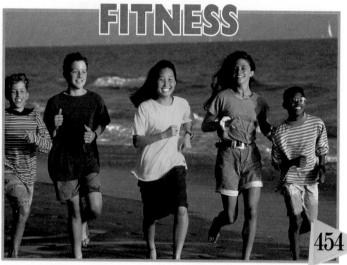

HEALTH and FITNESS

454

Connecting the Theme *People must make decisions about health issues every day. You'll learn how mathematics can help you make good health choices about nutrition, exercise, and adequate rest.*

HEART of the CITY

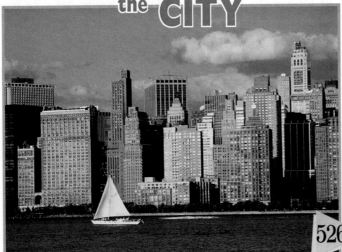

526

Connecting the Theme *Managing traffic, constructing sky-scrapers, and designing plazas all depend on mathematics. You'll see how mathematics can be used as a tool to help organize many aspects of city life.*

Module Features

MODULE PROJECT
Traffic Flow, pp. 527, 538, 561, and 577

CAREER CONNECTION
Computer Hardware Engineer, p. 537

TECHNOLOGY
Using Computer Drawing Software, p. 567

EXTENSION
Three-Dimensional Views, p. 550
Semi-Regular Tessellations, p. 575

Assessment Options

PORTFOLIO ASSESSMENT
EXTENDED EXPLORATION (E²):
Wrap It Up, p. 563
REFLECTING ON THE SECTION:
pp. 536, 550, 560, and 574

ONGOING ASSESSMENT
CHECKPOINTS: pp. 530, 533, 542, 546, 555, 557, 566, and 570
KEY CONCEPTS QUESTIONS: pp. 534, 547, 558, and 571
STANDARDIZED TESTING: pp. 551, 562, and 576

MODULE ASSESSMENT
REVIEW AND ASSESSMENT: pp. 578 and 579
REFLECTING ON THE MODULE: p. 579

ORGANIZATION OF THE BOOK

This book contains eight modules. To get an overview of the modules and their themes, look at the Table of Contents starting on p. iv.

THEME APPROACH

MODULES:
8 per book

MODULE **1**

MODULE **2**

MODULE **3**

MODULE **4**

MODULE **5**

MODULE **6**

MODULE **7**

MODULE **8**

SECTIONS:
4–6 per module

Section ①
Section ②
Section ③
Section ④

EXPLORATIONS:
1–3 per section

Exploration 1
Exploration 2
Exploration 3

PRACTICE:
for each exploration

Practice & Application Exercises

MODULE THEME & PROJECT

Each module's theme connects the mathematics you are learning to the real world. *Recreation* is the theme of Module 5. The Module Project that you'll work on is introduced at the beginning of the module.

Connecting Mathematics and the Theme
The math topics you'll be learning and the settings in which you'll be learning them.

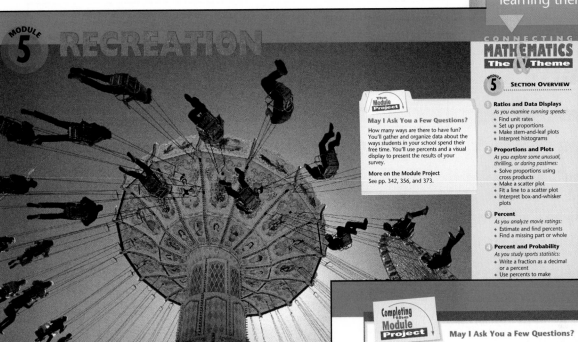

MODULE
5
RECREATION

The Module Project

May I Ask You a Few Questions?

How many ways are there to have fun? You'll gather and organize data about the ways students in your school spend their free time. You'll use percents and a visual display to present the results of your survey.

More on the Module Project
See pp. 342, 356, and 373.

CONNECTING
MATHEMATICS
The & Theme

5 **SECTION OVERVIEW**

1 **Ratios and Data Displays**
As you examine running speeds:
  ◆ Find unit rates
  ◆ Set up proportions
  ◆ Make stem-and-leaf plots
  ◆ Interpret histograms

2 **Proportions and Plots**
As you explore some unusual, thrilling, or daring pastimes:
  ◆ Solve proportions using cross products
  ◆ Make a scatter plot
  ◆ Fit a line to a scatter plot
  ◆ Interpret box-and-whisker plots

3 **Percent**
As you analyze movie ratings:
  ◆ Estimate and find percents
  ◆ Find a missing part or whole

4 **Percent and Probability**
As you study sports statistics:
  ◆ Write a fraction as a decimal or a percent
  ◆ Use percents to make

The Module Project

As you learn new math skills, you can apply them to your work on the Module Project. By the end of the module, you'll be able to complete the project and to present your results.

Completing the Module Project

May I Ask You a Few Questions?

You have gathered and organized data about the free time of students in your school. In order for your survey to be useful, you must now share your findings. In this module you have learned several ways to present data.

Choosing a Data Display Many magazines and newspapers display survey results in bar graphs, line plots, histograms, or tables. Often the data is in percent form. But no matter the form, the visual display of the data must be clear and informative.

7 Summarize your class survey data in a table. Present the data using fractions, decimals, and percents.

8 Make a general statement about the results shown in the table that you made in Project Question 7. Does the statement answer the topic question? Explain.

9 Decide what type of visual display, other than a table, would best organize your data. Create your display. Be sure to include a title.

10 Explain your choice of visual display in Project Question 9. Why do you think your choice is a good way to show the data? Does it answer the topic question as well as the table you created in Project Question 7? Why or why not?

11 If you were to organize another survey, what topic would you research? What would you do differently?

**ACTIVE
LEARNING**

SECTION ORGANIZATION

The diagram below illustrates the organization of a section:

Section ④

Setting the Stage	Exploration 1		
Exploration 2	Key Concepts	Practice & Application Exercises
Exploration 3		

Motivate   **Explore**   **Summarize**   **Practice**

Section ④ **Percent and Probability**

IN THIS SECTION
EXPLORATION 1
◆ Fractions, Decimals, and Percents
EXPLORATION 2
◆ Predicting Using Percents
EXPLORATION 3
◆ Multi-stage Experiments

Make Every Shot Count

Section Title and Math Focus
The title of Section 4 is *Make Every Shot Count*. Its math focus is *Percent and Probability*.

···Setting the Stage

Setting the Stage
begins with a reading, graph, activity, or game to introduce the section.

In 1996, over 127,000 cheerin...
tour of the USA Women's Nat...
"Dream Team" lived up to its...
against some of the nation's b...
scored an average of 96.4 poi...
average of 46.2 points! The te...
record for foul shots, called *fre*...
top five free-throw shooters are shown below.

The "Dream Team" was coached by Tara VanDerveer, shown above. Coaches usually choose the best free-throw shooter to attempt the free throw on a technical foul.

PLAYERS	FREE THROWS MADE (FTM)	FREE THROWS ATTEMPTED (FTA)
Sheryl Swoopes	27	33
Jennifer Azzi	58	64
Nikki McCray	28	35
Katy Steding	50	60
Teresa Edwards	13	15

Think About It

1 Suppose there are three seconds left on the clock and the score is tied when a technical foul is called on the other team. If you were head coach Tara VanDerveer, which player would you choose to attempt the free throw? Why?

2 Suppose a player made 1 free throw out of 1 attempt. Would that player be the best choice for the free throw? Why?

 Module 5 Recreation

EXPLORATIONS & KEY CONCEPTS

In the explorations you'll be actively involved in investigating math concepts, learning math skills, and solving problems.

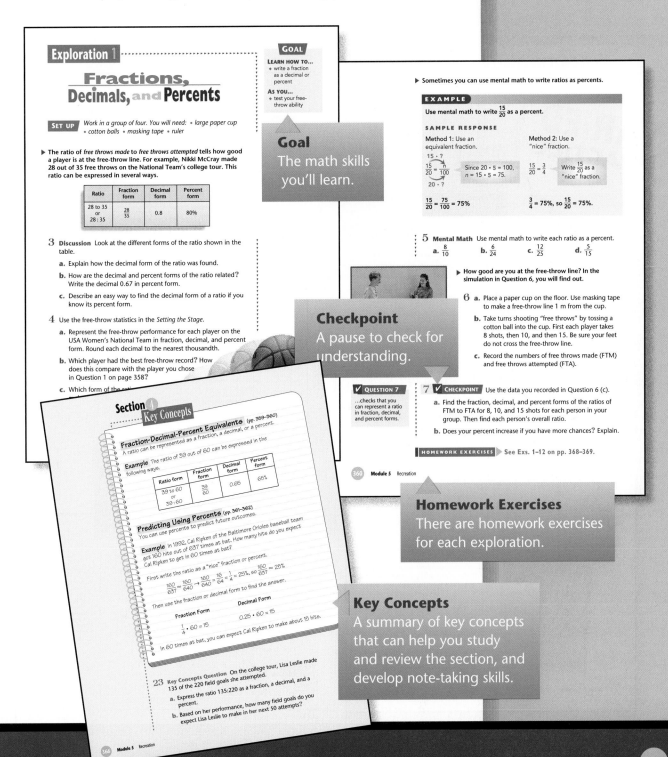

Exploration 1

Fractions, Decimals, and Percents

SET UP Work in a group of four. You will need: • *large paper cup* • *cotton balls* • *masking tape* • *ruler*

▶ The ratio of *free throws made* to *free throws attempted* tells how good a player is at the free-throw line. For example, Nikki McCray made 28 out of 35 free throws on the National Team's college tour. This ratio can be expressed in several ways.

Ratio	Fraction form	Decimal form	Percent form
28 to 35 or 28 : 35	$\frac{28}{35}$	0.8	80%

3 **Discussion** Look at the different forms of the ratio shown in the table.

 a. Explain how the decimal form of the ratio was found.

 b. How are the decimal and percent forms of the ratio related? Write the decimal 0.67 in percent form.

 c. Describe an easy way to find the decimal form of a ratio if you know its percent form.

4 Use the free-throw statistics in the *Setting the Stage*.

 a. Represent the free-throw performance for each player on the USA Women's National Team in fraction, decimal, and percent form. Round each decimal to the nearest thousandth.

 b. Which player had the best free-throw record? How does this compare with the player you chose in Question 1 on page 358?

 c. Which form of the rati...

GOAL

LEARN HOW TO...
 ◆ write a fraction as a decimal or percent

AS YOU...
 ◆ test your free-throw ability

Goal
The math skills you'll learn.

Checkpoint
A pause to check for understanding.

▶ Sometimes you can use mental math to write ratios as percents.

EXAMPLE

Use mental math to write $\frac{15}{20}$ as a percent.

SAMPLE RESPONSE

Method 1: Use an equivalent fraction.

$\frac{15}{20} = \frac{n}{100}$ Since 20 • 5 = 100, $n = 15 • 5 = 75$.

$\frac{15}{20} = \frac{75}{100} = 75\%$

Method 2: Use a "nice" fraction.

$\frac{15}{20} = \frac{3}{4}$ Write $\frac{15}{20}$ as a "nice" fraction.

$\frac{3}{4} = 75\%$, so $\frac{15}{20} = 75\%$.

5 **Mental Math** Use mental math to write each ratio as a percent.
 a. $\frac{8}{10}$ **b.** $\frac{6}{24}$ **c.** $\frac{12}{25}$ **d.** $\frac{5}{15}$

▶ How good are you at the free-throw line? In the simulation in Question 6, you will find out.

6 **a.** Place a paper cup on the floor. Use masking tape to make a free-throw line 1 m from the cup.

 b. Take turns shooting "free throws" by tossing a cotton ball into the cup. First each player takes 8 shots, then 10, and then 15. Be sure your feet do not cross the free-throw line.

 c. Record the numbers of free throws made (FTM) and free throws attempted (FTA).

✓ QUESTION 7

...checks that you can represent a ratio in fraction, decimal, and percent forms.

7 **✓ CHECKPOINT** Use the data you recorded in Question 6 (c).

 a. Find the fraction, decimal, and percent forms of the ratios of FTM to FTA for 8, 10, and 15 shots for each person in your group. Then find each person's overall ratio.

 b. Does your percent increase if you have more chances? Explain.

HOMEWORK EXERCISES ▶ See Exs. 1–12 on pp. 368–369.

Homework Exercises
There are homework exercises for each exploration.

Section 1
Key Concepts

Fraction-Decimal-Percent Equivalents (pp. 359–360)
A ratio can be represented as a fraction, a decimal, or a percent.

Example The ratio of 39 out of 60 can be expressed in the following ways.

Ratio form	Fraction form	Decimal form	Percent form
39 to 60 or 39 : 60	$\frac{39}{60}$	0.65	65%

Predicting Using Percents (pp. 361–362)
You can use percents to predict future outcomes.

Example In 1992, Cal Ripken of the Baltimore Orioles baseball team got 160 hits out of 637 times at bat. How many hits do you expect Cal Ripken to get in 60 times at bat?

First write the ratio as a "nice" fraction or percent.

$\frac{160}{637} \approx \frac{160}{640} \to \frac{160}{640} = \frac{16}{64} = \frac{1}{4} = 25\%$, so $\frac{160}{637} \approx 25\%$

Then use the fraction or decimal form to find the answer.

Fraction Form	Decimal Form
$\frac{1}{4} • 60 = 15$	0.25 • 60 = 15

In 60 times at bat, you can expect Cal Ripken to make about 15 hits.

23 **Key Concepts Question** On the college tour, Lisa Leslie made 135 of the 220 field goals she attempted.

 a. Express the ratio 135 : 220 as a fraction, a decimal, and a percent.

 b. Based on her performance, how many field goals do you expect Lisa Leslie to make in her next 50 attempts?

Key Concepts
A summary of key concepts that can help you study and review the section, and develop note-taking skills.

PRACTICE & APPLICATION

Practice and Application Exercises will give you a chance to practice the skills and concepts in the explorations and apply them in solving many types of problems.

VARIED PRACTICE

Balanced Practice
These exercises develop numerical and problem solving skills, and the ability to write about and discuss mathematics.

Consider the experiment of flipping a coin and rolling an 8-sided die. Shade a grid to find the probability of each event.

18. heads and the number 6
19. tails and a number less than 4
20. tails and an odd number
21. heads and a number greater than 2

22. Suppose this spinner is spun twice.

   a. **Writing** Which of the grids below could you shade to find the probability that the first spin will be red and the second spin will be blue? Explain.

   A. 10 × 10 grid   B. 3 × 3 grid   C. 3 × 6 grid

   b. Copy the grid you chose in part (a). Shade it to find the probability that the first spin is red and the second is blue.

23. A box contains two red and three blue marbles. Three marbles are removed from the box one after another without looking. After each marble is removed, its color is recorded and the marble is put back into the box before the next marble is removed.

   a. Copy and complete this tree diagram to show the outcomes of this experiment. Label each branch of the tree with the probability.

first marble
R
B

   b. Use the tree diagram to find the probability of each event.

    • removing three red marbles

Section ④
Practice & Application Exercises

1. **Basketball** In the 1996 NCAA women's college basketball championship game, Tennessee beat Georgia 83 to 65. The table shows some of the field-goal statistics for four Tennessee players from that game. Represent each player's field-goal performance in fraction, decimal, and percent forms. Round each decimal to the nearest thousandth.

Player	Field goals made	Field goals attempted
Goldsclaw	6	16
Conklin	5	8
Marciniak	5	13
T. Johnson	7	10

Baseball A player's batting average is the decimal form of the ratio of *number of hits* to *times at bat* rounded to the nearest thousandth.

Find the 1992 batting average for each player.

2. David Justice (Braves): 124 for 484

3. Barry Larkin (Reds): 162 for 533

4. Frank Thomas (White Sox): 185 for 573

5. Bip Roberts of the Cincinnati Reds and Jon Kruk of the Philadelphia Phillies both had .323 batting averages in 1992, which were high enough for third and fourth place in the National League batting average race. Roberts had 172 hits in 532 times at bat. Kruk had 164 hits in 507 times at bat. Which player was in third place? How did you find your answer?

Luis Ulacia is shown rounding third base after hitting a home run in the first inning of the game against the United States. ▼

6. **Olympics** On July 28, 1996, the United States Olympic baseball team lost to the defending Olympic championship team from Cuba by a score of 10–8. Find the batting average for each player in the game whose batting results are shown in the table. Represent each average in fraction, decimal, and percent form.

Player	Hits	Times at bat
Ulacia (Cuba)	2	5
Paret (Cuba)	1	3
Lee (U.S.A.)	3	4
Glaus (U.S.A.)	1	4

Reflecting on the Section
helps you pull together what you've learned in the form of an oral report, journal writing, visual thinking, research, or a discussion.

24. **Challenge** Suppose three marbles are removed from the box in Exercise 23 one after another, but each marble is not replaced before the next marble is removed. Repeat parts (a) and (b) of Exercise 23 for this experiment.

Reflecting ▶ on the Section

25. During her previous basketball games this season, Alyssa made 20 free throws in 40 attempts. She calculated her free-throw percent to be 50%. In today's game, she made 10 free throws out of 10 attempts, or 100%. Alyssa thinks her free-throw percent is now 75%. Is she correct? Explain.

Journal
Exercise 25 checks that you understand how to use percent to make predictions.

Spiral ▶ Review

Solve each proportion. (Module 5, p. 352)

26. $\frac{18}{12} = \frac{24}{x}$　　27. $\frac{3}{13} = \frac{x}{325}$　　28. $\frac{x}{100} = \frac{4}{5}$　　29. $\frac{5}{x} = \frac{2}{20}$

ADDITIONAL PRACTICE

At the end of every section, you'll find Extra Skill Practice. You can use these exercises to check that you understand important skills before starting the next section.

Section 4
Extra Skill Practice

Write each ratio as a fraction, a decimal, and a percent.

1. 1:3
2. 15:30
3. 16:20
4. 7:25
5. 12:18
6. 23:100
7. 4.5:10
8. 21:28
9. 14:64

Use mental math to write each fraction as a percent.

10. $\frac{111}{334}$
11. $\frac{13}{25}$
12. $\frac{9}{26}$
13. $\frac{2}{9}$
14. $\frac{7}{20}$
15. $\frac{20}{27}$
17. $\frac{9.5}{50}$
18. $\frac{6}{21}$

...se the probability that it will rain is $\frac{5}{7}$ each day for two ...utive days.

...at is the probability that it will not rain on a given day?

...ke a tree diagram to find all the possible outcomes of rain ...two consecutive days.

...a grid to show the probability of rain on two ...secutive days.

...at is the probability that it will rain one day and will *not* rain ...next day?

Standardized Testing ▶ Multiple Choice

1. Choose the letter(s) of the ratio(s) that is (are) *not* equivalent to 13.5%.

   A 0.135   B $\frac{5}{37}$ C 13.5 : 100   D $\frac{6}{36}$

2. A paper bag contains 4 plums and 12 nectarines. Without looking, Frida reaches into the bag and pulls out the first fruit she touches, which happens to be a plum. Then Pat takes a fruit from the bag in the same way. What is the probability that she will also get a plum?

   A $\frac{1}{16}$ B 25%   C $\frac{3}{16}$ D 20%

Standardized Testing

develops your ability to answer questions in different formats: multiple-choice, open-ended, free response, and performance task.

Spiral ▶ Review

Evaluate each expression when $a = -32$, $b = 4$, and $c = 6$.
(Module 2, p. 124)

47. $b - 3$
48. $3c - 27$
49. $2a + 5$
50. $2b + 15$
51. $a + c$
52. $a - 4b$

53. Susan and Claire worked a total of 20 hours. Susan earn... per hour. Claire earned $7.00 per hour. Together they e... $148.00 over the weekend. How many hours did Claire ... Tell what problem solving strategy you used. (Module 1, ...

Tell whether each number is divisible by 2, 5, and 10.
(Toolbox, p. 582)

54. 75   55. 215   56. 253   57. 630

Extension ▶▶

Equations with Variables on Both Sides

In this Section, the equations you solved had a variable on only one side of the equals sign. You can apply the ideas you learned to solve equations that have variables on both sides of the equals sign.

Describe how you would solve each equation modeled below.

58. $n + 1 = 2n$

59. $n + 6 = 2 + 2n$

60. $2n + 3 = 3n$

61. $n + 5 = 3 + 2n$

62. Solve each equation in Exercises 58–61 algebraically. Check each solution.

63. a. Does the equation $x + 35 = x + 13$ have a solution? Explain.

   b. Does the equation $x + 4 = 4 + x$ have a solution? Explain.

Extension

problems challenge you to extend what you have learned and to apply it in a new setting.

xvii

CALCULATORS & COMPUTERS

There are many opportunities to use calculators, as well as mental-math and paper-and-pencil methods. Special Technology pages show you how to use computer programs to explore concepts and solve problems in the module.

TOOLS FOR LEARNING

Using Calculators

Calculators can be especially useful as a problem solving tool. The questions on this page help make calculator use meaningful.

GOAL

LEARN HOW TO...
◆ multiply and divide decimals by powers of 10
◆ write numbers in scientific notation

AS YOU...
◆ look at calculator displays

KEY TERM
◆ scientific notation

Exploration 3

Scientific Notation

SET UP You will need: • Labsheet 4B
• calculator

▶ The number of digits a calculator can display is limited, but calculations with large (or small) numbers are still possible. A universal method is used to represent large and small numbers.

23 Try This as a Class For parts (a) and (b), describe how the results are displayed on a calculator as the steps are carried out.

a. Clear the calculator and then enter 10. Multiply by 10 and look at the result. Continue multiplying by 10 and looking at the result at least 20 times.

b. Clear the calculator and then enter 10. Divide by 10 and look at the result. Continue dividing by 10 and looking at the result at least 20 times.

c. What did the calculator display after completing part (a)? part (b)? Why does this happen?

24 Discussion Most calculators have a special way to display large and small numbers. Three displays for the same number are shown.

| 1E15 | 1e+15 | 1   15 |

hat number is represented by the displays?

rite this number in standard form.

hy is the number not displayed in standard form?

nd Quotients with Powers of 10 Suppose a calculator
3456e+13. This is the same as $1.23456 \cdot 10^{13}$, a decimal
ltiplied by a power of ten.

et 4B for Questions 25 and 26.

w the directions on Labsheet 4B to complete the *Product Table*.

TECHNOLOGY Using Spreadsheet Software

You can use most spreadsheets to create a bar graph for Question 16(a).

Step 1 Enter the data for the graph into the spreadsheet. The categories for the bars (the amounts of time in hours) should be entered in column A as text. The data for the lengths of the bars (the average mathematics proficiencies) should be entered in column B.

File Edit Format Calculate Options View

AVERAGE MATH PROFICIENCY

	A	B	C	D	E	F
1	Time (hours)	Average math proficiency				
2	1 or less	269				
3	2	268				
4	3	265				
5	4 or 5	260				
6	6 or more	245				

Step 2 To make a graph, highlight the data you entered and select the option that lets you make a chart. Then select the type of graph you want to make.

Options
Make Chart...
Protect Cells
Unprotect Cells
Add Page Break
Remove Page Break
Lock Title Position
Print Range...
Go To Cell...

Chart Options
Modify-
Axis
Series
Labels
General
Gallery-
Bar   Line   Scatter   Pie
Stacked   X-Y   X-Y   Pictogram
Bar   Line   Scatter

Step 3 Experiment with the labels, grid lines, and scale until the graph appears the way you want it to.

Eighth Grade Students' Television Viewing and Math Proficiency

Using Computers

Technology pages illustrate the use of spreadsheet, graphing, statistical, probability, and drawing software.

ASSESSMENT & PORTFOLIOS

In each module there are a number of questions and projects that help you check your progress and reflect on what you have learned. These pages are listed under *Assessment Options* in the Table of Contents.

E^2 stands for Extended Exploration— a problem solving project that you'll want to add to your portfolio.

Student Self-Assessment

EXTENDED E² EXPLORATION

FOR ASSESSMENT AND PORTFOLIOS

Wrap It Up

SET UP *You will need:* • paper bag • scissors • tape or glue • ruler

The Situation

Many of the products we buy in stores come in boxes. The shapes of boxes are chosen for various reasons, such as shelf size or ease of handling. Package designers must also think about the amount of material used to create them. Reducing the total area of the outside surface of the box is a major factor in any package design.

The Problem

What is the biggest box that can be wrapped using a paper bag?

Something to Think About

• What kind of space figure is a box?

• How can making a net help you solve the problem?

• What measure(s) do you need to maximize in order to produce the biggest box?

• Is there any other information you need to obtain before you can begin working on this problem? If so, what is it?

Present Your Results

Give an oral report describing how you created your box design. Include the volume and the surface area of the box. Be sure to display your net and the b[...]

Assessing Problem Solving

For each E^2, you can use the Student Self-Assessment Scales. They will help you become a better problem solver.

MODULE 5 Review and Assessment

Module Review and Assessment

Each module ends with exercises to help you review and assess what you've learned.

Write each rate as a unit rate. (Sec. 1, Explor. 1)

1. $\frac{95 \text{ min}}{11 \text{ mi}}$
2. $\frac{\$15}{4 \text{ lb}}$
3. $\frac{86 \text{ mi}}{3 \text{ gal}}$
4. $\frac{250 \text{ km}}{16 \text{ L}}$

Use the table for Exercises 5–7. (Sec. 1, Explor. 2)

5. Make a stem-and-leaf plot of the data. Be sure to include a key and a title.

6. Find the range, the mean, the median, and the mode for the data.

7. Colorado has about 160,000 acres of state parkland. Suppose you include Colorado in the list. How would your stem-and-leaf plot change?

Use the histogram for Exercises 8–10. (Sec. 1, Explor. 3)

Areas of State Parks in 10 States (In thousands)	
State	**Acres (in thousands)**
Alabama	48
Arkansas	45
Georgia	60
Hawaii	25
Idaho	44
Kansas	37
Maine	72
Montana	47
Rhode Island	8
Virginia	50

MODULE
1 **SECTION OVERVIEW**

1 Data Displays

As you consider Olympic athletes' decisions:

◆ Interpret bar and line graphs
◆ Make frequency tables

2 Sequences and Exponents

As you find patterns and use them to make predictions:

◆ Represent sequences with graphs and equations
◆ Predict terms of sequences
◆ Use exponents in expressions
◆ Find the volume of a cube

3 Probability

As you decide on a game strategy:

◆ Find theoretical and experimental probabilities of events

4 Problem Solving

As you predict the effect of lifestyle changes on health:

◆ Solve problems using a 4-step approach

5 Assessing Problem Solving

As you explore how to become a more creative problem solver:

◆ Evaluate solutions and make connections to other problems

6 Expressions and Representations

As you think about ways to improve your mathematical language skills:

◆ Use the order of operations to evaluate expressions
◆ Choose a bar or a line graph

The Module Project

Tune In to Data

How do television advertisers try to influence your choice? You'll collect data to research this question. For a presentation of what you have learned, you'll choose appropriate representations for your data.

More on the Module Project
See pp. 11, 38, 46, 69, and 71.

INTERNET
To learn more about the theme:
http://www.mlmath.com

1

Section 1   Data Displays

IN THIS SECTION

EXPLORATION 1
 ◆ Bar and Line Graphs

EXPLORATION 2
 ◆ Tallying Data

Going for the GOLD

◄‑‑‑*Setting the Stage*

Did you ever dream of winning an Olympic gold medal? Earning a spot on an Olympic team requires more than skill and a love of the sport.

A newspaper surveyed the 1994 United States Winter Olympics team about what they gave up for their sport. The graph shows the results.

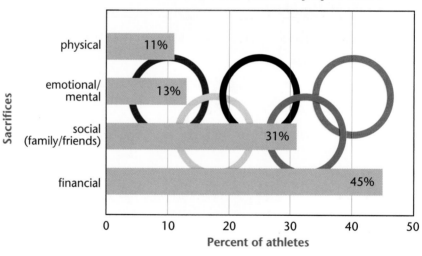

The Greatest Sacrifices for 114 Athletes on the 1994 U.S. Winter Olympics Team

physical — 11%
emotional/mental — 13%
social (family/friends) — 31%
financial — 45%

Sacrifices

Percent of athletes

▲
"What's vacation? Between skiing and school, I don't get too much time for it."
—Nikki Stone, freestyle skier

Think About It

1 What did most athletes feel was their greatest sacrifice? financial

2 The bar for athletes whose sacrifice was financial is about how many times as long as the bar for those who said it was physical?
about 4 times

▶ **Like athletes, you must make choices in situations you meet every day. In this module, you'll learn skills to help you make wise decisions.**

BAR and Line GRAPHS

GOAL

LEARN HOW TO...
- interpret data in percent form
- interpret bar and line graphs

AS YOU...
- explore data about the Olympics and education

KEY TERMS
- bar graph
- vertical axis
- percent
- horizontal axis
- line graph
- interval

Some of the choices you have in life are minor ones: *What should I wear today?* Others will be more important: *What classes should I take?* And some will even affect your well-being: *Is it okay for me to smoke?*

▸ **When you make a decision, you need information about the choices. Sometimes this information comes in the form of a bar graph, which displays data that fall into distinct categories.**

Use the bar graph on page 2 for Questions 3–7.

3 Every graph should have a title.

  a. Who was surveyed? **114 athletes on the 1994 U.S. Winter Olympics team**

  b. What information is displayed in the graph? **the athletes' greatest sacrifices**

4 Graphs should be clearly labeled. The categories for this bar graph appear along the **vertical axis**. What does the label "Financial" mean? **Sample Response: having to do with money**

▸ **The symbol % on the bar graph stands for *percent*. Percent means "per hundred" or "out of 100."**

> 45%
> 45 percent
> 45 per 100
> 45 out of 100

5 The **horizontal axis** of the bar graph is labeled with a scale of numbers. What do the numbers on this graph represent?

FOR▸HELP

with *percent*, see **TOOLBOX, p. 588**

5. the percent of athletes considering a particular sacrifice their greatest sacrifice

6 **Try This as a Class** Use the concept of percent.

  a. How many athletes responded to the survey? **114**

  b. Does 45% mean 45 athletes in this survey? Explain.

  c. In this survey, is 31% of the athletes *more than* or *less than* 31 athletes? Explain. **More than; Since 31% means 31 out of 100 and since more than 100 athletes were interviewed, 31% is more than 31 in this instance.**

6. b. No; Since 45% means 45 out of 100 and since more than 100 athletes were interviewed, 45% means more than 45 in this instance.

7 ✔ **CHECKPOINT** Compare the bars for two categories of the graph that you did not already compare. What does your comparison tell you about sacrifices made by the athletes surveyed? **Sample Response: The bar for social sacrifice is about 2.5 times as long as the bar for emotional/mental sacrifice; The number of athletes who felt their greatest sacrifice was social was about 2.5 times the number who thought it was emotional/mental.**

✔ **QUESTION 7**

...checks that you can interpret a bar graph with data in percent form.

▶ **Interpreting Line Graphs** A line graph is often used to display data that change over time. A double line graph can help you compare two sets of data. For Questions 8–12, use the graph below, which shows one result of a choice about education.

vertical scale

The scale is marked in equal-sized intervals.

horizontal scale

8 What information is displayed in the double line graph?
Sample Response: the average salaries of high school graduates and college graduates from 1978 to 1994

▶ Each step between grid lines on a scale is an **interval**. The horizontal and vertical axes are marked with different scales.

9 What is represented by each interval on the vertical scale? $5000

10 a. In about what year was the average salary of workers with a bachelor's degree $25,000? 1985

b. Estimate the average salary of workers with a high school diploma in 1990. about $18,000

11 What decisions might someone studying this graph be trying to make? Sample Response: whether or not to go to college

12. a. Sample Response: The average salary of both groups increases, but the salary of the bachelor's degree group shows a greater and faster increase.

...checks that you can interpret a line graph.

12 ✔ **CHECKPOINT** Think about the two groups of people represented in the graph.

a. How have annual salaries changed over time for each group?

b. How has the difference in average salaries between these two groups changed over time?
Sample Response: The difference becomes greater as time goes on.

HOMEWORK EXERCISES ▶ See Exs. 1–15 on pp. 8–9.

Exploration 2

Tallying **DATA**

SET UP *You will need:* • *Labsheet 1A* • *ruler*

GOAL

LEARN HOW TO...
◆ make a frequency table

AS YOU...
◆ gather and analyze data about time spent on homework

KEY TERMS
◆ frequency table
◆ frequency

▶ To "go for the gold" in school as well as in sports requires time for practice. An important decision you'll make this year is how much time to spend on homework each day.

13 Choose the letter of the phrase that best represents the amount of time you spent doing homework each day last year for all subjects. *Answers will vary.*

   A. did not usually have homework

   B. did not do assignments

   C. one half hour or less

   D. one hour

   E. two hours

   F. more than two hours

▶ You can use a **frequency table** like the one shown below to collect your classmates' answers to Question 13.

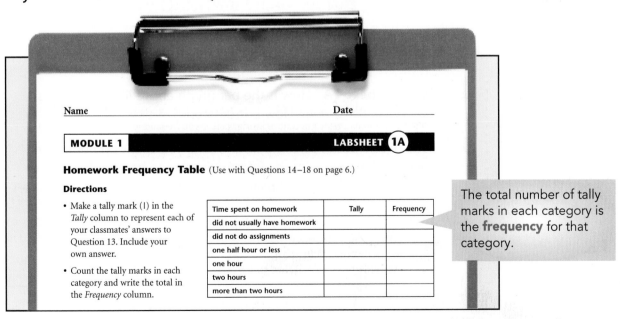

Name _____ Date _____

| MODULE 1 | LABSHEET **1A** |

Homework Frequency Table (Use with Questions 14–18 on page 6.)

Directions

• Make a tally mark (|) in the *Tally* column to represent each of your classmates' answers to Question 13. Include your own answer.

• Count the tally marks in each category and write the total in the *Frequency* column.

Time spent on homework	Tally	Frequency
did not usually have homework		
did not do assignments		
one half hour or less		
one hour		
two hours		
more than two hours		

The total number of tally marks in each category is the **frequency** for that category.

QUESTION 14

...checks that you can complete a frequency table.

14 ✔ **CHECKPOINT** Record each of your classmates' answers to Question 13 in the *Homework Frequency Table*. Answers will vary. Check student's work.

15 Use the data in the *Homework Frequency Table* to complete the *Homework Bar Graph*. Answers will vary. Check student's graphs.

FOR ▶ HELP

with *making a bar graph*, see **TOOLBOX, p. 594**

16 How did you choose the scale for the horizontal axis of the *Homework Bar Graph*? Sample Response: There were enough spaces to let each space represent one person.

17 How can you find the most frequent answer to Question 13 from the *Homework Frequency Table*? from the *Homework Bar Graph*? Find the greatest number of tally marks; Find the longest bar.

▶ **Comparing Bar Graphs** Before you decide how much time to spend on homework, it might help to compare the bar graph you made in Question 15 with a graph based on a national survey.

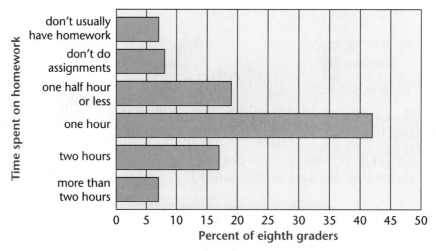

Total Time Eighth Graders Spent on Homework Each Day

18 **Use Labsheet 1A.** How is the bar graph above like your class's *Homework Bar Graph*? How is it different? Sample Response: The one hour bar is the longest; Percent of students is given instead of number of students.

19 Would it be better to compare the time you spent on homework each day last year with the information in the bar graph above or with your class's data? Explain your choice. Sample Response: my class's data; I don't know how many people were in the national survey or where they were from.

20 **Discussion** What other information would you want to have to help you decide how much time you should spend on homework? Why? Sample Response: the average grades of people in each category; to see if grades increase as time spent on homework increases

HOMEWORK EXERCISES ▶ See Exs. 16–21 on pp. 9–10.

Section 1
Key Concepts

Key Terms

Analyzing Bar and Line Graphs (pp. 2–4)

To make good choices, you need information. A bar graph displays data that fall into distinct categories. A line graph can show how data change over time.

bar graph

line graph

Example

The graph shows the percent of U.S. residents (the number of people per 100) who were 10 to 14 years old as of April 1 of each year.

> Every graph should have a title.

percent

Percent of U.S. Population 10 to 14 Years Old

> The scale along the vertical axis goes from 0% to 12%.

vertical axis

horizontal axis

> The horizontal axis is divided into 10-year intervals.

interval

Using Frequency Tables (pp. 5–6)

Frequency tables show how often each data item occurs.

frequency

Example

The frequency table and the bar graph show participation in the Vermont Youth Conservation Corps in 1992.

frequency table

Age	Tally	Frequency
17	III	3
18	JHT II	7
19	JHT JHT	10
20	JHT I	6
21	II	2

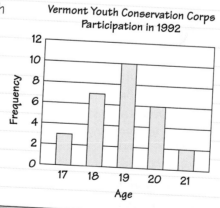

Vermont Youth Conservation Corps Participation in 1992

CLOSURE QUESTION

Describe what line graphs, bar graphs, and frequency tables show.

Line graphs show how data change over time, bar graphs show data that fall into distinct categories, and a frequency table shows how often data items occur.

21 **Key Concepts Question** For each graph above, state one fact that you can learn from the graph. Sample Response: The percent of U.S. residents who were 10 to 14 years old decreased between 1890 and 1950; The most common age for people who participated in the Vermont Youth Conservation Corps in 1992 was 19 years old.

YOU WILL NEED

For Exs. 28–30:
♦ graph paper

Baseball Cards Use the line graph below for Exercises 1–5.

Willie Mays excelled at all aspects of baseball. He hit 660 home runs, set stolen base records, and made a spectacular catch in the 1954 World Series.

WILLIE MAYS `51`
Outfield—New York Giants
Born: Fairfield, Ala. (Age 20)
Height: 5-11   Weight: 170
Bats: Right   Throws: Right
Signed by the Giants after graduating from high school in June 1950. Placed with their Trenton farm team. Appeared in 81 games, batting .353. Sent to the Minneapolis Millers of the American Association for the 1951 campaign. Willie was compiling an amazing record for the Millers when the Giants called him up. In the line-up for 35 games, he had batted a sensational .477.
No. 305 in the 1951 SERIES
BASEBALL PICTURE CARDS
©1951 Bowman Gum, Inc., Phila., Pa., U.S.A.

Price of a Willie Mays 1951 Bowman Rookie Card in Mint Condition

1. Estimate the price of a Willie Mays card in 1988. about $1300

2. In which year do you think the price of a Willie Mays card was about $2500? 1991

3. Estimate the price of a Willie Mays card in 1995. Explain how you arrived at your answer. about $4500; I extended the graph.

4. **Open-ended** Write a question of your own that can be answered by the information in the graph. Sample Response: How much did the value of the card increase between 1989 and 1993?

5. **Writing** Suppose an investor is deciding whether to buy a Willie Mays 1951 Bowman rookie card in mint condition. What are two facts about the history of its price from 1979 to 1993 that may affect the investor's decision? Sample Response: Why did the price increase slightly and then hold steady between 1979 and 1985? Why did the price increase between 1985 and 1993?

Estimation For each group of people surveyed, tell whether 23% of the group is *more than, less than,* or *equal to* 23 people.

6. 200 students more than

7. 75 pilots less than

8. 84 moviegoers less than

9. 570 dancers more than

10. 100 runners equal to

11. 23 writers less than

Job Changes The double bar graph displays some results of a survey that included 1053 people in Japan and 1002 people in the United States. Use the graph for Exercises 12–15.

12. What information is displayed in the graph? *the percent of 18 to 24 year olds in Japan and the U.S. who changed jobs*

13. In which country have more than 60% of the young adults surveyed never changed jobs? *Japan*

14. Compare the percent of young adults in Japan who changed jobs twice to the percent of young adults in the United States who changed jobs twice. *It is about $\frac{1}{3}$ as much.*

15. **Challenge** About how many young adults surveyed in the United States have changed jobs only once? *about 150*

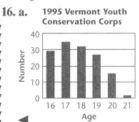

Job Changes among 18 to 24 year olds in Japan and in the United States

Percent of people surveyed (vertical axis, 0 to 70)

Number of job changes: none, one, two, three, four or more, no answer

Legend: ■ Japan ■ United States

16. The frequency table shows participation in the *Vermont Youth Conservation Corps* in 1995. This organization trains teenagers and young adults to carry out conservation and park management projects on public lands in Vermont.

Age	Tally	Frequency
16	JHT JHT JHT JHT JHT IIII	29
17	JHT JHT JHT JHT JHT JHT JHT	35
18	JHT JHT JHT JHT JHT JHT II	32
19	JHT JHT JHT JHT JHT II	27
20	JHT JHT JHT	15
21	I	1

16. a. **1995 Vermont Youth Conservation Corps**

Number (vertical axis, 0 to 40)
Age (horizontal axis): 16 17 18 19 20 21

◄ In 1995, Youth Corps crews completed 53,447 hours of work. They worked to clear trails, seed riverbanks, organize tourist information, install bat houses, and build tables and benches.

a. Make a bar graph of the data. *See above.*

b. How is your graph from part (a) like the bar graph on page 7? How is it different? *Sample Response: The bar for age 21 is the shortest; The bar for age 17 is the longest.*

c. Make a double bar graph of the 1992 data and the 1995 data.

d. Use your graph from part (c) to describe how participation in the organization has changed over time.
Sample Response: Participation by 17 to 20 year olds has at least doubled.

16. c. **Vermont Youth Conservation Corps**

Number (vertical axis, 0 to 40)
Age 16 17 18 19 20 21
Legend: □ 1992 ■ 1995

Make a frequency table for each set of data. 17–20. See Additional Answers.

17. Pieces of mail received each day for a month: 5, 6, 5, 10, 6, 8, 7, 8, 8, 5, 9, 7, 7, 8, 6, 7, 5, 9, 6, 7, 8, 6, 9, 6, 6, 5, 5

18. Scores on a five-point quiz: 5, 5, 4, 3, 4, 4, 2, 4, 4, 5, 3, 3, 4, 4, 3

19. Sizes of sweatshirts for a softball team: small, large, large, medium, medium, small, extra large, large, medium, large, medium, small, large, medium, large

20. Neighborhood pets: dog, dog, cat, none, none, dog, fish, horse, dog, cat, dog, gerbil, snake, none, cat, cat, cat, dog, fish, none

<table>
<tr><td>**RESEARCH**</td></tr>
<tr><td>Exercise 21 checks that you can interpret a bar graph.</td></tr>
</table>

Reflecting ▶ on the Section

Answers will vary. Check students' work.

21. a. Find an example of a bar graph in a newspaper or a magazine.

b. What is the title of the graph?

c. Are the axes clearly labeled? Explain.

d. What decision can the bar graph help a person make? State two facts shown by the graph that may affect the decision.

28. Sample Response:

29. Sample Response:

30. Sample Response:

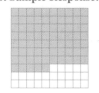

Spiral ◀▶ Review

Find the area of each rectangle. (Toolbox, p. 593)

22. 8 in. 5 in. 40 in.²

23. 6 yd 9 yd 54 yd²

24. 4 ft 5 ft 20 ft²

Find the fraction of each set that is shaded. (Toolbox, p. 584)

25. $\frac{3}{5}$

26. $\frac{4}{6}$ or $\frac{2}{3}$

27. $\frac{6}{8}$ or $\frac{3}{4}$

Draw each percent on a 100 grid on graph paper. (Toolbox, p. 588)

28. 20%

29. 38%

30. 75%

Tune In to Data

SET UP *Work in a group.*

How do you feel about television commercials? Do you watch too many? Over the next few weeks your group will research television commercials: how often they air, the types of products they advertise, how advertisers use them to influence you, and so on. For your project, your group will present the data you collect and what you learn from the data.

Frequency Tables You can use a frequency table to collect data about how often commercials air and the products they advertise.

 1 Decide the following with your group.
Answers will vary.
   a. Which two half-hour time slots will you observe each day? Example: 7:00 P.M. to 7:30 P.M. and 8:00 P.M. to 8:30 P.M.

   b. Pick one or two channels to track for five days (Monday–Friday). You'll track each channel during the same time slot each day.

   c. Who will observe the channels during the time slots each day?

 2 Create a frequency table for your observation periods.
Answers will vary.

 3 Collect the data for your observation period(s). Write down what you thought of the commercials you watched. Were they better or worse than the show they interrupted? Explain.
Answers will vary.

Observer: Lionel
Day of week: Tuesday
Time Slot: 7–7:30 pm   Channel: 8
Program: Star Trek
Notes:

Product advertised	Tally	Frequency
Cars	IIII	4
Food	II	2
Restaurants	I	1
Medicine	IIII	4
Cosmetics	I	1

Total number of commercials = 12

 The products advertised may be different for your time slot.

Section 1   Data Displays   **11**

Use the bar graph for Exercises 1–3.

1. About how many Internet hosts (or machine addresses) were there in January of 1994? **about 2,200,000**

2. Compare the number of Internet hosts in January of 1995 with the number in January of 1996. **about 4,600,000 more in January of 1996**

3. Do you think the data in the bar graph can be displayed in a line graph? Explain. **Yes; The graph is of data that changes over time.**

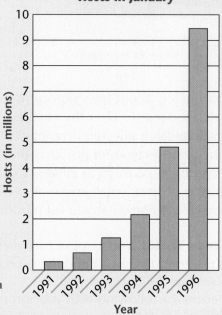

Number of Internet Hosts in January

Estimation For each group of people surveyed, tell whether 51% of the group is *more than*, *less than*, or *equal to* 51 people.

4. 25 artists **less than** 5. 51 musicians **less than**

6. 100 athletes **equal to** 7. 300 actors **more than**

Make a frequency table for each set of data.

8. The number of phone calls listed for each day on a month's bill: 2, 1, 3, 2, 4, 2, 1, 4, 5, 2, 5, 3, 2, 1, 2, 3, 6, 4, 5, 3, 2, 0, 2, 4, 1, 3, 4, 3, 1, 2 **See Additional Answers.**

9. The ages of a team of students cleaning up a neighborhood playground: 12, 11, 15, 12, 12, 13, 15, 14, 10, 11, 14, 15, 15, 12, 12, 13, 14, 10, 15, 12, 14, 14, 13, 11 **See Additional Answers.**

Study Skills ◀▶ Taking Notes

Taking notes allows you to keep a record of what you are learning. Be sure to take notes that make sense to you and that you will be able to understand later.

1. **a.** Look at your notes for this section. What ideas did you record?
   Sample Response: ideas about the differences between line and bar graphs
   b. What changes can you make to your notes so they are easier to use? Rewrite your notes for this section with these changes.
   Sample Response: Use fewer words and more diagrams; Check students' work.

Section ② Sequences and Exponents

IN THIS SECTION

EXPLORATION 1
◆ Modeling Sequences

EXPLORATION 2
◆ Exponents, Squares, and Cubes

PATTERNS and PREDICTIONS

Warm-Up Exercises
See page 14.

Setting the Stage ▶▶▶▶▶▶▶▶▶

Read the poem by Shel Silverstein and think about whether the boy is making "Smart" choices.

1. b. He increased the number of pieces of money by one with each trade.

Think About It

1 **a.** What was the boy trying to do? **get more money**

b. Explain the pattern he followed to make each trade. **See above.**

2 **a.** How much money did the boy lose altogether? **$.95**

b. For which trade did he lose the most money? **trading the dollar bill for two quarters**

3 What other trading choices might the boy have made? **See below.**

4 Follow the boy's pattern to list the trades he might make if his dad gives him a $20 bill. Answer Question 2 for these trades. **See below.**

SMART

My dad gave me one dollar bill
'Cause I'm his smartest son,
And I swapped it for two shiny quarters
'Cause two is more than one!

And then I took the quarters
And traded them to Lou
For three dimes—I guess he don't know
That three is more than two!

Just then, along came old blind Bates
And just 'cause he can't see
He gave me four nickels for my three dimes,
And four is more than three!

And I took the nickels to Hiram Coombs
Down at the seed-feed store,
And the fool gave me five pennies for them,
And five is more than four!

And then I went and showed my dad,
And he got red in the cheeks
And closed his eyes and shook his head—
Too proud of me to speak!

▶ Finding and using patterns to make predictions is an important problem-solving strategy. It can help you make good choices in a variety of decision-making situations.

3. Sample Response: 2 half dollars for a $1 bill, 4 quarters for 2 half dollars

4. Sample Response: a $20 bill for two $10 bills, two $10 bills for three $5 bills, three $5 bills for four $1 bills, four $1 bills for 5 quarters, 5 quarters for 6 dimes, 6 dimes for 7 nickels, 7 nickels for 8 pennies; $19.92; trading three $5 bills for four $1 bills

GOAL

LEARN HOW TO...
◆ model sequences
◆ make predictions

AS YOU...
◆ explore visual patterns

KEY TERMS
◆ sequence
◆ term
◆ term number
◆ equation
◆ variable

Exploration 1

Modeling Sequences

SET UP You will need: • Labsheets 2A and 2B • 25 square tiles or graph paper

▶ The boy in the poem followed a pattern to make his trades. You can follow a pattern to find numbers in a *sequence*. A **sequence** is an ordered list of numbers or objects, called **terms**.

The **term number** tells the position of each term in the sequence.

This symbol indicates that the pattern continues.

Term number	1	2	3	4	5	6	⋯	10	⋯	90
Shape sequence	□				?	?	⋯	?	⋯	?
Number sequence	1	3	5	7	?	?	⋯	?	⋯	?

The **4th term** of the number sequence is **7**.

WARM-UP EXERCISES

Write the next three numbers.

1. 5, 15, 25, 35, ...
   45, 55, 65

2. 300, 298, 296, 294, ...
   292, 290, 288

3. 2, 22, 222, 2222, ...
   22222, 222222, 2222222

4. 1, 3, 2, 4, 3, 5, 4, 6, ...
   5, 7, 6

5th

5 How are the number sequence and the shape sequence in the table related? The number in the number sequence gives the number of tiles in the shape.

6 **a.** Use square tiles (or draw a picture) to model the 5th term of the shape sequence.

   b. What is the 5th term of the number sequence? 9

7 **a.** What pattern can you use to predict the 6th term of the shape sequence? Sample Response: Add 1 tile to each row.

   b. Predict what the 6th term of the number sequence will be. 11

8 **Discussion** Share your patterns from Question 7(a). Predict the 10th and 90th terms of the number sequence. Present your method(s) to the class. 19, 179; Sample Response: The number in the number sequence is one less than twice the term number.

▶ **Graphing Sequences** Another way to explore a sequence is to set up a table of values and graph the values on a coordinate plane.

Sequence Table	
Term number	Term
1	1
2	3
3	5
4	7
5	9

Sequence Graph

9 a. Describe how the points are arranged on the graph.

Sample Response: The points lie along a straight line.

b. If the number sequence continues, how could your answer to part (a) help you predict the 6th and 7th terms?

9. b. Draw and then extend the line through the points. Read the value of the term from the graph.

10 ✔ **CHECKPOINT** Use **Labsheets 2A and 2B.**
You'll build models with square tiles (or draw pictures) and complete a table, make a graph, and write a word sentence for three *Building Patterns*.

See Additional Answers.

✔ **QUESTION 10**

...checks that you can model a sequence with a table, a graph, and a word sentence.

▶ In Question 7 you used a pattern to predict a term of the sequence 1, 3, 5, 7, ... You may have noticed that the number of squares in each term of the shape sequence is equal to 2 times the term number minus 1. For example:

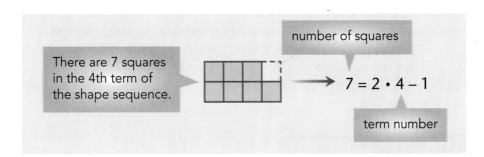

There are 7 squares in the 4th term of the shape sequence.

number of squares

$7 = 2 \cdot 4 - 1$

term number

▶ An **equation** such as $7 = 2 \cdot 4 - 1$ is a mathematical sentence stating that two quantities are equal. You can use *variables* to write an equation for a sequence. A **variable** is a quantity that is unknown or that changes. It can be represented by a letter or a symbol.

EXAMPLE

Write an equation for the sequence 1, 3, 5, 7, … . Use the equation to predict the 100th term of the sequence.

SAMPLE RESPONSE

Since the terms and the term numbers change, you can use variables to represent them. Let **t** = the term. Let **n** = the term number.

The term is equal to 2 times the term number minus 1.

$$t = 2 \cdot n - 1$$
or $$t = 2n - 1$$

> "2 times *n*" can be written $2 \cdot n$ or $2n$.

Use this equation to predict the 100th term of the sequence.

$$t = 2n - 1$$
$$= 2 \cdot 100 - 1$$
$$= 200 - 1$$
$$= 199$$

> For the **100th** term, the term number **n** is **100**.

The 100th term in the sequence 1, 3, 5, 7, … is 199.

---

12. a. For Pattern 1, let s = the total number of squares and n = the number of stories. Then, $s = 3n$. For Pattern 2, let s = the total number of squares and t = the number of squares in the tower. Then, $s = t + 3$. For Pattern 3, let s = the total number of squares and n = the number of stories. Then, $s = 3n + 1$.

11 How many squares are there in the 100th term of the shape sequence in the table on page 14? 199

12 ✔ **CHECKPOINT** **Use Labsheets 2A and 2B.**

a. Use your word sentences to write an equation for each *Building Pattern*. Be sure to identify what each variable represents.

b. Use your equations from part (a). Predict the total number of squares for Patterns 1 and 3 when there are 100 stories on the building and for Pattern 2 when the tower is 100 squares high. 300; 301; 103

✔ **QUESTION 12**

…checks that you can write an equation for a sequence and use it to make predictions.

▌ **HOMEWORK EXERCISES** ▶ See Exs. 1–11 on pp. 21–22.

EXPONENTS, SQUARES, and CUBES

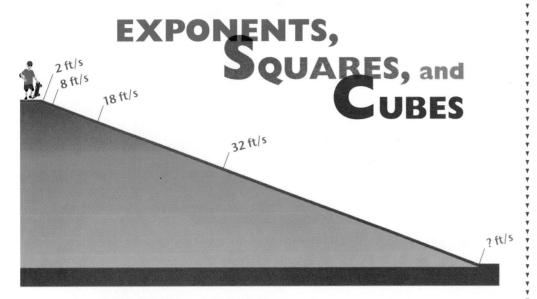

2 ft/s
8 ft/s
18 ft/s
32 ft/s
? ft/s

13 The boy is deciding whether to skateboard down the hill. The numbers show the speed he would be going at each distance from the hilltop. Would you skate down the hill? Why?

Sample Response: No; I'd be out of control at the bottom of the hill.

▸ In Exploration 1, you saw patterns involving addition, subtraction, and multiplication. In this Exploration you'll learn how to use exponents to find the skateboarder's speed at the bottom of the hill. **Exponents** can show a pattern of repeated multiplication.

base **exponent**

exponential form → $3^4 = 3 \cdot 3 \cdot 3 \cdot 3 = 81$ ← **standard form**

3 is used as a factor 4 times.

You read 3^4 as " 3 to the 4th **power**."

14 a. Copy and complete the table.

3^5 3^6

Term number	1	2	3	4	5	6
Exponential form of sequence	3^1	3^2	3^3	3^4	?	?
Standard form of sequence	3	9	27	?	?	?

81 243 729

b. If the sequence in part (a) continues, how could you use exponents to predict the 10th term? $3^{10} = 59{,}049$

▶ **Area Patterns** The squares in the shape sequence below are made up of small squares. Each side of a small square is 1 unit long. You can find a related number sequence for the area of each shape.

15 a. Sketch the next two shapes in the sequence.

b. How can you find the area of a square from the length of a side? area = length · length

c. If the sequence in the table continues, what are the first five terms of the number sequence for the area of each shape? 1, 4, 9, 16, 25

Term number	Shape sequence
1	□
2	⊞
3	⊞
4	?
5	?

✔ **QUESTION 16**

…checks that you can use exponents to write an equation for a sequence.

16. a. The base of each term is the side length of the shape in the corresponding term of the shape sequence; The numbers in the number sequence are the standard form of the expressions in the sequence. They give the area of each shape.

16 ✔ CHECKPOINT The following sequence is another way to represent the area pattern in the shape sequence above.

$$1^2, 2^2, 3^2, \ldots$$

You read 3^2 as "3 to the 2nd power" or as "3 squared."

a. How is this sequence related to the shape sequence above and to the number sequence you wrote in Question 15(c)?

b. Write an equation for the area of a square. Let s = the length of a side of a square. Let A = the area of the square. $A = s \cdot s$ or $A = s^2$

c. Use your equation from part (b) to find the area of a square that has sides of length 10 cm. 100 cm²

▶ **Volume Patterns** A **cube** is a space figure with six square surfaces. The sequence of cubes below has a related number sequence that gives the *volume* of each cube. The **volume** is the number of *unit cubes* that fill the figure.

Term number	1	2	3	…
Shape sequence				…

A unit cube is 1 unit long, 1 unit wide, and 1 unit high.

17 How many unit cubes make up each term in the shape sequence?

a. 1st term 1   **b.** 2nd term 8   **c.** 3rd term 27

▶ There are 1000 centimeter cubes in the large cube below, so its volume is 1000 cm³. (You read cm³ as "cubic centimeters.") Another way to find the volume of a cube besides counting unit cubes is to use an equation.

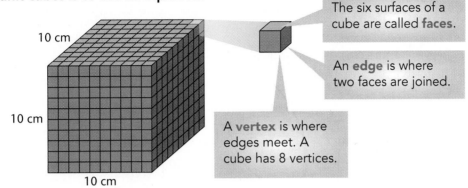

The six surfaces of a cube are called **faces**.

An **edge** is where two faces are joined.

A **vertex** is where edges meet. A cube has 8 vertices.

10 cm

10 cm

10 cm

18 Discussion Explain how the lengths of the edges of the large cube above can be used to find its volume.

volume = length · length · length

19 a. Write an equation for the volume of a cube. Let s = the length of an edge of a cube. Let V = the volume of the cube. $V = s \cdot s \cdot s$ or $V = s^3$

b. Use your equation from part (a) to find the volume of the first three cubes in the shape sequence at the bottom of page 18.

1 cubic unit, 8 cubic units, 27 cubic units

c. Describe how your answers in part (b) compare with those in Question 17. The numbers are the same.

20 ✔ CHECKPOINT Find the volume of a cube with edges of each length.

a. 1 cm 1 cm³   **b.** 5 in. 125 in.³   **c.** 50 m   **d.** 300 ft

125,000 m³   27,000,000 ft³

✔ QUESTION 20

...checks that you can find the volume of a cube.

21 The fifth term in the table below is the speed that the skateboarder on page 17 will reach at the bottom of the hill.

Speed (feet per second)	2	8	18	32	?
Exponential form	$1^2 \cdot 2$	$2^2 \cdot 2$	$3^2 \cdot 2$	?	?

a. Study the pattern in the table. Then write the 4th and 5th terms of the sequence in exponential form. $4^2 \cdot 2; 5^2 \cdot 2$

b. What will the skateboarder's speed be in feet per second when he reaches the bottom of the hill? What will his speed be in miles per hour? (*Hint:* 5280 ft = 1 mi) 50 ft/s; about 34 mi/h

c. What advice would you give this skateboarder?

Sample Response: Don't go down the hill.

HOMEWORK EXERCISES ▶ See Exs. 12–32 on pp. 23–24.

Section ② Key Concepts

sequence

term

term number

equation

variable

exponent

base

power

Sequences (pp. 14 and 15)

A sequence is an ordered list of numbers or objects, called terms. Each term has a term number that tells the term's position in the sequence.

Example Make a table and a graph for the sequence 5, 10, 15, 20, … .

Sequence Table

Term number	Term
1	5
2	10
3	15
4	20

Sequence Graph

The 4th term of the sequence is 20.

Equations and Variables (p. 16)

You can use variables to write an equation that shows how a term in a sequence is related to its term number. A variable is a letter or a symbol used to represent unknown quantities or quantities that change.

Example Write an equation for the sequence 5, 10, 15, 20, … .

The term t is 5 times the term number n.

$$t = 5 \cdot n$$
$$t = 5n$$

Exponents (p. 17)

An exponent tells you how many times a base is used as a factor. The value of any number to the 1st power is that number.

$$10^5 = 10 \cdot 10 \cdot 10 \cdot 10 \cdot 10 = 100{,}000$$

← 100,000 is the 5th power of 10.

base · exponent

22 Key Concepts Question Find the 20th term of the sequence represented by the equation $t = 5n$, where t is the term and n is the term number. 100

Section ②

Key Concepts

▶▶▶▶▶▶▶▶▶▶▶▶▶▶▶▶▶▶▶▶▶▶

Key Terms

Squares and Cubes (pp. 18–19)

The formulas for the area of a square and the volume of a cube can be written using exponents.

volume

Area of a Square

  s

$A = s \cdot s = s^2$

Volume of a Cube

s

$V = s \cdot s \cdot s = s^3$

cube
  face
  edge
  vertex

You read s^2 as "s squared."

You read s^3 as "s cubed."

Example Find the volume of a cube when the length of an edge is 8 ft.

  8 ft
8 ft
8 ft

$V = s^3$

$= 8^3$ ◀ exponential form

$= 8 \cdot 8 \cdot 8$

$= 512$ ◀ standard form

The volume is 512 ft^3.

exponential form

standard form

---

23 Key Concepts Question The length of an edge of a cube is 4 in. Find the volume of the cube and the area of one of its faces.
64 in.^{3}; 16 in.^{2}

CLOSURE QUESTION

Write the formulas for the area of a square and the volume of a cube in two ways, one of which uses exponents. State what each variable represents in the formulas.

Answer: Let s = the length of a side of the square or the cube, A = the area of the square, and V = the volume of a cube. Then A = s • s or A = s², and V = s • s • s or V = s³.

Section ②

Practice & Application Exercises ▶▶▶▶▶▶▶

Suppose the boy in the poem on page 13 begins with 2 bills. Then he trades them for 4 of the next lesser bill or coin, and so on, according to the pattern 2, 4, 6, 8, 10, ... (*Note:* He can trade for half dollars.) For each starting amount, how much will he lose altogether?

1. 2 one-dollar bills $1.88

2. 2 two-dollar bills $3.86

3. **Challenge** Assume that the boy in the poem finds someone to agree to any trade. Describe a pattern he can use so that he will not lose money overall on his trades although each trade is for the next lesser bill or coin. Sample Response: 3, 9, 27, 81, 243

4. d.

Term number	Term
1	2
2	5
3	8
4	11
5	14
6	17
7	20
8	23
9	26
10	29

4. Use the shape sequence in the table.

a. Draw pictures of the 5th and 6th terms of the sequence.

b. Write the number sequence that matches the first six terms of the shape sequence. 2, 5, 8, 11, 14, 17

c. Write a word sentence to describe a pattern you could use to predict the 7th term of the number sequence. **Sample Response: Multiply the term number by 3 and subtract 1.**

d. Make a table of values for the first 10 terms of the number sequence. Use it to make a graph of the sequence.

e. Use your graph to predict the 15th term of the number sequence. 44

Term number	Shape sequence
1	
2	
3	
4	
⋮	⋮

Write an equation for each word sentence. Use t for the term and n for the term number.

5. The term is six times the term number. $t = 6n$

6. The term is one less than the term number. $t = n - 1$

7. The term is five more than the term number. $t = n + 5$

8. The term is half the term number. $t = \frac{n}{2}$

For each sequence, make a table, draw a graph, and write an equation. Then predict the 100th term.

9. 7, 14, 21, 28, ...
See Additional Answers.

10. 199, 198, 197, 196, ...
See Additional Answers.

11. **Social Studies** Arizona and Oregon became states on the same day, February 14, but in different years. Arizona's first year as a state was Oregon's 54th year.

Arizona's years of statehood	1	2	3	4	...
Oregon's years of statehood	54	55	56	57	...

a. Arizona became a state in 1912. When did Oregon become a state? 1859

b. When Arizona celebrates 100 years of statehood, how many years will Oregon have been a state? 153

Write each product in exponential form.

12. $2 \cdot 2 \cdot 2$ 2^3 **13.** $3 \cdot 3$ 3^2 **14.** $7 \cdot 7 \cdot 7 \cdot 7 \cdot 7$ 7^5

Write each power in standard form.

15. 5^2 25   **16.** 4^3 64   **17.** 11^4 14,641   **18.** 6^5 7776

19. 10^6 1,000,000   **20.** 0^{15} 0   **21.** 1^{50} 1   **22.** 1592^1 1592

23. Predict the 100th term of the sequence $2^3, 4^3, 6^3, 8^3, \ldots$. 200^3

Find the volume of a cube with edges of each length.

24. 7 mm
343 mm³   **25.** 11 ft
1331 ft³   **26.** 80 cm
512,000 cm³   **27.** 25 in.
15,625 in.³

Chinese Noodles To make dragon's beard noodles, a chef takes noodle dough, stretches it, and then folds it in half. The chef repeats this process, making more noodles with each fold. An experienced noodle maker can stretch and fold the dough 8 times.

28. Suppose a chef folds the dough 8 times. How many noodles will there be? 256

29. How many folds are required to make about 500 noodles? 9

Number of folds	Number of noodles
1	2
2	4
3	8
⋮	⋮

30. a.

Area of a Square

Area (cm²) — 1600, 800, 0
Side length (cm) — 0, 20, 40

30. **a.** Copy and complete the table. Then graph the values.

See above.

Side length (cm)	10	20	30	40
Area of a square (cm²)	?	?	?	?

100 400 900 1600

    b. How does the area of a square change when you multiply the length of each side by 2? by 3? by 4? It is 4 times as large; 9 times as large; 16 times as large.

    c. Copy and complete the table. Then graph the values.

Edge length (cm)	10	20	30	40
Volume of a cube (cm³)	?	?	?	?

1000 8000 27,000 64,000

30. c.

Volume of a Cube

Volume (cm³) — 64,000, 32,000, 0
Side length (cm) — 0, 20, 40

    d. How does the volume of a cube change when you multiply the length of each edge by 2? by 3? by 4? It is 8 times as large; 27 times as large; 64 times as large.

    e. **Writing** Compare your answers to parts (b) and (d). Is the effect on area of doubling a side length the same as the effect on volume of doubling an edge length? Explain.

30. e. No; Sample Response: new area = (2 × original length) × (2 × original length) = 4 × original area; new volume = (2 × original edge length) × (2 × original edge length) × (2 × original edge length) = 8 × original volume

31. **Challenge** The volume of a cube is 700 cm³. Estimate the length of an edge. Explain your method.
about 8.88 cm; Sample Response: I used a calculator and trial and error.

Reflecting on the Section

32. Find the volume of the 5th shape in the sequence. The edge of each small cube is 5 cm long. 1875 cm³

5 cm
5 cm
5 cm

Spiral Review

Use the bar graph at the right.
(Module 1, pp. 2–3)   33. about $\frac{150}{750}$ or $\frac{1}{5}$

33. About what fraction of the votes did Rosa get?

34. Which person got about one third of the votes? Jordan

35–37. Sample responses are given.

Write an equivalent fraction for each fraction below. (Toolbox, p. 585)

35. $\frac{1}{2}$ $\frac{4}{8}$

36. $\frac{20}{25}$ $\frac{60}{75}$

37. $\frac{3}{7}$ $\frac{30}{70}$

Election Results

Candidates: Rosa, Franklin, Jordan, Alecia

Number of votes: 0 50 100 150 200 250 300

Career Connection

Trader: David Lei

David Lei is the president of a trading company that buys and sells goods around the world. To get the best price, he must try to keep shipping costs low.

38. Shipping costs can be based on the number of cubic meters of goods shipped. The table shows shipping costs determined this way.

Number of cubic meters	1	2	3	4
Shipping cost	$45	$90	$135	$180

   a. Write an equation for the cost c of shipping based on the number n of cubic meters of goods. $c = 45n$

   b. Extend the table to include the next 6 terms of the sequence. See below.

   c. Graph the data in your table. See Additional Answers.

b.	5	6	7	8	9	10
	225	270	315	360	405	450

39. Suppose it costs $1000 to ship a 57 m³ cargo container from Hong Kong to San Francisco. Use the graph you made in part (c) of Question 38. Predict when it becomes less expensive to pay for shipping by container rather than by the cubic meter. after 22 m³

Section ② Extra Skill Practice

Write an equation for each word sentence. Use *t* for the term and *n* for the term number.

1. The term is eight times the term number. $t = 8n$
2. The term is two more than the term number. $t = n + 2$
3. The term is five less than the term number. $t = n - 5$
4. The term is one third the term number. $t = \frac{1}{3}n$

For each sequence, make a table, draw a graph, and write an equation. Then predict the 100th term. 5–10. See Additional Answers.

5. 4, 8, 12, 16, …
6. 999, 998, 997, 996, …
7. 12, 13, 14, 15, …
8. 0, 1, 2, 3, …
9. $\frac{1}{2}$, 1, $\frac{3}{2}$, 2, …
10. 3, 5, 7, 9, …

Write each product in exponential form.

11. $5 \cdot 5$ 5^2
12. $2 \cdot 2 \cdot 2 \cdot 2$ 2^4
13. $3 \cdot 3 \cdot 3 \cdot 3 \cdot 3 \cdot 3$ 3^6
14. $5 \cdot 5 \cdot 5 \cdot 2$ $5^3 \cdot 2$
15. $3 \cdot 7 \cdot 7$ $3 \cdot 7^2$
16. $11 \cdot 3 \cdot 3$ $11 \cdot 3^2$

Write each power in standard form.

17. 9^2 81
18. 5^3 125
19. 2^5 32
20. 3^7 2187
21. 10^4 10,000
22. 1^{12} 1
23. 0^{26} 0
24. 862^1 862

Find the volume of a cube with edges of each length.

25. 2 in. 8 in.^{3}
26. 3 cm 27 cm^3
27. 15 m 3375 m^3
28. 400 ft 64,000,000 ft^3
29. 12 in. 1728 in.^{3}
30. 2 yd 8 yd^3
31. 52 cm 140,608 cm^3
32. 15 ft 3375 ft^3

Standardized Testing ◀▶ Open-ended

1. Write a sequence in which the terms follow a pattern that can be expressed using exponents. Sample Response: 1, 4, 9, 16, …

2. Write an equation for the sequence you wrote in Question 1. Use *t* for the term and *n* for the term number. Sample Response: $t = n^2$

Section ③ Probability

IN THIS SECTION

EXPLORATION 1
♦ What Are the Chances?

EXPLORATION 2
♦ Theoretical Probability

LIKELY or UNLIKELY?

·---·*Setting the Stage*

SET UP   *Work in a group of two or three. You will need:* • *Labsheet 3A* • *18 chips for each student* • *2 number cubes or dice*

Sometimes making a choice involves taking a chance. In the *Difference Game,* making smart choices improves your chances of winning.

DIFFERENCE GAME

♦ Each player begins with 18 chips and a copy of the *Game Board* on Labsheet 3A.

♦ Players start by placing their chips in the numbered columns on their *Game Boards.* The chips may be placed in any arrangement.

♦ Players take turns rolling the number cubes. The result of each roll is the difference between the numbers on the cubes.

♦ Each player who has a chip in the column for the difference rolled removes that chip from the *Game Board.* Each player may remove only one chip per roll.

♦ The first player to remove all of the chips from his or her *Game Board* is the winner.

▶ **Use Labsheet 3A.** Play the *Difference Game* three times. Use the *Frequency Table* to keep track of how many times the cubes are rolled.

Think About It ►►►►►►►►►►►►►►►►►►►►►►►►►►►►►►►►►►

1 The *Difference Game* involves both *choice* and *chance*. What part involves choice? What part involves chance?
  placing the chips; rolling the number cubes

2 Did you use the same arrangement of chips for every game? Why or why not?
  Sample Response: No; Some differences came up more often than others.

3 What can you do to help decide where to place your chips on the *Game Board*? Sample Response: Keep track of how often each difference comes up.

Exploration 1 ►►►►►►►►►►►►►►►►►►►►►►►►►►►►►

What Are the CHANCES?

SET UP *Work with a partner. You will need:* • *Labsheets 3A and 3B* • *18 chips* • *2 number cubes or dice*

GOAL

LEARN HOW TO...
• list the outcomes for an event
• find and compare experimental probabilities

AS YOU...
• analyze the *Difference Game*

KEY TERMS
• experiment
• outcome
• event
• probability
• experimental probability

► **In the *Difference Game*, you had to choose where to place your chips.**

4 **a.** Should you place any chips on the 6? Why or why not?
  Sample Response: No; The greatest difference that will come up is 5.
  b. Suppose a difference does not occur very often. Should you put many of your chips on that number? Explain.
  Sample Response: No; You probably won't get the chance to remove them.

► **To make good choices about where to put the chips, it helps to know your chances of getting a particular difference on a roll.**

5 **Use Labsheet 3B.** Answers will vary. Check students' work.

  a. Roll the number cubes 18 times. Record how often each difference occurs in the *Results of 18 Rolls* table.

  b. What differences seem to occur most often? least often?

  c. What fraction of the 18 rolls resulted in a difference of 2? Record your answer in the last column of the table.

  d. Repeat part (c) for the other differences from 0 through 6.

The difference is 6 − 2 = 4.

▶ When you rolled the number cubes and found each difference in Question 5(a), you were conducting an **experiment**. The result of an experiment is an **outcome**. For the roll shown, the outcome is a difference of 4. An **event** is any set of outcomes.

✔ **QUESTION 6**

...checks that you can list the outcomes for an event.

6 ✔ **CHECKPOINT** Suppose the experiment is to roll the number cubes and record the difference.

a. What are all the possible outcomes of the experiment?
a difference of 0, 1, 2, 3, 4, or 5

b. Which outcomes make up the event the *difference is even*?
a difference of 0, 2, or 4

▶ A **probability** is a number from 0 through 1 that tells how likely it is that an event will happen. Each of the fractions you wrote for Question 5 is an **experimental probability** because each was found by doing an experiment.

EXAMPLE

Suppose, that when you roll two number cubes 18 times you get a difference of 4 on 3 rolls. What is the experimental probability of getting a difference of 4?

SAMPLE RESPONSE

Since the difference is 4 on $\frac{3}{18}$ of the rolls, the experimental probability of a difference of 4 is $\frac{3}{18} = \frac{1}{6}$.

FOR ▶ HELP

with *writing fractions in lowest terms*, see
TOOLBOX, p. 585

7 **Discussion** **Use Labsheet 3B.** Look at the experimental probabilities in the last column of the *Results of 18 Rolls* table.

a. In the *Difference Game*, what does it mean to say the experimental probability of a 1 is $\frac{5}{18}$? $\frac{5}{18}$ of the rolls resulted in a difference of 1.

b. Which, if any, of the differences have a probability of 0?
Sample Response: 5 and 6

c. What does a probability of 0 mean? The outcome never occurred.

d. What is the probability that the difference is less than 7? Why? $\frac{18}{18}$ or 1; All possible outcomes are less than 7.

e. What do you think a probability of 1 means?
The event will always occur.

f. Is an event more likely to occur when its probability is *greater than* one half or *less than* one half? greater than one half

▶ **Use Labsheet 3B for Questions 8–10.** The *Results of 72 Rolls* frequency table is reproduced below.

8. Answers will vary. Check students' work.

8 a. Record the frequencies from the *Results of 18 Rolls* table in the column labeled *My Group* of the *Results of 72 Rolls* table. Then do the same with the frequencies of three other groups.

b. Complete the *Total frequency* column.

c. Complete the *Experimental probability* column.

Results of 72 Rolls (Use with Questions 8–10 on page 29.)

Difference	Group frequencies				Total frequency	Experimental probability
	My group	Group 1	Group 2	Group 3		
0						
1						
2						
3						
4						
5						
6						
			Total number of rolls →		72	

Add the frequencies for the four groups.

The total frequency is what fraction of the 72 rolls?

9 Discussion Use both the *Results of 72 Rolls* table and the *Results of 18 Rolls* table.

a. Compare the experimental probabilities in the two tables. How are the probabilities alike? How are they different?
Answers will vary. Check students' work.

b. Which set of probabilities do you think gives a better indication of how likely it is for each difference to occur? Why?
Sample Response: Results of 72 Rolls; More experiments were conducted.

10 Try This as a Class Use the probabilities in the *Results of 72 Rolls* table to predict how many times each difference 0 through 6 will occur in 18 rolls of the number cubes.

11 a. Discussion How can your answer to Question 10 help you decide where to place your chips in the *Difference Game*?

b. Use Labsheet 3A. Use the answers to Question 10 to place the 18 chips on a *Game Board*. Roll the number cubes until all the chips have been removed. How many times did you roll the number cubes? Compare the number of rolls with those in the *Frequency Table*. Sample Response: 33

FOR ▶ HELP

with *comparing fractions,* see
TOOLBOX, p. 586

10. Answers will vary. Sample Response: Suppose 9 of the 72 rolls resulted in a difference of 3. Then you would expect $\frac{9}{72}$ of 18 rolls, or about 2 rolls, to result in a difference of 3.

11. a. In each numbered column on the game board, place a number of chips equal to your prediction of how many times that difference would occur in 18 rolls.

HOMEWORK EXERCISES ▶ See Exs. 1–12 on pp. 34–35.

GOAL

LEARN HOW TO...
◆ find theoretical probabilities

AS YOU...
◆ explore outcomes when rolling one or two number cubes

KEY TERMS
◆ theoretical probability
◆ equally likely

Exploration 2

Theoretical PROBABILITY

SET UP *Work with a partner. You will need:* • *Labsheets 3C and 3D* • *2 number cubes or dice (red and blue)*

▶ **Sometimes probabilities can be determined without actually doing an experiment. Such probabilities are called theoretical probabilities.**

12 a. What are all the possible outcomes when a number cube is rolled once? 1, 2, 3, 4, 5, 6

b. Discussion The theoretical probability of rolling a 4 is $\frac{1}{6}$. Why do you think $\frac{1}{6}$ is the theoretical probability for this event?

12. b. The chance of rolling each of the six numbers is the same so theoretically, 1 out of every 6 rolls will be 4.

✔ QUESTION 13

...checks that you can find and compare probabilities.

13. a. Theoretical probabilities are all $\frac{1}{6}$. Sum of theoretical probabilties is 1. Experimental probabilities will vary.

13 ✔ CHECKPOINT **Use Labsheet 3C.**

a. Follow the directions for *Rolling One Number Cube* and completing the table. You'll be finding both experimental and theoretical probabilities.

b. How does the experimental probability of each outcome in the table compare with its theoretical probability?
Sample Response: They are close.

▶ **When the probability of two or more outcomes is the same, the outcomes are equally likely.**

14 Discussion Are all six possible outcomes equally likely when you roll one number cube? when you play the *Difference Game*? Why or why not? Yes; No; Sample Response: Some differences are more likely to occur than others.

15 Discussion Suppose that one of the number cubes used in the *Difference Game* is red and the other one is blue. You roll a red 1 and a blue 5 to get a difference of 4.

a. What other rolls result in a difference of 4? Possible answers: red 5, blue 1; red 6, blue 2; blue 6, red 2

b. Do you think the rolls that result in a difference of 4 are equally likely? Why or why not?
Sample Response: Yes; The 6 outcomes on each cube are equally likely, so combinations of the two cubes are equally likely.

You can use probability software to conduct experiments, such as rolling a die or number cube, tossing a coin, or spinning a spinner. The steps below show you how to gather data for 150 rolls of a die. You can use the results to answer Question 13 on page 30 without ever rolling a number cube or die.

Step 1   Select the type of experiment to run.

Step 2   Enter how many times to conduct the experiment. Then select how you would like to display the results.

Model

✓ **Dice**

Coins

Spinners

Jar of marbles

Choose the dice as the model for your experiment.

Enter 150 rolls.

Choose a table display.

Step 3   Run the experiment.

The *theoretical probability* is the probability, before the experiment, that each outcome will occur.

Frequency is the number of times the outcome occurred.

Experimental probability is also called *relative frequency*. It can be shown as a fraction, a decimal, or a percent.

Values	A Theor. Prob.	B Freq.	C Rel. Freq.
⚀	16.7%	28	18.7%
⚁	16.7%	27	18.0%
⚂	16.7%	23	15.3%
⚃	16.7%	23	15.3%
⚄	16.7%	23	15.3%
⚅	16.7%	26	17.3%
Sum:	100%	150	100%

Your table will show you data for 150 rolls of a die. You can choose to have it record the theoretical probability, the frequency, the experimental probability, or all three.

Use Labsheet 3D for Questions 16–18.

16 Suppose you roll a red number cube and a blue number cube. Record all the possible differences in the *Difference Chart*. Then answer parts (a)–(f) on the labsheet.   See Additional Answers.

17.

Theoretical Probabilities for the *Difference Game*
$P(0) = \frac{6}{36}$ or $\frac{1}{6}$
$P(1) = \frac{10}{36}$ or $\frac{5}{18}$
$P(2) = \frac{8}{36}$ or $\frac{2}{9}$
$P(3) = \frac{6}{36}$ or $\frac{1}{6}$
$P(4) = \frac{4}{36}$ or $\frac{1}{9}$
$P(5) = \frac{2}{36}$ or $\frac{1}{18}$
$P(6) = \frac{0}{36}$ or 0
Sum $= \frac{36}{36}$ or 1

Based on the results in the chart, the probability of rolling a difference of 4 is $\frac{4}{36}$, since there are a total of 36 possible outcomes and 4 of them, or $\frac{4}{36}$ of all the possible outcomes, are "4." This can be written as shown.

the probability of → rolling a difference of 4 →

$$P(4) = \frac{4}{36} \text{ or } \frac{1}{9}$$

17 Use the *Difference Chart* to complete the *Difference Game Theoretical Probability Table* that appears on Labsheet 3D.   See above.

18 Think back to the experimental probabilities for the *Difference Game* that you found in Question 8 on page 29.

How do those experimental probabilities compare with the theoretical probabilities you found in Question 17?
Sample Response: They are close.

19 Explain how knowing the theoretical probability of rolling a particular difference can help you make good choices in the *Difference Game*.
Sample Response: If, for example, a difference has a probability of $\frac{5}{18}$, put 5 chips on that difference.

Labsheet 3D content:

Name ___ Date ___

MODULE 1   LABSHEET 3D

Difference Chart (Use with Questions 16–18 on page 32.)

Directions Suppose you roll a red number cube and a blue number cube. Complete the *Difference Chart* below to show what difference results from each roll. An example is shown. Then answer the questions below.

a. Which difference occurs most often in the chart? Which occurs least often?

b. How many boxes are there to fill in on the chart (including the ones filled in for you)?

c. What fraction of the boxes contain a difference of 4?

d. What is the theoretical probability of rolling a difference of 4?

e. What fraction of the boxes contain a difference of 6?

f. What is the theoretical probability of rolling a difference of 6?

Blue \ Red	1	2	3	4	5	6
1					(5 – 1) 4	
2	1					
3						
4		(4 – 3) 1				
5						
6						

Difference Game Theoretical Probability Table
(Use with Questions 17 and 18 on page 32.)

Directions Complete the table at the right by finding the theoretical probability of each difference shown in the *Difference Chart* above. Then find the sum of the theoretical probabilities.

Theoretical Probabilities for the *Difference Game*
$P(0) =$
$P(1) =$
$P(2) =$
$P(3) =$
$P(4) = \frac{4}{36}$, or $\frac{1}{9}$
$P(5) =$
$P(6) =$
Sum $=$

HOMEWORK EXERCISES   See Exs. 13–30 on pp. 35–37.

Section 3

Key Concepts

Probability and Experimental Probability (pp. 27–29)

A probability is a number from 0 through 1 that tells how likely it is that an event will happen. An impossible event has a probability of 0. A certain event has a probability of 1.

Probabilities determined by repeating an experiment a number of times and observing the results are called experimental probabilities.

Example Suppose the spinner below was spun 60 times with the results shown in the table.

Outcome	Frequency
A	17
B	25
C	18

Since $\frac{17}{60}$ of the spins landed on A, the experimental probability of spinning an A is $\frac{17}{60}$. This can also be written as $P(A) = \frac{17}{60}$.

Theoretical Probability (pp. 30–32)

Probabilities that are determined without actually doing an experiment are theoretical probabilities.

Outcomes are equally likely if they have the same chance of occurring.

Example Since the spinner above is divided into 3 equal-sized sectors, all three possible outcomes A, B, and C on the spinner have the same chance of occurring, so they are equally likely.

The theoretical probability of spinning an A is $\frac{1}{3}$, or $P(A) = \frac{1}{3}$.

Key Terms

probability

impossible event

certain event

experiment

experimental probability

outcome

event

theoretical probability

equally likely

CLOSURE QUESTION

Explain the difference between experimental probability and theoretical probability.

Answer: Experimental probability is probability found by performing experiments. Theoretical probability is calculated probability, or probability that is determined without doing an experiment.

20 Key Concepts Question Use the spinner and the frequency table from the first Example. For each indicated event, find the experimental probability and the theoretical probability.

a. $P(B)$ $\frac{25}{60}$ or $\frac{5}{12}$; $\frac{1}{3}$ **b.** $P(A$ or $C)$ $\frac{35}{60}$ or $\frac{7}{12}$; $\frac{2}{3}$ **c.** $P(\text{not } A)$ $\frac{43}{60}$; $\frac{2}{3}$

Section 3

Practice & Application Exercises

YOU WILL NEED

For Ex. 6:
- coin

For Ex. 26:
- 25 toothpicks or drinking straws

For Ex. 38:
- bag and 8 cubes using 3 different colors

Estimation Tell whether you think the probability of each event is 0, 1, or between 0 and 1. If the probability is between 0 and 1, do you think it is *greater than* or *less than* $\frac{1}{2}$? Give a reason.

1–4. Answers will vary from 0 to 1. Check students' work.

1. The snow in your area will be great for snowboarding this weekend.

2. Someone in your household will make a long-distance phone call in the next week.

3. You'll go on a field trip during this school year.

4. You'll move in the next year.

5. Marta spun the spinner shown 26 times. She got an even number on 10 spins.

   a. Based on Marta's results, what is the experimental probability of getting an even number on a spin? $\frac{10}{26}$ or $\frac{5}{13}$

   b. Describe an event that has a probability of 1 and an event that has a probability of 0. Sample Response: The spinner stops on a number less than 9; The spinner stops on a number greater than 10.

6. a. One method for deciding between two choices is to toss a coin. What are all the possible outcomes when you toss a coin? **heads or tails**

b. Toss a coin 50 times. Record your results in a frequency table. Then find the experimental probability of getting heads and the experimental probability of getting tails. **Answers will vary, but the experimental probability, for both outcomes should be about $\frac{1}{2}$.**

Suppose you roll two number cubes. List at least three outcomes that will produce each event. **7–12. Sample Responses are given.**

7. a difference of 3
6 and 3, 5 and 2, 4 and 1

8. a difference of 0
6 and 6, 5 and 5, 4 and 4

9. a sum of 6
5 and 1, 4 and 2, 3 and 3

10. an even sum
5 and 1, 4 and 6, 2 and 2

11. a difference of 2 or more
6 and 1, 6 and 2, 6 and 3

12. a sum of 9 or more
4 and 5, 5 and 4, 5 and 6

13. Suppose a coin is tossed once.

a. Find the theoretical probabilities P(heads) and P(tails). $\frac{1}{2}; \frac{1}{2}$

b. How do the results of part (a) compare with the experimental probabilities you found in Exercise 6(b)? **Sample Response: They are about the same.**

14. a. Sample Response: losing the coin toss; Given only two choices, it seems at least 1 out of 21 guesses would have been correct.

b. Sample Response: No; It's impossible to change your luck.

14. Football Football teams toss a coin before each game. The team that wins the toss chooses whether to kick or receive the ball at the start of the game. The article shown describes a high school football team's unfortunate win/loss record both on the field and in the opening coin toss.

a. The article mentions an "improbable pair of losing streaks" with which a high school football team opened its 1983 season. Which of these losing streaks was more improbable in your opinion? Why?

b. The article says that ". . . . it's a whole lot easier to change one's luck than one's skill." Do you agree? Explain.

There's a Moral Here, Cougar Fans

… an improbable pair of losing streaks: The Cougars had lost not only 21 straight games but also, amazingly, every pregame coin toss over the same span. [The team] proceeded to lose its 22nd straight game, 58–0, the worst defeat in the school's history, but not before finally winning a coin flip. Which goes to show, we suppose, that it's a whole lot easier to change one's luck than one's skill.

Sports Illustrated,
September 5, 1983

Complete Exercise 15. Then for Exercises 16–24, find the theoretical probability of each event.

Outcome for blue cube	Outcome for red cube					
	1	2	3	4	5	6
6	?	?	?	?	11	?
5	?	?	?	?	?	?
4	5	?	?	?	?	?
3	?	?	?	?	?	?
2	?	?	?	?	?	?
1	?	?	?	?	?	?

15. Suppose you roll a red cube and a blue cube. Copy and complete the table to show the sums (outcomes) that can occur.

16. $P(2)$ $\frac{1}{36}$ 17. $P(6)$ $\frac{5}{36}$ 18. $P(1)$ $\frac{0}{36}$ or 0   19. $P(8)$ $\frac{5}{36}$

20. $P(3)$ $\frac{2}{36}$ or $\frac{1}{18}$ 21. $P(7)$ $\frac{6}{36}$ or $\frac{1}{6}$ 22. $P(4$ or $5)$ $\frac{7}{36}$ 23. $P(\text{even})$ $\frac{18}{36}$ or $\frac{1}{2}$

24. $P(\text{sum is even and greater than 6})$ $\frac{9}{36}$ or $\frac{1}{4}$

15. 7, 8, 9, 10, 12;
6, 7, 8, 9, 10, 11;
6, 7, 8, 9, 10;
4, 5, 6, 7, 8, 9;
3, 4, 5, 6, 7, 8;
2, 3, 4, 5, 6, 7

Native American Games Use the information below for Exercises 25 and 26.

Many Native American peoples developed games that involved probability. In several types of Native American stick games, one player separated an odd number of sticks into two bundles and a second player tried to guess, without counting, which bundle had an *even* number of sticks. A correct guess counted as a win.

25. Suppose you use 25 sticks to play a stick game like the ones described above.

25. a. 2, 4, 6, 8, 10, 12, 14, 16, 18, 20, 22, 24; 1, 3, 5, 7, 9, 11, 13, 15, 17, 19, 21, 23

   a. If there are 12 sticks in the bundle chosen by the second player, then he or she wins. List all possible outcomes that produce a win. Then list all possible outcomes that produce a loss.

   b. Find the theoretical probability of the second player's winning the stick game. $\frac{1}{2}$

26. **Home Involvement** Work with a partner.

   a. Play the stick game from Exercise 25 forty times. Use 25 straws or toothpicks for sticks. Use a table like the one shown to keep track of each game's results.   Answers will vary. Check students' work.

Event	Tally	Frequency
win	?	?
loss	?	?

   b. Use your results from part (a) to find the experimental probability of the second player's winning the stick game.
   Answers will vary. Check students' work.

   c. How does your answer to part (b) compare with your answer to Exercise 25(b)? Sample Response: It is close to the theoretical probability of $\frac{1}{2}$.

27. Suppose an experiment involves spinning the spinner once.

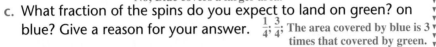

a. What are all the possible outcomes of the experiment?   green, blue

b. Are landing on green and landing on blue equally likely events? Why or why not?
No; Blue covers a larger area.

c. What fraction of the spins do you expect to land on green? on blue? Give a reason for your answer. $\frac{1}{4}$; $\frac{3}{4}$; The area covered by blue is 3 times that covered by green.

d. **Writing** Suppose you repeat the experiment 40 times. What results do you expect? Do you think the results will always match your expectations? Why or why not?

27. d. Sample Response: Spinning green about 10 times and blue about 30 times; No; Theoretical and experimental probabilities are seldom the same.

Challenge Sketch a spinner for each situation.

28. The possible outcomes are X and Y. The probability of spinning an X is two times the probability of spinning a Y.

28.

29. The possible outcomes are E, F, and G. The probability of spinning an E is $\frac{3}{4}$. The probability of spinning an F is $\frac{1}{8}$.

R e f l e c t i n g ◄►on the Section

Be prepared to discuss your response to Exercise 30 in class.

30. Suppose that the weather forecaster on television predicts that the chance of rain tomorrow is 70%. (Remember, 70% = $\frac{7}{10}$.)

a. Is tomorrow a good day to have a cookout? Explain.
No; It is likely to rain.

b. What is the probability it will not rain tomorrow?   30% or $\frac{3}{10}$

Discussion

Exercise 30 checks that you understand the meaning of probability.

S p i r a l ◄►Review

For each sequence, make a table, draw a graph, and write an equation. Then predict the 100th term. (Module 1, p. 20)

31. 10, 20, 30, 40, ...
See Additional Answers.

32. 16, 17, 18, 19, ...
See Additional Answers.

For Exercises 33–35, find each sum or difference. (Toolbox, p. 581)

33. 25.47 + 12.16
37.63

34. 2.45 + 9 + 3.1
14.55

35. 10 – 4.983
5.017

36. Find the mean of these travel times, in minutes, to get to school: 10, 18, 25, 36, 40, 15, 22, 34, 32, 18, 21, 29. (Toolbox, p. 595)
25 min

Predicting from a Sample

37. Suppose a bag contains 6 cubes: 3 red, 2 green, and 1 yellow. Suppose you pick a cube without looking in the bag.

   a. Find the theoretical probability of picking each color. See below.

   b. Find the sum of the three probabilities you found in part (a). 1

   c. Suppose you add more yellow cubes to the bag. How many should you add so that $P(\text{yellow}) = \frac{1}{2}$? Explain.

4; Since 5 out of 10 cubes would be yellow, $P(\text{yellow}) = \frac{5}{10} = \frac{1}{2}$.

37. a. $P(\text{red}) = \frac{3}{6} = \frac{1}{2}$, $P(\text{green}) = \frac{2}{6} = \frac{1}{3}$, $P(\text{yellow}) = \frac{1}{6}$

38. Home Involvement Work with a partner. One person should fill a bag with 8 cubes of 3 colors, without showing the other person. The second person should pick a cube, record the color, and put it back in the bag.

After repeating this experiment 20 times, the second person should use experimental probabilities to guess how many cubes of each color are in the bag.

Sample Response: The experimental probabilities were $P(\text{yellow}) = \frac{2}{20}$, $P(\text{red}) = \frac{6}{20}$, and $P(\text{green}) = \frac{12}{20}$. So, my guess is 1 yellow, 2 red, and 5 green.

Tune In to Data

SET UP *Work in a group. You will need your data from Project Question 3.*

Making Predictions from Data During the past week, you collected data about television commercials. Now you'll examine the data.

 4 Gather together all the data your group has collected.
Answers may vary. Check students' work.

 5 Study your group's data. Then discuss each question.

   a. Was the number of commercials about the same for each time slot? Answers may vary. Check students' work.

   b. What types of products were advertised? Were the same products advertised during each time slot?

   c. How do advertisers try to influence your choices?

   d. Can you make any predictions about the number of commercials and the products you might see advertised during your favorite program? Explain.

Extra Skill Practice

For Exercises 1–19, use the table and information below.

Suppose a bag contains 8 marbles, with 2 each of the colors red, yellow, blue, and green. An experiment involves picking a marble from the bag, recording its color, and putting it back in the bag. The table shows the results after the experiment has been repeated 100 times.

Outcome	Frequency
red	40
yellow	20
blue	28
green	12

Find the experimental probability of each event.

1. P(red) $\frac{40}{100} = \frac{2}{5}$

2. P(yellow) $\frac{20}{100} = \frac{1}{5}$

3. P(blue) $\frac{28}{100} = \frac{7}{25}$

4. P(green) $\frac{12}{100} = \frac{3}{25}$

5. P(not red) $\frac{60}{100} = \frac{3}{5}$

6. P(red or yellow) $\frac{60}{100} = \frac{3}{5}$

7. P(not green) $\frac{88}{100} = \frac{22}{25}$

8. P(brown) $\frac{0}{100} = 0$

9. P(not yellow) $\frac{80}{100} = \frac{4}{5}$

Find the theoretical probability of each event.

10. P(red) $\frac{2}{8} = \frac{1}{4}$

11. P(yellow) $\frac{2}{8} = \frac{1}{4}$

12. P(blue) $\frac{2}{8} = \frac{1}{4}$

13. P(green) $\frac{2}{8} = \frac{1}{4}$

14. P(not blue) $\frac{6}{8} = \frac{3}{4}$

15. P(blue or red) $\frac{4}{8} = \frac{1}{2}$

16. P(not yellow) $\frac{6}{8} = \frac{3}{4}$

17. P(brown) $\frac{0}{8} = 0$

18. P(not red) $\frac{6}{8} = \frac{3}{4}$

19. How many red marbles do you expect to get if you repeat the experiment 500 times? Did you use *experimental probability* or *theoretical probability* to find your answer? Explain.

    125; Sample Response: theoretical probability; Experimental probability can vary greatly for a small number of trials. As the number of trials increases, the experimental probabilities should begin to approach the theoretical probabilities. So when they can be calculated, it is better to use theoretical probabilities to make predictions.

Standardized Testing ◀▶ Performance Task

Suppose a coin bank contains only 8 quarters. One quarter is dated 1955, 1 quarter is dated 1975, 3 quarters are dated 1985, and 3 quarters are dated 1997. Shaking the coin bank causes one coin at a time to come out randomly.

1. What is the probability that the first coin to come out is dated 1975? Explain. $\frac{1}{8}$; One quarter out of 8 is dated 1975.

2. Suppose the first coin to come out is *not* dated 1985. What is the probability that the second coin to come out is dated 1985? Explain. $\frac{3}{7}$; There are 7 quarters left and 3 are dated 1985.

3. What is the probability that the last coin to come out is a quarter? Explain. 1; All the coins in the bank are quarters.

Section 4 Problem Solving

WARM-UP EXERCISES

Tell which problem solving strategy or strategies you would use to solve each problem.

1. finding a path through a maze
   work backward

2. deciding in what order you should deliver packages that are to be delivered to different locations
   make an organized list and make a diagram

3. trying to find your lost keys
   act it out (retrace your steps) and use logical reasoning

4. how you can rearrange the furniture in you room
   draw a diagram

What Can You EXPECT?

‹‹‹Setting the Stage

When you make a choice that affects your health or well-being, you may have to interpret information and analyze claims made by others.

The table displays data from a study. It shows how changing to an active lifestyle could lengthen a man's life span. In the study, an active lifestyle involves using 2000 or more Calories (Cal) per week on exercise.

Effects on Men of a Change to an Active Lifestyle	
Age when active lifestyle began	**Estimated increase in life span (years)**
35–39	2.51
40–44	2.34
45–49	2.10
50–54	2.11
55–59	2.02
60–64	1.75
65–69	1.35
70–74	0.72
75–79	0.42

Think About It

1 a. How many years could a man who begins an active lifestyle at age 67 expect to gain? 1.35 years

   b. Suppose a man begins exercising on his 67th birthday and wants to gain the additional years stated in the table above. What is the least number of total calories he will have to use on exercise by age 80? 1,352,000 calories

2 What do you notice about the estimated number of years gained as you read the table from top to bottom?
> Except for the age bracket 50–54, the number of years gained decreases.

3 The study shows how the choice to change from an inactive to an active lifestyle could affect the length of a man's life.

   a. What choices, other than amount of exercise, can people make that might affect the length of their lives?
> Sample Response: Stop smoking and eat a healthy diet.

   b. What are some factors that they might not be able to change?
> Sample Response: Air quality, work environment, family history

4 What does the table suggest to you about the effects of exercise?
> Sample Response: The sooner you begin to change to an active lifestyle, the more years of life you will gain.

Exploration 1 ▶▶▶▶▶▶▶▶▶▶▶▶▶▶▶▶▶▶▶▶▶▶▶

Four Steps to PROBLEM SOLVING

GOAL

LEARN HOW TO...
* recognize the steps of the 4-step approach to problem solving

AS YOU...
* solve a problem about exercise

SET UP *Work in a group of three.*

In response to the study, two doctors questioned whether the number of years gained would justify the time and effort needed to burn 2000 Cal per week. They explored the study's claim about years gained for a man beginning exercise at age 35 and continuing until age 80.

To investigate the claim, the doctors focused on stair-stepping. They found that it takes one second to climb 2 stairs, and that climbing 70 stairs burns 28 Cal.

▶ How did these doctors know how to evaluate the study's claim? Problem solving has been described as "what you do when you don't know what to do." Some people use a 4-step approach to solve problems, as you will do in Questions 5–8.

5 **a.** Discuss what the two doctors were trying to do. In your own words, state the problem the doctors tried to solve. Sample Response: Is the effect of exercising on life span worth the time and effort?

b. Make a list of information needed to solve this problem. Check off information you already have, and circle information you'll need to calculate or find. Sample Response: the effect of exercise on life span, the time and effort required to burn 2000 calories a week

6 Discuss how you would go about solving the problem. Sample Response: Find the amount of time needed to burn 2000 cal per week and present the data to people who stair-step in health clubs. Ask their opinion.

7 Solve the problem individually. Sample Response: about 42 min per week; About 70% of the 20 people I interviewed felt the gain was worth the time and effort.

8 Look back over your solution.

a. Check all your computations. Check students' work.

b. Does your solution answer the question your group asked? Explain. Sample Response: Yes; I got direct answers to the question I was asking.

c. Explain another way you could have solved the same problem.

d. The two doctors were interested in whether the gain in years is worth the time spent exercising. What do you think? Write a brief letter expressing your thoughts. Be sure to include your solution to the problem and how you found it. Answers will vary.

9 **Try This as a Class** Questions 5–8 illustrate the steps in the 4-step approach to problem solving. Describe each step by writing a short phrase about what you did for each question.

8. c. Sample Response: I could compare the number of days spent exercising to the number of days the life span increases.

9. Sample Response: Step 1: Understand the problem—In Question 5 we made sure that we understood the problem; Step 2: Make a plan—In Question 6 we planned how we would solve the problem; Step 3: Carry out the plan—In Question 7 we used the plan to solve the problem; Step 4: Look back—In Question 8 we looked back to see if we answered the question and looked at other possible ways to solve it.

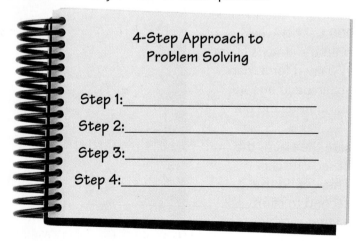

4-Step Approach to Problem Solving

Step 1:_____
Step 2:_____
Step 3:_____
Step 4:_____

HOMEWORK EXERCISES ▶ See Exs. 1–3 on p. 45.

Exploration 2

The LAST CARD Problem

SET UP *Work in a group. You will need 15 index cards numbered from 1 to 15.*

One of the steps in the 4-step approach is to make a plan to solve the problem. Making a plan often involves choosing a problem solving strategy such as *look for a pattern* or *use a model*. You might use one of these strategies as you explore the Last Card Problem.

▶ **The Last Card Problem** **Start with a stack of cards in numerical order from top to bottom. Then do as follows:**

First

Put the top card face up on the table.

Next

Put the next card on the bottom of the stack.

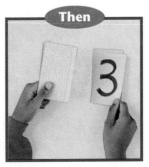

Then

Continue until all the cards are face up.

▶ **Can you predict what the last card will be if you know how many cards you start with?**

10 Suppose you start the Last Card Problem with six cards.

    a. Which card do you think will be last?
    Answers will vary. (The correct answer is 4.)
    b. Try the experiment with your cards. Were you right?
    Answers will vary.

11 Suppose you start the Last Card Problem with nine cards. What will be the number on the last card? 2

12 Suppose you start with 16 cards or 20 cards. What will be the number on the last card in each case? Explain your answers.
16, 8; Sample Response: I made a set of cards and did the problems.

HOMEWORK EXERCISES ▶ See Exs. 4–7 on pp. 45–46.

4-Step Approach to Problem Solving (p. 42)

Step 1: Understand the Problem
- Read the problem carefully, probably several times.
- Identify what the question is.
- Restate the problem in your own words.
- Identify the information needed to solve the problem, and determine if any of it is missing.

Step 2: Make a Plan
You may have to choose several problem solving strategies such as:
- try a simpler problem
- make an organized list
- act it out
- use logical reasoning
- make a picture or diagram
- make a table
- look for a pattern
- guess and check
- work backward
- use an equation

Step 3: Carry Out the Plan
- Solve the problem using the strategies you selected.
- You may need to change strategies.

Step 4: Look Back
- Check that you answered the question being asked.
- Check that your solution seems reasonable.
- Check that your work is accurate.
- Try to find another method to solve the problem and compare the results.
- Study the solution to see if the method can be generalized or extended to other situations or to solve other problems.

CLOSURE QUESTION

List each step in the 4-step Approach to Problem Solving in this section and briefly explain each step.

Answer: Understand the problem, make a plan, carry out the plan, look back. In the first step, you identify the question and gather the necessary information. In the second step, you decide on a problem solving strategy. In the third step, you solve the problem. In the fourth step, you check to make sure that your solution is accurate and makes sense.

Key Concepts Questions

13 **a.** Which strategies did you use when you solved the card problems in Question 12? **Sample Response: act it out, make a table, look for a pattern**

b. Why would you want to use more than one strategy?
Sample Response: one strategy may not work

14 Why is looking back an important step in problem solving?
Sample Response: It is easy to make and overlook a mistake.

Section 4

Practice & Application Exercises

1. Calculator Assume a person jogging 1 mi at a rate of 5 mi/h will burn 100 Cal.

   a. At this rate, how many minutes does it take to jog 1 mi? **12 min**

   b. At this rate, how many minutes per week must a person jog to burn 2000 Cal? **240 min**

   c. At age 35, a man changes to an active lifestyle. If he jogs regularly until age 80, how many minutes of his lifetime will he have to spend jogging to burn 2000 Cal per week?
   561,600 min

   d. **Writing** Is jogging as efficient as stair-stepping for increasing the number of years you live? Explain.
   No; It takes almost 6 times as long to burn 2000 cal jogging as it does stair-stepping.

2. **Geometry Connection**
   Three rhombuses with sides 1 in. long can be placed side by side as shown to form a figure with a

   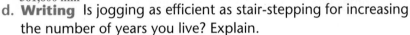

   perimeter of 8 in. If another figure is formed in the same way using 20 rhombuses, what will its perimeter be? **42 in.**

3. A pet shop has 12 dogs and cats. Each dog is fed 5 oz of pet chow per meal and each cat is fed 3 oz. It takes 42 oz of pet chow to feed all 12 animals one meal. How many dogs are there? **3 dogs**

4. Two cards are on a table. A 12 is written on one of the cards and a 9 on the other. Each card also has a number written on its back. By turning over one or both or neither of the cards and adding the two numbers showing, you can get each of these sums: 15, 16, 20, and 21. What number is written on the back of each card?

   4. 4 on the back of the 9 and 11 on the back of the 12, or 8 on the back of the 9 and 7 on the back of the 12

5. Natasha's scores on her first three quizzes were 88, 72, and 80. She reasons that if she scores high enough on the next quiz, then the mean of her quiz scores will be at least 90. Do you think Natasha's solution is reasonable? Why or why not?
   No; She would have to get a 120 on the next quiz.

6. **Challenge** Suppose you buy lunch for the drama club. You have enough money to buy 20 salads or 15 sandwiches. The members want 12 sandwiches. How many salads can you buy? **4 salads**

8. b. $P(R) = \frac{3}{6}$ or $\frac{1}{2}$,
$P(B) = \frac{2}{6}$ or $\frac{1}{3}$, $P(W) = \frac{1}{6}$

**7. Partial Sample
Response:** Use the
average life span to
convert the 13 years and
4 months to hours per
day. Convert the 2 years
and 7 months to minutes
per hour of television.
Decide if the results seem
reasonable; Yes; The
results from my
calculations seem
reasonable.

Reflecting ◀▷ on the Section

Be prepared to report on the following topic in class.

7. Describe a situation in daily life when you have had to solve a problem.
How was the process you used similar to the 4-step approach?
Answers will vary.

Spiral ◀▷ Review

8. The spinner shown is spun once and the color of the section that the
spinner lands on is recorded. **(Module 1, p. 33)**

a. What are all the possible outcomes of the experiment?
R, B, W

b. What is the theoretical probability of each outcome?

c. Suppose the spinner is spun 30 times. How many
times would you expect to get red? about 15

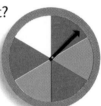

Use compatible numbers to estimate each quotient. **(Toolbox, p.583)**

9. $19\overline{)101}$ about 5   **10.** $83\overline{)164}$ about 2   **11.** $148\overline{)612}$ about 4

Working on the Module Project

Tune In to Data

6. Sample Response: Is the claim that the average American will watch
13 years and 4 months of television reasonable? If so, is it reasonable that
2 years and 7 months of that time could be spent watching commercials?;
the life span of the average American, the average number of minutes of
commercials per hour of television.

SET UP *Work in a group.*

Problem Solving Use the 4-step approach to determine
whether the following claim is valid.

> ❝The average American will spend 13 years and 4 months
> watching television. During that time, 2 years and
> 7 months will be spent watching commercials.❞

6 Describe the problem you need to solve. Identify any
information missing from the problem. See above.

7 Devise a plan and solve the problem. Do you think the
claim is valid? Why or why not? See above.

8 Look back. Find another way to verify your answer.
Sample Response: Take a survey to find out how much
television people watch. Record the number of minutes of
commercials during various time periods. Predict the totals over
a lifetime.

1. David earns $6.00 per hour plus $9.00 for every extra hour he works over 40 h per week. If David earned $285.00 last week, how many extra hours did he work? 5 h

2. Cynthia needs $1500 to buy a computer. The table shows how much money she had in October, November, and December. If this pattern continues, in what month will she be able to buy the computer? April

Month	Amount of money
October	$600
November	$750
December	$900

3. Jermaine sent a message to four friends. Two of the friends each sent the message to three other people and the other two friends each sent the message to five other people. Each of these other people then sent the message to one other person. How many people in all were sent the message? 36

4. Jenna and Elizabeth play soccer at a local playground. They are both on the soccer field today, but they have different schedules. Jenna plays every 2 days and Elizabeth plays every 4 days. How many times will they both be on the soccer field on the same day during the next eight weeks? 14

Standardized Testing ◀▶ Free Response

Suppose Jana plans on doing five events (Events A–E) at an athletic competition. The judges require that Event C be performed either first or last. In how many different orders can Jana perform her five events? 48 different orders

FOR ASSESSMENT AND PORTFOLIOS

THE Painted CUBE

A unit cube has edges 1 unit long.

The Situation See the Resource Book for a detailed discussion of this Extended Exploration

Katie, a student at the world's first orbiting middle school, noticed that unit cubes float in zero gravity. If she was careful, she could even build floating geometric shapes with the unit cubes.

One day Katie used the unit cubes to build a larger floating cube that was three units long on each edge. She then painted all the exposed faces of the unit cubes bright red. Unfortunately, just after she finished, she sneezed, scattering the unit cubes. No cubes remained attached to each other.

The Problem

When Katie gathers the cubes, how many cubes will she find that have exactly 6 faces painted red? 5 faces painted red? 4 faces painted red? 3 faces painted red? 2 faces painted red? 1 face painted red? 0 faces painted red? 0; 0; 0; 8; 12; 6; 1

Something to Think About

◆ How many unit cubes should she have in all? 27

◆ Does each unit cube have the same number of painted faces? No.

Present your Results

Write a summary that clearly explains how you solved the problem. Include any drawings or other representations that will help make your explanation clear to others. Sample Response: I used a model to find there was 1 cube with no painted faces, 6 with 1 painted face, 12 with 2 painted faces, and 8 with 3 painted faces.

The Assessment Scales on page 49 will help you and your teacher think about your work on this and other Extended Explorations (E²). The presentation scale will help you assess how well you present your results: Remember, a solution should always include an explanation of your work as well as your answer. In Sections 5 and 6, you will learn to use the other scales.

If your score is in the shaded area, explain why on the back of this sheet and stop.

☆ The star indicates that you excelled in some way.

 ## Problem Solving

❶ I did not understand the problem well enough to get started or I did not show any work.

❸ I understood the problem well enough to make a plan and to work toward a solution.

❺ I made a plan, I used it to solve the problem, and I verified my solution.

 ## Mathematical Language

❶ I did not use any mathematical vocabulary or symbols, or I did not use them correctly, or my use was not appropriate.

❸ I used appropriate mathematical language, but the way it was used was not always correct or other terms and symbols were needed.

❺ I used mathematical language that was correct and appropriate to make my meaning clear.

 ## Representations

❶ I did not use any representations such as equations, tables, graphs, or diagrams to help solve the problem or explain my solution.

❸ I made appropriate representations to help solve the problem or help me explain my solution, but they were not always correct or other representations were needed.

❺ I used appropriate and correct representations to solve the problem or explain my solution.

 ## Connections

❶ I attempted or solved the problem and then stopped.

❸ I found patterns and used them to extend the solution to other cases, or I recognized that this problem relates to other problems, mathematical ideas, or applications.

❺ I extended the ideas in the solution to the general case, or I showed how this problem relates to other problems, mathematical ideas, or applications.

 ## Presentation

❶ The presentation of my solution and reasoning is unclear to others.

❸ The presentation of my solution and reasoning is clear in most places, but others may have trouble understanding parts of it.

❺ The presentation of my solution and reasoning is clear and can be understood by others.

Section ⑤ Assessing Problem Solving

IN THIS SECTION

EXPLORATION 1
♦ Evaluating Solutions

EXPLORATION 2
♦ Making Connections

Creative Solutions

◄····Setting the Stage

The reading below describes how Alesia Revis and her friend Sylvester solved a problem.

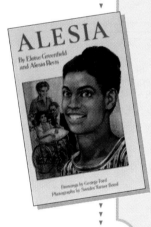

ALESIA

by Eloise Greenfield and Alesia Revis

A friend of mine named Sylvester came down to my office to have lunch with me today. When we left the cafeteria, we had to go through this corridor where the floor slopes uphill. It wasn't easy in our wheelchairs. My arms gave out, and then Sylvester said, "Hold on to my chair," and he pulled both of us. I should have held on with my left hand because my right arm is stronger and I could have helped roll my chair, but by the time I thought of it, we were halfway up the hill, and I was afraid that if I tried to switch hands I would roll backward and get hurt. Anyway, we made it. We got through it with nobody else's help and I was so proud of us.

Think About It

1 What problem did Alesia and Sylvester face?
getting up the incline in wheelchairs

2 Describe how their approach to the problem was like the 4-step approach to problem solving. **Sample Response: They recognized their problem and made a plan to solve it. They carried out their plan and then looked back to see how they could have used another plan.**

► **Alesia faced a special challenge related to getting around in a wheelchair. Having good problem solving skills can help you make good choices when you face your own challenges.**

Evaluating SOLUTIONS

▸ One way to improve your problem solving skills is to evaluate or assess your past experiences. You can use the Assessment Scales on page 49 to assess your work in mathematics. In this Section you'll evaluate solutions to the Last Card Problem from Section 4.

The problem solving scale helps you evaluate your approach to solving a problem.

A marker is used to draw a segment along the scale. This student scored at level 4 on this scale.

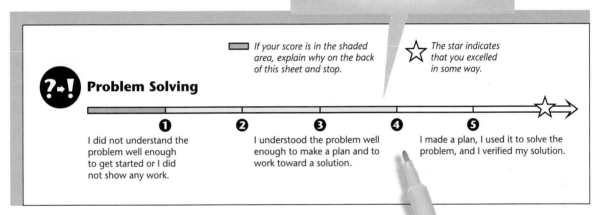

If your score is in the shaded area, explain why on the back of this sheet and stop.

☆ *The star indicates that you excelled in some way.*

?→! Problem Solving

❶ I did not understand the problem well enough to get started or I did not show any work.

❷

❸ I understood the problem well enough to make a plan and to work toward a solution.

❹

❺ I made a plan, I used it to solve the problem, and I verified my solution.

▸ When you assess your work using the problem solving scale, think about whether you:
　◆ understood the problem
　◆ made a plan
　◆ carried out the plan to solve the problem
　◆ looked back to verify your solution

3 **Try This as a Class** Discuss how the problem solving scale is related to the 4-step approach to problem solving you used in Section 4.
　Sample Response: Each part of the scale includes one or more of the four steps.

4 In Question 12 on page 43 of Section 4, you were asked to solve the Last Card Problem for 16 cards and for 20 cards. Suppose a group found the last card in each case but did not show any work. How would the group score on the problem solving scale? Why?
　1; They showed no work.

▶ **Here is how Kim's group approached the Last Card Problem.**

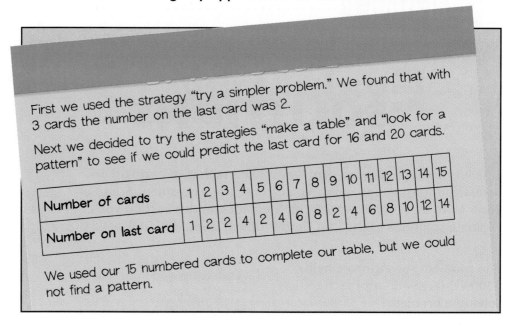

First we used the strategy "try a simpler problem." We found that with 3 cards the number on the last card was 2.

Next we decided to try the strategies "make a table" and "look for a pattern" to see if we could predict the last card for 16 and 20 cards.

Number of cards	1	2	3	4	5	6	7	8	9	10	11	12	13	14	15
Number on last card	1	2	2	4	2	4	6	8	2	4	6	8	10	12	14

We used our 15 numbered cards to complete our table, but we could not find a pattern.

5 **Discussion** If Kim's group stops without finding a solution, how should they score their work on the problem solving scale? Why?
Sample Response: 3; They understood the problem, made a plan, and worked toward a solution.

6 Describe any patterns you see in the table made by Kim's group.
Sample Response: Except for the instance using 1 card, the number of the last card is always even. The numbers on the last cards are in sequences of consecutive even integers.

▶ **When your approach to a problem does not help you find a solution, you may need to try a different method. As a new approach, Kim's group modeled each move for 6 cards.**

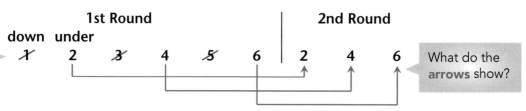

Why are **1, 3,** and **5** crossed out?

1st Round   **2nd Round**

down under

What do the **arrows** show?

7 **a.** Copy and complete the model. What number is crossed out next? What will be the last card? 2; 4

b. Use this method to solve the Last Card Problem for 16 cards and for 20 cards. 16; 8

✔ QUESTION 8

...checks that you can assess a solution using the problem solving scale.

8 **✔ CHECKPOINT** Suppose Kim's group uses the method above and finds the last card for 16 cards and for 20 cards. How should they score their work on the problem solving scale? Why?
4 if they made a plan and used it to solve the problem, but didn't verify their work; 5 if they did verify their work.

HOMEWORK EXERCISES See Exs. 1–3 on p. 56.

M[A]KING Connections

SET UP *You will need: • Labsheet 5A • marker for highlighting • your group's solution to Question 12 on page 43*

GOAL

LEARN HOW TO...
◆ use the connections scale

AS YOU...
◆ find ways to extend your solution to the Last Card Problem

▶ **When you solve problems, you sometimes see familiar patterns. The table shows patterns that Greg's group recognized while working on the Last Card Problem.**

Number of cards	1	②	3	④	5	6	7	⑧	9	10	11	12	13	14	15
Number on last card	1	2	2	4	2	4	6	8	2	4	6	8	10	12	14

9 a. Why do you think an X was drawn over the data for 1 card?
    The problem makes no sense using 1 card.

   b. Why do you think brackets were drawn under the table?
    to group sequences of consecutive even integers

   c. Why do you think circles were drawn around 2, 4, and 8?
    to show where a sequence ends

   d. Suppose you continue the table. What do you think the next circled number will be? Why? How would you describe the circled numbers?
    16; Each circled number is twice the circled number preceding it; powers of 2

▶ **Greg's group connected another mathematical topic, the powers of 2, to the Last Card Problem. You can use the connections scale to assess how well you make mathematical connections.**

Connections

❶ I attempted or solved the problem and then stopped.

❷ ❸ I found patterns and used them to extend the solution to other cases, or I recognized that this problem relates to other problems, mathematical ideas, or applications.

❹ ❺ I extended the ideas in the solution to the general case, or I showed how this problem relates to other problems, mathematical ideas, or applications.

You might score a 3 on the connections scale if you:
- recognize how the problem is related to other problems
- recognize connections to other mathematical topics
- extend the solution beyond the original problem

You might score a 5 on the connections scale if you:
- show how the problem or mathematics can be applied elsewhere
- extend the problem to the general case

10 **Discussion** Suppose a group solved the Last Card Problem for 16 cards and for 20 cards, and then stopped. How would the group score on the connections scale? Why?
1; They didn't use patterns or ideas to extend the solution.

QUESTION 11

...checks that you can assess a solution using the connections scale.

11 ✔ **CHECKPOINT** Suppose the group in Question 10 also explained how they used powers of 2 in their solution. How would the group score on the connections scale now? Why?
3; They recognized the problem relates to a mathematical idea but didn't extend the solution.

▶ **Extending Solutions** You can earn a higher score on the connections scale by extending or applying a solution.

12.b. Sample Response: The numbers on the last card are in sequences of consecutive even integers that begin with 2. A particular sequence ends when the number of cards is a power of 2; yes.

12 **a.** What is the next power of 2 after 16? 32

b. Look at the table on page 53. What pattern do you see? Does it continue for 17 cards, 18 cards, and so on?

Use Labsheet 5A for Questions 13 and 14.

13 **a.** Complete the *Last-Card Table* through 20 cards. 16, 2, 4, 6, 8

b. How could you verify (check) your answers?
Sample Response: Use a model or draw a diagram.

14 **a.** Without extending the table any more, predict the last card for a stack of 33 cards. 2

b. Complete the *Last-Card Table* through 33 cards. Compare your prediction in part (a) with your answer in the table.
10, 12, 14, 16, 18, 20, 22, 24, 26, 28, 30, 32, 2; They are the same.

15 **Discussion** For each situation, tell how you would assess a student's solution to Questions 12–14 on the connections scale.

a. The student's work includes everything in Questions 12–14. 4

b. The student's work identifies a pattern and shows how to use it with *any number* of cards (the general case). 5

16 **Use Labsheet 5A.**

   a. Use the *Two Assessment Scales* to assess your group's solution to Question 12 on page 43 of Section 4.   Check students' work.

   b. Explain why you rated your group as you did on each scale.
   Answers will vary.

17 **Discussion** When would you shade a scale as far as the ☆ ?
   Sample Response: when all the criteria of 5 were met and the student developed a unique variation of the Last Number Problem

HOMEWORK EXERCISES ▶ See Exs. 4–7 on pp. 56–57.

Section 5
Key Concepts

The purpose of the Assessment Scales is to help you evaluate your solutions to problems and increase your problem solving ability.

Problem Solving Scale (pp. 51–52)
The problem solving scale is used to assess how well you apply the 4-step approach to problem solving.

Connections Scale (pp. 53–55)
The connections scale helps assess the connections you make to other problems, mathematical concepts, or applications.

Example Here are two ways Greg's group could have scored at level 5 on the connections scale:

• The group extended the Last Card Problem to determine the number on the last card no matter how many cards they used (general case).

• The group explained why the last card drawn equals the number of cards in the stack only when the number of cards is a power of 2.

CLOSURE QUESTION

When assessing your work, how could you score a 5 on the Problem Solving Scale? on the Connections Scale?

Answer: Sample Response: If I made a plan, used it to solve the problem, and verified my work.; If I extended the ideas in the solution to a general case, or I showed how the problem relates to other problems, mathematical ideas, or applications.

18 **Key Concepts Question** What problem solving strategies were used in this Section to solve the Last Card Problem?
   Try a simpler problem; Act it out; Use logical reasoning; Make a picture or diagram; Make a table; Look for a pattern.

1. B; Sample Response:

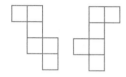

4. 1, 6, 2, 10, 3, 7, 4, 9, 5, 8; Sample Response: Working backwards from the answer, I filled in a chart like that on page 52.

1. **Visual Thinking** Choose the letter(s) of the pattern(s) that can be folded into a cube. Then draw two other patterns that will work.

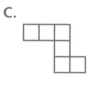

A.

B.

C.

2. Suppose next semester you want to take music, advanced science, creative writing, and basketball. Music is held periods 1, 2, and 4 only. Advanced science is offered periods 2, 3, and 4. Creative writing meets periods 1, 2, and 3, while basketball is offered periods 1, 3, and 4. List all the possible ways you could take these four classes. MSWB, MWSB, MWBS, WMSB, WMBS, WSBM, BMWS, BSWM, BWSM

3. **Use Labsheet 5B.** Assess your work in Exercises 1 and 2 using the problem solving scale. Answers will vary.

4. Suppose you have 10 cards numbered from 1 to 10. How would you order the cards so that when you follow the procedure below, the cards are in numerical order in a pile on a table, with the 1 at the bottom and the 10 at the top? (*Note:* Your solution should explain what you did and why you did it.)

♦ Place the top card face up on a table.
♦ Put the second card on the bottom of the stack.
♦ Place the third card face up on the table.
♦ Put the fourth card on the bottom of the stack, and so on, until all cards are on the table.

5. **Use Labsheet 5B.** Assess your work in Exercise 4 using the *Two Assessment Scales.* Give reasons why you rated your work the way you did, and describe what you could do to improve your solution.

6. **Challenge Use Labsheet 5A.** How could you use the patterns in the *Last-Card Table* to determine the number on the last card no matter how many cards you started with?

Reflecting ◀▶ on the Section

Write your response to Exercise 7 in your Journal.

7. The problem solving scale used in this section can be used to assess activities other than mathematics. Explain how the problem solving scale can be used to assess your performance in one activity you perform regularly. Activities to consider are science homework, chores, sports, or music.
   Answers will vary.

Spiral ◀▶ Review

8. Juanita was taking archery. One day she shot 6 arrows at the target shown. Each arrow hit the target. Which of the following numbers could have been her score: 5, 32, 19, 56, 47? Explain your reasoning. (Module 1, p. 44)

Replace each _?_ with the correct measure.
(Toolbox, p. 592; Table of Measures, p. 597)

9. 9 h = _?_ min 540   10. 4 yd = _?_ in. 144   11. 48 oz = _?_ lb 3

12. 60 ft = _?_ yd 20   13. 5 lb = _?_ oz 80   14. 3600 s = _?_ h 1

Estimation Estimate the value of each expression. Explain how you made each estimate. (Toolbox, pp. 582–583)

15. 236 · 18
about 4800; 240 · 20 = 4800

16. 2683 ÷ 91
about 30; 2700 ÷ 90 = 30

17. 236 + 481 + 352
about 1070; 240 + 480 + 350 = 1070

18. 1917 – 398
about 1500;
1900 – 400 = 1500

19. 51 · 122
about 6000;
50 · 120 = 6000

20. 104 + 92 + 113
about 300;
100 + 90 + 110 = 300

5. **Sample Response:** My problem solving score is 5 because I made a plan to solve the problem and verified my answer. My connections score is 3. I used the patterns I saw in the Last Card Problem to solve this problem. I couldn't, however, generalize beyond this particular solution.

Journal

Exercise 7 checks that you can use the problem solving scale to assess your work.

6. **Sample Responses:** Find the closest power of 2 and use the even number sequence pattern to find a solution. If the number of cards is 251, for example, start with 256, the power of 2 closest to 251. We know that if there are 256 cards, the number on the last card is 256. Work backwards from the column for 256 to set up a partial table to find the number on card 251, which will be 246; Subtract the greatest power of 2 that is less than the number of cards in the deck and multiply the difference by 2. For example, 251 – 128 = 123 and 123 · 2 = 246. The last card has the number 246 on it.

8. Eliminate 5, 19, and 47 because the sum of 6 odd integers is an even integer. Eliminate 56 because the highest possible score is 54 (9 · 6). A score of 32 is possible because one possible way to score it is 5 · 5 + 7 = 32.

Section 5

1. **a.** Suppose you have quarters, dimes, and pennies with a total value of $1.19. How many of each coin can you have without being able to make change for a dollar? 4 pennies, 4 dimes, and 3 quarters or 4 pennies, 9 dimes, and 1 quarter

   b. Show that the combination of coins that you found in part (a) is the largest amount of money in these 3 coins that you can have without being able to make change for a dollar.

   1. b. If there were one more of any of the coins, the change could be made. If, for example, there were 5 pennies, 4 dimes, and 3 quarters, the change would be 5 pennies, 3 quarters, and 2 dimes. If there were 4 pennies, 5 dimes, and 3 quarters, the change would be 5 dimes and 2 quarters.

   c. What score would you give your work in parts (a) and (b) on the problem solving scale on page 51?
   Answers will vary.

2. **a.** **Visual Thinking** Find the total number of triangles in the diagram. 37

   b. What score would you give your solution in part (a) on the problem solving scale on page 51?
   Answers will vary.

3. **a.** A book states that the average person in the United States will spend 1091 h in movie theaters in his or her lifetime. Do you think this claim is correct? Explain. (Assume the average lifespan of a person living in the United States is 74.9 years.)

   Yes; If the average movie is 2.5 h long, this is about 436 movies or about 7 per year from age 12 on.

   b. What score would you give your solution in part (a) on the problem solving and connections scales on pages 51 and 53?
   Answers will vary.

Standardized Testing ▶ Free Response

b. Yes; Alex could look at the table to see whether any combination of a sandwich, a dessert, and a drink costs exactly $3 or $4, which would make it possible to spend exactly $12. No combination costs exactly $4, but Alex could pay $3 per person for a deluxe sandwich, an apple, and water and treat 4 friends for exactly $12.

Suppose Alex has $12. He wants to use as much of the $12 as possible to treat some friends to a picnic lunch. Each person will get a sandwich, a dessert, and a drink.

a. Explain how Alex could find the number of friends he can invite and the combination of menu items to serve.
See below.

b. Is there a different way to solve this problem? Explain.
See above.

c. Alex wants to treat 4 friends to the same menu next month, and 5 friends the month after that. Can he use the solution from part (a) to help him find out how much money he needs each time? Explain.

Yes; He can take the price of the combination he chooses and multiply by 4 or 5.

Pine Point Specials	
Sandwich	
regular	$1.89
deluxe	$2.33
Dessert	
Cookie	$.89
Apple	$.67
Drink	$.75
(no charge for water)	

a. Alex could make an organized list of the (8) possible combinations and find the cost of each combination. He could then use estimation or mental math strategies to find the combination that would feed a whole number of friends at a total cost that comes closest to $12 without going over. Using this approach, he would find that he could serve 4 people a deluxe sandwich, an apple, and water for $3 each and spend a total of exactly $12.

Section 6 Expressions and Representations

The Clear CHOICE

WARM-UP EXERCISES

Simplify.

1. $87 + 258 + 390$ 735
2. $12 \cdot 42 \cdot 71$ 35, 784

Tell whether to use a table, line graph, or bar graph.

3. To show changes over time. line graph

4. To find an exact value. table

5. To compare data. bar graph

Setting the Stage ▸▸▸▸▸▸▸▸▸▸▸▸▸▸▸▸▸▸▸▸▸▸▸▸▸▸▸▸▸▸▸▸▸▸▸

Communicating your ideas and decisions clearly and correctly is an important skill. When you solve a problem and explain your solution, you should choose the words, symbols, and pictures you use carefully. The cartoon shows how important this can be.

CALVIN AND HOBBES © 1990 Watterson. Dist. by UNIVERSAL PRESS SYNDICATE. Reprinted with permission. All rights reserved.

1. a. $6 + 3$, y, square number, square, side, measure, diagonal, numbers and 2; not all are accurate and appropriate. For example, a square has four equal sides, so labeling it with sides 6 and 3 is inaccurate.

Think About It

1 What mathematical terms and picture does Hobbes (the tiger) use? Are they accurate and appropriate? Explain.

2 a. Write an explanation telling Calvin how to solve his problem.

  b. What choices did you make when deciding how to present your explanation? Did you use pictures? words? symbols?

  c. Was your explanation clear and appropriate? Explain.
  Sample Response: Yes; my 5 year-old brother understood it.

2. a. Sample Response: The "+" sign means "and" or "plus". So asking "What's 6 + 3?" is a short way of asking "If I have 6 pencils, for example, and then somebody gives me 3 more, how many pencils do I have altogether?" Now use some pencils to help you figure out the answer.

b. Sample Response: whether the symbols or the arithmetic were the problem, whether to use drawings or objects; no; yes; yes

▶ **In this Section, you will examine ways to assess and improve your mathematical communication skills.**

ORDER of OPERATIONS

▶ Mathematics has its own language of words and symbols. You probably used mathematical language to explain how to solve Calvin's problem. You can use the mathematical language scale from the Assessment Scales on page 49 to assess how well you use mathematical vocabulary and symbols.

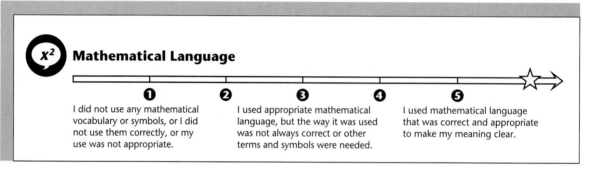

x^2 **Mathematical Language**

❶ I did not use any mathematical vocabulary or symbols, or I did not use them correctly, or my use was not appropriate.

❸ I used appropriate mathematical language, but the way it was used was not always correct or other terms and symbols were needed.

❺ I used mathematical language that was correct and appropriate to make my meaning clear.

3 Why is it important that mathematical symbols, words, and rules be used correctly when you solve a problem? **Sample Response: If they are not used correctly, the problem may be misunderstood.**

4 a. What score do you think Hobbes should give himself for his explanation of how to find 6 + 3? Why? **1; Symbols and vocabulary were used incorrectly.**

b. What score would you give your explanation and why? **Sample Response: 5; My explanation used correct and appropriate mathematical language.**

▶ In Calvin's problem, 6 + 3 is a numerical *expression*. An **expression** is a mathematical phrase that can be formed using numbers, variables, and operation symbols.

5 Discussion For parts (a) and (b), in what order must you do the operations to get the answers given?

a. 5 + 2 • 25 = 175 Add, then multiply. **b.** 5 + 2 • 25 = 55 Multiply, then add.

c. The expression 5 + 2 • 25 can be used to represent the total value (in cents) of a nickel and two quarters. Which of the answers from parts (a) and (b) gives the correct value? **b**

▶ To **evaluate** a numerical expression, you carry out the mathematical operations in the correct order. This order is known as the **order of operations.**

6 **Discussion** Discuss the order in which the operations were performed in each case to get the correct answer.

a. $3 \cdot 6 + 27 = 45$ Multiply, then add.

b. $36 - 24 \div 4 = 30$ Divide, then subtract.

c. $12 \div 3 + 10 = 14$ Divide, then add.

d. $15 + 12 \cdot 6 = 87$ Multiply, then add.

e. $12 \div 6 \cdot 2 = 4$ Divide, then multiply.

f. $36 - 15 + 5 = 26$ Subtract, then add.

g. $3 \cdot 4 - 54 \div 6 = 3$ Multiply, divide, then subtract.

h. $48 \div 4 - 6 \cdot 2 = 0$ Divide, multiply, then subtract.

7 Use correct and appropriate language to state a rule that describes the order of operations for an expression containing addition, subtraction, multiplication, and division.

Do all multiplications and divisions in order from left to right. Then go back and do all additions and subtractions in order from left to right.

▶ **Grouping Symbols** Operations within grouping symbols such as parentheses and brackets are carried out first. A fraction bar indicates that you carry out operations in the numerator separately from those in the denominator. Then you divide numerator by denominator.

8 For each expression, in what order were the operations carried out to get 35**?**

a. $[15 - (6 + 4)] \cdot 7 = 35$
$6 + 4; 15 - 10; 5 \cdot 7$

b. $\dfrac{(8 + 6) \cdot 5}{8 - 6} = 35$
$8 + 6; 14 \cdot 5; 8 - 6; 70 \div 2$

9 **Try This as a Class** Discuss where grouping symbols and exponents fit into the order of operations to get the correct answers shown.

a. $3 \cdot (6 + 4) = 30$

b. $2 \cdot 3^2 = 18$

c. $(2 \cdot 3)^2 = 36$

d. $2 \cdot (3 + 4)^2 = 98$

e. $[(5 - 4)^6 + 2] \cdot 8 = 24$

f. $\dfrac{48 \div (7 - 3)}{24 - 18} = 2$

9. The order is as follows: operations within grouping symbols, exponents, multiplication and division in order from left to right, addition and subtraction in order from left to right.

10 Use parentheses to rewrite $54 \div 6 - 3 \cdot 2$ so the result is 12.
$(54 \div 6 - 3) \cdot 2$

11 ✔ **CHECKPOINT** Evaluate each expression.

a. $9 + 2 \cdot 4$ 17

b. $10 \div 2 + 16 \div 8$ 7

c. $\dfrac{(12 - 5) \cdot 6}{6 + 1}$ 6

d. $[(5 - 3)^3 \div (7 - 5)] \cdot 5^2$ 100

✔ **QUESTION 11**

... checks that you can follow the order of operations to evaluate expressions.

HOMEWORK EXERCISES ▶ See Exs. 1–17 on p. 66.

GOAL

LEARN HOW TO...
- use the representations scale
- decide when a line graph is appropriate

AS YOU...
- explore television viewing habits

Exploration 2

Representations

▶ Equations, tables, graphs, and diagrams are representations that can be used to help explain solutions. You can use the representations scale to assess how well you use representations.

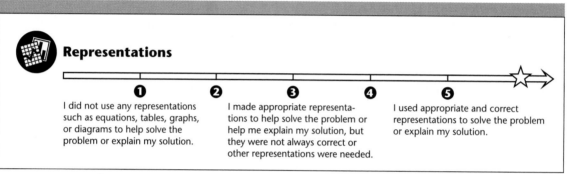

Representations

❶ ❷ ❸ ❹ ❺

❶ I did not use any representations such as equations, tables, graphs, or diagrams to help solve the problem or explain my solution.

❸ I made appropriate representations to help solve the problem or help me explain my solution, but they were not always correct or other representations were needed.

❺ I used appropriate and correct representations to solve the problem or explain my solution.

12 In the cartoon on page 59, Hobbes used a picture in his explanation to Calvin. What score do you think Hobbes should give himself on the representations scale? Why?
2; A diagram was used, but it wasn't appropriate.

▶ George is in the seventh grade. He thinks this table he saw in a newspaper can help him decide whether to change his television viewing habits to improve his mathematics proficiency next year.

Eighth Grade Students' Reports on Amount of Time Spent Watching Television Each Day (1990)		
Amount of time (hours)	Percent of students	Average mathematics proficiency
1 or less	12%	269
2	21%	268
3	22%	265
4 to 5	28%	260
6 or more	16%	245

The highest possible score is 500.

Percents are rounded to the nearest whole percent.

13 **Discussion** George thinks that on average he watches 3.5 h of television each day. Does he fit into any of the categories for "Amount of time"? Explain. Answers will vary. Sample Response: He probably would be in either the 3 h category or the 4 to 5 h category, but the table does not make it clear how data that fell in between categories were counted.

▶ **George made a line graph to compare his television viewing habits with those of eighth graders. On the graph he plotted data from the table and a point G to represent himself.**

Time Spent Watching Television Each Day

14 **Try This as a Class** Using his graph, George made the following observation. "I watch 3.5 h of TV per day. From my graph, I can see that 25% of eighth graders watch the same amount of TV."

a. How did George get 25%? Is his observation correct? Explain.

b. Does George's graph accurately represent the data from the table? Explain.

c. Is a line graph an appropriate way to represent this data? Explain. No; A line graph includes data points between intervals on the horizontal axis.

d. Is there a better way to represent the data? Explain.
Yes; A bar graph would show only the appropriate data points.

15 ✔ **CHECKPOINT** If the graph above is the only representation George used to explore the situation, how do you think he should score himself on the representations scale? Why?
2; He used a graph but it wasn't appropriate.

16 George also wants to investigate whether the amount of time spent watching television is related to the average mathematics proficiency.

a. Make a bar graph of the mathematics proficiency data. Include a title for the graph and label the axes.

b. What observation(s) might George make using your bar graph? Average math proficiency decreases as the time spent watching television increases.

c. Why is a bar graph more appropriate than a line graph for these data? Sample Response: The bar graph does not include data points in the intervals between categories on the horizontal axis, which would be inappropriate given the way the data are grouped.

14. a. He read the percent on the vertical axis that corresponds to the point G on the graph; No; If you add the percents corresponding to the six points plotted on the graph, the total is 125% rather than 100%.

b. No; The data for the five categories in the table are plotted correctly, but connecting the points with segments implies that you can find the percent of students who watched television for an amount of time in the intervals between the categories, and this is not correct.

✔ **QUESTION 15**

... checks that you can use the representations scale.

16. a. 8th Graders, Math Proficiency and Time Spent Watching TV

You can use most spreadsheets to create a bar graph for Question 16(a).

Step 1   Enter the data for the graph into the spreadsheet. The categories for the bars (the amounts of time in hours) should be entered in column A as text. The data for the lengths of the bars (the average mathematics proficiencies) should be entered in column B.

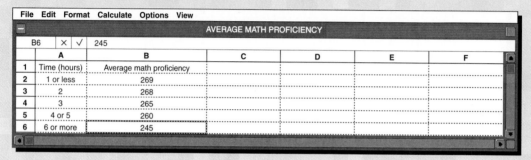

	A	B	C	D	E	F
1	Time (hours)	Average math proficiency				
2	1 or less	269				
3	2	268				
4	3	265				
5	4 or 5	260				
6	6 or more	245				

Step 2   To make a graph, highlight the data you entered and select the option that lets you make a chart. Then select the type of graph you want to make.

Step 3   Experiment with the labels, grid lines, and scale until the graph appears the way you want it to.

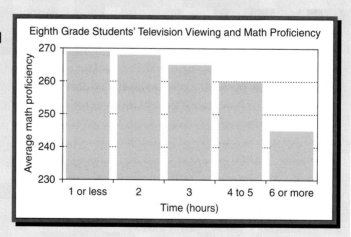

17 a. Nationwide, about half of the eighth graders who took the mathematics proficiency test in 1990 scored above 262, and about half scored below. George watches 3.5 h of TV each day. Based on these facts and the bar graph you made in Question 16(a), do you think George should change how much TV he watches? Why?

b. Suppose George decides to watch less TV. Can he be certain that his mathematics proficiency will change? Explain.
Sample Response: No; There must be other factors, such as time spent studying, or what he decides to do with his time.

17. a. Sample Response: Yes; Since George watches about 3.5 h of TV each day, his score is likely to be between 265 and 260, or about 262. A little less TV and more studying would mean he has a greater chance of scoring above the national average.

> **HOMEWORK EXERCISES** ▶ See Exs. 18–26 on pp. 67–68.

Section 6
Key Concepts

Key Terms

Mathematical Language Scale (p. 60)
The mathematical language scale assesses how well you use mathematical vocabulary and symbols.

expression

Order of Operations (pp. 60–61)
It is important to use the correct order of operations when evaluating expressions.

Example

order of operations

- First, evaluate expressions set apart by grouping symbols. Start with the innermost pair of symbols.
- Next evaluate all powers.
- Then do all multiplication and division in order from left to right.
- Finally, do all addition and subtraction in order from left to right.

$3 + [11 + (7 - 4)]^2 \div 7$
$3 + [11 + 3]^2 \div 7$
$3 + 14^2 \div 7$
$3 + 196 \div 7$
$3 + 28$
31

evaluate

Representations Scale (pp. 62–63)
The representations scale assesses how well you use equations, tables, graphs, and diagrams to help solve a problem or explain your solution.

CLOSURE QUESTION

State the Order of Operations.

Answer: Complete operations inside parentheses, evaluate powers, do multiplication and division from left to right, do addition and subtraction from left to right.

18 Key Concepts Question Describe the steps you follow to evaluate $3 + 5 \cdot (6 - 3)^2$. Subtract 3 from 6 $(6 - 3 = 3)$, square the difference $(3^2 = 9)$, multiply the square by 5 $(5 \cdot 9 = 45)$, and add 3 to the product $(3 + 45 = 48)$.

YOU WILL NEED

For Ex. 18(b):
♦ Labsheet 6A

For Exs. 31–34:
♦ ruler

◀◀◀◀◀◀◀◀ **Practice & Application Exercises**

Evaluate each expression using the order of operations.

1. $48 - 6 \cdot 7$ 6
2. $9 \cdot (6 + 5) - 9$ 90
3. $9 \cdot 8 - 64 \div 8$ 64
4. $12 + 16 \div 2^2 - 2$ 14
5. $27 \div (12 - 9) \cdot 9$ 81
6. $(6 - 4)^2 \cdot (12 + 3)$ 60
7. $\dfrac{(10 - 8) \cdot 9}{5 + 1}$ 3
8. $\dfrac{70 \div (12 - 5)}{15 \div 3}$ 2
9. $3^3 \div [6^2 - (16 + 8)]$ 2.25

10. Write and evaluate an expression to represent the value (in cents) of 2 half-dollars, 5 quarters, 6 nickels, 3 dimes, and 3 pennies.
$2(50) + 5(25) + 6(5) + 3(10) + 3(1) = 288$

Use grouping symbols to make each statement true.

11. $28 - 9 \cdot 2 = 38$
$(28 - 9) \cdot 2 = 38$

12. $6 + 5 \cdot 3 - 2 = 11$
$6 + 5 \cdot (3 - 2) = 11$

13. $6 + 6 \div 2 \cdot 6 - 1 = 30$
$(6 + 6) \div 2 \cdot (6 - 1) = 30$

14. $4 \cdot 5 - 4^2 + 3 = 1$
$(4 \cdot 5) - (4^2 + 3) = 1$

15. **Challenge** Use grouping symbols to make the statement
$2 + 7^2 - 3^2 \div 3^2 - 1 \cdot 5 = 35$ true. $[2 + (7^2 - 3^2) \div (3^2 - 1)] \cdot 5 = 35$

16. *Pizza by the Inch* sells square pizza. The smallest pizzas are 5 in. on each side and sell for $1.99. The next size is a 10 in. by 10 in. for $4.99. The largest pizza costs $19.99 and has 20 in. sides.

   a. Which size is the best buy? Justify the operations you used to make your decision.

   b. Use the mathematical language scale on page 60. What score would you give your solution to part (a)?   Answers will vary.

17. **Geometry Connection** Read these instructions:

   "Draw a closed, four-sided flat figure that has sides that are segments that are all the same length and that has corners that are all the same shape."

   a. Write instructions for the same task using fewer words.   Draw a square.

   b. Compare your instructions with the given ones in terms of correctness and appropriateness. Both sets of instructions are correct. One is appropriate for someone who doesn't know what a square is and the other is not.

16. a. the medium or large; Sample Response: I multiplied to find the area of each pizza. Then I rounded the price of each pizza up by 1¢. Finally, I divided the price of each pizza by the area to get the price per square inch. The large and medium pizza both cost about $.05/in.^{2} The small pizza costs about $.08/in.^{2}

18. A circus has unicycles and tricycles. There are 25 cycles, with a total of 51 wheels.

   a. How many of each type of cycle does the circus have?
      12 unicycles, 13 tricycles

   b. **Use Labsheet 6A.** Use the *Three Assessment Scales* to assess your solution to part (a). Answers will vary.

Use the line graph for Exercises 19–21.

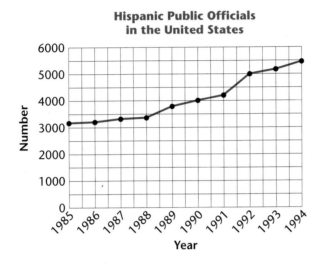

Hispanic Public Officials in the United States

19. What was the approximate number of Hispanic public officials in the year 1990? 4000

20. In what year was the number of Hispanic public officials about 5000? 1992

21. **Interpreting Data** Describe any trends in the data that the line graph helps you see.

21. Sample Response: There was a sharp increase in the number of Hispanic public officials between 1991 and 1992. Overall, the number of Hispanic public officials has increased over the years 1985–1994.

22. **Choosing a Data Display**
Decide whether a double bar graph or a double line graph is the most appropriate representation of the data in the table. Explain.
Double bar graph; There are no values for the categories between the six that are given.

Teens' Weekly Spending, 1994		
Goods or services	Boys	Girls
Food, snacks	$10.10	$6.50
Clothing	$6.19	$10.65
Entertainment	$4.35	$3.45
Records, tapes, CDs	$1.55	$1.80
Grooming/cosmetics	$1.10	$3.35

23. A student used the diagram below to show that

$$2(3 + 4) = 2 \cdot 3 + 2 \cdot 4.$$

Use the representations scale on page 62 to assess the student's diagram. What do you think the student's score should be? Why?

$$2(3 + 4) \quad = \quad 2 \cdot 3 \quad + \quad 2 \cdot 4$$

Sample Response: 3; The first diagram would be clearer if brackets were used to show the top row is composed of 3 squares plus 4 squares.

24. A student was trying to choose the most accurate and appropriate diagram from the following to show that $\frac{2}{3}$ of 6 is 4. Which should the student choose and why?

A. ⬤⬤◯   B. ⬤⬤⬤⬤◯◯   C. ⬤⬤ ⬤⬤ ◯◯

C; The diagram shows 6 objects divided into 3 groups and 2 out of 3 of the groups are clearly labeled.

25. Create Your Own Make a diagram to show that $2 \cdot 3 = 3 \cdot 2$. Then use the representations scale on page 62 to assess your diagram. ◯◯◯ / ◯◯◯ = ◯◯◯ ; Answers will vary.

Reflecting ◀▷**on the Section**

Be prepared to discuss your response to Exercise 26 in class.

26. It is not always easy to give walking or driving directions to help someone find a certain location. **Check students' work.**

a. Write instructions and draw a corresponding map to explain to someone how to get from your school to another location. Choose a location that requires at least five steps in your instructions.

b. Give your instructions and map to someone else who is familiar with your school and the location you chose. Have that person assess your work.

c. Did the person find that your instructions and map were correct and appropriate? that your meaning was clear? Make adjustments if needed. How did the assessment help you improve?

For Exercises 27–30, suppose each face of a cube was painted either red, white, or blue. The cube was rolled 60 times and the results were recorded in the table. Find each experimental probability.
(Module 1, p. 33)

Outcome	Frequency
red	20
white	33
blue	7
total	60

27. P(red) $\frac{20}{60}$ or $\frac{1}{3}$ 28. P(white) $\frac{33}{60}$ or $\frac{11}{20}$ 29. P(blue) $\frac{7}{60}$

30. How many faces do you think were painted each color? Explain your thinking. (Module 1, pp. 44 and 55)

Use a ruler to draw a segment of each length. (Toolbox, p. 591)

31. $1\frac{1}{2}$ in.   32. $5\frac{3}{4}$ in.   33. $6\frac{7}{8}$ in.   34. $3\frac{5}{16}$ in.

31–34. Check students' drawings.

30. 2 red, 3 white, 1 blue; Using the experimental probabilities, 1 out of 3 or 2 out of 6 faces are red, about 1 out of 2 or 3 out of 6 are white, and the remaining face is blue.

Tune In to Data

Displaying Data A visual display of the data you gathered about television commercials can help people quickly understand what you have learned from the data.

9 Look over the data from Module Project Question 4. What patterns or trends, if any, do you notice in the data? Answers will vary.

10 Discuss how you will display your data. Will a table, a bar graph, or a line graph help people see the patterns or trends you identified in your data?
 Sample Response: bar graph

11 Create representations that accurately display the patterns or trends you identified in two different sets of your data.
 Check students' work.

SET UP

• Work in a group.
• You will need your group's data from Module Project Question 4.

Evaluate each expression using the correct order of operations.

1. $32 - 2 \cdot 10$ 12

2. $4 \cdot (7 - 5) + 6$ 14

3. $6 \cdot 3 - 30 \div 5$ 12

4. $9 + 50 \div 5^2 \cdot 4$ 17

5. $26 - (2^3 + 12) + 4^2$ 22

6. $(3 + 7)^2 \cdot (8 - 5)^2$ 900

7. $\dfrac{16 \div (2 + 6)}{3 - 2}$ 2

8. $\dfrac{17 + (9 - 4)}{18 \div 9}$ 11

9. $\dfrac{(40 + 8) \div 8}{7 - 4}$ 2

10. $2 + [(8 + 7) \div 5] + 8 - 4$ 9

11. $8 + [(4^2 - 1^2) - 12] \cdot 10$ 38

Use grouping symbols to make each statement true.

12. $30 - 10 \div 5 = 4$ $(30 - 10) \div 5 = 4$

13. $3 + 12 \cdot 6 = 90$ $(3 + 12) \cdot 6 = 90$

14. $24 \div 2 + 2 = 6$ $24 \div (2 + 2) = 6$

15. $3^2 + 5^2 \div 2 = 17$ $(3^2 + 5^2) \div 2 = 17$

16. a. Make a graph of the data in the table. See below.

   b. Does the graph help you quickly understand the relationships among the data in the table? Explain.

1996 AKC Registrations	
Breed of Dog	Number Registered
Pomeranian	39,712
German shepherd	79,076
beagle	56,946
dachshund	48,426
poodle	56,803

Sample Response: Yes; The differences in the numbers registered are immediately obvious from the graph.

16. a.

1996 AKC Registration

Standardized Testing ◀▶ Multiple Choice

1. Which expression has the same value as $3 \cdot 4^3$? B

   (A) $12 \cdot 12 \cdot 12$ (B) $3 \cdot 4 \cdot 4 \cdot 4$ (C) $3 \cdot 3 \cdot 3 \cdot 4 \cdot 4 \cdot 4$

2. A rectangular planter is 6 in. high, 20 in. long, and 9 in. wide. Suppose a gardener fills the planter $\frac{1}{4}$ full of potting soil. Which expression could be used to find the amount of soil needed? B

   (A) $4(20 + 9 + 6)$ (B) $20 \cdot 9 \cdot \frac{6}{4}$ (C) $20 + 9 + \frac{6}{4}$ (D) $4(20 \cdot 9 \cdot 6)$

Completing the Module Project

Tune In to Data

In this module, you have collected and analyzed data about television commercials. To complete the project, your group will present the data you collected and what you have learned from it.

12–16. Answers may vary. Check students' work.

12 With your group, discuss what you learned from the data you collected. Be sure to discuss the following topics:

- the number of commercials shown at various times
- the types of products commercials advertise
- how advertisers use commercials to influence your decisions
- the "average lifetime" claim about television viewing

13 How might you communicate this information to the class? Brainstorm with your group on ways to present your data and what you learned from it.

14 What other ideas do you have for preparing a group presentation that you would add to the list on the notebook?

15 Work as a team to prepare a presentation of the information you gathered on television commercials.

16 Present your facts about commercials to the class.

SET UP

- *Work in a group.*
- *You will need your group's data and tables or graphs from Module Project Questions 4 and 11.*

Ideas for Preparing a Group Presentation

1. Everyone should participate in the presentation.
2. Presentation
   - possible types:
     - lecture
     - news show
     - panel discussion
     - skit
     - song
     - commercial
   - use representations (tables, graphs, diagrams, and so on)

You will need: • *graph paper* (Ex. 8)

Use the line graph for Exercises 1–5.
(Sec. 1, Explor. 1)

Value of a Stock on the First of the Month

1. What was the value on January 1? $15

2. When was the value $30? March 1, June 1

3. During what months did the value decrease? March and April

4. During what month did the value increase the most? May

5. What do you think the value of the stock will be on December 1? Why?
about $47.50; The value of the stock is increasing at a rate of about $2.50/month.

6. Make a frequency table for the following set of data. (Sec. 1, Explor. 2) See Additional Answers.

   Amounts withdrawn in one hour from an automatic teller machine: $20, $50, $20, $10, $30, $40, $100, $30, $50, $30

7. Look at the sequences below. (Sec. 2, Explors. 1 and 2) See Additional Answers.

   a. How is the number sequence related to the shape sequence?

   b. Make a table for the number sequence. Extend it to include the fourth term.

   c. There is a pattern in the first four terms of the sequence that is related to exponents. Add another row to your table. Write the first four terms in exponential form. Describe the pattern.

   d. Use the pattern you identified in part (c) to find the fifth term. Write it in both exponential form and standard form.

   e. Predict the 50th term in the number sequence.

8. Make a table, draw a graph, and write an equation for the sequence 6, 12, 18, 24, … . Then predict the 100th term.
   (Sec. 2, Explor. 1) See Additional Answers.

9. Find the volume of a cube when the length of an edge is 9 cm.
   (Sec. 2, Explor. 2) 729 cm³

Use the spinner for Exercises 10–13.

10. George spun the spinner 50 times. His results are shown in the table. Find the experimental probability for each outcome. (Sec. 3, Explor. 1)

Outcome	Tally	Frequency
red	JHT JHT IIII	14
blue	JHT JHT	10
green	JHT JHT JHT JHT JHT I	26

$P(\text{red}) = \frac{14}{50} \text{ or } \frac{7}{25}, P(\text{blue}) = \frac{10}{50} \text{ or } \frac{1}{5}, P(\text{green}) = \frac{26}{50} \text{ or } \frac{13}{25}$

Suppose an experiment consists of spinning the spinner once and recording the color the spinner lands on. (Sec. 3, Explor. 2)

11. List the possible outcomes of the experiment.

red, blue, green

12. Find the theoretical probability of each outcome.

$P(\text{red}) = \frac{1}{4}, P(\text{blue}) = \frac{1}{4}, P(\text{green}) = \frac{1}{2}$

13. Suppose you spin the spinner 60 times. About how many times would you expect it to stop on red? about 15

14. Use the 4-step approach to solving problems to find the total number of triangles of any size in the shape shown at the right. Explain your solution. (Sec. 4, Explor. 1)

14. 26; There are 16 triangles that are 1 triangle high, 6 that are 2 triangles high, 3 that are 3 triangles high, and 1 that is 4 triangles high.

15. Assess your work in Exercise 14 using the problem solving scale on page 49. (Sec. 5. Explor. 1)   Answers will vary.

Evaluate each expression without using a calculator. (Sec. 6, Explor. 1)

16. $20 - 4 \cdot 5$ 0

17. $3 \cdot (4 + 5) \cdot 6$ 162

18. $2 + 54 \div 3^2 - 2$ 6

19. Suppose a group of hikers are walking west. To avoid a steep slope, they walked 3 km north, 2 km west, 2 km north, 4 km west, and 5 km south. How many fewer kilometers would the hikers have walked if they did not have to avoid the steep slope?

(Sec. 6, Explor. 2)   10

R e f l e c t i n g ◀▶on the Module

20. **Writing** Write a letter to an adult member of your family describing what you have done in this module. Discuss the mathematics you learned. You may also want to talk about what you liked most and least about the module.

Answers will vary. Check students' work.

SEARCH and RESCUE

MODULE 2   SECTION OVERVIEW

1 Looking at Angles

As you learn a rescue skill:
- Name and measure angles
- Classify angles
- Use supplementary and complementary angles

2 Integers and Coordinates

As you study elevation:
- Compare integers
- Find opposites and absolute values of integers
- Identify and plot points in a coordinate plane

3 Integer Addition and Subtraction

As you explore wind-chill temperatures:
- Use a model to work with integers
- Add and subtract integers

4 Function Models

As you compare rescue options:
- Model a function with a table, an equation, or a graph
- Evaluate expressions with variables

5 Addition and Subtraction Equations

As you explore backpack weights:
- Write addition and subtraction equations
- Solve equations using models and inverse operations

The Module Project

Planning a Search

You'll imagine that you are a member of a search and rescue team and develop a search strategy for finding a lost person. You'll write a newspaper article about planning your search.

More on the Module Project
See pp. 86, 99, 114, and 143.

INTERNET
To learn more about the theme:
http://www.mlmath.com

75

Section ① Looking at Angles

IN THIS SECTION

EXPLORATION 1
♦ Measuring Angles

EXPLORATION 2
♦ Angle Relationships

HEADING OUT

WARM-UP EXERCISES

Illustrate each term with a drawing and state its dimension.

1. point

   •; no dimensions

2. line
   ⟷ ; 1 dimension

3. plane

   ;
   2 dimensions

4. cube
   ; 3 dimensions

◄‹‹ *Setting the Stage*

In the book *Hatchet* by Gary Paulsen, Brian Robeson is going to visit his father in northern Canada. The 13-year-old is a passenger in a two-person plane when suddenly the pilot has a heart attack.

HATCHET *by Gary Paulsen*

[Brian] looked at the dashboard of the plane, studied the dials and hoped to get some help, hoped to find a compass, but it was all so confusing, a jumble of numbers and lights.

. . .

He tried to figure out the dials. . . . He thought he might know which was speed—it was a lighted number that read 160—but he didn't know if that was actual miles an hour, or kilometers, or if it just meant how fast the plane was moving through the air and not over the ground.

. . .

When the pilot had jerked he had moved the plane, but Brian could not remember how much or if it had come back to its original course. Since he did not know the original course anyway and could only guess at which display might be the compass—the one reading 342—he did not know where he had been or where he was going. . . .

▶ When a plane goes down or a hiker is lost in the wilderness, search and rescue (SAR) teams are called in to search for and rescue survivors. Some of the tools and the strategies that SAR teams use involve mathematics.

1 **a.** Brian thinks the speed of the plane might be 160 miles per hour or 160 kilometers per hour. Which is faster? 160 mi/h

b. How could Brian use the plane's speed to estimate its location?

2 Why do you think Brian "hoped to find a compass"?
A compass would enable Brian to determine in what direction the plane was flying.

3 What would you do in this situation if you were Brian? What information would help you? I would get on the radio and try to get some help either with flying the plane or reviving the pilot.

1. b. Find the approximate distance traveled since takeoff by multiplying the speed of the plane by the time in flight. The plane would be near the circumference of a circle with radius equal to the distance traveled and with its center at the point of takeoff.

Exploration 1 ▸▸▹▹▹▹▹▹▹▹▹▹▹▹▹▹▹▹▹▹▹▹▹▹

MEASURING ANGLES

SET UP *You will need:* • *Labsheet 1A* • *protractor* • *ruler*

GOAL

LEARN HOW TO...
◆ name and measure angles
◆ classify angles

AS YOU...
◆ learn a skill SAR team members need

KEY TERMS
◆ ray
◆ angle
◆ vertex
◆ degree
◆ right angle
◆ straight angle
◆ acute angle
◆ obtuse angle

▸ **To find their way through unfamiliar territory, SAR team members may need to use a navigational compass. Knowing about *rays* and *angles* can help you understand how to read a compass.**

A **ray** is part of a line. It starts at an endpoint and goes on forever in one direction.

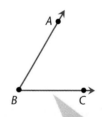

Ray *BA* is written $\overrightarrow{BA}$. Always write the endpoint first.

This angle is formed by $\overrightarrow{BA}$ and $\overrightarrow{BC}$.

4 **Discussion** Use the angles shown above and at the right.

a. Point *B* is the *vertex* of the angle shown above. Point *E* is the vertex of the angle at the right. What do you think *vertex of an angle* means?

b. Which rays form the angle at the right?
$\overrightarrow{ED}$ and $\overrightarrow{EF}$

4. a. The vertex is the endpoint of the rays forming the angle.

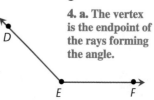

▶ **Naming Angles** An **angle** is formed by two rays with a common endpoint called the **vertex** of the angle. You can name an angle using labeled points and the angle symbol, ∠.

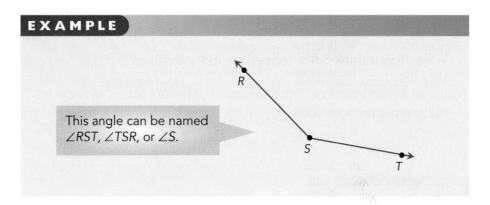

EXAMPLE

This angle can be named ∠RST, ∠TSR, or ∠S.

5. b. The vertex of the angle in the Example, ∠RST, is S. The vertex of ∠SRT is R. So, ∠RST and ∠SRT are not the same angle.

5 a. Which rays form the angle in the Example? Which point is the vertex? $\overrightarrow{SR}$ and $\overrightarrow{ST}$; S

b. The angle in the Example cannot be named ∠SRT. Why not? (*Hint*: Think about the points in the order in which they appear.)

✔ QUESTION 6

...checks that you know how to name angles.

6 ✔ CHECKPOINT Look back at the angles on page 77. Name each angle in three different ways. ∠ABC, ∠CBA, ∠B; ∠DEF, ∠FED, ∠E

▶ **Measuring Angles** Imagine one ray of an angle rotating around the vertex while the other ray is fixed in place. You can measure the angle by measuring the amount of rotation. An angle is measured in units called *degrees*.

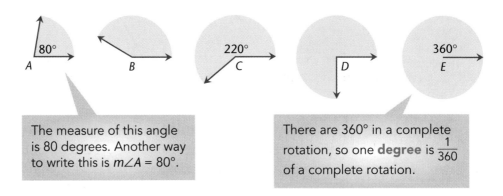

The measure of this angle is 80 degrees. Another way to write this is m∠A = 80°.

There are 360° in a complete rotation, so one **degree** is $\frac{1}{360}$ of a complete rotation.

7 What is the measure of half of a complete rotation? What do you think an angle with that measure looks like? 180°; a line

8 Estimation Estimate the measure of each angle.

a. ∠B About 150°   **b.** ∠D About 270°

You can use a protractor to measure and draw angles. To draw an angle whose measure is 45°, follow these steps:

Step 1 Create one side of the angle by drawing a ray. The endpoint will be the vertex of the angle.

Step 2 Place the center of the protractor on the vertex. Line up the ray with the base line of the protractor, at 0°.

Step 3 Follow the numbers as they increase from 0°. Mark a point at 45°.

Step 4 Draw a second ray from the vertex through the point.

9. 135° is the marking for an angle that is formed by a clockwise rotation starting from a ray that has the same endpoint as the one in Step 1 but extending in the opposite direction. 45° is the measure of the angle that was formed starting with the ray in Step 1 and rotating counter-clockwise; Since angles can be formed with either clockwise or counter-clockwise rotations, two scales are needed.

10. $m\angle A = 90°$, $m\angle B = 50°, m\angle C = 70°$, $m\angle D = 120°$, $m\angle E = 150°, m\angle F = 180°$
a. an angle that measures 90°
b. an angle that measures 180°
c. an angle that measures more than 0° and less than 90°
d. an angle that measures more than 90° and less than 180°

11.
90° right angle
30° acute angle
130° obtuse angle
180° straight angle

9 Try This as a Class The ray drawn in Step 4 above passes through the number 135. Why is the measure of the angle not 135°? Why do you think there are two sets of numbers on the protractor?

10 Use Labsheet 1A. Measure each angle on the Labsheet. Use your results to answer parts (a)–(d) below about *Types of Angles*.

  a. What is a **right angle**?   **b.** What is a **straight angle**?

  c. What is an **acute angle**?   **d.** What is an **obtuse angle**?

11 ✔ CHECKPOINT Draw a right angle, an acute angle, an obtuse angle, and a straight angle. Find the measure of each angle.
Samples are given.

✔ QUESTION 11

…checks that you can draw and measure different types of angles.

HOMEWORK EXERCISES ▶ See Exs. 1–14 on p. 84.

GOAL

LEARN HOW TO...
- use supplementary angles and complementary angles

AS YOU...
- find compass headings

KEY TERMS
- supplementary angles
- complementary angles

Exploration 2

ANGLE RELATIONSHIPS

SET UP *Work with a partner. You will need:*
• Labsheets 1B and 1C • protractor • ruler

▶ To locate a lost person, a search and rescue team needs to first develop a search strategy before sending out search parties in different directions. The SAR team can use a *compass heading* to describe each direction. Like angles, headings are measured in degrees.

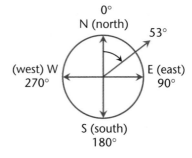

The needle on a magnetic compass points to the *north magnetic pole*, which is determined by Earth's magnetic field. Throughout this module, north (N) always refers to magnetic north.

Headings are always measured in a clockwise direction starting from north, which is at 0°. This compass diagram shows a heading of 53°.

```
            0°
         N (north)
                      53°
(west) W ─────┼───── E (east)
 270°                   90°
         S (south)
           180°
```

12. a. Sample Response: On both a compass and a protractor, one degree is $\frac{1}{360}$ of a rotation; a compass shows a complete rotation and a protractor shows one half of a rotation.

12 Discussion Use the compass diagram above.

a. How is the degree scale on a magnetic compass like the scale on a protractor? How is it different?

b. North (N) has a heading of 0°. What heading is used for east? for south? for west?   90°; 180°; 270°

c. What heading, other than 0°, could you use for north? 360°

► North, south, east, and west are the *principal directions.* Knowing their headings can help you estimate other headings.

13 **Use Labsheet 1B.** For each of the *Heading Diagrams*, estimate the heading by drawing a ray. Compare methods with your partner.
Check students' drawings. See exact answers for Question 20.

► You can use principal directions to plot actual headings on a map. Two methods to plot a heading of 220° are shown below.

Method 1 Start at north. Use a protractor to draw ∠A.

Method 2 Start at south. Use a protractor to draw ∠B.

A heading of 220°

14 **a.** Use the compass diagrams above. Without using a protractor, find *m∠A* and *m∠B.* Explain how you found each measure.

b. What is the sum of *m∠A* and *m∠B?* Explain.
180°; Taken together, ∠A and ∠B form a half circle or half rotation.

14. a. *m∠A* = 140° and *m∠B* = 40°; Sample response: Since the measure of the entire circle is 360°, *m∠A* = 360° − 220°. Since the measure of half the circle is 180°, *m∠B* = 180° − *m∠A* or 180° − 140°.

► Angles *A* and *B* in the diagrams above are *supplementary angles.* Two angles are **supplementary angles** if the sum of their measures is 180°.

15 Two of the angles below are supplementary. Name these angles.
∠ABC and ∠KLM

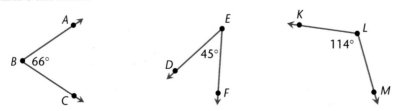

16 ✔ **CHECKPOINT** Suppose ∠W and ∠Y are supplementary. Find *m∠Y* if *m∠W* = 75°. 105°

✔ **QUESTION 16**

...checks your understanding of supplementary angles.

17. a. $m\angle C = 50°$ and $m\angle D = 40°$; Sample response: Since $m\angle C = 360° - 310° = 50°$ and $m\angle C + m\angle D = 360° - 270° = 90°$, $m\angle D = 90° - 50° = 40°$.

17 **a.** Use the compass diagram. Without using a protractor, find $m\angle C$ and $m\angle D$. Explain how you found each angle measure.

b. What is the sum of $m\angle C$ and $m\angle D$? 90°

▶ Angles *C* and *D* in the diagram above are *complementary angles*. Two angles are **complementary angles** if the sum of their measures is 90°.

18 Two of the angles below are complementary. Name these angles.
∠QRS and ∠WXY

✔ QUESTION 19

…checks your understanding of complementary angles.

19 ✔ **CHECKPOINT** Suppose ∠S and ∠T are complementary. Find $m\angle T$ if $m\angle S = 15°$. 75°

20 **Use Labsheet 1B.** For each of the *Heading Diagrams*, use a protractor to draw a ray for the heading. See Additional Answers.

21 **Use Labsheet 1C.** In the reading from *Hatchet* on page 76, Brian guesses that the 342 on the display might be a compass heading. Follow the directions on Labsheet 1C for *Plotting a Heading* on a map of northern Canada like the one shown.
Check students' work.

CLOSURE QUESTION

How are individual angles classified and what are two ways that pairs of angles are classified?

Sample Response: Individual angles are classified by determining whether their measures are between 0° and 90°, equal to 90°, between 90° and 180°, or equal to 180°. Pairs of angles are classified as complementary or supplementary by determining whether the sum of their measures is 90° or 180°.

HOMEWORK EXERCISES ▷ See Exs. 15–30 on pp. 84–85.

Section 1

Key Concepts

Rays and Angles (pp. 77–78)

An angle is formed by two rays that have a common endpoint. The common endpoint of the rays is the vertex of the angle. ∠QRS is formed by $\overrightarrow{RQ}$ and $\overrightarrow{RS}$.

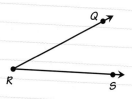

angle

ray

vertex

Measuring and Classifying Angles (pp. 78–79)

Angles are measured in degrees. A complete rotation is 360 degrees, or 360°. An angle can be classified by its measure.

degree

Example

This is a right angle symbol.

$m\angle C = 30°$

$m\angle D = 110°$

right angle
Its measure is 90°.

straight angle
Its measure is 180°.

acute angle
Its measure is greater than 0° but less than 90°.

obtuse angle
Its measure is greater than 90° but less than 180°.

right angle

straight angle

acute angle

obtuse angle

Supplementary and Complementary (pp. 80–82)

Two angles are supplementary angles if the sum of the measures of the angles is 180°.

Two angles are complementary angles if the sum of the measures of the angles is 90°.

supplementary angles

complementary angles

∠ABC and ∠CBD are supplementary.

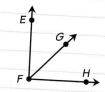

∠EFG and ∠GFH are complementary.

22. a. right; Sample Response: Since ∠M and ∠N are supplementary angles, the sum of the measures of the two angles is 180°. Since $m\angle M = m\angle N$, each angle must measure 90°. So, each angle is a right angle.

22. b. acute; Sample Response: Since ∠X and ∠Y are complementary angles, the sum of the measures of the two angles is 90°. So, each angle must measure less than 90°. Since an angle that measures greater than 0° but less than 90° is an acute angle, each angle is an acute angle.

22 Key Concepts Question For each situation, classify the angles as *acute*, *obtuse*, or *right*. Explain.

a. ∠M and ∠N are supplementary angles and $m\angle M = m\angle N$.
See above.

b. ∠X and ∠Y are complementary angles.

YOU WILL NEED

For Exs. 5–14:
◆ protractor

For Exercises 1–6, use the diagram.

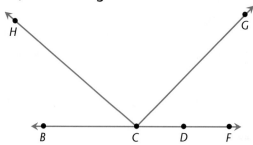

1. Name the ray that passes through point *H*. $\overrightarrow{CH}$

2. Name two rays that have point *D* as an endpoint. $\overrightarrow{DF}, \overrightarrow{DB}$

3. Name three angles that have $\overrightarrow{CH}$ as a side. ∠*BCH*, ∠*HCG*, ∠*HCF*

4. Name all the angles that have vertex *C*.
   ∠*BCH*, ∠*HCG*, ∠*GCF*, ∠*BCG*, ∠*HCF*, ∠*BCF*

5. Name an acute angle and find its measure.
   Possible answers: ∠*BCH*, 40°; ∠*GCF*, 45°

6. Name an obtuse angle and find its measure.
   Possible answers: ∠*BCG*, 135°; ∠*HCF*, 140 °; ∠*HCG*, 95°

Draw an angle with each measure. Then classify each angle as *acute, obtuse, right,* or *straight.*

7. 90°   90° right angle

8. 85°   85° acute angle

9. 138°   138° obtuse angle

10. 150°   150° obtuse angle

11. 53°   53° acute angle

12. 180°   180° straight angle

13. 100°   100° obtuse angle

14. 30°   30° acute angle

Estimation For Exercises 15 and 16, estimate the heading on each compass diagram.

15.   About 135°

16.   About 315°

17. 338°; Sample Response: The two planes are flying in opposite directions from *Q*. So, their combined flight paths form a line that cuts a compass diagram in half. The heading of the second plane, then, is equal to the heading of the first plane plus 180°, or 338°.

17. **Writing** A plane flies from point *Q* with a heading of 158°. Another plane flies from point *Q* in the opposite direction. Find the heading of the second plane. Explain your thinking.

Use the diagram on the photo.

18. Name three pairs of
    supplementary angles.

19. Name two pairs of
    complementary angles.
    ∠CBK and ∠KBH; ∠GBF and ∠FBD

20. Estimate the measure of the
    angle between the minute
    hand and the hour hand.
    About 210° or 150°

For each angle measure:
a. Find the measure of a supplementary angle.
b. Find the measure of a complementary angle, if possible.

21. 15°   22. 63°   23. 45°   24. 38°

25. 87°   26. 125°   27. 95°   28. 115°

29. **Challenge** ∠F and ∠G are complementary angles. Suppose the
    measure of ∠F is 10° more than the measure of ∠G. Find m∠F.   50°

18. Possible answers:
∠CBD and ∠DBG;
∠GBF and ∠FBC; ∠GBK
and ∠KBH; ∠CBH and
∠GBH

21. a. 165° b. 75°
22. a. 117° b. 27°
23. a. 135° b. 45°
24. a. 142° b. 52°
25. a. 93° b. 3°
26. a. 55° b. not possible
27. a. 85° b. not possible
28. a. 65° b. not possible

Reflecting ▶on the Section

Be prepared to report on the following topic in class.

30. Describe two ways to locate a 290° heading. Use these methods
    to estimate headings of 290° on two separate compass diagrams.
    Measure 110° west of south or measure 70° west of north.

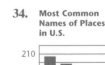

Oral Report

Exercise 30 checks
your understanding
of angle measures.

Spiral ◀▶Review

Evaluate each expression. (Module 1, p. 65)

31. 48 − 32 ÷ 8 44   32. 30 ÷ (6 − 4) 15   33. 6 + 4² 22

34. **Displaying Data** Make a bar graph of the data. (Toolbox, p. 594)

The Most Common Names of Places in the United States			
Name	Midway	Fairview	Oak Grove	Five Points
Number	207	192	150	145

Find the perimeter of a rectangle with the given dimensions.
(Toolbox, p. 593)

35. length = 5 ft, width = 2 ft   36. length = 16 in., width = 7 in.
    14 ft   46 in.

34. **Most Common
    Names of Places
    in U.S.**

Planning a Search

Gina Roberts is a pilot who lives in Laverton, a small town in the outback of western Australia. She has flown solo before, but now she is ready for her longest flight ever—440 mi to visit a friend in Nullagine.

Only 1.5 hours after Gina's takeoff, the Laverton airport tower receives a distress call. Gina is experiencing engine trouble. She gives her location as 185 mi from Laverton at a heading of 344°. Then communication is lost.

For your module project, you'll imagine that you are a member of a search and rescue (SAR) team and use your new mathematical skills to develop a search strategy for finding Gina.

Using Headings A storm is approaching, and Gina's chances of survival depend on a quick and well-planned search. You can use her last known heading to begin planning a search strategy.

Use Project Labsheet A. Use the *Regional Map* to answer Questions 1–4.

 On the *Regional Map*, find Gina's location when radio communication was lost. Mark this spot with an X. **Check students' work.**

 A search plane will be sent out from Wiluna. Find the distance and heading it must fly to reach location X. **About 85 mi, 50°**

 The search plane holds enough fuel to travel 560 mi and must return to Wiluna. Use the *Regional Map* to plan a search pattern to find the missing plane. Be sure to include headings and distances for each leg of the search. **See above.**

 For each heading, tell which city a plane leaving Wiluna will fly over.

 a. 265°   b. 135°   c. 355°
    Nannine   **Laverton**   **Nullagine**

SET UP

You will need:
- Project Labsheet A
- protractor

3. Sample Response:
Fly from Wiluna to X, 85 mi on a heading of 50°. At X fly 20 mi on a heading of 344°, 10 mi on 254°, 30 mi on 164°, 20 mi on 74°, 40 mi on 344°, 30 mi on 254°, 50 mi on 164°, 40 mi on 74°, 60 mi on 344°, 50 mi on 254°, 53 mi on 164°, and fly back to Wiluna about 52 mi on about 230°.

Section 1
Extra Skill Practice

You will need: • *protractor* (Exs. 4–8)

For Exercises 1–4, use the diagram.

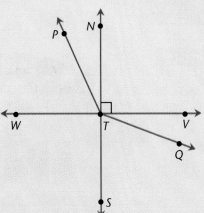

1. Name two rays that pass through point W. $\overrightarrow{TW}, \overrightarrow{VW}$

2. Name the endpoint of ray $\overrightarrow{NS}$. *N*

3. Name all the acute angles that have $\overrightarrow{TQ}$ as a side. ∠VTQ, ∠STQ

4. Name an obtuse angle and find its measure. Possible answers: ∠WTQ, 160°; ∠PTQ, 135°; ∠PTV, 115°; ∠NTQ, 110°

Draw an angle with each measure. Then classify the angle as *acute*, *obtuse*, *right*, or *straight*.

5. 180° straight angle   6. 28° acute angle   7. 65° acute angle   8. 155° obtuse angle

9. Name a complementary angle and a supplementary angle to ∠NTP in the diagram above. ∠WTP, ∠PTS

For each angle measure:
a. Find the measure of a supplementary angle.
b. Find the measure of a complementary angle, if possible.

10. 72°   a. 108°   b. 18°

11. 163°   a. 17°   b. not possible

12. 35°   a. 145°   b. 55°

13. 56°   a. 124°   b. 34°

Study Skills ▸ Determining Your Learning Style

There are many ways to learn—by listening, reading, looking at pictures, writing, watching, doing, and so on—with others or on your own. The way you learn best is your *learning style*.

1. List several activities that you do well. Tell how you learned to do each one. Based on your answers, describe your learning style. Check students' work.

This book contains activities and questions that fit different learning styles. Find an example of each in Module 1. Check students' work.

2. hands-on activity   3. group activity   4. reading selection

5. Discussion question   6. Writing exercise   7. Visual Thinking exercise

Section ② Integers and Coordinates

IN THIS SECTION

EXPLORATION 1
◆ Comparing Integers

EXPLORATION 2
◆ Coordinate Graphing

WARM-UP EXERCISES

Compare the two given numbers. Use <, >, or =.
1. 21 _?_ 12   >
2. 8 _?_ 6   >
3. 6 _?_ 8   <
4. 4.00 _?_ 4   =
5. 0.09 _?_ 0.0900 =
6. 0 _?_ 0.1   <

SEARCHING FOR INTEGERS

·‹·Setting the Stage

One tool that search and rescue teams use to plan a search is a *contour map*. A contour map shows the elevation and the steepness of a land area. These factors are important because they affect the walking or hiking conditions of an area. In the map below, the change in elevation between contour lines is 10 ft.

This is a peak.

The elevation along this contour line is 50 ft above sea level.

Think About It

1 What is the elevation at point *A*? How did you determine it?
80 ft; Point *A* is two contour lines below 100 or 3 contour lines above 50.

2 How can you use a contour map to tell if a region is relatively flat?
If the contour lines on the map are not close together, the region is relatively flat.

3 What is the highest elevation shown on the map? 162 ft

4 What symbol sets an elevation below sea level apart from an elevation above sea level? The symbol "–" indicates an elevation below sea level.

Exploration 1

COMPARING
INTEGERS

GOAL

LEARN HOW TO...
- compare integers
- find opposites and absolute values of integers

AS YOU...
- learn about elevation

KEY TERMS
- positive
- negative
- integer
- inequality
- opposite
- absolute value

▶ One way to think about elevations above and below sea level is to say that those above sea level are greater than 0 or **positive**, and that those below sea level are less than 0 or **negative**.

200 ft above sea level. The elevation is 200 ft or "positive 200."

200 ft below sea level. The elevation is –200 ft or "negative 200."

5 Rewrite each elevation using symbols instead of words.

   a. Mount Rainier, Washington: 14,410 ft above sea level   14,410 ft

   b. Venice Beach, California: at sea level   0 ft

   c. Makaweli Reef, Hawaii: 116 ft below sea level   –116 ft

▶ The numbers you have been using are *integers*. The **integers** are the numbers ... , –3, –2, –1, 0, 1, 2, 3, ... You can also show the integers on a number line.

The arrowheads mean the integers go on forever in both directions.

negative integers   positive integers

0 is neither positive nor negative.

6 Use the number line shown above.

   a. List the next five integers on the right side of the number line.
     8, 9, 10, 11, 12

   b. List the next five integers on the left side of the number line.
     –8, –9, –10 –11, –12

Lake Assal

Mt. Kilimanjaro

▶ **Comparing Integers** The highest elevation in Africa is 19,340 ft at the peak of Mount Kilimanjaro. The lowest elevation in Africa is –512 ft at the surface of Lake Assal. These two elevations can be compared with an **inequality**, which is a mathematical sentence stating that one quantity is greater than or less than another.

The elevation of Mt. Kilimanjaro	is greater than	the elevation of Lake Assal.

$$19{,}340 > -512$$

The elevation of Lake Assal	is less than	the elevation of Mt. Kilimanjaro.

$$-512 < 19{,}340$$

▶ You can use a number line to help compare two integers.

EXAMPLE

The integers increase as you go from left to right on a number line.

Write two inequalities to compare –7 and –3.

SAMPLE RESPONSE

Graph the numbers on a number line.

–7 is **less than** –3.	or	–3 is **greater than** –7.
–7 < –3	or	–3 > –7

7 a. Where on a number line are the integers less than –7? List four integers less than –7 in increasing order.
Integers less than –7 are to the left of –7; Sample Response: –11, –10, –9, –8

b. Where on a number line are the negative integers greater than –7? Give an example of a negative integer greater than –7.
Negative integers greater than –7 are to the right of –7 and to the left of 0 ; –5

8 Write two inequalities to compare the numbers in each pair.

a. 25 and 26
25 < 26, 26 > 25

b. –76 and 123
–76 < 123, 123 > –76

c. –22 and –23
–23 < –22, –22 > –23

9 ✔ **CHECKPOINT** Replace each _?_ with > or <. You may want to use a number line.

a. 6 _?_ –8 >

b. –1 _?_ –2 >

c. 3 _?_ 9 <

d. –5 _?_ 0 <

e. –9 _?_ –5 <

f. 3 _?_ –3 >

✔ QUESTION 9

...checks that you can compare two integers.

10 Look back at the elevations on the map on page 88.

a. What do you notice about the distances of points *B* and *C* from sea level? The distances are the same.

b. Where would these elevations be located on a number line?
Point *B* would be at 30 and Point *C* would be at –30.

▶ Two numbers that are the same distance from 0 but on opposite sides of 0 on a number line are **opposites**. The opposite of 0 is 0.

EXAMPLE

The opposite of 3 is –3.

11 7 and –7 are opposites but 2 and –1 are not. Why not?

11. Since 7 and –7 are the same distance from 0 but on opposite sides of 0 on a number line, they are opposites. 2 and –1 are on opposite sides of 0 on a number line, but they are not the same distance from 0. So, they are not opposites.

12 ✔ **CHECKPOINT** Find the opposite of each integer.

a. 10 –10   **b.** 0 0   **c.** –8 8

d. –235 235   **e.** 51 –51   **f.** –103 103

✔ **QUESTION 12**

...checks that you can find the opposite of an integer.

▶ The **absolute value** of a number is the distance from the number to 0 on a number line.

EXAMPLE

You read |–4| as "the absolute value of negative four."

$|-4| = 4$ and $|4| = 4$

|———— 4 units ————|———— 4 units ————|

$$-4 \quad -3 \quad -2 \quad -1 \quad 0 \quad 1 \quad 2 \quad 3 \quad 4$$

13 What is the absolute value of –100? of 100? How do they compare? 100, 100; They are the same.

14 ✔ **CHECKPOINT** Find each absolute value.

a. |–5| 5   **b.** |–9| 9   **c.** |12| 12

d. |0| 0   **e.** |–12| 12   **f.** |17| 17

✔ **QUESTION 14**

...checks that you can find the absolute value of an integer.

15 The elevations of two points both have an absolute value of 150. What can you say about the elevations? Both elevations could be below sea level, both could be above sea level, or one could be below and the other above sea level.

16 Can the absolute value of a number be negative? Explain.
No; Since a distance is always positive or zero, and since absolute value is a distance, absolute value cannot be negative.

HOMEWORK EXERCISES ▶ See Exs. 1–50 on pp. 95–97.

GOAL

LEARN HOW TO...
- identify and plot points in a coordinate plane

AS YOU...
- work with parallel and perpendicular lines

KEY TERMS
- plane
- intersect
- parallel
- perpendicular
- coordinate plane
- origin
- ordered pair
- coordinate

Exploration 2

COORDINATE Graphing

SET UP *You will need graph paper.*

In 1912, the giant passenger ship *Titanic* struck an iceberg and sank. The wreck was found in 1985 after searchers combed the waters with a sonar device. The searchers used latitude and longitude lines to mark the location of the *Titanic* so they could find it again.

▶ **For small areas, searchers often lay a grid over a map of the search area. The grid is made up of *parallel* and *perpendicular* lines.**

A **plane** can be thought of as a flat surface that goes on forever.

Two lines **intersect** if they meet or cross each other.

Two lines in a plane are **parallel** if they do not intersect.

Two lines are **perpendicular** if they intersect at 90° angles.

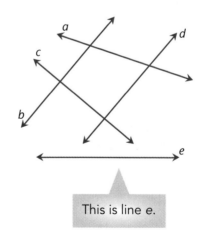

This is line *e*.

17 Which lettered pairs of lines above appear to be parallel to each other? perpendicular to each other? *b* and *d*; *c* and *b*, *c* and *d*

18 The drawings of lines *d* and *e* above do not intersect. Are lines *d* and *e* parallel to each other? Explain. No; If *d* is extended, it will intersect *e*.

19 In the paragraph about the *Titanic*, what type of paths does the phrase "combed the waters" suggest? parallel paths (as the teeth on a comb)

▶ Searchers can use a *coordinate system* based on a grid to give directions and report their findings.

EXAMPLE

A **coordinate plane** is a grid with a horizontal axis and a vertical axis that intersect at the **origin**. An **ordered pair** of numbers, called **coordinates**, can be used to identify and plot points in a coordinate plane. Point *P* has coordinates (**3, –2**).

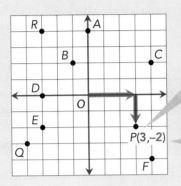

The **first coordinate** in an ordered pair gives a point's location left or right of the vertical axis.

The **second coordinate** gives the location up or down from the horizontal axis.

Use the coordinate plane in the Example for Questions 20–25.

20 Describe how the grid lines in a coordinate plane are related to each other. The vertical lines are parallel, the horizontal lines are parallel, and the vertical lines are perpendicular to the horizontal lines.

21 The coordinates of point *R* are (–3, 4). Describe what the coordinates tell you about point *R*. Point *R* is 3 units to the left of the vertical axis and 4 units above the horizontal axis.

22 What are the coordinates of point *Q*? (–4, –3)

23 Do the coordinates (2, 5) and (5, 2) describe the location of the same point? Explain.

24 What are the coordinates of the origin? Why do you think it is called the origin? (0, 0); To locate a point on the coordinate plane, you start at the origin. It is the point at which things originate or begin.

25 ✔ **CHECKPOINT** Give the coordinates of points *A* through *F*.
A(0, 4), B(–1, 2), C(4, 2), D(–3, 0), E(–3, –2), F(4, –4)

26 Plot each point in a coordinate plane.

    a. *W*(4, –1)   **b.** *X*(–1, 4)   **c.** *Y*(–3, –3)

    d. *Z*(5, 4)   **e.** *S*(–2, 2)   **f.** *T*(2, –1)

23. No; (2, 5) describes a point 2 units to the right of the vertical axis and 5 units above the horizontal axis and (5, 2) describes a point 5 units to the right of the vertical axis and 2 units above the horizontal axis.

26. a.–f.

✔ **QUESTION 25**

…checks that you can identify the coordinates of a point.

HOMEWORK EXERCISES ▶ See Exs. 51–59 on pp. 97–98.

Key Terms

integer

  negative

  positive

inequality

opposite

absolute value

plane

intersect

parallel

perpendicular

Integers (pp. 89–91)

The integers are the numbers:

negative integers	zero	positive integers
... , −4, −3, −2, −1	0	1, 2, 3, 4, ...

The opposites of the counting numbers.

The counting numbers.

You can write inequalities to compare integers. (p. 90)

1 is greater than −5 because 1 is farther to the right.

Example −5 < 1 or 1 > −5

Opposites are the same distance from 0 but on opposite sides of 0 on a number line. The opposite of 5 is −5. The opposite of 0 is 0. (p. 91)

The absolute value of a number is the distance between the number and 0 on a number line. The absolute value of 0 is 0. (p. 91)

Example The absolute value of −3 is written |−3|. Because −3 and 3 are both 3 units from 0 on a number line, |−3| = |3| = 3.

Line Relationships (p. 92)

Two different lines in a plane either intersect or are parallel. When they intersect at a 90° angle, the lines are perpendicular.

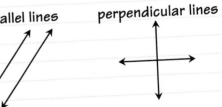

Intersecting lines   parallel lines   perpendicular lines

27. The opposite of an integer is the same distance from 0 as the integer, but it is on the opposite side of 0 on the number line. The absolute value of an integer is the distance on the number line between the integer and 0. The absolute value of an integer is always positive or zero, but the opposite of an integer such as 3 may be negative.

27 **Key Concepts Question** Explain the difference between the opposite of an integer and the absolute value of an integer.

Section ②

▸▸▸▸▸▸▸▸▸▸▸▸▸▸▸▸▸▸▸▸▸▸▸▸▸▸▸▸

Key Terms

Graphing in a Coordinate Plane (p. 93)

An ordered pair is used to locate a point in a coordinate plane.
The first coordinate indicates the horizontal position of the point.
The second coordinate indicates the vertical position of the point.

ordered pair

coordinate plane

coordinate

Example

The first coordinate is read along the **horizontal axis**.

The second coordinate is read along the **vertical axis**.

The point (0, 0) is called the origin.

CLOSURE QUESTION

How do perpendicular and parallel lines help you determine the coordinates of a point in a coordinate plane?

origin

Sample Response: The axes of a coordinate plane are perpendicular lines. One is horizontal and the other is vertical. First move parallel to the horizontal axis to determine how far to the left or right of the vertical axis the point is. This tells you the first coordinate of the point. Then move parallel to the vertical axis to determine how far above or below the horizontal axis the point is. This tells you the second coordinate of the point.

28 **Key Concepts Question** Describe how to locate the point with coordinates (–5, –3). How are the points (–5, 3) and (–5, –3) related? Start at the origin. Move five units to the left and then move three units down; the points (–5, 3) and (–5, –3) are on the same vertical line, but one point is above the horizontal axis and the other is below it.

Section ②

Practice & Application Exercises

▸ ▸ ▸ ▸ ▸ ▸ ▸ ▸

YOU WILL NEED

For Exs. 56 and 59:
♦ graph paper

For each description in words, represent the change using an integer and an appropriate unit of measure.

1. You add $25 to your savings. $25

2. The speed of a car decreases 15 mi/h. –15 mi/h

3. The stock market drops five points. –5 points

4. Water in a swimming pool rises 6 in. 6 in.

5. Sample Response: The word *abundantes* suggests *abundance*, which means *having more than enough.* The word suits a positive number. The word *defectivi* suggests *defective*, which means *lacking in something.* The word suits a negative number.

5. Writing The term *negative number* developed over time. In thirteenth century China, a diagonal stroke drawn through the right-hand digit of a number showed it was negative. In 1600, John Napier of Scotland called positive and negative numbers *abundantes* and *defectivi*. Why do you think he chose these terms?

Replace each ? with > or <.

6. 7 _?_ 0 >

7. 0 _?_ –4 >

8. 29 _?_ 35 <

9. –8 _?_ 13 <

10. 4 _?_ –21 >

11. –50 _?_ –75 >

Temperature Use the temperature scales to give an approximate temperature, in degrees Celsius and in degrees Fahrenheit, for each situation.

12. the outside temperature today
Sample Response: 80°F or 27°C

13. the temperature of a slightly cool room Sample Response: 60°F or 16°C

14. the temperature on a very cold day in your city or town
Sample Response: 30°F or –1°C

For each pair of temperatures below, identify the colder temperature.

15. –40°F, –39°F –40°F

16. –18°C, –21°C –21°C

17. 33°F, 0°C 0°C

18. 80°F, 40°C 80°F

19. 50°F, 5°C 5°C

20. –10°C, 10°F 10°F

Find the next three terms of each sequence.

21. 8, 6, 4, 2, ... 0, –2, –4

22. –15, –23, –31, –39, ... –47, –55, –63

23. –250, –200, –150, –100, ... –50, 0, 50

24. Copy and complete the table by describing each opposite situation. Then describe each situation and its opposite using integers and appropriate labels.

Situation	Opposite situation	Appropriate integers
1000 ft above sea level	1000 ft below sea level	1000 ft, –1000 ft
20 min in the past	20 min in ? the future	–20 min, 20 min
50 mi north	? 50 mi south	50 mi, –50 mi
10 yd gain in football	10 yd loss ? in football	10 yd, –10 yd

Find the opposite of each integer.

25. 6 _–6_   **26.** –4 _4_   **27.** –9 _9_   **28.** 18 _–18_

29. –24 _24_   **30.** 76 _–76_   **31.** 0 _0_   **32.** –306 _306_

Algebra Connection You read *–x* as "the opposite of *x*." Find the value of *–x* for each value of *x*.

33. *x* = 4 _–4_   **34.** *x* = –8 _8_   **35.** *x* = –100 _100_ **36.** *x* = 42 _–42_

Find the absolute value of each integer.

37. –8 _8_   **38.** 5 _5_   **39.** 0 _0_   **40.** 19 _19_

41. –62 _62_   **42.** 96 _96_   **43.** 514 _514_   **44.** –1025 _1025_

Replace each _?_ with > or <.

45. |–7| _?_ |5| _>_   **46.** –5 _?_ 10 _<_   **47.** |–9| _?_ |–2| _>_

48. |3| _?_ |–8| _<_   **49.** 16 _?_ –16 _>_   **50.** –9 _?_ –10 _>_

Map Reading Use this map of Puerto Barrios, Guatemala.
Sample Responses are given.

51. Name two streets that are parallel.
Calle 13 and Calle 14

52. Name two streets that are perpendicular.
Calle 14 and Avenida 8a

53. Name two streets that intersect but are not perpendicular. Calle Rufino Barrios and Calle 15

54. Writing Why do you think streets are laid out in a grid in some cities?

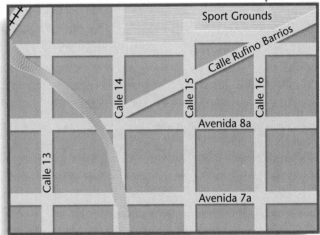

It is easier to give and follow directions for finding places in a city laid out in grids.

55.

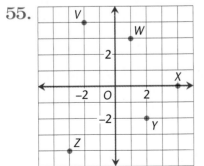

a. Identify the coordinates of the points *V* through *Z* in the coordinate plane. *V*(–2, 4), *W*(1, 3), *X*(4, 0), *Y*(2, –2), *Z*(–3, –4)

b. Which two points in the plane have first coordinates that are opposites? second coordinates that are opposites? *V* and *Y*, *V* and *Z*

56.

57.

58.

59.

63.

Average Monthly Fahrenheit Temperature in Aswan, Egypt (°F)

56. Graph each ordered pair in a coordinate plane. Draw segments to connect the points in alphabetical order. Then connect point *N* back to point *A* to form a closed figure.

A(6, 6)	*B*(8, 0)	*C*(6, 0)	*D*(8, –2)
E(6, –4)	*F*(–4, –4)	*G*(–6, 0)	*H*(–10, –4)
K(–10, 6)	*L*(–6, 2)	*M*(–2, 6)	*N*(2, 6)

Challenge Three different lines, *x*, *y*, and *z*, lie in a plane. For each situation, make a sketch and decide how line *x* is related to line *z*.

57. Line *x* is parallel to line *y*. Line *y* is parallel to line *z*.
Line *x* is parallel to line *z*.

58. Line *x* is perpendicular to line *y*. Line *y* is perpendicular to line *z*.
Line *x* is parallel to line *z*.

Reflecting ◀▶ on the Section

59. In a coordinate plane, the points (2, 1), (2, –2), and (–5, –2) are three corners of a rectangle. Without plotting the points, determine the coordinates of the fourth corner. Then plot the points on graph paper. Were you correct? (–5, 1)

Spiral ◀▶ Review

For each angle measure, find the measure of a complementary angle.
(Module 2, p. 83)

60. 43° 47°   **61.** 82° 8°   **62.** 26° 64°

63. Displaying Data Make a line graph of the data.
(Toolbox, p. 595)

Average Monthly Temperatures in Aswan, Egypt			
January	60°F	July	93°F
February	65°F	August	92°F
March	72°F	September	89°F
April	80°F	October	82°F
May	88°F	November	72°F
June	91°F	December	64°F

Find each sum or difference. (Toolbox, p. 587)

64. $\frac{2}{5} + \frac{1}{5}$ $\frac{3}{5}$ **65.** $\frac{1}{4} + \frac{2}{4}$ $\frac{3}{4}$ **66.** $\frac{7}{9} - \frac{2}{9}$ $\frac{5}{9}$ **67.** $\frac{5}{6} - \frac{4}{6}$ $\frac{1}{6}$

Working on the Module Project

Planning a Search

SET UP *You will need Project Labsheet B.*

Elevation and Search Areas When the search and rescue (SAR) team finds the plane, there is no sign of Gina, and her backpack is missing. To narrow down the search area, the team uses data organized into *Probability Zones* to predict where Gina will be found in relation to the *Point Last Seen* (PLS). The data are based on what other people in similar situations have done, and on the elevation of the area.

Use Project Labsheet B. Use the *Probability Zones* and the *Map of Point Last Seen* to answer Questions 5–8. The location of the plane is the PLS.

 5 The search plane locates Gina's downed plane at the X on the *Map of Point Last Seen*. Would the search pattern you developed on page 86 of Section 1 have located Gina's plane?
Answers will vary. Check students' work.

 6 a. What is the probability of finding a lost person between 2 and 3 mi downhill from the PLS? 2%

b. What is the probability of finding a lost person within 4 mi of the PLS? 96%

 7 Create and describe a search plan for an 8 person SAR team. Be sure to think about:

♦ how you would divide your team

♦ the amount of area that can be covered on foot

♦ the short amount of time available (4 hours until dark)

♦ areas that you will not bother to search and why
Answers will vary. Check students' work.

 8 On the *Map of Point Last Seen*, shade the areas covered by your search plan.
Check students' work.

Rewrite each value using symbols instead of words.

1. Elevation of Salton Sea Airport, California: 85 ft below sea level –85 ft

2. Lowest recorded temperature, Vostok, Antarctica: 89°C below zero –89°C

Replace each ? with > or <.

3. 4 _?_ 7 <   4. –9 _?_ –17 >   5. 7 _?_ –7 >   6. 29 _?_ 0 >

7. –65 _?_ 0 <   8. –40 _?_ –1 <   9. –50 _?_ 11 <   10. –6 _?_ –18 >

11. –14 _?_ 14 < 12. –31 _?_ –23 < 13. 0 _?_ –40 >   14. –87 _?_ 87 <

For each integer:
a. Find its opposite.
b. Find its absolute value.

15. 8 –8, 8   16. –1 1, 1   17. –16 16, 16   18. 85 –85, 85   19. –2001 2001, 2001

20. 461 –461, 461   21. –93 93, 93   22. 5 –5, 5   23. –72 72, 72   24. 55 –55, 55

For Exercises 25–28, use the diagram.

25. Which line is parallel to line *c*? perpendicular to line *c*? d, a

26. Are lines *b* and *d* parallel? Explain.

27. Identify the coordinates of four points where pairs of lines intersect.

28. Identify the coordinates of the point where line *d* intersects each axis.

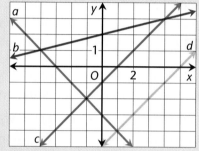

26. If *b* and *d* are extended, they will intersect. So, they are not parallel.
27. *a* and *b* intersect at (–4, 1), *b* and *c* at (4, 3), *c* and *a* at (–1, –2), and *d* and *a* at (1, –4).
28. *d* intersects the horizontal axis at (5, 0) and the vertical axis at (0, –5).

Standardized Testing ◀▶ Open-Ended

For each pair of integers, write a word problem that contains measurements that the integers can represent.

1. –5, 18   2. –206, 157

1. Sample Response: A man weighed 160 lb. He lost 5 lb and then gained 18 lb. How much did he then weigh?

2. Sample Response: In 1989, the population of a town was 5557. During the year, 206 people moved out of the town and 157 people moved in. What was the population of the town at the end of 1989?

For each temperature, describe the type of clothing that would be appropriate to wear outdoors, and name two outdoor activities that people might participate in.

3. 30°C People would probably be wearing shorts or other summer clothing. They might be swimming or just sitting outside to stay cool.

4. –1°C People would be wearing winter coats or jackets. They might be skiing or making a snowman.

5. –10°F People would be wearing layers and layers of clothing trying to stay warm. The only people involved in outdoor activities would be those who had to work outdoors (like a police officer directing traffic).

Section ③ Integer Addition and Subtraction

IN THIS SECTION

EXPLORATION 1
◆ Modeling Integer Operations

EXPLORATION 2
◆ Adding Integers

EXPLORATION 3
◆ Subtracting Integers

A CALL FOR HELP

Setting the Stage ▶▶▶▶▶▶▶▶▶▶

A hiker is injured and a passerby on the same trail uses a cellular phone to call for help.

"Help! A hiker is injured along Emerson trail, about 5 miles from Crystal Falls."

Think About It

1 Can rescue workers tell where the caller is from the information given? If not, what else would the caller need to tell them?
No; the rescuers have to know in what direction from Crystal Falls the injured hiker is.

2 Moves along a number line can be used to model a hiker hiking along a trail.

   a. How is describing the location of a hiker on a trail like describing the position of a point on a number line?
   Both location descriptions give distance from a reference point.

   b. Describe another travel situation you can model by moving on a number line. What point would you use as 0? What would be the positive and negative directions?

Search and rescue work can involve life-threatening situations. The ability to clearly communicate information, such as location, is very important. Rescuers must give instructions to those in danger and follow directions to avoid becoming lost themselves.

▶ Rescuers use integers when they work with wind-chill charts. In this section, you will learn to add and subtract integers as you use your skill at following directions.

WARM-UP EXERCISES

Use mental math to add or subtract.
1. $14 + 9$ 23
2. $5 + 15 + 10$ 30
3. $8 + 3 + 17$ 28
4. $16 - 4$ 12
5. $27 - 16$ 11
6. $38 - 19$ 19

2. b. Sample Response:
Traveling between floors of a building in an elevator; the ground floor; the positive direction would be above ground; the negative direction would be below ground.

LEARN HOW TO...
- use a model to work with integers

AS YOU...
- take hikes along a number line

Exploration 1

Modeling **INTEGER** Operations

SET UP *Work in a group of four. You will need:*
• Labsheets 3A, 3B, and 3C • scissors • three paper clips

▶ **In this activity, you'll explore what happens when you move in different ways along a number line.**

3 **Use Labsheets 3A and 3B.** Follow the directions on Labsheets 3A and 3B to set up a number line and build three spinners. Then follow the steps below to practice hiking on the number line. Each group member should have a turn as the hiker.

First Three members of the group spin the spinners and give the directions to the hiker in the following order.

1 Start at the number shown on the START spinner.

START
0 | –3
2 | 1
3 | –2
–1 | 0

2 Face the direction shown on the DIRECTION spinner.

DIRECTION
FACE THE – DIRECTION | FACE THE + DIRECTION

– means to face the negative direction.

+ means to face the positive direction.

3 Move in the way described on the MOVE spinner.

MOVE
0 | –1
–2 | 3
1 | –3
0 | 2

3 means move forward 3 units. –3 means move backward 3 units.

| NEGATIVE DIRECTION | –6 | –5 | –4 | –3 | –2 | –1 | 0 | 1 | 2 | 3 | 4 | 5 | 6 | POSITIVE DIRECTION |

Then The hiker follows the instructions and calls out the number he or she finishes at on the number line.

4 Use Labsheet 3C. Continue taking turns hiking on the number line. Record each hike and the finishing position until you complete the *Table of Hikes*. Check students' work.

5 Discussion Why is it not necessary to label one of the 0's on the MOVE spinner as –0?
0 units forward is the same as 0 units backward; that is 0 = –0.

HOMEWORK EXERCISES ▶ See Exs. 1–5 on pp. 110.

Exploration 2 ▶▶▶▶▶▶▶▶▶▶▶▶▶▶▶▶▶▶▶▶▶▶▶▶▶▶▶▶▶▶

Adding **INTEGERS**

GOAL

LEARN HOW TO...
◆ add integers
◆ use properties of addition

AS YOU...
◆ analyze hikes along a number line

KEY TERMS
◆ commutative property of addition
◆ associative property of addition

SET UP *You will need Labsheet 3C with data from Question 4.*

▶ **Adding Integers with the Same Sign** The "hikes" you took in Exploration 1 can help you think about adding integers. Addition of integers can be modeled on a number line with an arrow.

EXAMPLE

Find the sum –3 + (–5).

Start at –3.	Face the positive direction.	Move backward 5 units.
–3	+	(–5)

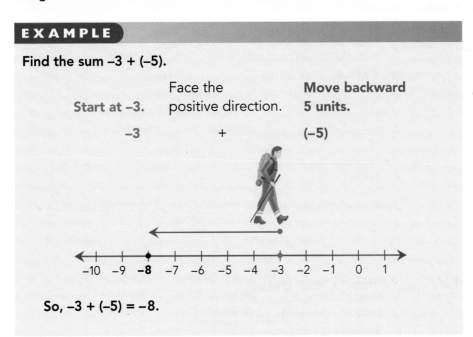

So, –3 + (–5) = –8.

7. a.

7. b.

6 **Use Labsheet 3C.** In the *Table of Hikes*, can you find a hike that models the addition of two negative integers? If so, write the addition problem and the sum. Sample Response: $-3 + (-1) = -4$

7 Draw a number line and an arrow to find each sum.

    a. $2 + 9$ **b.** $-7 + (-2)$

8 **Try This as a Class** Think about adding two integers with the same sign.

    a. Is the sum of two positive integers *positive* or *negative*? positive

    b. Is the sum of two negative integers *positive* or *negative*? negative

    c. Explain how to add two negative integers.
    Add the absolute values of the two integers. Put a negative sign in front of the sum.

9 Suppose a student recorded a hike as $-6 + 0$. What did the student do on that turn? The student started at -6 and stayed there.

10 Find each sum. Use a number line if necessary.

    a. $5 + 0$ 5   **b.** $0 + (-2)$ -2 **c.** $-3 + 0$ -3 **d.** $0 + 0$ 0

✔ **QUESTION 11**

…checks that you understand what happens when you add 0 and a number.

11 ✔ **CHECKPOINT** What is the sum of 0 and a number?
The sum is the number itself.

▶ **Adding Integers with Different Signs** You can also model addition of a positive integer and a negative integer on a number line.

EXAMPLE

Find the sum $-4 + 10$.

Start at -4.	Face the positive direction.	Move forward 10 units.
-4	$+$	10

So, $-4 + 10 = 6$.

12 Use a number line to find each sum.

    a. $4 + (-6)$ **b.** $-3 + 6$ **c.** $-5 + 5$

12. a.   **b.**   **c.**

13 Try This as a Class Think about adding two integers with different signs.

    a. When is the sum positive? negative?

    b. Explain how to add any two integers with different signs.

14 Give MOVE instructions so that the hiker stops at 0. Write each answer in words and as a number.

    a. Start at 5. Face the positive direction. Move backward 5 units; –5

    b. Start at –3. Face the positive direction. Move forward 3 units; 3

15 a. How is each answer in Question 14 related to the starting point? The number that gives the instruction is the opposite of the number at the starting point.

    b. When is the sum of two integers zero? When the integers are opposites.

16 ✔ **CHECKPOINT** Find each sum.

    a. 22 + (–13) 9   **b.** –18 + (–17) –35   **c.** –19 + 7 –12

    d. 31 + (–40) –9   **e.** –16 + 16 0   **f.** –7 + (–7) –14

17 Use a number line to find the sum 10 + (–4). How does this compare with the sum in the Example on page 104? The sums are the same.

18 Find each sum.

    a. –3 + 2 –1   **b.** 2 + (–3) –1

    c. (–2 + 8) + 15 21   **d.** –2 + (8 + 15) 21

19 How do the expressions in parts (a) and (b) of Question 18 compare? How do the sums compare? The expressions contain the same integers, but the integers are in a different order; the sums are the same.

20 How do the expressions in parts (c) and (d) of Question 18 compare? How do the sums compare? The expressions contain the same integers in the same order, but the integers are grouped differently; the sums are the same.

▶ **Properties of Addition** The **commutative property of addition** says that you can change the order of numbers in an addition problem and still get the same sum. The **associative property of addition** says that you can change the grouping when you add numbers and still get the same sum.

21 Discussion Use properties of addition and mental math to find the value of the expression –4 + 3 + 6 + 4 + (–6). 3

▌ **HOMEWORK EXERCISES** ▶ See Exs. 6–23 on pp. 110–111.

---

13. a. The sum is positive if the absolute value of the positive integer is greater than the absolute value of the negative integer; the sum is negative if the absolute value of the negative integer is greater than the absolute value of the positive integer.

13. b. Subtract the absolute values of the two integers and use the sign of the integer with the greater absolute value.

…checks that you know how to add integers.

Exploration 3

Subtracting **INTEGERS**

▶ When rescuers respond to a call for help, they must be prepared for the weather conditions. On cold and windy days, they might refer to a wind-chill chart like the one shown below. The difference between the thermometer reading and the temperature felt by the body can be great enough to endanger victims and rescuers.

22 a. The wind-chill temperature for a thermometer reading of 30°F and a 20 mi/h wind speed is shown on the wind-chill chart below. Find the wind-chill for 20°F and a 15 mi/h wind. –5°F

b. To find out how much colder it feels with the wind blowing, write a subtraction expression to represent the difference between the thermometer reading and the wind-chill temperature you found in part (a). 20°F – (–5)°F

Step 1 Find the thermometer reading.

Step 2 Read down the column to find the wind speed.

Estimated wind speed	Actual thermometer reading (°F)								
	40	**30**	**20**	**10**	**0**	**–10**	**–20**	**–30**	**–40**
Calm	40	30	20	10	0	–10	–20	–30	–40
5 mi/h	37	27	16	6	–5	–15	–26	–36	–47
10 mi/h	28	16	4	–9	–21	–33	–46	–58	–70
15 mi/h	22	9	–5	–18	–36	–45	–58	–72	–85
20 mi/h	18	4	–10	–25	–39	–53	–67	–82	–96
25 mi/h	16	0	–15	–29	–44	–59	–74	–88	–104

Wind-chill Temperature (°F)

Step 3 Where the row and the column meet, you'll find the wind-chill temperature that you would feel.

- Little danger if properly clothed
- Increasing danger
- Great danger

▶ To find the difference between thermometer readings and wind-chill temperatures, you may need to subtract integers. You have already done this in some of your "hikes" in Exploration 2.

23 a. Give START, DIRECTION, and MOVE instructions for a hike on a number line that would be recorded as the subtraction expression you wrote for part (b) of Question 22. Where would the hike end? *Start at 20. Face the negative direction. Move backward 5 units; at 25*

b. How can you change the instructions you gave in part (a) so the hiker starts at the same place, but faces the positive direction, and still ends up at the same finishing position? *Start at 20. Face the positive direction. Move forward 5 units.*

c. Write an expression to represent the hike in part (b). *20 + 5*

d. Look at your answer to part (c). How can 20 – (–5) be rewritten as an addition problem? What is the sum? *20 + 5; 25*

e. How much colder is the wind-chill temperature of –5°F than the thermometer reading of 20°F? *25°F*

▶ **Subtracting Integers on a Number Line** The number line can help you see that every subtraction problem has a related addition problem with the same answer.

EXAMPLE

Find the difference –5 – 3.

Start at –5.   Face the negative direction.   Move forward 3 units.

–5   –   3

So, –5 – 3 = –8.

---

24 Discussion What addition problem can be shown with the same diagram as in the Example? Describe how your answer can be interpreted as adding the opposite. *–5 + (–3); subtracting 3 is the same as adding –3.*

25 Draw a number line to find the difference 2 – 4. What addition problem can be shown with the same diagram? *2 + (–4)*

26 a. Think about the START, DIRECTION, and MOVE commands for the problem –5 – (–3). Draw a number line diagram showing the subtraction.

-6 -5 -4 -3 -2 -1 0 1 2

b. What is the result of –5 – (–3)? _–2_

c. Write the related addition problem that has the same result as –5 – (–3). _–5 + 3_

27 What related addition problem has the same result as 2 – (–8)? _2 + 8_

✔ **QUESTION 28**

…checks that you know how to subtract integers.

28 ✔ **CHECKPOINT** Find each difference.

a. 1 – 5 _–4_   **b.** 4 – (–6) _10_   **c.** –3 – 2 _–5_

d. 2 – 3 _–1_   **e.** –3 – (–6) _3_   **f.** 4 – (–1) _5_

▶ 🖩 Calculator **You can use a calculator to add and subtract integers. For example, to find the sum 3 + (–8), you can use the following key sequence.**

[3] [+] [8] [+⊝–] [=] [–5.]

29 What does the [+⊝–] key do? _It changes the sign of the number that was just entered._

30 Replace each _?_ with the correct number.

a. [9] [–] [2] [+⊝–] [=] _?_ _11_

b. [4] [+⊝–] [+] [5] [=] _?_ _1_

31 Evaluate each expression using a calculator.

a. 84 – (–19) _103_   **b.** –63 + 27 _–36_

c. 90 – 14 + (–47) _29_   **d.** 32 + (–51) – (–18) _–1_

32 Suppose the thermometer reading is 10°F and there is a 5 mi/h wind. A rescue worker wants to know how much colder it will feel if the wind speed increases to 20 mi/h. Use the wind-chill chart on page 106 and a calculator.

a. Find the wind-chill temperature for the wind speed of 5 mi/h. _6°F_

b. Find the wind-chill temperature for the wind speed of 20 mi/h. _–25°F_

c. Find the difference between your answer to part (a) and your answer to part (b). _31°F_

d. Interpret your answer to part (c) in relation to the situation.
It will feel 31°F colder.

HOMEWORK EXERCISES ▶ **See Exs. 24–47 on pp. 111–113.**

Section 3
Key Concepts

Number-Line Models (pp. 102–108)
You can think of addition and subtraction as hikes on a number line.

Example $2 + (-6) = -4$ $2 - 6 = -4$

Adding Integers (pp. 103–105)
To add two integers with the same sign, add the absolute values of the integers. The sum has the same sign as the integers you are adding.

Examples $8 + 5 = 13$ and $-3 + (-7) = -10$

To add two integers that have different signs, subtract the smaller absolute value from the greater one. The sum has the same sign as the integer with the greater absolute value.

Examples $9 + (-6) = 3$ and $4 + (-5) = -1$

> The answer is negative because $|4| < |-5|$.

The sum of **0 and a number** is that number. The sum of **a number and its opposite** is 0. Reordering and regrouping can help you find sums of more than two numbers using mental math. (pp. 104–105)

Subtracting Integers (pp. 106–108)
You can rewrite a subtraction problem as an addition problem. To subtract an integer, add its opposite.

Examples $6 - (-9) = 6 + 9 = 15$ and $5 - 7 = 5 + (-7) = -2$

33 **Key Concepts Question** Find a possible value of *x* in each case.

a. $3 + x$ is positive.   **b.** $3 + x$ is 0. –3   **c.** $3 + x$ is negative.
   See above.   See above.

d. $3 - x$ is positive.   **e.** $3 - x$ is 0. 3   **f.** $3 - x$ is negative.
   See above.   See above.

---

33 a. Possible answers: any number greater than –3

c. Possible answers: any number less than –3

d. Possible answers: any number, positive or negative, that is less than 3

f. Possible answers: any number greater than 3

properties of addition

   commutative

   associative

CLOSURE QUESTION

How does absolute value help you to add two integers?

Answer: Absolute value is helpful if the numbers you are adding have different signs. The sum will have the same sign as the number with the greater absolute value. If the numbers have different signs and equal absolute values, then they are opposites and their sum is 0, which is neither positive nor negative.

Practice & Application Exercises

A hiker on a number line follows each set of directions. Determine where the hiker will finish. Record the moves as an addition problem with its sum or as a subtraction problem with its difference.

1. Start at –4. Face the positive direction. Move backward 2 units.
$-6; -4 + (-2) = -6$

2. Start at 5. Face the positive direction. Move forward 6 units.
$11; 5 + 6 = 11$

3. Start at 0. Face the negative direction. Move forward 8 units.
$-8; 0 - 8 = -8$

4. Start at –3. Face the negative direction. Move backward 7 units.
$4; -3 - (-7) = 4$

5. Suppose the hiker shown below is given the instructions "Start at 2, face the negative direction, and move forward 3."

| NEGATIVE DIRECTION | –6 | –5 | –4 | –3 | –2 | –1 | 0 | 1 | 2 | 3 | 4 | 5 | 6 | POSITIVE DIRECTION |

    a. Where does the hiker stop after following the instructions? -1

    b. If the hiker starts at 2, what other set of instructions can be given so the hiker finishes at the same location?
    Start at 2. Face the positive direction. Move backward 3 units.

    c. What set of instructions can be given so the hiker remains at 2?
    Sample Response: Start at 2. Face the positive direction. Move forward 0 units.

Find each sum.

6. $-2 + (-5)$ -7 7. $0 + (-17)$ -17 8. $12 + 3$ 15

9. $-18 + (-3)$ -21 10. $19 + 36$ 55 11. $-11 + 0$ -11

12. $-9 + (-10) + 8$ -11 13. $-13 + 8 + (-4)$ -9 14. $6 + 0 + (-6)$ 0

For a correct answer on a TV game show, a positive dollar amount is added to a player's score. For an incorrect answer, a negative dollar amount is added. For Exercises 15–17, suppose the players have the scores shown.

15. If Danessa answers a $600 question correctly, what will be her new score?
300

16. Use the scores on page 110. If Mike answers a $600 question incorrectly, what amount is added to his score? What is his new score? −600; −200

17. Suppose both Jonah and Mike answer the last question, worth $300, incorrectly, but Danessa gives the correct answer. Use the scores on page 110. Who wins? What is each player's final score? Mike; Danessa's score is 0, Jonah's −900, and Mike's 100

For Exercises 18 and 19, write and evaluate an addition expression to model each situation.

18. A team loses 8 yd on one play of a football game and gains 3 yd on the next. Find the total number of yards gained or lost. −8 + 3 = −5; 5 yd loss

19. A company loses $30,000 in the first quarter of a year, then gains $43,000 in the second quarter. Find the total amount of money gained or lost in that time. −$30,000 + $43,000 = $13,000; $13,000 gain

Mental Math Find each sum mentally. Use properties of addition.

20. −2 + 0 + (−9) + 9 −2

21. −13 + 8 + (−2) + (−8) −15

22. −9 + 7 + 12 + (−7) + 9 12

23. 5 + (−12) + (3 + 12) 8

Rewrite each subtraction problem as the related addition problem that has the same answer.

24. 7 − 2
7 + (−2)

25. −10 − (−2)
−10 + 2

26. 0 − 6
0 + (−6)

27. 9 − (−17)
9 + 17

28. **Wind Chill** Refer to the wind-chill chart on page 106 to determine the difference between the thermometer reading and the wind-chill temperature for each condition in the chart below.

Estimated wind speed	Actual thermometer reading	Wind-chill temperature
10 mi/h	−30°F	? −58°F
25 mi/h	40°F	? 16°F

difference 28°F
24°F

29. **Estimation** Estimate the wind-chill temperature for a thermometer reading of 15°F and a wind speed of 20 mi/h.
About −17°F

Find each difference.

30. 9 − (−13) 22

31. −12 − 5 −17

32. −7 − 13 −20

33. −7 − (−13) 6

34. 12 − 7 5

35. 12 − (−7) 19

The highest point in the United States is Mount McKinley, in Alaska. It has an elevation of 20,320 ft.

The deepest lake in the world is Lake Baikal in central Siberia, Russia. It has a depth of 5712 ft.

The lowest point in the United States is in Death Valley, California. It has an elevation of –282 ft.

Geography Use the information above for Exercises 36 and 37.

36. What is the difference in elevation between Mount McKinley and Death Valley? 20,602 ft

37. The deepest point of Lake Baikal is 4219 ft below sea level. How high above sea level is the surface of the lake? 1493 ft

38. Weather The most unusual temperature rise ever recorded occurred in Spearfish, South Dakota, on January 22, 1943. The temperature was –4°F at 7:30 A.M. and 45°F at 7:32 A.M. How many degrees did the temperature rise during those 2 minutes? 49°F

Evaluate each expression.

39. 7 – (–10) + 8 25   **40.** –13 + 4 – 9 –18   **41.** 19 + (–5) – 3 11

42. (5 – 16) – (–2) –9 **43.** (16 – 5) – (–2) 13 **44.** 16 – [5 – (–2)] 9

45. Look back at the expressions in Exercises 42–44 and their values. Tell whether there are commutative and associative properties of subtraction. No.

46. Challenge Find a path through Integer Woods for the hiker. The hiker can move only horizontally or vertically from integer to integer. The sum of the numbers in a path must equal the exit number.
–3→4→–8→3→–9

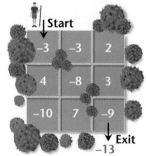

Start

–3	–3	2
4	–8	3
–10	7	–9

Exit –13

Reflecting on the Section

Write your response to Exercise 47 in your journal.

47. a. Suppose you started at 4 on a number line and wanted to move in the positive direction. What numbers could you add? What numbers could you subtract?

   any positive number; any negative number

   b. Suppose you started at 4 on a number line and wanted to move in the negative direction. What numbers could you add? What numbers could you subtract?

   any negative number; any positive number

   c. Using a number line, explain why subtracting an integer is like adding its opposite.

Spiral Review

48. Graph these ordered pairs in a coordinate plane:
    A(–3, 1), B(4, 1), C(4, –2), and D(–3, –2). (Module 2, p. 95)

Mental Math Find each sum or difference mentally. (Toolbox, p. 581)

49. 2.36 + 0.98 3.34   50. 87.41 – 19.95   51. 14.32 – 7.75 6.57
                            67.46

Find the next three terms of each sequence. (Module 1, p. 20)

52. 31, 27, 23, 19, ... 15, 11, 7   53. 25, 36, 49, 64, ... 81, 100, 121

Journal

Exercise 47 checks your understanding of integer addition and subtraction.

47. c. Sample Response: The directions for 3 – (–2) are as follows: start at 3, face the negative direction, and move backward 2 units. The directions for 3 + 2 are as follows: start at 3, face the positive direction, and move forward 2 units. Both sets of directions result in ending at 5.

3 – (–2)

3 + 2

48.

Extension ▶ ▶

Consecutive Integers

If you count by ones beginning with any integer, you get a set of consecutive integers.

Example:

–2, –1, 0, 1 are consecutive integers.

4, 5, 6 are consecutive integers.

54. The sum of three consecutive integers is –57. What are the three integers? –20, –19, –18

55. The sum of eight consecutive integers is 12. What are the eight integers? –2, –1, 0, 1, 2, 3, 4, 5

Working on the Module Project

Planning a Search

SET UP *You will need Project Labsheet C.*

Hiking on a Coordinate Grid When a searcher finds a clue, the search and rescue team organizes a new phase of the search. The team sets up a coordinate grid with the location of the clue as its origin. Then team members hike at a steady pace along the grid lines, hoping to find the person they are searching for, or another clue.

Use Project Labsheet C. A searcher found an empty juice box at point *C* on the map. Use the *Search Grid* and the *Revised Search Grid* to answer Questions 9 and 10.

 9 Eight searchers, S1 through S8, hiked along the lines of the *Search Grid* at a steady rate of 2 mi/h, and searcher S4 found footprints in the mud at point *F*. How long did it take searcher S4 to reach this point? **45 min**

Kendenura Hill
632
Beyondie Lakes
Ten Mile Lake
558
600
Point Last Seen ✕
Yibbie Range
650
•658

C •

0 1 2 3 4 5 6 7 8 9 10
Miles

 10 The team established a *Revised Search Grid*. This square region is 1 mi on a side and point *F* is the origin. Check students' work.

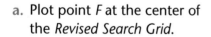

  a. Plot point *F* at the center of the *Revised Search Grid*.

  b. Draw the paths on the *Revised Search Grid* that you think each of the eight searchers should follow. Keep in mind these facts.

    ♦ The searchers walk at the same rate (2 mi/h).

    ♦ The searchers walk along grid lines only.

    ♦ There are about 1.5 hours of daylight remaining.

    ♦ The searchers will begin at point *F* and return to point *F* after 1 hour to revise the plan, if necessary.

Section 3
Extra Skill Practice

A hiker on a number line follows each set of directions. Determine where the hiker will finish. Record the moves as an addition problem with its sum or as a subtraction problem with its difference.

1. Start at –2. Face the positive direction. Move forward 5 units. $-2 + 5 = 3$

2. Start at 4. Face the negative direction. Move backward 2 units. $4 - (-2) = 6$

3. Start at –1. Face the negative direction. Move forward 3 units. $-1 - 3 = -4$

Find each sum.

4. $5 + 7$ 12
5. $-6 + (-3)$ –9
6. $0 + (-5)$ –5
7. $-12 + 9$ –3
8. $28 + (-37)$ –9
9. $-13 + 18$ 5
10. $-58 + 58$ 0
11. $-52 + (-48)$ –100
12. $45 + (-37)$ 8
13. $-78 + 68$ –10
14. $-84 + (-96)$ –180
15. $49 + (-49)$ 0

Mental Math Find each sum using mental math. Use properties of addition.

16. $-25 + 6 + 0 + (-6)$ –25
17. $14 + (-9) + (26 + 9)$ 40
18. $3 + 14 + (-3) + (-4)$ 10
19. $-2 + 12 + (-8) + (-2)$ 0
20. $-6 + (-14) + 21 + 9$ 10
21. $17 + (-8) + (-12) + (-17)$ –20

Evaluate each expression.

22. $3 - 7$ –4
23. $0 - (-6)$ 6
24. $-5 - 3$ –8
25. $13 - (-8)$ 21
26. $-22 - 6$ –28
27. $-2 - (-18)$ 16
28. $29 - 33$ –4
29. $-15 - (-5)$ –10
30. $9 - (-6) - 7$ 8
31. $-8 - 4 + (-18)$ –30
32. $29 + (-17) - (-3)$ 15
33. $-6 + 7 - (-5)$ 6
34. $9 - 12 - 11$ –14
35. $-16 + (-7) - (-14)$ –9

Standardized Testing ◀▶ Multiple Choice

1. Point *B* lies halfway between points *A* and *C*. What is the coordinate of point *C*? B

   A 6   B 8   C 10   D 14

2. Evaluate $-14 + 3 - (-17) + (-4) - 11$. C

   A –12   B 8   C –9   D –5

A PHONE CHAIN

The Situation See the Resource Book for a detailed discussion of this Extended Exploration

When a search and rescue team is needed, all members of the search and rescue team must be notified as quickly as possible. This is often accomplished through a phone chain. In a phone chain, the first person calls two people. Each of those people call two more people. Each of those people call two more people and so on, until everyone in the search and rescue team is notified of the emergency.

The Problem

Estimate the least amount of time it would take using a phone chain like the one described above to notify all the members in a 55-person search and rescue team. Sample Response: about 10 minutes

Something to Think About

♦ How might a table or drawing help you solve this problem?

♦ Could you modify the procedure to shorten the total amount of time involved? If so, how?

♦ What are some assumptions you might need to make about phone calls?

Sample Response: A table or drawing could help visualize the situation; yes, put a limit on the length of each phone call; you have to assume all phone calls are the same length of time and all phone calls are answered.

Present Your Results

Describe what you did to solve the problem. Explain why you solved it this way. Show any drawings, diagrams, charts, or tables that you used to solve the problem. Why do you think your solution is accurate?

Sample Response: I drew a diagram because I can visualize the problem and figure out the solution better that way. I think my solution is accurate because I checked over the problem several times, looking for errors in my thinking and math.

Section 4 Function Models

IN THIS SECTION

EXPLORATION 1
◆ Modeling a Function

EXPLORATION 2
◆ Graphing a Function

URBAN RESCUE

Setting the Stage ▸ ▸ ▸ ▸ ▸ ▸ ▸ ▸ ▸

A bus is caught in raging flood waters…people are trapped on top of a burning skyscraper… a plane crashes into an icy river…

These are just some of the emergency situations in urban areas requiring the skills of helicopter rescue personnel.

▲ A helicopter transports someone to a hospital.

▲ Police practice their helicopter-rescue skills.

Think About It

1 What kinds of skills do you think are important for members of a rescue team to have? **Sample Response: the ability to follow directions, physical strength and agility, problem solving skills, interpersonal skills**

2 What factors do you think affect the response time of emergency vehicles in urban rescue situations? **Sample Response: traffic and weather conditions, the cooperation or lack of cooperation of people in the path of the emergency vehicles, the skills and quickness of the emergency personnel**

3 What are some advantages and disadvantages of using helicopters instead of other emergency vehicles for urban rescues?

3. Sample Response: Emergency personnel in helicopters could get directly to victims on the top of a building. However, helicopters might have difficulty landing or getting to victims who were on a busy street, surrounded by skyscrapers.

▶ **In this section you'll explore how tables, equations, and graphs are used to understand search and rescue situations and to make decisions.**

GOAL

LEARN HOW TO...
- model a function with a table or an equation
- evaluate expressions with variables

AS YOU...
- explore distance, rate, and time

KEY TERMS
- evaluate
- equation
- function

Exploration 1

Modeling a FUNCTION

▶ **Travel time is critical in emergency situations. During medical emergencies, helicopters travel 2 miles per minute (mi/min). Ambulances travel at whatever speed (rate) the traffic will allow.**

4 **a.** Suppose an ambulance travels 55 miles per hour (mi/h). How far will it go in 1 hour? in 2 hours? in 3 hours? 55 mi; 110 mi; 165 mi

b. What method did you use to answer part (a)?
Answers will vary. Check students' work.

▶ **The table shows the distances traveled by a helicopter going 2 mi/min for different travel times.**

Distances Traveled for Various Travel Times

Time (minutes)	Distance (miles)
10	2 · 10 = 20
20	2 · 20 = 40
30	2 · 30 = 60
t	2t = d

The expression $2t$ shows how to use travel time t to find distance traveled d.

5 An expression can be formed using variables as well as numbers and operation symbols.

a. What operation is used in the expression $2t$ in the table? multiplication

b. What does the expression $2t$ tell you about how to use the rate 2 mi/min and a travel time to find the distance traveled?
Multiply the rate by the travel time to find the distance traveled.

▶ You can **evaluate** an expression that has a variable by substituting a value for the variable and performing the operations.

EXAMPLE

Evaluate 2*t* when *t* = 40 to find the distance traveled in 40 min by a helicopter going 2 mi/min.

SAMPLE RESPONSE

$$2t = 2(40)$$

> Substitute **40** for *t* and then multiply.

$$= 80$$

A helicopter going 2 mi/min will travel 80 mi in 40 min.

▶ When two expressions are equal, you can write an **equation** to express the relationship. For example:

Distance traveled is rate × time.
$$d = rt$$

6 Use an ambulance's rate of 55 mi/h for parts (a) and (b).

   a. Make a table of the distances traveled in 4, 5, 6, and *t* hours.

   b. Write an equation relating distance traveled and travel time.
   $$d = 55t$$

▶ A **function** is a relationship between input and output. For each input, there is exactly one output. Output depends on input. For example, the distance traveled depends on the travel time.

6. a.

Hours driven	Miles Traveled
4	220
5	275
6	330
t	55*t*

① Select an **input** value. (a time in minutes)

② Apply a rule. (multiply by 2 mi/min)

③ Write the **output** value. (a distance in miles)

t = 40

$$d = 2t$$
$$d = 2(40)$$

d = 80

7 **Discussion** Use the function in the diagram.

   a. What input values make sense for this function when *t* represents a time and *d* represents a distance?
   Both *t* and *d* can be 0 or any positive number.

   b. Explain why the output will always be 80 when *t* = 40.
   The product of 2 and 40 is always 80.

8 Try This as a Class Suppose a group of *s* searchers includes four relatives of a lost boy along with *m* members of an SAR team.

   a. In words, describe the relationship between *m* and *s*. The number of searchers *s* is 4 more than the number of members of the SAR team *m*.

   b. What type of numbers make sense as values for *m* and *s*? Both *m* and *s* must be positive integers and *s* must be greater than 4.

✔ **QUESTION 9**

...checks that you can model a function with a table or an equation.

9 ✔ **CHECKPOINT** Make a table using three possible input values for *m* to model the situation in Question 8. Then write an equation relating *m* and *s*.

9.

Number of members of SAR team *m*	Number of searchers *s*
3	7
6	10
8	12

$s = m + 4$

▶ **Expressions with Two Operations** Some situations can be modeled using expressions that involve two operations.

10 Suppose a helicopter starts 50 mi from its destination and travels 2 mi/min. Let *t* = the number of minutes the helicopter travels.

   a. What does the expression 2*t* model? how far the helicopter has traveled in *t* minutes

   b. What does the expression 50 – 2*t* model? how far the helicopter is from its destination after *t* minutes

   c. Which two operations are involved in the expression 50 – 2*t*? multiplication and subtraction

---

EXAMPLE

Evaluate 50 – 2*t* when *t* = 5.

SAMPLE RESPONSE

$$50 - 2t = 50 - 2(5)$$

Substitute **5** for **t**.

$$= 50 - 10$$

$$= 40$$

Multiply before you subtract.

---

11 **a.** Evaluate 50 – 2*t* when *t* = 10, *t* = 20, and *t* = 30. 30, 10, –10

   b. What values of *t* make sense in the situation in Question 10? numbers greater than or equal to 0 and less than or equal to 25

   c. Can 50 – 2*t* be a rule for a function? Why or why not? Yes; for each input value *t*, there is only one output value.

✔ **QUESTION 12**

... checks that you can write and evaluate an expression to model a situation.

12 ✔ **CHECKPOINT** By noon an ambulance has traveled 40 mi from its starting point and continues to travel at 55 mi/h.

   a. Let *t* = the travel time since noon. Write an expression to model the total distance the ambulance has traveled. 40 + 55*t*

   b. Use the expression to find the distance traveled by 2:00 P.M. 150 mi

HOMEWORK EXERCISES ▶ See Exs. 1–24 on pp. 125–126.

SET UP *You will need:* • Labsheet 4A • a ruler

Emergency medical technicians (EMTs) at an accident scene must decide how to transport someone to a hospital that provides the right care.

The diagram below gives information about a highway accident scene. The ambulance at the scene and a medical helicopter nearby can both handle the emergency. In this exploration you'll see which vehicle will get to the hospital sooner.

The ambulance can travel an average of 1 mi/min.

| Mile 0 | Mile 10 | Mile 36 |

14. 26 min; Sample Response: the ambulance has to travel 36 – 10 = 26 mi and it takes it one minute to travel one mile, so it takes 26 min to travel 26 mi.

13 **Use Labsheet 4A.**
Use the *Location Table*.

   a. Complete the *Location Table* to show the ambulance's location after various travel times.
     See Additional Answers.

   b. Write an equation that relates the variables *m* and *t* in the table. $t = m - 10$
                             or $m = 10 + t$

14 **Discussion** How long will it take the ambulance to reach the hospital? Explain how you got your answer. See above.

15 **Use Labsheet 4A.** Plot the values from the *Location Table* on the *Location Grid*. Draw a line through the points to the edge of the grid.
See Additional Answers.

Name Yoshi Sato   Date 10-8   LABSHEET **4A**

MODULE 2

Location Table (Use with Question 13 on page 121.)

Directions Complete the table to show the ambulance's location (mile marker) at various times. Use the information in the diagram on page 121.

				Ambulance Location					
					12	16	20	24	t
									m
Travel time (minutes)	0	4	8						
Location (mile marker)	10	14							

Location Grid (Use with Questions 15–18 on pages 121–122.)

Directions Plot the values from the table above on the grid below. Draw a line through the points to the edge of the grid.

Rescue Vehicle Location

(Location (mile marker) vs. Travel time (minutes))

16. a. The locations range from mile 0, where the helicopter is, to mile 36, where the hospital is.
b. The emergency vehicles begin travelling at time 0, and we estimated the ambulance would reach the hospital in 26 min so we went a little beyond 26 min on the horizontal axis.

16 **a.** The values on the vertical axis of the *Location Grid* range from 0 to 36 mi. Why do you think these values were chosen?

b. Why do you think the values used on the horizontal axis were chosen?

c. What mile marker will the ambulance be at in 10 min? 20

d. In Question 14 you figured out how long it would take the ambulance to reach the hospital. Does your answer match what is shown on your graph? Explain. Yes; the point which corresponds to mile 36 has a travel time of 26 min.

✔ **QUESTION 17**

...checks that you can model a function with a graph

17. a.

Helicopter Location

Travel Time (minutes)	Location (mile marker)
0	0
4	8
8	16
12	24
16	32
20	40
24	48
t	m

---

17 ✔ **CHECKPOINT** Suppose the helicopter in the diagram below is chosen for the trip to the hospital.

a. Make a table of values like the one for the ambulance to show the helicopter's location m at various travel times t.

b. Write an equation that relates the variables m and t. $m = 2t$

c. Plot the values from your table on the Location Grid. Draw a line through the points. See Additional Answers.

The helicopter can travel an average of 2 mi/min.

| Mile | Mile | | Mile |
| 0 | 10 | | 36 |

▶ You can compare functions by graphing them on the same grid. The lines on your *Location Grid* can help you decide which vehicle will get to the hospital sooner.

18 **a.** The rescue vehicles start at different locations. How is this shown on your *Location Grid*? The lines start at different points on the Location axis.

b. The two lines on your graph *intersect* (cross). What are the coordinates of the point where the lines intersect? What do the coordinates tell you about the situation? (10, 20); after 10 min, both vehicles are at mile marker 20.

c. Which vehicle will get to the hospital sooner? How much sooner? Explain how you got your answers. the helicopter; 8 min sooner; Sample Response: reading the travel time for the 36 mi marker from the graph, the travel time for the helicopter is only 18 min, while the ambulance is 26 min.

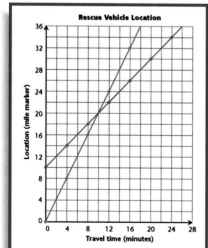

HOMEWORK EXERCISES See Exs. 25–36 on pp. 126–128.

You can also use a graphing calculator or graphing software to make and analyze the graphs in this exploration.

Step 1 To graph a function, you enter its equation, using X for the input variable and Y for the output variable.

The equations you wrote for Questions 13(b) and 17(b) can be entered where the screen shows Y1 and Y2.

Step 2 To set the *viewing window* for your graph, enter the values you want shown along each axis. Then graph.

Enter the minimum, maximum, and scale values for X and Y.

These values affect the **horizontal axis**.

These values affect the **vertical axis**.

Step 3 Use the TRACE feature to estimate values for the function in Questions 16(c) and 18(b), or use the INTERSECTION or the TABLE feature to find exact values.

Use the arrow keys to trace along a line and see coordinates of points.

A minimum value of 0 and an increase of 2 in each step were chosen for this table.

Key Terms

evaluate

Evaluating Expressions (pp. 118–120)

To evaluate an expression that has a variable, substitute a value for the variable and perform the operations.

Example A family on a 1200-mile road trip has traveled for *t* hours at *r* miles per hour. This expression represents the distance left to travel:

$$1200 - rt$$

← distance traveled = rate × time

To find the distance left to travel after 9 h at an average rate of 45 mi/h, evaluate $1200 - rt$ when $r = 45$ and $t = 9$.

$$
\begin{aligned}
1200 - rt &= 1200 - 45 \cdot 9 \\
&= 1200 - 405 \\
&= 795 \text{ (mi)}
\end{aligned}
$$

Substitute 45 for *r* and 9 for *t*. Then simplify.

19.

function

Modeling Functions (pp. 118–122)

A function is a relationship between input and output. For each input, there is exactly one output. Output depends on input. You can model a function in many ways.

Example A number *y* is one less than twice another number *x*.

equation

Table (p. 118)

input x	0	1	2
output y	−1	1	3

This table shows only a few of the possible values for *x* and *y*.

Equation (p. 119)

$$y = 2x - 1$$

Graph (pp. 121–122)

CLOSURE QUESTION

Suppose you are graphing a function and that you are using the first coordinates to represent input values. Can two different points have the same first coordinates? Explain.

Answer: No. For a function, there is only one output value for each input value.

19 Key Concepts Question The equation $d = 1200 - 45t$ models the situation in the first example, when *d* is the distance left to travel at an average rate of 45 mi/h. Graph the equation using reasonable values. See above.

Section 4

Practice & Application Exercises

YOU WILL NEED

For Exs. 25–27, 29–31, 34, 43, and 44:
♦ graph paper

For Ex. 35:
♦ graphing calculator

Choose the letter of the expression that models each situation.

1. At a box office, the price of a ticket is p dollars. What is the price at a ticket outlet that charges an extra $2 per ticket? **C**

   A. $2p$ B. $p - 2$ C. $p + 2$

2. A *fathom* is equal to 6 ft. How many feet are there in n fathoms? **A**

   A. $6n$ B. $n \div 6$ C. $6 \div n$

Write an expression that models each situation.

3. The price of a compact disk is p dollars. What is the price after a $3 increase? $p + 3$

4. **Geometry Connection** The measure of an angle is x degrees. What is the measure of a complementary angle? $90 - x$

Evaluate each expression when $a = 3$, $b = 5$, and $c = -7$.

5. $40a$ 120   6. $25b$ 125   7. $120 \div b$ 24

8. $75 \div a$ 25   9. $a + 18$ 21   10. $b - 9$ –4

11. $c + 14$ 7   12. $b + c$ –2   13. $c - b$ –12

14. **Recreation** The *Texas Folklife Festival* celebrates cultural diversity with music, dance, crafts, costumes, and food.

TEXAS FOLKLIFE FESTIVAL

The table models the relationship between the number of tickets sold n and the amount of money collected c.

a. Copy and extend the table to include the amounts collected for these values of n: 25, 30, 35, and 40.

Tickets sold	Amount collected ($)
0	0
5	40
10	80
15	120
20	160
n	c

b. Write an equation to model the relationship between the number of tickets sold and the amount collected. $c = 8n$

c. How much money is collected when 23 tickets are sold? $184

d. What type of numbers make sense as values for n? 0 or any positive integer

14 a.

Tickets Sold	Amount Collected
0	0
5	40
10	80
15	120
20	160
25	200
30	240
35	280
40	320

Evaluate each expression when $x = 10$, $y = -4$, and $z = 2$.

15. $2z + 4$ 8

16. $5x - 22$ 28

17. $3z - x$ –4

18. $2z + y$ 0

19. $4x + y$ 36

20. $x - 9z$ –8

21. $y + 8z$ 12

22. $y - 3x$ –34

23. $xz - y$ 24

24 a.

Number of Nights	Total Cost
1	$34
2	$43
3	$52
4	$61
5	$70

24. Travel It costs $10 for a person up to 17 years of age to join American Youth Hostels, and $15 to buy a required sleeping sack. Worldwide, the average cost to stay in a hostel is $9 per night.

  a. Make a table that shows the costs for 1, 2, 3, 4, and 5 nights.

  b. Write an equation to model the relationship between the number of nights n spent in a hostel and the total cost c. $c = 9n + 25$

PONY EXPRESS !

CHANGE OF TIME!   REDUCED RATES!

10 Days to San Francisco!

LETTERS

WILL BE RECEIVED AT THE

OFFICE, 84 BROADWAY,

NEW YORK,

Up to **4** P. M. every **TUESDAY,**

AND

Up to 2½ P. M. every **SATURDAY,**

Which will be forwarded to connect with the PONY EXPRESS leaving ST. JOSEPH, Missouri,

Every **WEDNESDAY** and **SATURDAY** at 11 P. M.

▲

The Pony Express delivered mail for only 18 months. In 1861, a telegraph line to California made the service unnecessary.

25. Social Studies The table shows ways that mail traveled across the United States in the early to late 1860s. See Additional Answers.

Covered Wagon 2 mi/h   Stage Coach 5 mi/h   Pony Express 10 mi/h   Railroad 22 mi/h

  a. Choose one of the rates given above. Make a table showing the distances traveled for travel times of 0, 1, 2, 3, 4, 5, and 6 hours.

  b. Use the rate you chose in part (a). Write an equation to model the distance traveled d in relation to travel time t.

  c. Graph the data from your table in part (a) on graph paper. Label each axis with reasonable values. Include axis titles and a graph title.

  d. Use coordinates to label the point on your graph that shows the distance traveled in 4.5 hours.

26.

27.

Copy and complete the table of values for each equation. Then graph each equation in a coordinate plane.

26. $y = x + 2$

x	−2	−1	0	1	2
y	? 0	? 1	? 2	? 3	? 4

27. $y = 2x - 5$

x	0	2	4	6	8
y	? –5	? –1	? 3	? 7	? 11

28. Open-ended Describe a situation that can be modeled by one of the equations in Exercises 26 and 27. Tell what values make sense for the variables in that situation. **See below.**

Make a table of values for each equation when $x = -1$, $x = 0$, **and** $x = 1$. **Then graph each equation in a coordinate plane.**
See Additional Answers.

29. $y = x + 3$ **30.** $y = x - 4$ **31.** $y = 2 - x$

32. Interpreting Data The graph models two mountain bike trips. Riders with equal skills are riding on different trails.

Mountain Bike Trips

a. **Writing** Who is traveling on the easier trail? Explain your thinking.
See below.

b. How far does each rider travel in 2 hours? Is this consistent with your answer to part (a)?
Rider 1: 16 miles, Rider 2: 8 miles; yes

c. Make a table of values for each trip.
See Additional Answers.

d. Write an equation for each trip.
Rider 1: $d = 8t$; Rider 2: $d = 4t$

33. Challenge Describe how you can use the graph in Exercise 32 to find the rate at which each rider is traveling. **Find the coordinates of any point. Divide the second coordinate (distance) by the first coordinate (time).**

34. Bowling Costs Some bowling alleys charge by the hour. Rashida compared the costs per hour for two people to bowl together at two different bowling alleys.

Bowling Alley A:

$4 for 2 pairs of shoes plus $17 per hour

Bowling Alley B:

$2 for 2 pairs of shoes plus $18 per hour

a. Let x = the bowling time (in hours). Let y = the total charge (in dollars). Use them to model each option with an equation.
For Bowling Alley A, $y = 17x + 4$, and for Bowling Alley B, $y = 18x + 2$.

b. Graph your equations from part (a) on one coordinate grid.
See Additional Answers.

c. When is Bowling Alley A less expensive?
when the bowling time is more than 2 h

d. When are the charges the same for both bowling alleys?
when the bowling time is 2 h

35. Graphing Calculator Repeat Exercise 34 for the following situation: the hourly rate for Bowling Alley B is $18.50, but all other conditions stay the same. **See Additional Answers.**

28. Sample Response for Exercise 26: Susan has two more CDs than Fritz; x can be any integer greater than or equal to 0; y can be any integer greater than or equal to 2; for Exercise 27: Elgin has five less than twice as many marbles as Luann; x can be any integer greater than 2; y can be any positive integer.

32. a. Rider 1; Sample Response: For any travel time shown on the graph, the distance traveled by Rider 1 is greater than the distance traveled by Rider 2.

Discussion

Exercise 36 checks that you understand some ways to model a function.

Reflecting ▶on the Section

Be prepared to discuss your response to Exercise 36 in class.

36. In this section, you've seen functions modeled with tables, equations, and graphs. Describe the advantages and disadvantages of each type of model. Sample Response: A table helps in organizing data, and equations enable you to find corresponding values of the variables quickly and easily. However, neither a table nor an equation helps you to visualize how one variable changes as the other changes. A graph enables you to visualize change, but a graph does not directly give you values of the variables.

Spiral ▶Review

Find each sum or difference. (Module 2, p. 109)

37. $-18 + (-42)$ -60 38. $-6 - (-13)$ 7   39. $-10 - 7$ -17

Suppose you roll an eight-sided die with faces labeled 1 to 8 and all outcomes are equally likely. Find the theoretical probability of each event. (Module 1, p. 33)

40. $P(3)$ $\frac{1}{8}$ 41. $P(9)$ 0   42. $P(\text{odd number})$ $\frac{4}{8}$ or $\frac{1}{2}$

43. Make a table, draw a graph, and write an equation for the sequence 6, 7, 8, 9, … . Then predict the 100th term.
(Module 1, p. 20)

Place in Sequence p	1	2	3	4
Value v	6	7	8	9

 ; $v = p + 5$; 105

44. a.

Age	3	4	5	6	7	8	9	10	11	12	13	14
Systolic Blood Pressure– Lower Limit	76	78	80	82	84	86	88	90	92	94	96	98

Career ▪ Connection

Paramedic: Scott Rosenfeld

One of the greatest challenges paramedic Scott Rosenfeld faces is treating an injured child. To find out whether the injury has resulted in shock, he can measure the injured child's blood pressure to see whether it's too low.

44. Scott Rosenfeld can use a formula to estimate whether a child's *systolic* blood pressure is below a "safe" limit. The formula applies to children over two years old through their early teens:

Lower limit for systolic blood pressure = 70 + (2 × child's age)

a. Make a table of values and a graph to show the relationship between systolic blood pressure and age. See above.

b. What are reasonable input and output values for the situation?
Input values: integers between 2 and 15; output values: integers between 75 and 99

16. Sample Response:

Miles to library x	3	4	5
Miles to mall y	6	8	10

$y = 2x$

17. Sample Response:

Number x	1	2	3
Number y	8	10	12

$y = 2x + 6$

You will need: • *graph paper* (Exs. 18–21)

Write an expression that models each situation.

1. Luisa is 5 cm taller than Ruth. Ruth is n centimeters tall. How tall is Luisa? $n + 5$

2. Brian drove for 3 hours at r miles per hour. How far did he drive? $3r$

Evaluate each expression when $x = 2$, $y = 4$, and $z = -3$.

3. $25x$ 50
4. $64 \div y$ 16
5. $z + 3$ 0
6. $x - 12$ –10

7. $y \div x$ 2
8. $2 + z$ –1
9. $9y$ 36
10. $-5 - y$ –9

11. $2y + 5$ 13
12. $15x - 7$ 23
13. $z - xy$ –11
14. $3x + y$ 10

Model each relationship between x and y with a table and an equation. For the table, use three input values that make sense.

15. Sample Response:

Nearby House Number x	4	6	10
House Number y	2	4	8

$y = x - 2$

15. A house number y is 2 less than a nearby house number x.

16. The distance to the mall is y miles. The distance to the library is x miles. The distance to the mall is twice the distance to the library. See above.

17. A number y is 6 more than twice another number x. See above.

Make a table of values for each equation when $x = -1$, $x = 0$, and $x = 1$. Then graph each equation in a coordinate plane. See Additional Answers.

18. $y = x$
19. $y = x + 1$
20. $y = 1 - x$
21. $y = x + 4$

Standardized Testing ▶ Free Response

The Kartanel family took a 4-hour car trip from Praitis to Veloysha.

Use the map and the graph to describe the Kartanels' trip during each hour. Tell as much about the trip as you can. (You may want to think about their average speed for each hour and why they slowed down or sped up.) See Additional Answers.

Section ⑤ Addition and Subtraction Equations

IN THIS SECTION

EXPLORATION 1
◆ Write and Model Equations

EXPLORATION 2
◆ Using Inverse Operations

SEARCHING FOR A SOLUTION

WARM-UP EXERCISES

Use mental math to solve each equation.
1. $n + 6 = 10$ $n = 4$
2. $27 - p = 14$ $p = 13$
3. $r \times 7 = 42$ $r = 6$
4. $44 \div y = 4$ $y = 11$
5. $9 \cdot b = 72$ $b = 8$
6. $\frac{x}{4} = 20$ $x = 80$

‹‹‹**Setting the Stage**

Have you ever felt as if your arms would break if you had to carry your books another minute? Just how much extra weight do you carry at school? Students at Monte Cassino Middle School in Tulsa, Oklahoma, weighed their backpacks and discovered that they carry anywhere from 11 lb to 26 lb.

Search and rescue (SAR) teams find creative ways to keep the contents of their backpacks as light as possible. Backpack weights for SAR team members vary according to each member's fitness, the search area, and the time of year.

Towels are cut in half.

Toothbrush handles are sawed off.

Think About It

1 How have the items shown above been made lighter? **Excess bulk and weight were eliminated by, for example, cutting towels in half and sawing toothbrush handles in half.**

2 About how many of your math books would it take to reach a weight of 26 lb? **Sample Response: about 8**

3 What are some ways that you could reduce the weight of the materials that you carry with you during the day?

4 Estimate how many pounds of school materials you carry home with you on a typical day. Explain how you made your estimate.
Sample Response: about 20 lb; five textbooks, weighing an average of 3 lb each, would total 15 lb, plus an additional 5 lb for notebooks, a calculator, and other stuff

3. Sample Response: Instead of putting everything I need for the whole day in my backpack, I could just carry what I need for my morning classes. The rest would go in my locker. After lunch, I could go to my locker, put what I don't need anymore in my locker, and pack what I do need for my afternoon classes.

Exploration 1

WRITE AND MODEL EQUATIONS

SET UP *You will need algebra tiles.*

GOAL

LEARN HOW TO...
◆ write addition and subtraction equations
◆ solve addition equations using models

AS YOU...
◆ examine the contents of a backpack

KEY TERMS
◆ solution of an equation
◆ solve an equation

Weather conditions affect what an SAR team member must carry. In a cold climate, a team member may need to carry 6 lb of warm clothing. In a hot climate, the 6 lb of clothing might be traded for 5 lb of extra water and 1 lb of sunscreen and insect repellent.

This trade can be modeled in several ways.

Verbal statement	Weight of extra water	plus	weight of sunscreen and insect repellent	equals	weight of warm clothing
Equation	5 lb	+	1 lb	=	6 lb
Balance model					

> The water, sunscreen, and insect repellent can replace the warm clothing.

5 **Try This as a Class** Use the balance model above.

a. Why can the rescuer exchange the warm clothing for water, sunscreen, and insect repellent? The weight of the clothing and the combined weights of the water, sunscreen, and insect repellent are the same.

b. Why does the balance scale work as a model for an equation? When a scale is balanced, the items on either side of the scale have the same weight. Similarly, the equal sign in an equation tells us that the items on either side of the equation have the same value.

Section 5 Addition and Subtraction Equations **131**

▶ **Equations Involving Variables** Suppose a rescuer can carry 25 lb. The rescuer has a 6 lb tent, a 4 lb sleeping bag, a 5 lb backpack, plus other items. Here are two ways to model the situation, where *x* represents the weight of the other items.

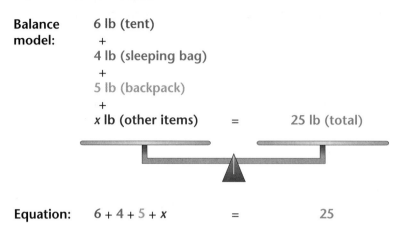

Balance model:

6 lb (tent)
+
4 lb (sleeping bag)
+
5 lb (backpack)
+
x lb (other items)   =   25 lb (total)

Equation: 6 + 4 + 5 + *x*   =   25

6. b. Sample Response: I added the weight of the tent, the sleeping bag, and the backpack and got 15 lb. These three items plus the other items must weigh 25 lb. So, I thought, "What do I have to add to 15 lb to get 25 lb?" and I got 10 lb.

6 a. What is the unknown weight *x* the rescuer could carry? **10 lb**

   b. Explain how you found the value of *x* in part (a).

▶ Balance models can help you visualize an equation and remember that both sides represent the same amount. Equations can be used to model a variety of situations.

> ### EXAMPLE
>
> Suppose an SAR team with 30 members includes 14 men. Let *w* = the number of women on the team. Write an equation to model the total number of SAR team members.
>
> **SAMPLE RESPONSE**
>
> | Number of women | plus | number of men | equals | total number on SAR team |
> |:---:|:---:|:---:|:---:|:---:|
> | w | + | 14 | = | 30 |

7 a. Why is 20 not a reasonable value for *w* in the Example?
   The sum of 20 + 14 is 34, which is greater than 30.
   b. What is the unknown number of women on the team in the Example? **16**

8 Suppose an SAR team with 30 members includes 12 women. Choose a variable to represent the number of men on the team and write an equation to model the situation.
   If *m* represents the number of men on the team, then $m + 12 = 30$.

▶ Sometimes equations that model a situation involve subtraction.

> **EXAMPLE**
>
> Between midnight and 2:00 A.M., the temperature dropped 4°F. At 2:00 A.M. the temperature was –1°F. Write an equation to model the situation.
>
> **SAMPLE RESPONSE**
>
> | Temperature at midnight (°F) | minus | drop in temperature (°F) | equals | temperature at 2:00 A.M. (°F) |
> |:---:|:---:|:---:|:---:|:---:|
> | t | – | 4 | = | –1 |

9 Find the temperature at midnight for the situation in the Example. 3°F

10 ✔ **CHECKPOINT** An SAR team ate 56 meals. They had 6 meals left over. Write a subtraction equation to model the situation. Use one variable and tell what it represents.

$n - 56 = 6$; n represents the number of meals they started with.

11 Describe a situation that each equation could model.

   a. $w + 3 = 8$ **b.** $15 - c = 4$

▶ **Algebra Tiles** You can use algebra tiles to model equations. The ▬ tile represents the variable. The ▪ tile represents 1.

> **EXAMPLE**
>
> You model the equation $x + 5 = 8$ with algebra tiles as follows:
>
>

12 a. Use algebra tiles to model the Example above. Remove two ▪ tiles from the side of the equation with the ▬ . What must you do to the other side to keep the equation balanced?

Remove two tiles from the other side of the equation.

   b. How many ▪ tiles must ▬ represent in the Example above for the equation to be balanced? How did you get your answer?

✔ **QUESTION 10**

...checks that you can use equations to model situations.

11. a. Sample Response: There are 8 kittens at the animal shelter. Three are males. How many are females?

11. b. Sample Response: Josh had to solve 15 equations for homework. He has 4 equations left. How many has he solved?

12. b. 3; Sample Response: I took 5 square tiles away from each side of the equation. Since the scale is balanced, the variable tile must represent 3 square tiles.

▶ A value of a variable that makes an equation true is a **solution of the equation**. The process of finding solutions is called **solving an equation**.

13 a. Write an equation represented by the algebra tile model. $4 = x + 2$

■■■■ = ■ + ■■

b. Using algebra tiles, get the ■ tile for the model in part (a) alone on one side of the equation while keeping the two sides balanced. Describe your method.
   Sample Response: I took 2 tiles off the right side, so I took 2 tiles off the left side.

c. Solve the equation you wrote in part (a). 2

✔ **QUESTION 14**

...checks that you can use a model to solve an addition equation.

14 ✔ CHECKPOINT Repeat Question 13 for this algebra tile model.

■ + ■■■ = ■■■■■■

a. $x + 3 = 6$
b. Sample Response: I took 3 tiles off the left side, so I took 3 off the right side.
c. 3

HOMEWORK EXERCISES ▶ See Exs. 1–17 on pp. 138–139.

GOAL

LEARN HOW TO...
♦ use inverse operations to solve addition and subtraction equations
♦ check solutions

AS YOU...
♦ explore weight limits for a backpack

KEY TERMS
♦ inverse operations

◄◄ **Exploration 2**

USING INVERSE OPERATIONS

In rough country, a rescuer can carry a total of only 18.5 lb. The rescuer has 7 lb of essential equipment plus some additional equipment. Let x = the number of pounds of additional equipment.

15 a. Write an addition equation that represents the situation above. $x + 7 = 18.5$

b. What can you do to both sides of the equation to get x alone?
   Subtract 7 from both sides of the equation.

c. Why is it difficult to represent this situation with a model?
   Sample Response: It is not possible to represent 18.5 with tiles.

▶ Addition and subtraction are **inverse operations**. They "undo" each other. Inverse operations are helpful in solving equations.

Here are keys to solving an equation:

 ◆ Use inverse operations to get the variable alone on one side.
 ◆ Keep the equation balanced by keeping both sides equal.

▶ **When you use symbols and variables to solve an equation, you are solving the equation *algebraically*.**

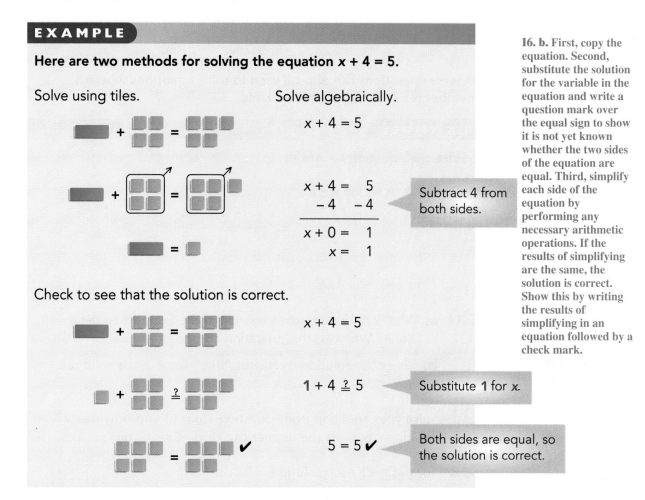

EXAMPLE

Here are two methods for solving the equation $x + 4 = 5$.

Solve using tiles.

Solve algebraically.

$$x + 4 = 5$$

$$\begin{aligned} x + 4 &= 5 \\ -4 &\quad -4 \\ \hline x + 0 &= 1 \\ x &= 1 \end{aligned}$$

Subtract 4 from both sides.

Check to see that the solution is correct.

$$x + 4 = 5$$

$$1 + 4 \overset{?}{=} 5$$

Substitute 1 for *x*.

$$5 = 5 \checkmark$$

Both sides are equal, so the solution is correct.

16. b. First, copy the equation. Second, substitute the solution for the variable in the equation and write a question mark over the equal sign to show it is not yet known whether the two sides of the equation are equal. Third, simplify each side of the equation by performing any necessary arithmetic operations. If the results of simplifying are the same, the solution is correct. Show this by writing the results of simplifying in an equation followed by a check mark.

16 **a.** In the Example, what was done to the equation to get *x* alone? Four tiles were taken from each side of the equation.

 b. Describe the steps in checking the solution.
 Why is a question mark included in the check process?

 c. Why is it important to check the solution? Sample Response: Checking enables you to find out if your answer is right or wrong.

17 Tim solved the equation $x + 47 = 65$ as shown at the right. Check to see whether Tim's solution is correct. Yes.

$$\begin{aligned} x + 47 &= 65 \\ -47 &\quad -47 \\ \hline x + 0 &= 18 \\ x &= 18 \end{aligned}$$

...checks that you understand how inverse operations can help you solve equations.

18 ✔ **CHECKPOINT** Solve. Check each solution.

a. $n + 18 = 102$ 84   **b.** $-2 = a + 5$ –7

19 **Try This as a Class** Use the equation $h + (-3) = 5$.

a. What would you do to both sides of the equation to "undo" the addition to get h alone? Subtract –3 from each side of the equation.

b. How could you use addition to solve this equation?
Add 3 to each side of the equation.

c. Use your method from part (b) to solve the equation $y + (-8) = 16$. 24

▶ Inverse operations can also be used to solve equations where a number is subtracted from a variable.

EXAMPLE

Solve the equation $x - 4 = -1$.

SAMPLE RESPONSE

$$\begin{array}{r} x - 4 = -1 \\ + 4 \quad + 4 \\ \hline x + 0 = \quad 3 \\ x = \quad 3 \end{array}$$

Add 4 to both sides.

---

20 **a.** What was done to the equation in the Example to get x alone? Why was this operation chosen? 4 was added to each side of the equation; addition "undoes" subtraction.

b. Check the solution by substituting 3 for x. Is the solution correct? Yes.

21 Solve your equation from Question 15(a) to find how many additional pounds the rescuer can carry. Check your solution. 11.5 lb

22 Solve. Check each solution.

a. $n - 3 = 6$ 9 **b.** $z - 1 = -4$ –3 **c.** $-6 = k - 7$ 1 **d.** $p - (-2) = 4$ 2

...checks that you understand how to verify a solution.

23 ✔ **CHECKPOINT** A student's solution of the equation $x - 7 = -2$ is 9. A check of this solution is shown. What does the check tell you? What is the solution of the equation? The solution is incorrect; 5

check
$x - 7 = -2$
$9 - 7 \overset{?}{=} -2$
$2 \overset{?}{=} -2$

HOMEWORK EXERCISES ▶ See Exs. 18–46 on pp. 139–140.

Key Terms

Modeling Equations (pp. 131–134)

Balance models can help you visualize an equation and remember that the expressions on either side of an equation must be equal. Algebra tile models can help you solve (find a solution of) an equation.

Using Inverse Operations to Solve (pp. 134–136)

The goal when you solve an equation is to get the variable alone on one side of the equation.

One method that can help you reach the goal is to use inverse operations. Inverse operations "undo" one another. Addition and subtraction are inverse operations.

Remember that any operation done on one side of an equation must also be done on the other side to keep the equation balanced.

Example Subtraction "undoes" addition when you solve an equation.

Solve $n + 3 = 8$.

$$n + 3 = 8$$
$$\underline{-3 \quad -3}$$
$$n + 0 = 5$$
$$n = 5$$

Subtract 3 from both sides.

Check that $n = 5$.

$$n + 3 = 8$$
$$5 + 3 \stackrel{?}{=} 8$$
$$8 = 8 \checkmark$$

Substitute your solution in the equation.

Example Addition "undoes" subtraction when you solve an equation.

Solve $n - 6 = -2$.

$$n - 6 = -2$$
$$\underline{+6 \quad +6}$$
$$n + 0 = 4$$
$$n = 4$$

Add 6 to both sides.

Check that $n = 4$.

$$n - 6 = -2$$
$$4 - 6 \stackrel{?}{=} -2$$
$$-2 = -2 \checkmark$$

24 **Key Concepts Question** Explain how the steps in the Examples keep each equation "balanced" and help to solve each equation.

In the first Example, subtracting 3 from each side of the equation keeps the equation balanced and leaves *n* alone on the left side of the equation. In the second Example, adding 6 to each side of the equation keeps the equation balanced and and leaves *n* alone on the left side of the equation.

CLOSURE QUESTION

Describe how to choose an operation to solve an addition or subtraction equation.

Answer: Choose the inverse operation. If a number is added to the variable on one side of the equation, then subtract that number from both sides. If a number is subtracted from the variable on one side of the equation, then add that number to both sides.

YOU WILL NEED

For Exs. 5–7 and 31:
♦ algebra tiles

Write an equation that each model represents.

1. ▪ + ▪▪/▪▪ = ▪▪▪▪/▪▪▪▪ $x + 4 = 8$

2. ▪ + ▪▪▪ = ▪▪▪▪ $y + 3 = 4$

3. **Open-ended** Describe a situation that can be modeled by the equation $n + 4 = 6$. Be sure to tell what the variable represents.

4. **Open-ended** Describe a situation that can be represented using a subtraction equation. Write an equation to model the situation. Use one variable and tell what it represents.

Make an algebra tile model that represents each equation. Then use the model to help you find each solution.

5. $x + 2 = 4$ 2   6. $3 + x = 4$ 1   7. $10 = x + 2$ 8

3. Sample Response: Of the 6 pets belonging to the Tracey family, 4 are iguanas. If n represents the number of pets that are not iguanas, what is the value of n?

4. Sample Response: After eating 5 muffins, Tanya had 12 muffins left. Find the number of muffins m Tanya had originally; $m - 5 = 12$.

Social Studies In 1933, the 20th Amendment to the Constitution set January 20 as the inauguration date for the President, and January 3 as the inauguration date for members of Congress. Write an addition equation to model each situation. Let y = the number of years served.

8. Dwight D. Eisenhower, the first President limited to two terms by a later amendment to the Constitution, served from 1953 to 1961.
$y + 1953 = 1961$

9. Barbara Jordan, the first African-American woman from a Southern state elected to the House of Representatives, served from 1973 to 1979.
$y + 1973 = 1979$

10. Dalip Singh Saund, the first Asian-American elected to the House of Representatives, served from 1957 to 1963. $y + 1957 = 1963$

11. Geometry Connection Use the diagram below.

    a. Write an addition equation that describes the relationship between the angles. $x + 150 = 180$

    b. Write a subtraction equation that describes the relationship between the angles. $180 - x = 150$

Write an addition equation to model each situation. Use one variable and tell what it represents.

12. The track team gets 2 new members, raising the membership to 20. **Let** m represent the number of old members. So, $m + 2 = 20$.

13. Of the 12 people in the 200 yd dash, 5 of them set a new "personal best."

14. Alicia won 3 medals. She now has 17.
Let m represent the number of medals Alicia originally had. So, $m + 3 = 17$.

13. Let n represent the number of people in the dash who did not set a "personal best." So, $n + 5 = 12$.

Write a subtraction equation to model each situation. Use one variable and tell what it represents.

15. Anna sold 70 prints. She had 8 left over.
Let n represent the number of prints that Anna originally had. So, $n - 70 = 8$.

16. After paying $5.75 for lunch, John received $4.25 in change.
Let t represent the amount of money John had originally. So, $t - 5.75 = 4.25$.

17. The number of customers on a paper route drops to 28 after 4 people cancel their subscriptions to the newspaper.
Let p represent the number of original subscribers. So, $p - 4 = 28$.

Solve. Check each solution.

18. $a + 19 = 47$ 28   **19.** $8 + w = 110$ 102   **20.** $q - 26 = 37$ 63

21. $53 = v - 19$ 72   **22.** $b + 27 = -16$ -43   **23.** $z - 25 = -2$ 23

24. $-15 = n + 32$ -47 **25.** $-16 + d = 24$ 40   **26.** $y - 18 = -66$ -48

27. $74 = -8 + h$ 82   **28.** $c - (-6) = -7$ -13 **29.** $1 = k - (-1)$ 0

30. Is 6 a solution of the equation $-8 + n = 2$? Explain.
No; substituting 6 for n gives $-8 + 6$ or -2 on the left side, and $-2 \neq 2$.

31. Challenge Write an equation that the model below represents. Then use algebra tiles to solve the equation. Use symbols to record what you do at each step. $2x + 3 = 11$; $2x + 3 - 3 = 11 - 3$, $2x = 8, \frac{2x}{2} = \frac{8}{2}, x = 4$

FOR▶HELP

with *adding and subtracting decimals*, see

TOOLBOX, p. 581

32. Let *b* represent the balance in the account before the withdrawal. So, $b - 165 = 357.49$. The solution is $522.49.

Banking For Exercises 32–34, write an equation to model each banking situation. Identify the variable you use. Solve each equation and check your solution.

32. Shellie withdrew money from her bank account to buy a used mountain bike. What was the balance in her account before the withdrawal?

33. Darius is saving money for a trip with the Spanish club. What was the increase in his savings this month? Let *d* represent Darius' deposit. So, $1271.63 + d = 1453.95$; $182.32.

34. Darius expected his ending balance to be $1450.24. What was the amount of interest he forgot to include? Let *i* represent the interest received. So, $1453.95 - 1450.24 = i$; $3.71.

35. Writing Describe how you would solve the equation $n - 49.75 = 682.94$ using a calculator. Add 682.94 and 49.75.

Choosing a Method Tell whether you would use mental math, paper-and-pencil, or a calculator to solve each equation. Then solve.

36.–44. Sample responses are given.

36. $17.3 + a = 62.1$
paper and pencil; 44.8

37. $b - 11 = 4$
mental math; 15

38. $c + 95 = 88$
mental math; –7

39. $x + 8 = -2$
mental math; –10

40. $y - 237 = 54$
paper and pencil; 291

41. $12 = z - 8.1$
mental math; 20.1

42. $-10 + r = 13$
mental math; 23

43. $11 = 6 + s$
mental math; 5

44. $t - 8 = -20.5$
calculator; –12.5

45. Geometry Connection Two angles are complementary. One angle has a measure of 37°. Let *a* = the measure of the other angle.

a. Write an addition equation to represent the situation. $a + 37 = 90$

b. Solve your equation from part (a). Check your solution. 53

RESEARCH

Exercise 46 checks that you understand how to write and solve equations.

Reflecting ◀▶on the Section

46. Research the terms of three former members of Congress from your own state who were elected after 1933 and who served full terms. Let *y* = the number of years served. Write and solve both an addition equation and a subtraction equation to model each situation. Check each solution. Answers will vary. Check students' work.

Evaluate each expression when $a = -32$, $b = 4$, **and** $c = 6$.

(Module 2, p. 124)

47. $b - 3$ 1

48. $3c - 27$ –9

49. $2a + 5$ –59

50. $2b + 15$ 23

51. $a + c$ –26

52. $a - 4b$ –48

53. Susan and Claire worked a total of 20 hours. Susan earned $8.00 per hour. Claire earned $7.00 per hour. Together they earned $148.00 over the weekend. How many hours did Claire work? Tell what problem solving strategy you used. (Module 1, p. 44)

12 h; Strategies will vary. Check students' work.

Tell whether each number is divisible by 2, 5, and 10.

(Toolbox, p. 582)

54. 75

75 is divisible by 5.

55. 215

215 is divisible by 5.

56. 253

253 is not divisible by 2, 5, or 10.

57. 630

630 is divisible by 2, 5, and 10.

Extension ▶ ▶

Equations with Variables on Both Sides

In this Section, the equations you solved had a variable on only one side of the equals sign. You can apply the ideas you learned to solve equations that have variables on both sides of the equals sign.

59. Remove one rectangular tile from each side of the equation and then remove two square tiles from each side. (The two steps can be reversed.)

Describe how you would solve each equation modeled below.

58. $n + 1 = 2n$ Remove one rectangular tile from each side of the equation.

59. $n + 6 = 2 + 2n$

Remove three square tiles from each side of the equation and then remove one rectangular tile from each side. (The two steps can be reversed.)

60. $2n + 3 = 3n$ Remove two rectangular tiles from each side of the equation.

61. $n + 5 = 3 + 2n$

62. Solve each equation in Exercises 58–61 algebraically. Check each solution. The solution for 58 is 1; for 59, 4; for 60, 3; and for 61, 2.

63. **a.** Does the equation $x + 35 = x + 13$ have a solution? Explain.

No; adding 35 to a number will never give the same result as adding 13 to the same number.

b. Does the equation $x + 4 = 4 + x$ have a solution? Explain.

Yes; any number increased by 4 is the same as 4 increased by the number. Every number is a solution.

Write an equation that each model represents.

1. ■ + ■■■■■ = ■■■■■■ $x + 5 = 6$

2. ■ + ■■ = ■■■■■ $y + 2 = 5$

3. ■■■■■■ = ■ + ■ $6 = 1 + m$

Write an addition or subtraction equation to model each situation. Use one variable and tell what it represents.

4. Alexis blew out 11 candles, but 2 remained lit.

4. Let c represent the original number of candles. So, the equations are $11 + 2 = c$ and $c - 11 = 2$.

5. Jill picked 53 apples. She and her brother together had 85 apples.

6. Oscar spent $5 and has $14 remaining.

5. Let b represent the number of apples Jill's brother picked. So, the equations are $53 + b = 85$ and $85 - b = 53$.

7. Jenn needs 8 points in her last turn of bowling to tie the high score of 121.

6. Let m represent the amount of money Oscar originally had. So, the equations are $5 + 14 = m$ and $m - 5 = 14$.

Solve. Check each solution.

7. Let s represent the number of points Jenn has before she takes her last turn. So, the equations are $8 + s = 121$ and $121 - s = 8$.

8. $a + 14 = 32$ 18   9. $q - 21 = 29$ 50   10. $y - 5 = -6$ –1   11. $b + 28 = -15$ –43

12. $6 + f = 24$ 18   13. $43 = v - 13$ 56   14. $z - 60 = -12$ 48   15. $-12 = n + 43$ –55

16. $-10 + d = 17$ 27   17. $54 = -18 + h$ 72   18. $c - (-5) = -9$ –14   19. $3 = k - (-3)$ 0

20. $46 + m = -23$ –69   21. $-19 = -14 + t$ –5   22. $s - (-12) = 25$ 13   23. $11 = -7 + p$ 18

Standardized Testing ◀▶ Performance Task

At soccer practice one day, Heidi, Jen, and Sheila together took a total of 36 shots. Heidi took 3 more shots than Jen did. Sheila took 3 fewer shots than Jen did.

During the same practice, Heidi, Jen, and Sheila combined for a total of 10 goals. Jen scored a goal on 1 out of every 3 shots she took. Heidi scored 1 fewer goal than Jen did. Sheila scored the same number of goals as Heidi did.

Sue, who is the goalie, says that based on their performance during practice, Jen is the most likely to score during the game. Do you agree with Sue? Present a convincing argument to support your answer.

Sample Response: I don't agree with Sue. Heidi's goals to shots ratio was $\frac{3}{15}$ or $\frac{1}{5}$, Jen's was $\frac{4}{12}$ or $\frac{1}{3}$, and Sheila's was $\frac{3}{9}$ or $\frac{1}{3}$. Sue's reasoning seems to be that the person who had the highest goals to shots ratio during practice will be the person most likely to score during the game. Since Sheila and Jen had the same ratio, they are equally likely to be that person.

Completing the Module Project

Planning a Search

Throughout this module, you have used mathematics to help searchers locate a lost person. When someone is lost, searchers throughout the world use these and other techniques in their race against time. Did you know that victims are found alive more than 95% of the time? Careful planning and the good use of mathematics make this possible.

Now you'll learn where Gina was found and decide whether your search plan would have located her. To complete your module project, you'll write a newspaper article about planning a search.

 11 The point *F* on the grid at the right is the spot where searchers found footprints in the mud. A searcher found Gina resting at point (2, −4) on this grid.

    a. Did you include the point where Gina was found in the last part of your search plan in Question 10 on page 114? Sample Response: No

    b. If your answer to part (a) was *No*, what adjustments to your search plan would have located Gina?
Sample Response: In planning a new search grid, don't include areas that have been previously searched.

0 0.1 0.2 0.3 0.4 0.5 0.6 0.7 0.8 0.9 1

Miles

12 Write a newspaper article about the search and rescue of Gina. Describe the search procedures. Be sure to include a description of how mathematics was used in the search.

Sample Response: Gina Roberts, a Laverton pilot, was rescued yesterday after engine trouble forced her to land while in flight to Nullagine. Based on the plane's last known location and heading, the initial air search effort was confined to the Central area. Using standard search and rescue procedure, a ground rescue crew further narrowed the search using a series of increasingly smaller search grids. Roberts was found unharmed in the vicinity of Ten Mile Lake.

You will need: • *protractor* (Ex. 4) • *graph paper* (Exs. 12–15 and 30)

For Exercises 1–4, use the diagram at the right.

1. Name two acute angles. (Sec. 1, Explor. 1) Possible answers: ∠FCB, ∠BCE, ∠ACD

2. Name two obtuse angles. (Sec. 1, Explor. 1) Possible answers: ∠ACB, ∠DCF, ∠DCE

3. Name two straight angles. (Sec. 1, Explor. 1) ∠ACE, ∠DCB

4. a. Find the measure of ∠BCE. (Sec. 1, Explor. 1) 45°

   b. Name and find the measure of a complementary angle and a supplementary angle to ∠BCE.
   (Sec. 1, Explor. 2) ∠BCF or ∠ACD, 45°; ∠ACB or ∠DCE, 135°

5. During the 1994 Winter Olympics, athletes competed underground in an ice hockey stadium. Parts of the stadium are 50 m below ground level. The stadium was built inside Norway's newly-created Gjøvik cavern.

   How can you use integers to describe this situation? Be sure to indicate what positive integers, negative integers, and zero represent. (Sec. 2, Explor. 1) If 0 represents ground level, then negative integers represent meters below ground level, and positive integers represent meters above ground level. So, the stadium was built at –50 m.

6. List the following integers in order from least to greatest:
   –2, 8, 14, 0, –5, –10, 6. (Sec. 2, Explor. 1) –10, –5, –2, 0, 6, 8, 14

Find the opposite and the absolute value of each integer.
(Sec. 2, Explor. 1)

7. 5 –5; 5

8. –1 1; 1

9. 72 –72; 72

10. –303 303; 303

11. Ski jumpers practice creating an ideal body position to maximize the length of their jumps, as shown in the drawing. (Sec. 2, Explor. 2)

11. a. If a line were drawn through the jumper's upper body and another through the skis, the lines would not intersect.

   a. What does it mean to say that the jumper's upper body is almost parallel to the skis?

   b. How would the skier look if his or her body were perpendicular to the skis?
   The skier would be standing up straight.

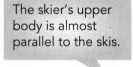

The skier's upper body is almost parallel to the skis.

Graph each ordered pair in the same coordinate plane. (Sec. 2, Explor. 2) See Additional Answers.

12. (3, 2)

13. (–1, 4)

14. (–5, –5)

15. (–4, 1)

Evaluate each expression. (Sec. 3, Explors. 2 and 3)

16. $-3 + 7$ 4
17. $-8 + (-4)$ -12
18. $6 + (-10)$ -4
19. $4 - 15$ -11

20. $-15 - (-12)$ -3
21. $2 - (-5)$ 7
22. $-8 + 13 - 2$ 3
23. $-8 - 7 - 4$ -19

Evaluate each expression when $x = 3$, $a = 6$, $b = -3$, **and** $y = 1$.
(Sec. 4, Explor. 1)

24. $10x$ 30
25. $a - b$ 9
26. $3 \div y$ 3

27. $2x - 23$ -17
28. $3a + b$ 15
29. $4x + 2y$ 14

30. The average speed of a recreational skier is 15 mi/h, or 22 ft/s. The fastest speed of a speed skier is 139 mi/h, or approximately 204 ft/s.
(Sec. 4, Explor. 2)

Time (seconds)	Distance traveled (feet)	
	Recreational skier	Speed skier
10	? 220	? 2040
20	? 440	? 4080
30	? 660	? 6120
40	? 880	? 8160

  a. Copy and complete the table to show the distance traveled in feet by each skier in 10 s, 20 s, 30 s, and 40 s.

  b. Write an equation that shows the relationship between d, the distance traveled in feet, and t, the time in seconds for each skier.
  For the recreational skier, $d = 22t$, for the speed skier, $d = 204t$.

  c. Graph your equations from part (b) on the same coordinate grid. Draw lines connecting the points for each skier.

  d. Use your graph to find out which skier will travel farthest in 45 s. How much farther will the skier go? the speed skier; about 8000 ft

30. c.

31. Julian bought 45 baseball cards. He now has 315. Write an equation to model the situation. Identify the variable you use.
(Sec. 5, Explor. 1) Let b represent the original number of baseball cards. So, $b + 45 = 315$.

Solve. Check each solution. (Sec. 5, Explors. 1 and 2)

32. $d - 33 = 18$ 51
33. $25 + f = 17$ -8
34. $-2 + k = -7$ -5

35. $s - (-4) = 10$ 6
36. $-1 + x = -8$ -7
37. $15 = w - 6$ 21

Reflecting ▷ on the Module

38. Writing Write a letter to one of your other teachers describing what you have done in this module. Discuss how the mathematics you learned might be used in that teacher's class. You may also want to talk about what you liked most and least about the module. Answers will vary. Check students' work.

A Universal Language

$$3x = 36$$

$$\frac{3x}{3} = \frac{36}{3}$$

$$4y = 16$$

$$x = 12$$

$$\frac{w}{2} = 7$$

Secret Codes

History is full of stories in which victory depends on breaking a secret code. You'll use a key to read messages in actual secret codes. Then you'll use the universal language of mathematics to create your own secret code.

More on the Module Project
See pp. 160, 175, 214, and 227.

① Factors, Divisibility, and Multiples
As you explore numbering patterns on clocks and calendars:
- Find prime factorizations
- Find common factors and multiples

② Fractions and Tree Diagrams
As you compare mathematics lessons from around the world:
- Add and subtract fractions
- Use tree diagrams to find probabilities

③ Fractions and Mixed Numbers
As you work with a monetary system used in colonial America:
- Add and subtract mixed numbers

④ Decimals and Exponents
As you learn about people who invented new ways to write decimals and powers:
- Write a decimal as a fraction
- Use integer exponents to write numbers in scientific notation

⑤ Metric Units of Length
As you explore a universal system of measurement:
- Convert metric lengths

⑥ Triangles and Equations
As you examine the use of symbols on national flags:
- Construct triangles
- Solve equations that involve multiplication and division

INTERNET
To learn more about the theme:
http://www.mlmath.com

Section 1 Factors, Divisibility, and Multiples

IN THIS SECTION

EXPLORATION 1
◆ Prime Factorization

EXPLORATION 2
◆ Common Factors

EXPLORATION 3
◆ Common Multiples

Warm-Up Exercises
See page 149.

It's UNIVERSAL

▲
The movement of shadows cast by the sun as it moved across the sky was used to indicate the passing hours.

Stone structures such as the 4000 year old Stonehenge in England were some of the earliest clocks. ▶

◄◄◄ *Setting the Stage*

Throughout history, people have watched and recorded the natural signs all around them. The Konso of central Africa described certain parts of the day by the activity that took place at that time. Their name for the period between 5:00 P.M. and 6:00 P.M., *kakalseema*, means "when the cattle return home."

The system of dividing the day into 24 hours came from the ancient Egyptians. They divided night into 12 hours, numbered the daytime hours 1–10, and assigned dawn and dusk 1 hour each.

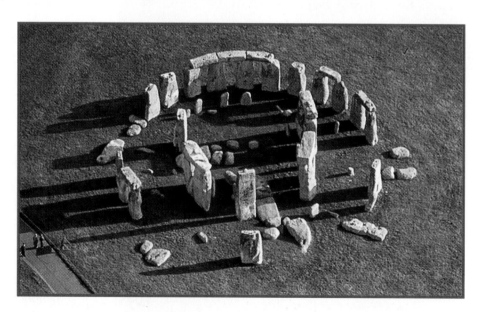

▶ Often called the "universal language," mathematics provides a way to communicate in a clear and precise way about time, money, measurements, shapes, and many other things.

Think About It ▸▸▸▸▸▸▸▸▸▸▸▸▸▸▸▸▸▸▸▸▸▸▸▸▸▸▸▸▸▸▸

1 What daily activities divide your day? Do these activities fall in one-hour intervals (8:00 to 9:00 A.M., 9:00 to 10:00 A.M., etc.)?

2 The Egyptian hours were not all the same. The summer daytime hours lasted longer than the winter daytime hours. Why do you think the hours were not equal?

Sample Response: The time from dawn to dusk is longer in the summer than in the winter. So, if both times were divided into 10 segments, the summer segments would be longer than the winter segments.

Exploration 1 ▸▸▸▸▸▸▸▸▸▸▸▸▸▸▸▸▸▸▸▸▸▸▸▸▸▸▸▸▸▸

Prime Factorization

SET UP *You will need Labsheet 1A.*

▶ **Although our day is divided into 24 hours, the faces of many clocks show only 12 hours. In this exploration you'll explore different possibilities for clock faces and decide which one is best.**

3 **Use Labsheet 1A.** See Additional Answers.

   a. On the clock face below, 4 jumps were made to get back to the START position. How large is each jump?

   b. Follow the directions on Labsheet 1A to complete the *Dot Jumping Table*.

   c. Discussion Look at your results. How are the number of jumps, the jump size, and the number of dots related?

   d. If you made jumps of 7 dots on a circle with 24 dots, would you land on START after one time around the circle? Why or why not?

START
4th jump   1st jump
3rd jump   2nd jump

---

1. Sample Response: meals, afternoon and morning classes, after school activities, night time relaxation; No.

GOAL

LEARN HOW TO...
  ◆ find factors
  ◆ find the prime factorization of a number

AS YOU...
  ◆ explore different clock faces

KEY TERMS
  ◆ factor
  ◆ divisible
  ◆ prime
  ◆ composite
  ◆ prime factorization

WARM-UP EXERCISES

Multiply.
  1. 6×120 720
  2. 15×48 720
  3. 30×24 720

Divide.
  4. $256 \div 8$ 32
  5. $256 \div 16$ 16
  6. $256 \div 4$ 64

4. a. 1 group of 12, 12 groups of 1, 2 groups of 6, 6 groups of 2, 3 groups of 4, 4 groups of 3

4 **Use Labsheet 1A.**

   a. Use your table to find all the ways of dividing the 12 months of the year into groups with the same number of months.

   b. Which method of dividing the months most closely follows the way the year is divided into seasons? 4 groups of 3

▶ In the dot-jumping activity, you found the *factors* of 12, 13, 14, and 15 by determining the number and the size of the jumps needed to land on START. For example, on a circle with 12 dots, you return to START after 6 jumps of size 2. This shows that 6 and 2 are factors of 12.

When one whole number divides another whole number with no remainder, the first number is a **factor** of the second. This also means that the second number is **divisible** by the first.

EXAMPLE

You can make an organized list to find all the factors of 36.

| Start a list with 1 and the number. | $1 \cdot 36 \Rightarrow 1,$ | 36 |

| | $2 \cdot 18 \Rightarrow 1, 2,$ | 18, 36 |

| Then, think of the next pair of factors. | $3 \cdot 12 \Rightarrow 1, 2, 3,$ | 12, 18, 36 |

| | $4 \cdot 9 \Rightarrow 1, 2, 3, 4,$ | 9, 12, 18, 36 |

| | $6 \cdot 6 \Rightarrow 1, 2, 3, 4, 6, 9, 12, 18, 36$ |

---

5 **a.** How do you know when you have found all the factors?
   when the first number in the factor pair has been previously listed
   b. Why is the factor 6 not listed twice?
   To list 6 twice would be repetitious.

▶ In the dot-jumping activity, you found that 13 had only two factors, 1 and 13. If a number has only two factors, 1 and itself, then it is **prime**. If a number has more than two factors, then it is **composite**. The numbers 0 and 1 are neither prime nor composite.

6 Tell whether each number is *prime* or *composite*.

   a. 2   **b.** 20   **c.** 23   **d.** 32
   prime   composite   prime   composite

7 Find all the factors of each number. Tell which factors are prime.

   a. 20   **b.** 35   **c.** 78   **d.** 120
   1, 2, 4, 5, 10, 20;   1, 5, 7, 35;   1, 2, 3, 6, 13,   1, 2, 3, 4, 5, 6, 8, 10,
   prime: 2, 5   prime: 5, 7   26, 39, 78;   12, 15, 20, 24, 30, 40,
                                    prime: 2, 3, 13   60, 120; prime: 2, 3, 5

▶ When you write a number as a product of prime factors, you are writing the **prime factorization** of the number.

8. d. First, look for a 2 in the prime factors. Use the remaining prime factors to find what you multiply 2 by to get 36. Since $(2)(2 \cdot 3 \cdot 3) = 2 \cdot 18 = 36$, 2 and 18 are factors of 36. Repeat the process for 3 and 4 as follows: $(3)(2 \cdot 2 \cdot 3) = 3 \cdot 12$, so 3 and 12 are factors of 36. $(2 \cdot 2)(3 \cdot 3) = 4 \cdot 9$, so 4 and 9 are factors of 36. Since 5 is not listed as a prime factor, 5 is not a factor of 36. But, $(2 \cdot 3)(2 \cdot 3) = 6 \cdot 6$, so 6 is a factor of 36.

8 Discussion Jorge used a factor tree to help him write the prime factorization of 36. Look at Jorge's factor tree below.

4 and 9 are factors of 36, but they are not prime.

All the circled factors are prime.

2 • 2 • 3 • 3 is the prime factorization of 36.

a. Why do you think another row was added after 4 and 9?
  4 and 9 are not prime numbers.

b. Suppose you drew a factor tree for 36 starting with the factors 2 and 18. Would you get the same prime factorization as Jorge? Explain. Yes; $18 = 2 \cdot 9 = 2 \cdot 3 \cdot 3$, so the prime factorization is $2 \cdot 2 \cdot 3 \cdot 3$.

c. How can you write the prime factorization of 36 using exponents? $2^2 \cdot 3^2$

d. How can you use the prime factorization of 36 to find other factors of 36? See above.

FOR ◀ HELP
with *exponents*,
see
MODULE 1, p. 20

9 ✔ **CHECKPOINT** Find all the factors of each number. Then write the prime factorization of each number. See below.

a. 18   **b.** 30   **c.** 64   **d.** 100

✔ **QUESTION 9**
…checks that you can find factors and write prime factorizations.

10 a. Many clock faces show only 12 hours, and the hours are repeated to make a 24-hour day. What other clock faces could be used to keep time? Give the number of hours on each clock face and how many times the hours would have to be repeated to make a 24-hour day. 1, 24; 24, 1; 2, 12; 3, 8; 8, 3; 4, 6; 6, 4

b. Which clock face do you think would be best to use? Why?
  Sample Response: the clock face with 24 h; The numbers used for the hours would not be duplicated.

9. a. 1, 2, 3, 6, 9, 18; $2 \cdot 3 \cdot 3$
b. 1, 2, 3, 5, 6, 10, 15, 30; $2 \cdot 3 \cdot 5$
c. 1, 2, 4, 8, 16, 32, 64; $2 \cdot 2 \cdot 2 \cdot 2 \cdot 2 \cdot 2$
d. 1, 2, 4, 5, 10, 20, 25, 50, 100; $2 \cdot 2 \cdot 5 \cdot 5$

HOMEWORK EXERCISES ▶ See Exs. 1–34 on pp. 157–158.

GOAL

LEARN HOW TO...
• use divisibility rules to find factors
• find the greatest common factor of two or more numbers

AS YOU...
• explore the Chinese calendar

KEY TERM
• greatest common factor (GCF)

Exploration 2

Common Factors

SET UP / *You will need Labsheet 1B.*

The Chinese developed an interesting method for making divisions of time. They named each year after one of twelve animals. For example, 1977 was the year of the Snake. The next year of the Snake was 12 years later, in 1989. In the Chinese calendar, a 60-year cycle allows the 12 different animals to repeat 5 times.

11 According to the Chinese calendar, when is the next year of the Snake after 1989? 2001

12 For which animal is the year of your birth named? Answers will vary.

▶ **Divisibility Rules** To determine some factors of a number, you can use divisibility rules. For example, a number divisible by 10 has a 0 in the ones place.

13 Discussion Without dividing, how can you tell that a number is divisible by 2? by 5? If it is even; If it ends in a 0 or 5.

14 Use Labsheet 1B.

a. Complete the *Divisibility-by-Nine Table* and look for a pattern involving the sum of the digits.

b. Write a rule for telling whether a number is divisible by 9. If the sum of the digits is divisible by 9, the number is divisible by 9.

c. Use your calculator to try the rule you wrote in part (a) with other numbers.

d. Write a rule for telling whether a number is divisible by 3. (*Hint:* The rule is similar to the rule for 9.) If the sum of the digits is divisible by 3, the number is divisible by 3.

15 On the notebook at the right, a student wrote a divisibility rule for 6. Is this rule correct? Why or why not? Yes; Since 6 = 2 · 3, a number must be divisible by both 2 and by 3 to be divisible by 6.

> A number is divisible by 6 if the ones digit is even and the sum of the digits is divisible by 3.

16 The responses in the second column of the table indicate whether the numbers in the first column are divisible by 4.

a. Copy the table and use a calculator to tell whether the numbers in the third column are divisible by 4. See table.

Divisible by 4?				
24	yes	224	?	Yes
34	no	334	?	No
36	yes	136	?	Yes
60	yes	460	?	Yes
66	no	866	?	No
72	yes	1572	?	Yes
84	yes	2784	?	Yes

b. How are the numbers in the third column related to the numbers in the first column?

c. Write a rule for telling whether a number is divisible by 4.

d. List some 3-digit and 4-digit numbers and test your rule. Does it work?

17 ✔ **CHECKPOINT** Use divisibility rules to tell whether each number is divisible by 2, 3, 4, 5, 6, 9, and 10.

a. 1362   b. 5220   c. 1268   d. 375

18 Write a rule for divisibility by 12 and test your rule with some 3-digit and 4-digit numbers. (*Hint:* Think about the divisibility rule for 6.) If a number is divisible by 3 and by 4, the number is divisible by 12. Example: Since 207 is divisible by 3 but not by 4, it shouldn't be divisible by 12. 207 ÷ 12 = 17 R3; It isn't divisble by 12.

14. a. 1 + 8 = 9; 9 + 1 + 8 = 18; 9, 1, 5, 3; 9 + 1 + 5 + 3 = 18; 7 + 1 + 1 + 2 + 7 + 2 + 0 + 7 = 27; 9, 4, 3, 2, 8, 0, 3, 0, 7; 9 + 4 + 3 + 2 + 8 + 0 + 3 + 0 + 7 = 36

c. Sample Response: Since 4 + 6 + 5 + 3 = 18 and 18 is divisible by 9, any four digit number combining these digits is divisible by 9. Examples: 5643 and 3465

16. b. The digits in the tens and ones places are the same.

c. Sample Response: If the last 2 digits are divisible by 4, the number is divisible by 4.

d. Sample Response: 4124 ÷ 4 = 1031, 142 ÷ 4 = 35.5; Yes.

17. a. 1362 is divisible by 2, 3, and 6.

b. 5220 is divisible by 2, 3, 4, 5, 6, 9, and 10.

c. 1268 is divisible by 2 and 4.

d. 375 is divisible by 3 and 5.

✔ **QUESTION 17**

...checks that you can tell whether a number is divisible by 2, 3, 4, 5, 6, 9, and 10.

▶ Numbers often have some factors in common. The **greatest common factor (GCF)** of two or more numbers is the greatest factor that is common to those numbers.

19. a. Factors of 42: 1, 2, 3, 6, 7, 14, 21, 42; Factors of 56: 1, 2, 4, 7, 8, 14, 28, 56

19 **a.** Use divisibility rules to help list all the factors of 42 and 56.

b. What factors do 42 and 56 have in common? 1, 2, 7, 14

c. Which is the greatest common factor you found in part (b)? 14

✔ QUESTION 20

...checks that you can find the GCF of two or more numbers.

20 ✔ **CHECKPOINT** Find the GCF of each group of numbers.

a. 24, 4 4   **b.** 7, 12 1   **c.** 28, 32, 36 4

21 What other numbers of animals could the Chinese have used to complete the 60-year cycle? (*Hint:* Use the factors of 60.)
1, 2, 3, 4, 5, 6, 10, 15, 20, 30, or 60

❘ HOMEWORK EXERCISES ▸ See Exs. 35–55 on p. 158.

GOAL

LEARN HOW TO...
♦ find the least common multiple of two or more numbers

AS YOU...
♦ work with a January calendar

KEY TERMS
♦ multiple
♦ least common multiple (LCM)

Exploration 3

Common Multiples

SET UP *You will need Labsheet 1C.*

▶ In Explorations 1 and 2, you found factors of numbers. For example, 12 = 2 · 6, so 2 and 6 are factors of 12. A **multiple** of a whole number is the product of that number and any nonzero whole number. For example, 12 is a multiple of 2 and a multiple of 6.

EXAMPLE

You can make a partial list of the multiples of 6.

$$1 \cdot 6 = 6$$
$$2 \cdot 6 = 12$$
$$3 \cdot 6 = 18$$
$$4 \cdot 6 = 24$$
$$\vdots$$

The multiples of 6 are 6, 12, 18, 24, ...

Use Labsheet 1C for Questions 22–25.

22 **a.** Follow the directions on Labsheet 1C to find the multiples of 1, 2, and 3.

b. Which spaces on the *Calendar of Multiples* have both a ② and a ③? 6, 12, 18, 24, 30

▶ Each of the numbers you listed in Question 22(b) is a multiple of 2 and a multiple of 3. The least number that is a multiple of two or more numbers is the **least common multiple (LCM)** of those numbers.

23 Use the *Calendar of Multiples* to find the LCM of 2 and 3. 6

24 Complete the calendar by placing a ④ in the spaces containing multiples of 4, a ⑤ in the spaces with multiples of 5, and so on. Continue until you have marked the calendar with the multiples of all the numbers up to and including 31. See Additional Answers.

25 **a.** List the common multiples of 3, 4, and 6 shown on the calendar.
12, 24
b. What is the least common multiple of 3, 4, and 6? 12

26 ✔ CHECKPOINT   Find the LCM of 10 and 15. Then explain how you found it.   30; Sample Response: List the multiples of 10 and the multiples of 15. Then find the least common multiple.

27 **a.** Write the prime factorization of 10 and of 15. $10 = 2 \cdot 5$; $15 = 3 \cdot 5$

b. List the prime numbers that are factors of 10, of 15, or of both. Do not list any factor more than once. Find the product of these factors. 2, 3, 5; 30

c. How does your answer to part (b) compare with the LCM of 10 and 15 you found in Question 26? It is the same.

28 **a.** The LCM of 6 and 18 is 18. Find another pair of numbers whose LCM is one of the original numbers. Sample Response: 6 and 24

b. The LCM of 6 and 5 is 30. Find another pair of numbers whose LCM is the product of the numbers. Sample Response: 3 and 4

29 The Dogon people of West Africa used astronomical observations to mark the passage of time. For example, they chose their leader when Jupiter (about a 12-year orbit) and Saturn (about a 30-year orbit) completed an orbit around the sun together. How often did they choose a leader?
every 60 years

HOMEWORK EXERCISES ▶ See Exs. 56–68 on p. 159.

22. a. Multiples of 1: 1–31; Multiples of 2: 2, 4, 6, 8, 10, 12, 14, 16, 18, 20, 22, 24, 26, 28, 30; Multiples of 3: 3, 6, 9, 12, 15, 18, 21, 24, 27, 30

CLOSURE QUESTION

Explain what is meant by factor and greatest common factor, and by multiple and least common multiple. Then tell how prime factorization involves prime numbers and composite numbers.

Sample Response: A factor is a whole number that can divide another whole number with a remainder of zero. The greatest common factor is the largest factor that divides two or more given numbers. A multiple of a whole number is the product

✔ **QUESTION 26**

...checks that you can find the LCM of two numbers.

of that whole number and any other whole number (excluding 0). The least common multiple is the least number that is a multiple of two or more given whole numbers. The prime factorization of a composite number is the product of its prime factors.

A Dogon man stands on the Bandiagara Cliffs in Mali, Africa.
▼

Key Terms

factor

prime

prime
factorization

composite

divisible

greatest
common
factor (GCF)

multiple

least common
multiple (LCM)

Prime Factorization (pp. 149–151)

Every whole number other than 0 or 1 is either prime or composite.

The prime factorization of a number is the product of its prime factors.

Example

24 is a composite number. $24 = 2 \cdot 2 \cdot 2 \cdot 3$ 2 and 3 are prime numbers.

Divisibility and Common Factors (pp. 152–154)

A number is divisible by...	
3	if the sum of the digits is divisible by 3.
4	if the number formed by the tens and ones digits is divisible by 4.
6	if it is divisible by both 2 and 3.
9	if the sum of the digits is divisible by 9.

The GCF of two or more numbers can be found by listing their factors.

Example

The factors of 48: **1, 2, 3, 4, 6,** 8, **12,** 16, 24, 48
The factors of 36: **1, 2, 3, 4, 6,** 9, **12,** 18, 36
The GCF of 48 and 36 is 12.

Multiples (pp. 154–155)

The LCM of two or more numbers can be found by listing their multiples.

Example

Multiples of 8: 8, 16, **24,** 32, 40, **48,** …
Multiples of 12: 12, **24,** 36, **48,** …
The LCM of 8 and 12 is 24.

---

30 **Key Concepts Question** Replace each _?_ with 2, 4, or 8 to make each statement true.

a. _?_ and _?_ are factors of _?_ . 2, 4, 8

b. _?_ and _?_ are multiples of _?_ . 4, 8, 2

c. The LCM of _?_ and _?_ is _?_ . 2, 4, 4 (or 4, 8, 8 or 2, 8, 8)

d. _?_ is prime; _?_ and _?_ are composite. 2, 4, 8

Section 1
Practice & Application Exercises

YOU WILL NEED

For Exs. 72–74:
◆ protractor

Find all the factors of each number.

1. 12   **2.** 27   **3.** 45   **4.** 53

5. 64   **6.** 71   **7.** 100   **8.** 124

9. 121   **10.** 144   **11.** 150   **12.** 225

13. The number 25 has an odd number of factors. Find five other numbers that have an odd number of factors. What pattern do you notice? Sample Response: 36, 49, 64, 81, 100; Perfect squares have an odd number of factors.

Tell whether each number is *prime* or *composite*.

14. 3   prime   **15.** 8   composite   **16.** 12   composite   **17.** 19   prime

18. 21   composite   **19.** 31   prime   **20.** 33   composite   **21.** 47   prime

Find the prime factorization of each number.

22. 16 $2 \cdot 2 \cdot 2 \cdot 2$ **23.** 28 $2 \cdot 2 \cdot 7$ **24.** 30 $2 \cdot 3 \cdot 5$ **25.** 36 $2 \cdot 2 \cdot 3 \cdot 3$

26. 46 $2 \cdot 23$ **27.** 50 $2 \cdot 5 \cdot 5$ **28.** 75 $3 \cdot 5 \cdot 5$ **29.** 170 $2 \cdot 5 \cdot 17$

30. Cheerleading Two guidelines for high school cheerleading are listed. Suppose a 32-person squad is planning pyramids with backward dismounts. What is the greatest possible number of backward dismounts the squad can perform at the same time? 5

Cheerleading Guidelines
- All pyramids are limited to two persons high.
- All backward dismounts from pyramids must use three catchers.

dismount   *catchers*

31. Challenge Ann Chang's class has 24 students and Mark McKay's class has 36 students. The two classes are going to a museum together. At the museum the students will be divided into smaller groups. Each group must contain students from both classes, and the students from each class must be divided evenly among the groups. List all the possible ways the groups can be set up.

---

*Answer key (margin):*

1. 1, 2, 3, 4, 6, 12
2. 1, 3, 9, 27
3. 1, 3, 5, 9, 15, 45
4. 1, 53
5. 1, 2, 4, 8, 16, 32, 64
6. 1, 71
7. 1, 2, 4, 5, 10, 20, 25, 50, 100
8. 1, 2, 4, 31, 62, 124
9. 1, 11, 121
10. 1, 2, 3, 4, 6, 8, 9, 12, 16, 18, 24, 36, 48, 72, 144
11. 1, 2, 3, 5, 6, 10, 15, 25, 30, 50, 75, 150
12. 1, 3, 5, 9, 15, 25, 45, 75, 225

31. 2 groups of 30 (12 from Ann Chang's class and 18 from Mark McKay's), 3 groups of 20 (8 from Chang's and 12 from McKay's), 4 groups of 15 (6 and 9), 6 groups of 10 (4 and 6), 12 groups of 5 (2 and 3)

Geometry Connection For each rectangle:

a. Find the area and the perimeter.

b. Find the length and width of a rectangle with the same area and a smaller perimeter.

c. Find the length and width of a rectangle with the same area and a greater perimeter. *Sample Responses are given.*

32.

6 in.

2 in.

a. 12 in.²; 16 in.
b. 3 in. by 4 in.
c. 1 in. by 12 in.

33.

10 m

3 m

a. 30 m²; 26 m
b. 5 m by 6 m
c. 2 m by 15 m, or 1 m by 30 m

34.

9 ft

4 ft

a. 36 ft²; 26 ft
b. 6 ft by 6 ft
c. 1 ft by 36 ft, 2 ft by 18 ft, or 3 ft by 12 ft

Tell whether each number in Exercises 35–42 is divisible by each of the numbers 2, 3, 4, 5, 6, 9, and 10.

35. 77 none **36.** 96 2, 3, 4, 6 **37.** 112 2, 4 **38.** 275 5

39. 300 2, 3, 4, 5, 6, 10 **40.** 414 2, 3, 6, 9 **41.** 780 2, 3, 4, 5, 6, 10 **42.** 1075 5

43. Make and test a rule for divisibility by 8. (*Hint:* Think about the divisibility rule for 4.)

44. List five numbers that are divisible by 25. Then list five numbers that are divisible by 100. Use your results to write divisibility rules for 25 and for 100.

Find the greatest common factor of each group of numbers.

45. 9, 12 3 **46.** 14, 21 7 **47.** 15, 30 15

48. 64, 48 16 **49.** 53, 71 1 **50.** 48, 120 24

51. 60, 75, 90 15 **52.** 96, 180, 192 12 **53.** 78, 104, 117 13

54. a. Can two even numbers have a GCF of 1? Explain.
No; The GCF must be at least 2 because 2 must be a factor of both numbers.

b. Can two odd numbers have a GCF of 1? Explain.
Yes; If the two numbers are prime or if they have no common factors other than 1, such as 9 and 25.

55. **Create Your Own** Jupiter has short days and long years. Using our time, a Jupiter day is only 9 h 55 min long. One Jupiter year is about 4333 Earth days.

Jupiter's orbit

sun

a. Design a calendar for a year that contains 4333 Earth days. Tell the numbers of days in a month and months in a year. *Sample Response: a calendar with 56 months, each 76 days long, and one month, 77 days long*

b. **Writing** Explain why you designed your calendar as you did.
Sample Response: 56 months × 76 days/month + 1 month × 77 days/month = 4333 days

43. If the number formed by the last 3 digits of the number is divisible by 8, the entire number is divisible by 8. Example: 9416 ÷ 8 = 1177

44. Sample Response: 50, 75, 100, 125, 150; 100, 200, 300, 400, 500; If the number ends in 25, 50, 75, or 00, the number is divisible by 25. If the number ends in 00, the number is divisible by 100.

Find the least common multiple of each group of numbers.

56. 2, 4 4   **57.** 4, 6 12   **58.** 6, 8 24

59. 8, 10 40   **60.** 12, 15 60   **61.** 20, 25 100

62. 5, 7, 10 70   **63.** 9, 18, 36 36   **64.** 8, 14, 28 56

65. Lucinda made just one list to find the LCM of 14, 36, and 63. Describe how she can find the LCM by listing the numbers 63, 126, 189, and 252. See above.

66. The price for one type of sticker is 25¢ each. Another type costs 35¢ per sticker. Suppose the same amount of money is spent on each type. What is the least total amount that can be spent? $3.50, $1.75 for each type of sticker.

67. **a.** Antonio asks if there is such a thing as a greatest common multiple. What would you tell him?
See below.
b. Is there a least common divisor? Explain.
Yes; Every whole number is divisible by 1, and 1 is the smallest whole number that can be a divisor, so 1 is the least common divisor of any set of whole numbers.

Reflecting on the Section

68. Explain how the problem of finding the number of ways to arrange desks in rows with the same number of desks in each row is related to factors, divisibility, and multiples. See below.

Spiral Review

Solve. Check each answer. (Module 2, p. 137)

69. $x + 38 = 90$ 52   **70.** $z - 53 = 798$ 851   **71.** $-102 = y - 47$ –55

Find the measure of each angle. Then classify each angle as *acute*, *obtuse*, *right*, or *straight*. (Module 2, p. 83)

72. 90°; right   **73.** 30°; acute   **74.** 120°; obtuse

Find each sum or difference. (Toolbox, p. 587)

75. $\frac{1}{5} + \frac{2}{5}$ $\frac{3}{5}$ **76.** $\frac{5}{8} - \frac{3}{8}$ $\frac{2}{8}$ **77.** $\frac{10}{23} - \frac{7}{23}$ $\frac{3}{23}$ **78.** $\frac{12}{35} + \frac{8}{35}$ $\frac{20}{35}$

65. Since the numbers listed are all multiples of 63, start with the lowest number and see if the number is divisible by both 14 and 36. If it is, that is the LCM. If it isn't, repeat the process with the next larger number in the list. Continue in this way until the LCM (252) is found.

25¢ each

35¢ each

Visual THINKING

Exercise 68 checks that you can apply ideas about factors, divisibility, and multiples.

67. a. No; If x is any common multiple of a set of numbers, then $2 \cdot x$ is also a common multiple, and it is greater than x. So there is always a greater common multiple.

68. Sample Response: A number's factors are those numbers by which the original number is divisible with no remainder. So, the number of rows and the number of desks in each row are factors of the total number of desks. The product of a number and any nonzero whole number is a multiple of the original number. So, the total number of desks is a multiple of the number of rows and of the number of desks in each row.

Beginning the Module Project

Secret Codes

Have you ever learned sign language? Do you understand Russian? There are over 6500 languages used throughout the world and no one can possibly understand them all. This can be an advantage when people are trying to keep communications secret.

Using the Language of Mathematics During World War II, the U.S. Marine Corps used the Navajo language as a code, since it was known only to the Navajo people. As you work through this module, you'll see how the universal language of mathematics can be used to design codes. For your project, you'll create your own code and test it with members of your class.

▲ Two Marines using the Navajo code during the battle for Bougainville in 1943

Code	Translation	Meaning
lo-tso	whale	Battleship
besh-lo	iron fish	Submarine
lo-tso-yazzie	small whale	Cruiser

The Roman Emperor Julius Caesar created a code in which each letter was replaced by another letter that was three places farther on in the alphabet. Applying the Caesar shift code to the English alphabet results in the code key below.

Original letter	A	B	C	D	E	F	G	H	I	J	K	L	M	N	O	P	Q	R	S	T	U	V	W	X	Y	Z
Code letter	D	E	F	G	H	I	J	K	L	M	N	O	P	Q	R	S	T	U	V	W	X	Y	Z	A	B	C

1 Use the code key to decode each message.

　a. XQGHUVWDQG WKH SUREOHP
　　　Understand the problem.
　c. FDUUB RXW WKH SODQ
　　　Carry out the plan.

　b. GHYLVH D SODQ
　　　Devise a plan.
　d. ORRN EDFN
　　　Look back.

2 A different shift code was used for the following message. Decode the message. Then describe any strategies you used.

DRO MKOCKB MYNO SC OKCI DY ECO　The Caesar code is easy to use; I guessed "the" was the first word in the message. So, I wrote in D as the code letter for T and filled in the rest of the chart.

3 How many possible shift codes are there for our alphabet? 25

Section 1

Extra Skill Practice

Find all the factors of each number. See Additional Answers.

1. 18
2. 24
3. 51
4. 180
5. 72
6. 169
7. 84
8. 75
9. 108
10. 125
11. 91
12. 56

Find the prime factorization of each number. See Additional Answers.

13. 24
14. 35
15. 81
16. 88
17. 90
18. 105
19. 120
20. 128
21. 54
22. 80
23. 48
24. 60

Tell whether each number is divisible by each of the numbers 2, 3, 4, 5, 6, 9, and 10.

25. 42 2, 3, 6
26. 56 2, 4
27. 87 3
28. 96 2, 3, 4, 6
29. 124 2, 4
30. 1585 5
31. 1620 2, 3, 4, 5, 6, 9, 10
32. 2560 2, 4, 5, 10

Find the greatest common factor of each group of numbers.

33. 9, 27 9
34. 12, 36 12
35. 15, 20 5
36. 72, 90 9
37. 64, 96, 144 16
38. 88, 110, 143 11
39. 98, 105, 112 7
40. 45, 135, 225 45

Find the least common multiple of each group of numbers.

41. 6, 9 18
42. 8, 12 24
43. 9, 15 45
44. 16, 20 80
45. 2, 5, 8 40
46. 4, 6, 9 36
47. 6, 10, 12 60
48. 8, 12, 16 48

Study Skills ◀▶ Using Mathematical Language

Some words have similar meanings in everyday language and in mathematics. Some have quite different meanings.

1. Look at the list of words below. Tell the meaning of each word in everyday language. Check students' work.

   a. axes
   b. factor
   c. negative
   d. mean
   e. origin
   f. variable

2. Explain how the meaning of each word in Exercise 1 is either similar to or different from its meaning in mathematics. (*Hint:* Use the Glossary.) Check students' work.

Section ② Fractions and Tree Diagrams

IN THIS SECTION

EXPLORATION 1
◆ Comparing Fractions

EXPLORATION 2
◆ Adding and Subtracting Fractions

EXPLORATION 3
◆ Tree Diagrams and Probability

WARM-UP EXERCISES

Write the fraction represented by the shading in each figure.

1. $\frac{1}{4}$

2. $\frac{3}{8}$

3. $\frac{2}{6}$

4. $\frac{10}{10}$

5. $\frac{0}{3}$

1. Sample Response: that $\frac{1}{4}$ of 3 is the same as $\frac{3}{4}$ of 1 or $\frac{3}{4}$; from the photo, the diagrams, and the fractions in the text

2. Sample Response: Thomas's mother made a stack of 3 pancakes, cut the stack into fourths, and told Thomas and his sister Heike that they could each eat $\frac{3}{4}$ of a pancake. Heike wanted $\frac{3}{4}$ of the top pancake, but Thomas explained that she would still get $\frac{3}{4}$ of a pancake if he gave her $\frac{1}{4}$ of the stack.

Mathematically Speaking

‹‹‹ *Setting the Stage*

Sprechen Sie Deutsch? (Can you speak German?) Maybe not, but see how much you can understand of this page from a German mathematics book.

13.2. Der Bruch als Teil mehrerer Ganzen

1. Mutter hat 3 Pfannkuchen gebacken und in Viertel geteilt. Heike und Thomas dürfen sich jeder $\frac{3}{4}$ Pfannkuchen nehmen. Heike will sich von den obersten Kuchen $\frac{3}{4}$ abnehmen. Thomas kann es einfacher. Er nimmt sich 3 übereinanderliegende Viertel, von jedem Kuchen also $\frac{1}{4}$, das sind auch $\frac{3}{4}$ Pfannkuchen.

2. Der Bruch $\frac{3}{4}$ kann also auf zwei verschiedene Arten entstehen:

a. Ein Pfannkuchen wird in vier gleiche Teile geteilt. 3 Teile davon werden zu einem Bruch zusammengefaßt: $\frac{3}{4}$ **Pfannkuchen**.

b. Drei Pfannkuchen werden aufeinandergelegt und geviertelt. Es liegen dann jeweils 3 Viertelstücke aufeinander, das sind: $\frac{3}{4}$ **Pfannkuchen**.

Think About It

1 What mathematics concept is presented in the German text? How do you know?

2 Tell a story that could go with the pictures.

Comparing Fractions

GOAL

LEARN HOW TO...
- write fractions in lowest terms
- compare fractions using least common denominators

AS YOU...
- read a flow chart

KEY TERMS
- equivalent fractions
- lowest terms
- least common denominator

▶ As you saw from the page of the German book, mathematical ideas can be communicated without language. Many of the same numerals, diagrams, and symbols are used in different countries. Students all over the world use >, <, and = to compare numbers.

3 Use the circle diagrams to compare the fractions. Replace each _?_ with >, <, or =.

a. $\frac{1}{4}$ _?_ $\frac{1}{8}$ >   **b.** $\frac{2}{4}$ _?_ $\frac{4}{8}$ =   **c.** $\frac{3}{4}$ _?_ $\frac{7}{8}$ <

▶ Fractions that represent the same amount are **equivalent fractions**. To write a fraction in **lowest terms**, you need to find an equivalent fraction where the greatest common factor of the numerator and denominator is 1.

FOR ▶ HELP

with *equivalent fractions*, see
TOOLBOX, p. 585

4 Which fractions in Question 3 are equivalent fractions? Are they in lowest terms? Explain. $\frac{2}{4}$ and $\frac{4}{8}$; No; In each fraction, the GCF of the numerator and denominator is greater than 1.

5 Use this example from a German mathematics lesson.

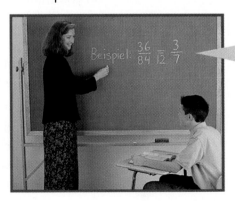

Beispiel means "example."

a. Find the GCF of 36 and 84. 12

b. Is $\frac{36}{84}$ in lowest terms? How do you know? No; The GCF of the numerator and denominator is greater than 1.

c. Find the GCF of 3 and 7. 1

d. Is $\frac{3}{7}$ in lowest terms? How do you know? Yes; The GCF of the numerator and denominator is 1.

6. a. **Sample Response:** The numerator and denominator of $\frac{36}{84}$ are to be divided by 12.

b. To write a fraction in lowest terms, divide both the numerator and denominator by their GCF.

✔ **QUESTION 7**

...checks that you can write a fraction in lowest terms.

6 Discussion Use the German example: $\frac{36}{84} = \frac{3}{7}$.
12

a. Although fraction concepts are universal, sometimes a slightly different notation is used. Why do you think the number 12 is printed underneath the equals sign in the example?

b. How can the idea of greatest common factor be used to find an equivalent fraction in lowest terms?

7 ✔ CHECKPOINT Write each fraction in lowest terms.

a. $\frac{10}{18}$ $\frac{5}{9}$ **b.** $\frac{12}{27}$ $\frac{4}{9}$

8 How can you use your answers to Question 7 to compare $\frac{10}{18}$ and $\frac{12}{27}$? Compare $\frac{5}{9}$ and $\frac{4}{9}$.

▶ **Comparing Fractions** The *flow chart* below appears in a Bulgarian mathematics book in a lesson about comparing fractions.

9 Try This as a Class Look at the examples shown along the left and right sides of the flow chart. See Additional Answers.

a. What do you think the question in the shaded box is asking?

b. For the example on the right, why do you think the third box of the flow chart is skipped? What do you think are the instructions in the third box?

c. Why are fifteenths used to compare the two fractions on the left side?

d. In the fourth box, what parts of the fractions are compared to find the greater fraction? Why?

▶ One way to compare fractions is by finding the *least common denominator*. The **least common denominator** of two fractions is the least common multiple of the denominators.

EXAMPLE

Compare $\frac{5}{8}$ and $\frac{7}{12}$.

SAMPLE RESPONSE

> 24 is the LCM of 8 and 12.

First Find a common denominator.

The least common denominator of $\frac{5}{8}$ and $\frac{7}{12}$ is 24.

Next Rename each fraction as an equivalent fraction with the common denominator.

$$\frac{5}{8} = \frac{5 \cdot 3}{8 \cdot 3} = \frac{15}{24} \quad \text{and} \quad \frac{7}{12} = \frac{7 \cdot 2}{12 \cdot 2} = \frac{14}{24}$$

Then Compare the fractions that have the same denominator.

$$\frac{15}{24} > \frac{14}{24}, \text{ so } \frac{5}{8} > \frac{7}{12}$$

---

10 In the Example, two fractions are renamed using the least common denominator. How does this method compare with the Bulgarian method? The methods are the same.

11 **Create Your Own** Create a flow chart of your own for comparing fractions. Include two examples that show how to use your flow chart. In one example, use fractions that have a common denominator. In the other example, use fractions that do not have a common denominator. See Additional Answers.

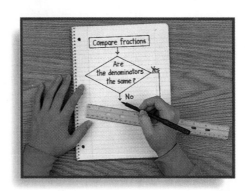

12 ✔ **CHECKPOINT** Compare each pair of fractions. Replace each _?_ with >, <, or =.

a. $\frac{3}{5}$ _?_ $\frac{3}{4}$ <   b. $\frac{2}{5}$ _?_ $\frac{1}{5}$ >   c. $\frac{2}{3}$ _?_ $\frac{11}{15}$ <

d. $\frac{19}{20}$ _?_ $\frac{54}{60}$ >   e. $\frac{7}{18}$ _?_ $\frac{5}{12}$ <   f. $\frac{55}{90}$ _?_ $\frac{11}{18}$ =

✔ **QUESTION 12**

...checks that you can compare fractions.

HOMEWORK EXERCISES ▶ See Exs. 1–30 on pp. 171–173.

Exploration 2

Adding and Subtracting
Fractions

SET UP *You will need Labsheet 2A.*

▶ **Models for adding and subtracting fractions are also universal. See the examples below from an Australian textbook and a Japanese textbook.**

Australian textbook:

For example, for $\dfrac{3}{8} + \dfrac{2}{8}$

Japanese textbook:

数直線を使って考えましょう。

答え $\dfrac{4}{5}\,\ell$

13 a. how to add fractions that have the same denominator

a. Explain what the examples are trying to show.

b. What makes these examples universal? The drawings and numbers can be understood even though you may not be able to to read the words.

c. Write the equation each example represents. Australian textbook:
$\dfrac{3}{8} + \dfrac{2}{8} = \dfrac{5}{8}$,

Japanese textbook:
$\dfrac{1}{5} + \dfrac{3}{5} = \dfrac{4}{5}$

14 a. Explain how to add two fractions that have the same denominator without using a diagram. *Add the numerators.*

b. Explain how to subtract two fractions that have the same denominator without using a diagram. *Subtract the numerators.*

FOR ▶ HELP

with *adding and subtracting like fractions,* see
TOOLBOX, p. 587

15 Find each sum or difference. Write each answer in lowest terms.

a. $\frac{3}{10} + \frac{5}{10}$ $\frac{4}{5}$ **b.** $\frac{1}{4} + \frac{1}{4}$ $\frac{1}{2}$ **c.** $\frac{5}{8} - \frac{3}{8}$ $\frac{1}{4}$ **d.** $\frac{11}{12} - \frac{7}{12}$ $\frac{1}{3}$

16 Why is it difficult to use models to find each answer?

a. $\frac{1}{2} + \frac{1}{5} = \underline{\ ?\ }$

It is not apparent what fractional part is shaded in the diagram showing the sum.

b. $\frac{2}{3} - \frac{1}{4} = \underline{\ ?\ }$

It is not obvious which part of the circle is shaded in the diagram showing the difference.

c. $\frac{1}{3} + \frac{1}{8} = \underline{\ ?\ }$

The diagram showing the sum essentially is just a repetition of the problem.

17 Estimation Use the models in Question 16. Which of the following choices is closest to the sum in part (a)? the difference in part (b)? the sum in part (c)? *D, B, B*

A. less than $\frac{1}{4}$ **B.** greater than $\frac{1}{4}$ but less than $\frac{1}{2}$

C. greater than $\frac{3}{4}$ **D.** greater than $\frac{1}{2}$ but less than $\frac{3}{4}$

18 Use Labsheet 2A. Use the *Equivalent Fraction Models* to find exact answers to the problems in Question 16. $\frac{7}{10}, \frac{5}{12}, \frac{11}{24}$

19 Estimation Estimate whether each sum or difference is *greater than*, *less than*, or *equal to* $\frac{1}{2}$.

a. $\frac{1}{5} + \frac{7}{10}$ **b.** $\frac{1}{3} + \frac{1}{6}$ **c.** $\frac{15}{16} - \frac{1}{8}$ **d.** $\frac{2}{3} - \frac{1}{4}$

greater than   *equal to*   *greater than*   *less than*

20. Change the fractions to equivalent fractions with the same denominators. Then add or subtract the numerators.

20 Discussion How can equivalent fractions be used to find the exact sum or difference of two fractions?

21 ✔ **CHECKPOINT** Find the exact sum or difference for each expression in Question 19. $\frac{9}{10}, \frac{1}{2}, \frac{13}{16}, \frac{5}{12}$

✔ **QUESTION 21**

…checks that you can add and subtract fractions with unlike denominators.

HOMEWORK EXERCISES ▶ See Exs. 31–43 on p. 173.

LEARN HOW TO...
- use a tree diagram to find outcomes and probabilities

AS YOU...
- think about choosing marbles from a jar

KEY TERM
- tree diagram

Exploration 3

TREE Diagrams
and
Probability

▶ The example below is written in Spanish, but the *tree diagram* is universal. **Tree diagrams** can be used to display the possible outcomes of an experiment.

La probabilidad del evento de sacar primero la azul, luego la verde, y por último la roja es de $\frac{1}{6}$.

$$P(E) = \frac{1}{6}$$

azul

verde

roja

22. a. Sample Response: A jar contains an azul, a verde, and a roja marble. The three marbles are drawn from the jar one at a time without looking.

22 a. What experiment does the tree diagram above represent?

b. How many possible outcomes are there? 6

c. Why is the probability of the circled combination of marbles equal to $\frac{1}{6}$? Of the 6 possible outcomes, one is the circled outcome.

d. What event does the E in $P(E) = \frac{1}{6}$ describe?
taking out the marbles in the following order: azul, verde, roja

23 Try This as a Class Look at the branches in the tree diagram on page 168.

a. Why are there three branches coming from the jar of marbles?

b. Why does each of the three marbles in the first column have two branches extending to the right?

c. Why does each of the marbles in the second column have only one branch extending to the right?

d. Is a marble replaced after it is chosen? How can you tell?

Some events for the experiment on page 168 are listed below. Use these events for Questions 24–27.

Event J: taking an *azul* marble out of the jar first, then a *roja* marble, then a *verde* marble

Event K: taking out a *roja* marble first

Event L: not taking out a *verde* marble last

Event M: taking out any combination of three marbles that includes an *azul* marble

24 Use the tree diagram to find each theoretical probability.

a. $P(J)$ $\frac{1}{6}$ **b.** $P(K)$ $\frac{1}{3}$ **c.** $P(L)$ $\frac{2}{3}$ **d.** $P(M)$ 1

25 ✔ CHECKPOINT Suppose three marbles are taken out of the jar one at a time and each marble is *replaced* in the jar before the next one is taken out.

a. Draw a tree diagram to list all the possible outcomes. Use a *verde*, an *azul*, and a *roja* marble. See Additional Answers.

b. How does this tree diagram differ from the one on page 168?
The second and third branches each contain 3 outcomes.

c. Use the tree diagram you drew for part (a) to find the theoretical probabilities of events J, K, L, and M. $\frac{1}{27}, \frac{1}{3}, \frac{2}{3}, \frac{19}{27}$

26 When a marble is *not replaced* after it is taken out of the jar, $P(azul, azul, azul) = 0$. What is the probability of this event when a marble *is replaced* after it is taken out? $\frac{1}{27}$

27 Discussion Compare the probabilities of events J, K, L, and M in Question 24 with those in Question 25(c). Are there any events for which the probabilities did not change? Explain.

HOMEWORK EXERCISES ▶ See Exs. 44–48 on p. 174.

23. **a.** There are 3 possible choices for picking the first marble: azul, verde, or roja.
b. Once 1 marble is taken out, 2 outcomes are possible when the next marble is drawn.
c. Once the first and second marbles are taken out, there can be only 1 outcome for the third marble.
d. No; There would be 3 possible outcomes shown in the second branch of the tree.

✔ QUESTION 25

…checks that you can use a tree diagram to list outcomes and find probabilities.

27. Yes; Event K remains the same in both Questions, so $P(K)$ is the same. In Question 24(c), $P(L) = \frac{4}{6} = \frac{2}{3}$. In Question 25(c), $P(L) = \frac{18}{27} = \frac{2}{3}$.

Key Terms

equivalent
fractions

lowest terms

least common
denominator

Equivalent Fractions (pp. 163–164)

Equivalent fractions can be found by multiplying or dividing the numerator and denominator of a fraction by the same number.

Example To write the fraction $\frac{27}{36}$ in lowest terms, find an equivalent fraction where the GCF of the numerator and denominator is 1.

The **GCF** of 27 and 36 is **9**.

$$\frac{27}{36} = \frac{27 \div 9}{36 \div 9} = \frac{3}{4}$$

The **GCF** of 3 and 4 is **1**.

Comparing Fractions (pp. 164–165)

Fractions can be compared by renaming them as equivalent fractions using the least common denominator.

Example $\frac{5}{8} = \frac{25}{40}$ and $\frac{13}{20} = \frac{26}{40}$

The **least common denominator** of $\frac{5}{8}$ and $\frac{13}{20}$ is **40**.

$$\frac{25}{40} < \frac{26}{40}, \text{ so } \frac{5}{8} < \frac{13}{20}$$

Adding and Subtracting Fractions (pp. 166–167)

One way to add or subtract fractions is to rename them using a common denominator.

Example $\frac{2}{7} + \frac{3}{14} = \frac{2 \cdot 2}{7 \cdot 2} + \frac{3}{14}$

The **least common denominator** is **14**.

$$= \frac{4}{14} + \frac{3}{14}$$

$$= \frac{7}{14}$$

$$= \frac{1}{2}$$

28. Sample Response: The first step in both cases is to rename the fractions as fourteenths. Then, depending on the problem, the numerators are either subtracted or added.

28 **Key Concepts Question** Refer to the last Example above. How is a method for finding $\frac{2}{7} - \frac{3}{14}$ like the method shown for finding $\frac{2}{7} + \frac{3}{14}$? How is it different?

Section ② Key Concepts

Tree Diagrams (pp. 168–169)

A tree diagram can be used to find the outcomes of an experiment and to find probabilities.

Example Suppose event A is choosing a pink ball first and choosing a green ball second.

Experiment 1
First ball chosen is replaced.

Experiment 2
First ball chosen is not replaced.

$P(A) = \frac{1}{4}$

$P(A) = \frac{1}{2}$

29 Key Concepts Question In Experiment 1 above, find the probability that a green ball will be chosen second. $\frac{1}{2}$

Section ②
Practice & Application Exercises

Write each fraction in lowest terms.

1. $\frac{3}{15}$ $\frac{1}{5}$ 2. $\frac{14}{21}$ $\frac{2}{3}$ 3. $\frac{6}{8}$ $\frac{3}{4}$ 4. $\frac{9}{15}$ $\frac{3}{5}$

5. $\frac{18}{42}$ $\frac{3}{7}$ 6. $\frac{34}{119}$ $\frac{2}{7}$ 7. $\frac{150}{390}$ $\frac{5}{13}$ 8. $\frac{160}{256}$ $\frac{5}{8}$

9. **Challenge** Suppose a fraction has a numerator that is 28 less than its denominator. The fraction written in lowest terms is $\frac{2}{3}$. What is the fraction? $\frac{56}{84}$

History For Exercises 10–12, use the data in the table. Write each fraction in lowest terms.

10. the fraction of rulers who reigned more than 40 years $\frac{3}{4}$

11. the fraction of rulers who reigned 45 years $\frac{1}{4}$

12. the fraction of rulers who reigned less than 47 years $\frac{1}{2}$

Salote Tupou III became Queen of Tonga at age 18. Tonga consists of three main island groups in the Pacific Ocean east of Fiji.

Long Reigning Woman Rulers		
Ruler	Country	Years reigned (as of 1996)
Victoria (1837–1901)	United Kingdom	64
Wilhelmina (1890–1948)	Netherlands	58
Afua Koba (1834–1884)	Asante Empire	50
Salote Tupou III (1918–1965)	Tonga	47
Elizabeth II (1952–present)	United Kingdom	45
Elizabeth I (1558–1603)	England	45
Maria Theresa (1740–1780)	Habsburg Empire	40
Maria I (1777–1816)	Portugal	39

Mental Math For Exercises 13–15, you'll use mental math to compare special pairs of fractions.

13. a. The fractions $\frac{3}{16}$ and $\frac{3}{14}$ have the same numerator. How can you tell which fraction is greater without finding a common denominator? Since $\frac{1}{14}$ of something is larger than $\frac{1}{16}$ of the same thing, $\frac{3}{14} > \frac{3}{16}$.

   b. If two fractions have the same numerator, how can you tell which fraction is greater? The fraction with the smaller denominator is greater.

   c. Use your answer to part (b) to find a fraction that is greater than $\frac{5}{25}$ but less than $\frac{5}{19}$. Sample Response: $\frac{5}{21}$

14. See Additional Answers.
14. a. **Visual Thinking** Explain how the diagram shows that $\frac{11}{12} > \frac{7}{8}$.

   b. Make a diagram to compare $\frac{2}{3}$ and $\frac{3}{4}$.

   c. Suppose the difference between the numerator and the denominator of each fraction you are comparing is 1, as in parts (a) and (b). How can you tell which fraction is greater?

   d. Use part (c) to find three fractions greater than $\frac{15}{16}$ but less than 1.

15. b. Sample Response: Divide the denominator of the fraction by 2. If the numerator is less than the quotient, the fraction is less than $\frac{1}{2}$. If the numerator is more than the quotient, the fraction is more than $\frac{1}{2}$.

15. a. Tell whether each of the fractions $\frac{10}{18}$, $\frac{12}{25}$, and $\frac{59}{100}$ is *greater than* or *less than* $\frac{1}{2}$. greater than; less than; greater than

   b. Describe a general method for comparing a fraction with $\frac{1}{2}$.

Estimation Tell whether each fraction is closer to 0, $\frac{1}{2}$, or 1.

16. $\frac{1}{15}$ 0   17. $\frac{3}{8}$ $\frac{1}{2}$ 18. $\frac{11}{12}$ 1   19. $\frac{2}{5}$ $\frac{1}{2}$

Choosing a Method Tell whether you would use *mental math*, *estimation*, or *paper-and-pencil* to compare each pair of fractions. Then replace each _?_ with >, <, or =. Sample choices are given.

20. $\frac{5}{7}$ _?_ $\frac{5}{9}$
mental math; >

21. $\frac{15}{16}$ _?_ $\frac{13}{16}$
mental math; >

22. $\frac{3}{7}$ _?_ $\frac{6}{11}$
estimation or paper and pencil; <

23. $\frac{24}{32}$ _?_ $\frac{3}{4}$
mental math; =

24. $\frac{7}{10}$ _?_ $\frac{5}{8}$
mental math; >

25. $\frac{3}{8}$ _?_ $\frac{1}{3}$
estimation or paper and pencil; >

26. $\frac{5}{18}$ _?_ $\frac{7}{16}$
paper and pencil; <

27. $\frac{5}{6}$ _?_ $\frac{6}{7}$
mental math; <

28. $\frac{10}{21}$ _?_ $\frac{15}{28}$
estimation or paper and pencil; <

Graph each set of numbers on a number line. Then list them in numerical order.

29. $\frac{1}{2}, \frac{1}{8}, \frac{3}{4}, \frac{5}{8}$ See Additional Answers.

30. $\frac{1}{3}, \frac{1}{2}, \frac{1}{6}, \frac{5}{6}, \frac{2}{3}$ See Additional Answers.

Find each sum or difference. Write each answer in lowest terms.

31. $\frac{1}{3} + \frac{1}{8}$ $\frac{11}{24}$ 32. $\frac{3}{5} + \frac{4}{15}$ $\frac{13}{15}$ 33. $\frac{3}{4} - \frac{7}{10}$ $\frac{1}{20}$ 34. $\frac{6}{7} - \frac{3}{4}$ $\frac{3}{28}$

35. $\frac{1}{9} + \frac{2}{3}$ $\frac{7}{9}$ 36. $\frac{3}{7} - \frac{1}{21}$ $\frac{8}{21}$ 37. $\frac{5}{12} - \frac{7}{18}$ $\frac{1}{36}$ 38. $\frac{3}{22} + \frac{1}{11}$ $\frac{5}{22}$,

39. $\frac{1}{2} + \frac{1}{3} + \frac{1}{2} + \frac{2}{3}$ 2   40. $\frac{1}{15} + \frac{1}{10} + \frac{2}{15} + \frac{3}{10}$ $\frac{3}{5}$

41. **Writing** Two students added the fractions $\frac{1}{4}$ and $\frac{5}{12}$ incorrectly. Look at their solutions. Describe the errors that were made and explain how to correctly add the fractions.

Bill

$$\frac{1}{4} + \frac{5}{12} = \frac{6}{16}$$

Janell

$$\frac{1}{4} + \frac{5}{12} = \frac{6}{12}$$

42. A student spent half an hour walking and a quarter of an hour jogging. What part of an hour did the student spend on these two activities? $\frac{3}{4}$

43. Town officials reported that $\frac{3}{4}$ of the eligible voters voted *Yes* on a proposed addition to the middle school, $\frac{1}{20}$ voted *No*, and $\frac{1}{5}$ did not vote. Does this report cover all of the eligible voters? Explain.
Yes; $\frac{3}{4} + \frac{1}{20} + \frac{1}{5} = \frac{20}{20}$

41. Bill added the numerators and then added the denominators of the fractions. Janell may have realized that the least common denominator of the fractions was 12, but she didn't write $\frac{1}{4}$ as an equivalent fraction with 12 as the denominator. The correct solution is $\frac{1 \cdot 3}{4 \cdot 3} + \frac{5}{12} = \frac{3}{12} + \frac{5}{12} = \frac{8}{12}$ and $\frac{8 \div 4}{12 \div 4} = \frac{2}{3}$.

For Exercises 44–47, use the tree diagram. A magician's hat holds three items. You take them out, one at a time.

44. a. How many outcomes are possible for the experiment? 6

 b. Does this experiment involve replacement? Explain.   No; If replacement were involved, after one of the items was chosen it could be chosen again.

45. Suppose you add a fourth object to the hat. Then you take out two objects, one at a time, without replacing the first object taken.

 a. Draw a tree diagram to show the possible outcomes. How many outcomes are possible? See Additional Answers.

 b. Describe two events that have different probabilities of occurring. Give the probability of each event.
 Sample Response: P(flowers, scarf) $= \frac{1}{12}$. P(flowers, not scarf) $= \frac{2}{12}$ or $\frac{1}{6}$.

46. 16; Sample Response: Yes; Since there are more possible outcomes, P(flowers, scarf) would decrease $\left(\text{to } \frac{1}{16}\right)$, but flowers, not scarf would increase $\left(\text{to } \frac{3}{16}\right)$.

46. In Exercise 45(a), how many outcomes would there be if the first object was put back into the hat before the second object was taken out? Would this affect the events you described in Exercise 45(b) or their probabilities? Why or why not?

47. Look at your tree diagram for Exercise 45(a). Event A is taking a card out first and taking a scarf out second. Event B is taking flowers out first and taking a card out second. Find the probability of each event.

 a. P(A) $\frac{1}{12}$ **b.** P(B) $\frac{1}{12}$ **c.** P(A or B) $\frac{1}{6}$

Oral Report

Exercise 48 checks that you understand and can apply models to add and subtract fractions.

Reflecting ◀▶ on the Section

Be prepared to report on the following topic in class.

48. An exchange student arrives in your math class.   See Additional Answers.

 a. Draw a model to show the student how $\frac{1}{2} + \frac{1}{3}$ can be rewritten using a common denominator.

 b. Use your model to show the student how to find $\frac{1}{2} + \frac{1}{3}$.

 c. Explain how the model can also be used to find $\frac{1}{2} - \frac{1}{3}$.

Find the GCF of each pair of numbers. (Module 3, p. 156)

49. 10, 12 2   **50.** 36, 90 18   **51.** 19, 50 1

Write each power in standard form. (Module 1, p. 21)

52. 10^2 100   **53.** 2^5 32   **54.** 1^{99} 1

Find each sum or difference. (Toolbox, p. 587)

55. $5\frac{1}{3} + 7\frac{1}{3}$ $12\frac{2}{3}$ **56.** $2\frac{3}{7} + 8\frac{1}{7}$ $10\frac{4}{7}$ **57.** $8\frac{4}{5} - 5\frac{1}{5}$ $3\frac{3}{5}$

Working on the Module Project

Secret Codes

Using Tree Diagrams The numeral "10000" may mean "ten thousand" to you, but it can also represent one or more letters of a coded word. In the Huffman code, a series of 0s and 1s, along with a code tree, is used to create a code.

SET UP

Work with a partner.

Each digit of a code number, either a 0 or a 1, tells you which branch to follow at each fork on the tree. In the code tree below, 1 means "follow the right branch" and 0 means "follow the left branch." The path for T is highlighted on the tree.

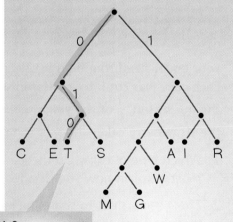

0 1 0 represents the letter T.

 4 a. What letter does 10000 represent? M

 b. Would splitting 10000 into 100 and 00 produce two letters? Why? No; There are no letters at the forks given in the coded directions.

 5 Write the Huffman code for SECRET. Do not leave spaces between each coded letter.
011001000111001010

A code tree must contain the letters in the message, but it can have other letters, too.

 6 Create your own code tree and encode a message to your partner. Then decode your partner's message using his or her code tree.
Answers will vary.

Write each fraction in lowest terms.

1. $\dfrac{9}{12}$ $\dfrac{3}{4}$
2. $\dfrac{2}{22}$ $\dfrac{1}{11}$
3. $\dfrac{46}{69}$ $\dfrac{2}{3}$
4. $\dfrac{10}{35}$ $\dfrac{2}{7}$
5. $\dfrac{27}{243}$ $\dfrac{1}{9}$

6. $\dfrac{25}{125}$ $\dfrac{1}{5}$
7. $\dfrac{15}{31}$ $\dfrac{15}{31}$
8. $\dfrac{12}{28}$ $\dfrac{3}{7}$
9. $\dfrac{36}{52}$ $\dfrac{9}{13}$
10. $\dfrac{5}{100}$ $\dfrac{1}{20}$

Replace each ? with >, <, or =.

11. $\dfrac{5}{11}$ __?__ $\dfrac{9}{22}$ >
12. $\dfrac{8}{10}$ __?__ $\dfrac{7}{8}$ <
13. $\dfrac{2}{3}$ __?__ $\dfrac{2}{18}$ >
14. $\dfrac{3}{5}$ __?__ $\dfrac{5}{9}$ >

15. $\dfrac{2}{7}$ __?__ $\dfrac{1}{3}$ <
16. $\dfrac{7}{9}$ __?__ $\dfrac{3}{4}$ >
17. $\dfrac{10}{16}$ __?__ $\dfrac{6}{10}$ >
18. $\dfrac{6}{15}$ __?__ $\dfrac{8}{20}$ =

Find each sum or difference. Write each answer in lowest terms.

19. $\dfrac{3}{8}+\dfrac{9}{16}$ $\dfrac{15}{16}$
20. $\dfrac{1}{12}+\dfrac{2}{3}$ $\dfrac{3}{4}$
21. $\dfrac{11}{18}-\dfrac{1}{3}$ $\dfrac{5}{18}$
22. $\dfrac{4}{5}+\dfrac{1}{6}$ $\dfrac{29}{30}$

23. $\dfrac{3}{4}-\dfrac{1}{12}$ $\dfrac{2}{3}$
24. $\dfrac{4}{5}-\dfrac{2}{7}$ $\dfrac{18}{35}$
25. $\dfrac{7}{15}+\dfrac{3}{10}$ $\dfrac{23}{30}$
26. $\dfrac{20}{33}+\dfrac{5}{22}$ $\dfrac{5}{6}$

27. Suppose you are taking the numbers 1, 2, 3, and 4 out of a hat to pick the order for members of a relay team. See Additional Answers.

   a. Would it make sense to put each number back in the hat before taking out the next number? Why or why not?

   b. Draw a tree diagram to show all the possible outcomes.

   c. What is the probability that runner 2 goes first and runner 4 goes second?

Standardized Testing ◀▶ Performance Task

Four equal-sized round layer cakes were served at a special event. Each cake was cut into a different number of equal-sized slices. After the guests left, $\dfrac{1}{8}$ of the yellow cake, $\dfrac{3}{16}$ of the chocolate cake, $\dfrac{1}{6}$ of the strawberry cake, and $\dfrac{3}{9}$ of the pineapple cake remained.

1. Which type of cake had the least amount left over? Which had the most? Explain how you decided. the yellow cake; the pineapple cake; Sample Response: I wrote each fraction as a decimal and compared the decimals.

2. The 4 servers get to share the leftover cake. Draw a tree diagram that shows all the possible ways they can share the cakes *if there is only one slice of each type left* and *they do not cut up the slices.* How would your solution change if the two assumptions in italic type were not stated? See Additional Answers.

Section 3 Fractions and Mixed Numbers

Two Bits for your Thoughts

IN THIS SECTION

EXPLORATION 1
◆ Renaming Fractions and Mixed Numbers

EXPLORATION 2
◆ Adding and Subtracting Mixed Numbers

Warm-Up Exercises
See page 178.

Setting the Stage ▸▸▸▸▸▸▸▸▸▸▸▸▸▸▸▸▸▸▸▸▸▸▸▸▸▸▸▸▸▸▸▸▸▸▸

SET UP *Work in a group. You will need:* • *Labsheet 3A*
• *shopping list and coins from Labsheet 3B*

$\frac{1}{8}$ of a Spanish dollar was called 1 *bit*.

Imagine buying a shirt with a basket of carrots. This method of exchange, called *bartering*, does not always work well. What one person may want to use for barter, another person may not need. Instead, coins and bills with agreed-on values have become the "universal language" of trade.

The picture shows a Spanish dollar. This was the main money used for trade in colonial America. Often these coins were cut into 2, 4, or 8 equal-sized pieces to make change.

Use Labsheets 3A and 3B. What was it like to shop in colonial America? Follow the directions on the labsheets and use your *Shopping Lists and Coins* (Spanish dollars and bits) to purchase items from the *Colonial Price List*.

Think About It

1 How much money did you have when you began shopping? How much did you have after you made your purchases?
   See Additional Answers.

2 Did you have enough money to buy everything on your list? If not, which items did you decide not to buy and why?
   Sample Response: I had to buy fewer candles and less expensive gifts.

3 Did you always have the correct change? If not, describe how you paid for the item(s). **Sample Response: No; I got change from a friend.**

WARM-UP EXERCISES

Write each fraction in lowest terms.

1. $\frac{4}{16}$ $\frac{1}{4}$

2. $\frac{14}{105}$ $\frac{2}{15}$

3. $\frac{4}{9}$ $\frac{4}{9}$

Add or subtract. Write each answer in lowest terms.

4. $\frac{4}{5} + \frac{1}{8}$ $\frac{37}{40}$

5. $\frac{7}{24} + \frac{1}{8}$ $\frac{5}{12}$

6. $\frac{1}{2} - \frac{1}{9}$ $\frac{7}{18}$

Exploration 1

Renaming Fractions and Mixed Numbers

If you had lived in colonial America, a knowledge of fractions and *mixed numbers* would have helped you when you made purchases with Spanish dollars.

4 Suppose a colonial merchant had 11 bits.

    a. If the merchant combined bits to make Spanish dollars, how many Spanish dollars and how many leftover bits did the merchant have? **1 dollar and 3 bits left over**

    b. What fraction represents the leftover bits? $\frac{3}{8}$

▶ **Fractions as Mixed Numbers** You can use the same thinking as in Question 4 to write fractions as *mixed numbers*. A **mixed number** is the sum of a nonzero whole number and a fraction between 0 and 1.

EXAMPLE

Suppose you have 21 bits and you want to exchange the bits for whole Spanish dollars and bits.

21 bits is the same as 21 eighths of a Spanish dollar.

$$\frac{21}{8} = \frac{8}{8} + \frac{8}{8} + \frac{5}{8}$$
$$= 2 + \frac{5}{8}$$
$$= 2\frac{5}{8}$$

Think: How many eighths make a **whole**? How many eighths are left?

5 What mixed number is equal to $\frac{15}{4}$? If necessary, use the coins or make a sketch. $3\frac{3}{4}$

6 Discussion Explain how to find each part when you write a fraction as a mixed number.

    a. the whole number <small>Use the whole number part of the quotient obtained when the numerator is divided by the denominator.</small>

    b. the numerator of the fraction <small>Use the remainder of the division. If there is no remainder, the answer contains no fractional part.</small>

    c. the denominator of the fraction <small>Use the denominator of the original fraction.</small>

7 ✔ **CHECKPOINT** Write each fraction as a whole number or as a mixed number in lowest terms.

    a. $\frac{13}{8}$ $1\frac{5}{8}$ **b.** $\frac{18}{4}$ $4\frac{1}{2}$ **c.** $\frac{34}{5}$ $6\frac{4}{5}$ **d.** $\frac{16}{2}$ 8

✔ QUESTION 7

...checks that you can write a fraction as a mixed number.

▶ **Mixed Numbers as Fractions** Suppose a colonist has 3 Spanish dollars and 7 bits and wants to buy an item that costs 27 bits. Does the colonist have enough money? One way to find out is to look at the total number of bits.

3 Spanish dollars and 7 bits   =   __?__ **bits**

8 a. How many total bits does the colonist have? 31

    b. Explain how to find the number of eighths in $3\frac{7}{8}$ dollars without counting the individual bits.
    <small>Sample Response: Multiply 3 by 8 and add 7.</small>

9 The diagram shows $8\frac{2}{3}$. Use your method from Question 8(b) to write $8\frac{2}{3}$ as a fraction: $8\frac{2}{3} = \frac{?}{3}$. 26

10 Discussion Explain how to find each part when you write a mixed number as a fraction. <small>See above.</small>

    a. the denominator   **b.** the numerator

10. a. <small>Use the denominator of the fraction in the mixed number.</small>
   b. <small>Add the numerator of the fraction to the product of the whole number and the denominator of the fraction.</small>

11 ✔ **CHECKPOINT** Write each mixed number as a fraction.

    a. $2\frac{3}{4}$ $\frac{11}{4}$ **b.** $3\frac{5}{6}$ $\frac{23}{6}$ **c.** $10\frac{1}{2}$ $\frac{21}{2}$ **d.** $14\frac{2}{3}$ $\frac{44}{3}$

✔ QUESTION 11

...checks that you can write a mixed number as a fraction.

▌ **HOMEWORK EXERCISES** ▶ See Exs. 1–26 on pp. 184–185.

Exploration 2

Adding and Subtracting Mixed Numbers

12 Suppose you are a colonial merchant and have sold some food for $3\frac{1}{2}$ Spanish dollars and some other goods for 2 dollars and 5 bits.

▲ income from food

a. How many whole dollars do you have? 5

b. Can you combine the broken pieces to equal another dollar? If so, describe how. (*Hint:* How many bits equal $\frac{1}{2}$ of a dollar?)

c. How many total dollars and leftover bits do you have? Write your answer as a mixed number of dollars.

▲ income from other goods

12. b. Yes; $\frac{1}{2}$ dollar + 4 bits = \$1

c. 6 dollars and 1 bit; $\$6\frac{1}{8}$

American colonists buying and selling goods at an outdoor marketplace ▶

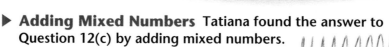

▶ **Adding Mixed Numbers** Tatiana found the answer to Question 12(c) by adding mixed numbers.

13 **Discussion** Study Tatiana's work.

13. a. To be added, the fractions in the problem must have a common denominator.

b. $5\frac{9}{8} = 5 + \frac{9}{8} =$ $5 + 1\frac{1}{8} = 6\frac{1}{8}$

a. Based on what you know about adding fractions, explain why $3\frac{1}{2}$ is rewritten as $3\frac{4}{8}$.

b. Explain why $5\frac{9}{8} = 6\frac{1}{8}$.

c. How does your answer to Question 12(c) compare with Tatiana's answer? It is the same.

$$3\frac{1}{2} = 3\frac{4}{8}$$
$$+ 2\frac{5}{8} = + 2\frac{5}{8}$$
$$5\frac{9}{8} = 5 + \frac{8}{8} + \frac{1}{8}$$
$$= 6 + \frac{1}{8}$$
$$= 6\frac{1}{8}$$

14 ✔ **CHECKPOINT** Find each sum.

    a. $7\frac{1}{8} + 8\frac{2}{3}$ $15\frac{19}{24}$ **b.** $4\frac{3}{4} + 1\frac{5}{12}$ $6\frac{1}{6}$ **c.** $3\frac{4}{5} + 12\frac{1}{2}$ $16\frac{3}{10}$

✔ **QUESTION 14**

...checks that you can add mixed numbers.

▶ **Subtracting Mixed Numbers** When subtracting mixed numbers, you may have to rewrite the fraction part.

15 Suppose you have $4\frac{5}{8}$ Spanish dollars and you buy a fiddle for $3\frac{1}{4}$ dollars.

amount you have

cost of a fiddle

$4\frac{5}{8}$ **dollars**   – $3\frac{1}{4}$ **dollars**

    a. How many whole dollars do you have left?   1

    b. How many bits do the remaining pieces equal? (*Hint*: How many bits equal $\frac{1}{4}$ of a Spanish dollar?)   3

    c. How much money will you have left altogether? Write your answer as a mixed number of Spanish dollars. $1\frac{3}{8}$ **dollars**

16 ✔ **CHECKPOINT** Find each difference.

    a. $7\frac{1}{2} - 2\frac{3}{8}$ $5\frac{1}{8}$ **b.** $10\frac{2}{3} - 6\frac{2}{5}$ $4\frac{4}{15}$ **c.** $24\frac{1}{2} - 20\frac{1}{3}$ $4\frac{1}{6}$

✔ **QUESTION 16**

...checks that you can subtract mixed numbers.

17 **Discussion** Suppose a colonist has $4\frac{1}{2}$ Spanish dollars and wants to buy an item for 2 Spanish dollars and 5 bits.

    a. How many dollars and bits will the colonist have left after buying the item? (*Hint:* Think about how a Spanish dollar can be traded for bits.)   1 dollar and 7 bits

    b. Write your answer to part (a) as a mixed number. $1\frac{7}{8}$

▶ **Subtracting with Regrouping** Mixed number subtraction problems may involve *regrouping*, where one whole is written as a fraction.

EXAMPLE

You can use a model to help you find the difference $3\frac{1}{4} - 1\frac{3}{4}$.

Not enough fourths to subtract $\frac{3}{4}$.

Trade one whole for $\frac{4}{4}$.

Regroup wholes and fourths.

$$3\frac{1}{4} \quad = \quad 2 + \frac{4}{4} + \frac{1}{4} \quad = \quad 2\frac{5}{4}$$
$$-\ 1\frac{3}{4} \quad = \quad -\quad 1 \quad \frac{3}{4} \quad = \quad -\ 1\frac{3}{4}$$

$$1\frac{2}{4} = 1\frac{1}{2}$$

---

18. a. Step 1—Change to fractions with a common denominator:
$4\frac{1}{2} = 4\frac{1 \cdot 4}{2 \cdot 4} = 4\frac{4}{8}$;
Step 2—There aren't $\frac{5}{8}$ to subtract so trade one whole for $\frac{8}{8}$:
$4\frac{4}{8} = 3 + 1 + \frac{4}{8} = 3 + \frac{8}{8} + \frac{4}{8}$;
Step 3—Regroup:
$3 + \left(\frac{8}{8} + \frac{4}{8}\right) = 3\frac{12}{8}$.

19. a. Write the fractional parts of the mixed numbers as equivalent fractions with a common denominator. If the numerator in the number being subtracted is the greater of the two numerators in the problem, rename the first mixed number by taking 1 from the whole number part of the mixed numeral and rewriting it as a fraction with the same denominator as that in the mixed numeral. Then add this fraction to the fractional part of the mixed numeral. Subtract the whole number parts of the mixed numbers. Then subtract the numerators of the fractional parts and write the difference over the common denominator.

18 a. Write an explanation of each step.

| Step 1 | Step 2 | Step 3 |

$$4\frac{1}{2} \quad = \quad 4\frac{4}{8} \quad = \quad 3 + \frac{8}{8} + \frac{4}{8} \quad = \quad 3\frac{12}{8}$$
$$-\ 2\frac{5}{8} \quad = \qquad\qquad\qquad\qquad\qquad = \quad -\ 2\frac{5}{8}$$

b. Find the difference $4\frac{1}{2} - 2\frac{5}{8}$. Compare it with your answer to Question 17(b). $1\frac{7}{8}$; They are the same.

19 Try This as a Class Think about subtracting mixed numbers.

a. Write a sequence of steps for subtracting mixed numbers.

b. Follow the steps you wrote in part (a) to find $3\frac{3}{4} - 1\frac{1}{8}$ and $4 - 1\frac{3}{4}$. Revise the steps if necessary. $2\frac{5}{8}$; $2\frac{1}{4}$

20 ✔ **CHECKPOINT** Find each difference.

a. $4\frac{1}{8} - 2\frac{3}{8}$ $1\frac{3}{4}$ **b.** $13 - 2\frac{3}{4}$ $10\frac{1}{4}$ **c.** $25\frac{4}{9} - 8\frac{1}{3}$ $17\frac{1}{9}$ **d.** $10\frac{3}{4} - 7\frac{4}{5}$ $2\frac{19}{20}$

HOMEWORK EXERCISES ▶ See Exs. 27–43 on pp. 185–187.

✔ **QUESTION 20**

…checks that you can subtract any mixed numbers.

Section 3

Key Concepts

▶▶▶▶▶▶▶▶▶▶▶▶▶▶▶▶▶▶▶▶▶▶▶▶▶▶

Renaming Fractions and Mixed Numbers (pp. 178–179)

Example Write $\frac{11}{3}$ as a mixed number.

$$\frac{11}{3} = \frac{3}{3} + \frac{3}{3} + \frac{3}{3} + \frac{2}{3}$$

$$= 1 + 1 + 1 + \frac{2}{3}$$

$$= 3\frac{2}{3}$$

Example Write $2\frac{1}{4}$ as a fraction.

$$2\frac{1}{4} = 1 + 1 + \frac{1}{4}$$

$$= \frac{4}{4} + \frac{4}{4} + \frac{1}{4}$$

$$= \frac{9}{4}$$

mixed number

Adding and Subtracting Mixed Numbers (pp. 180–182)

Example Find $7\frac{2}{3} + 2\frac{1}{2}$.

$$7\frac{2}{3} = \quad 7\frac{4}{6}$$

$$+ 2\frac{1}{2} = + 2\frac{3}{6}$$

$$9\frac{7}{6} = 9 + \frac{6}{6} + \frac{1}{6}$$

$$= 9 + 1 + \frac{1}{6}$$

$$= 10\frac{1}{6}$$

Write the fraction as the sum of two fractions between 0 and 1.

Example Find $5\frac{2}{9} - 2\frac{5}{9}$.

$$5\frac{2}{9} = \quad 4\frac{11}{9}$$

$$- 2\frac{5}{9} = - 2\frac{5}{9}$$

$$2\frac{6}{9} \text{ or } 2\frac{2}{3}$$

Regroup so there are enough ninths to subtract $\frac{5}{9}$.

CLOSURE QUESTION

How is addition and subtraction of mixed numbers like addition and subtraction of whole numbers? How is it different?

Sample Response: You add and subtract the whole number parts of mixed numbers just like you add and subtract whole numbers, but you also need to add and subtract the fractional part of mixed numbers, and you don't need to do this with whole numbers.

---

21 Key Concepts Question Matt uses the method shown at the right to subtract mixed numbers.

a. Explain Matt's method.

b. Compare this method with the method shown in this section.
Sample Response: This method seems simpler.

c. Which method would you use to find $25\frac{3}{8} - 19\frac{7}{8}$? Why?

Sample Response: The method of this section; The arithmetic is simpler.

$$5\frac{1}{3} = \quad \frac{16}{3}$$

$$- 1\frac{2}{3} = - \frac{5}{3}$$

$$\frac{11}{3} = 3\frac{2}{3}$$

21. a. Change the fractions to improper fractions with a common denominator. Subtract the numerators. Write the answer as a whole number or a mixed number.

Section ③

Practice & Application Exercises

Write each fraction as a mixed number.

1. $\frac{23}{5}$ $4\frac{3}{5}$

2. $\frac{22}{7}$ $3\frac{1}{7}$

3. $\frac{42}{10}$ $4\frac{1}{5}$

4. $\frac{47}{15}$ $3\frac{2}{15}$

Describe the error that was made when each fraction was written as a mixed number. Give the correct mixed number.

5. $\frac{8}{3} = 1\frac{5}{3}$

6. $\frac{11}{4} = 3\frac{1}{4}$

7. $\frac{31}{2} = 15$

8. $\frac{27}{5} = 5\frac{5}{2}$

5. The fraction is not between 0 and 1; $2\frac{2}{3}$

6. The division was done incorrectly; $2\frac{3}{4}$

7. The remainder was ignored; $15\frac{1}{2}$

8. The numerator and denominator of the fraction were switched; $5\frac{2}{5}$

Write each mixed number as a fraction.

9. $1\frac{1}{8}$ $\frac{9}{8}$

10. $2\frac{2}{5}$ $\frac{12}{5}$

11. $4\frac{4}{9}$ $\frac{40}{9}$

12. $8\frac{5}{6}$ $\frac{53}{6}$

13. $9\frac{2}{5}$ $\frac{47}{5}$

14. $12\frac{1}{4}$ $\frac{49}{4}$

15. $14\frac{1}{2}$ $\frac{29}{2}$

16. $17\frac{2}{3}$ $\frac{53}{3}$

Replace each _?_ with the correct mixed number or fraction.

17. A 66 in. tall gorilla stands __?__ ft tall. $5\frac{1}{2}$

The gorilla is the largest living primate. ▶

18. A 992 lb polar bear weighs __?__ tons. $\frac{62}{125}$

◄ The greatest weight recorded for a polar bear in the wild was an amazing 2210 lb!

19. A 270 lb ostrich weighs __?__ tons.

The ostrich is the largest living bird. ▶ $\frac{27}{200}$

20. A 126 in. tall African elephant stands __?__ ft tall. $10\frac{1}{2}$

◄ The African bush elephant is the largest living land animal.

FOR ▶ HELP

with *conversions*, see

TABLE OF MEASURES, p. 596

Choose a Method Tell whether you would use *mental math*, *estimation*, or *paper-and-pencil* to compare each fraction and mixed number. Then replace each ? with >, <, or =.   Sample choices are given.

21. $2\frac{4}{5}$? $\frac{7}{3}$
mental math; >

22. $\frac{17}{2}$? $8\frac{3}{4}$
mental math; <

23. $3\frac{1}{4}$? $\frac{13}{2}$
mental math; <

24. $\frac{31}{6}$? $5\frac{1}{6}$
mental math; =

25. $\frac{32}{3}$? $10\frac{5}{7}$
paper and pencil; <

26. $4\frac{1}{2}$? $\frac{5}{2}$
estimation; >

Use the ruler to help you evaluate each expression.

FOR ▶ HELP
with *reading a ruler*, see
TOOLBOX, p. 591

$1\frac{3}{8}$ + $1\frac{3}{4}$ = $3\frac{1}{8}$

27. $1\frac{1}{2} + 1\frac{1}{4}$ $2\frac{3}{4}$

28. $2\frac{1}{8} - 1\frac{1}{4}$ $\frac{7}{8}$

29. $4 - 2\frac{1}{4} - \frac{1}{8}$ $1\frac{5}{8}$

Find each sum or difference.

30. $15 + 4\frac{7}{12}$ $19\frac{7}{12}$

31. $12 - 1\frac{1}{3}$ $10\frac{2}{3}$

32. $10\frac{3}{4} + 23\frac{1}{16}$ $33\frac{13}{16}$

33. $5\frac{1}{3} - 2\frac{1}{4}$ $3\frac{1}{12}$

34. $\frac{7}{8} + 3\frac{1}{2}$ $4\frac{3}{8}$

35. $9\frac{9}{11} + 13\frac{5}{22}$ $23\frac{1}{22}$

36. Giant bamboo can grow up to $1\frac{1}{2}$ ft in a day.

a. Suppose a 3 ft giant bamboo plant grew $1\frac{1}{2}$ ft one day, $1\frac{1}{3}$ ft the next day, and $\frac{3}{4}$ ft on each of the next 2 days. How tall would the plant be then? $7\frac{1}{3}$ ft

b. Suppose a $5\frac{1}{2}$ ft giant bamboo plant grew $1\frac{1}{4}$ ft one day, 1 ft the next day, and $\frac{7}{8}$ ft on each of the next 3 days. How tall would the plant be then? $10\frac{3}{8}$ ft

◀ There are more than 1000 kinds of bamboos. Some bamboos can reach 100 ft in height.

FOR ▶ HELP

with *perimeter*,
see
TOOLBOX, p. 591

Algebra Connection For each figure, write an equation relating the perimeter and the lengths of the sides. Then solve to find x.

37. perimeter = 8 in.

$3\frac{1}{3}$ in.

2 in.

x

$8 = x + 5\frac{1}{3};\ 2\frac{2}{3}$

38. perimeter = 14 ft

$3\frac{3}{7}$ ft   4 ft

x

$14 = 3\frac{3}{7} + 4 + x$
$6\frac{4}{7} = x$

39. perimeter = $18\frac{1}{2}$ in.

x 8 in.

$7\frac{1}{2}$ in.

$18\frac{1}{2} = x + 15\frac{1}{2};\ 3$

40. perimeter = 15 ft

2 ft x

7 ft

$15 = x + 9;\ 6$

41. Industrial Technology Nancy cut a piece of wood $8\frac{3}{8}$ in. long from a piece 20 in. long. Since Nancy used a saw blade that was $\frac{1}{16}$ in. thick, she allowed $\frac{1}{16}$ in. extra for the cut.

a. How much wood is left over? $11\frac{9}{16}$ in.

b. If Nancy had started with a piece of wood $10\frac{1}{2}$ in. long, how much wood would be left over? $2\frac{1}{16}$ in.

c. Why is it important to know the thickness of the saw blade?

41. c. So you know
exactly how much
wood is left.

42. Sample Response:

Maria needs $10\frac{3}{8}$ cups of
flour for some bread she
is making. If she has
$3\frac{1}{4}$ cups, how much more
flour does she need?;
$7\frac{1}{8}$ cups

42. Open-ended Write a problem that can be solved using the equation $3\frac{1}{4} + x = 10\frac{3}{8}$. Then solve the equation.

Reflecting ◄►on the Section

Write your response to Exercise 43 in your journal.

Journal

Exercise 43 checks that you understand and can apply fractions.

43. The Spanish dollar is no longer used as a form of money, but fractions are still important in many monetary systems.

- a. What fractional parts of a United States dollar are represented by the value of the coins we use today? $\frac{1}{100}, \frac{1}{20}, \frac{1}{10}, \frac{1}{4}, \frac{1}{2}$

- b. For which coin does the coin's name tell its value? Explain.
  quarter and half dollar; Each name tells what fraction of a dollar the coin represents.

Spiral ◄►Review

Find each sum or difference. (Module 3, p. 170)

44. $\frac{1}{4} + \frac{2}{3}$ $\frac{11}{12}$ 45. $\frac{5}{9} - \frac{1}{6}$ $\frac{7}{18}$ 46. $\frac{4}{5} - \frac{2}{15}$ $\frac{2}{3}$ 47. $\frac{7}{12} + \frac{11}{18}$ $1\frac{7}{36}$

Find each sum or difference. (Toolbox, p. 581)

48. 0.249 + 1.806
2.055

49. 2.35 − 1.7
0.65

50. 3.0102 − 0.098
2.9122

51. What is the measure of each angle formed when a Spanish dollar is cut into 4 equal-sized pieces? into 8 bits? (Module 2, p. 83)
90°; 45°

Connection

Composer: Maia

One of Maia's compositions, *Key Vibrations, Symphony #1*, contains several music styles. Composers like Maia need to count beats and measures in music. A $\frac{4}{4}$ *time signature* means there are 4 beats in a *measure*. A whole note (o) is a complete measure in $\frac{4}{4}$ time. A half note (♩) is half a measure in $\frac{4}{4}$ time, and so on, for quarter notes (♩), eighth notes (♪), and sixteenth notes (♬).

52. Using a $\frac{4}{4}$ time signature, write the number of measures represented by each set of notes.

a. 1♩ + 2♩'s 1   b. 1o + 6♪'s + 4♬'s 2   c. 3♩'s + 6♪'s + 3♩'s 3

measure

$\frac{1}{4} + \frac{1}{4} + \frac{1}{4} + \frac{1}{4} = \frac{4}{4}$

time signature

Write each fraction as a mixed number.

1. $\frac{8}{5}$ $1\frac{3}{5}$

2. $\frac{7}{3}$ $2\frac{1}{3}$

3. $\frac{7}{4}$ $1\frac{3}{4}$

4. $\frac{11}{2}$ $5\frac{1}{2}$

5. $\frac{23}{3}$ $7\frac{2}{3}$

6. $\frac{15}{2}$ $7\frac{1}{2}$

7. $\frac{66}{5}$ $13\frac{1}{5}$

8. $\frac{92}{9}$ $10\frac{2}{9}$

9. $\frac{30}{7}$ $4\frac{2}{7}$

10. $\frac{45}{8}$ $5\frac{5}{8}$

11. $\frac{51}{5}$ $10\frac{1}{5}$

12. $\frac{31}{25}$ $1\frac{6}{25}$

Write each mixed number as a fraction.

13. $2\frac{4}{5}$ $\frac{14}{5}$

14. $5\frac{1}{2}$ $\frac{11}{2}$

15. $9\frac{3}{7}$ $\frac{66}{7}$

16. $4\frac{2}{3}$ $\frac{14}{3}$

17. $8\frac{1}{4}$ $\frac{33}{4}$

18. $12\frac{2}{5}$ $\frac{62}{5}$

19. $20\frac{1}{6}$ $\frac{121}{6}$

20. $2\frac{5}{8}$ $\frac{21}{8}$

21. $30\frac{4}{5}$ $\frac{154}{5}$

22. $45\frac{1}{2}$ $\frac{91}{2}$

23. $64\frac{1}{3}$ $\frac{193}{3}$

24. $100\frac{7}{9}$ $\frac{907}{9}$

Find each sum or difference and write the answer in lowest terms.

25. $1\frac{1}{3}+2\frac{3}{4}$ $4\frac{1}{12}$

26. $2\frac{2}{5}+3\frac{1}{8}$ $5\frac{21}{40}$

27. $4\frac{1}{2}-4\frac{1}{4}$ $\frac{1}{4}$

28. $5\frac{5}{7}+6\frac{3}{7}$ $12\frac{1}{7}$

29. $4\frac{5}{9}-2\frac{2}{3}$ $1\frac{8}{9}$

30. $10\frac{1}{4}-8\frac{1}{6}$ $2\frac{1}{12}$

31. $9+2\frac{1}{5}$ $11\frac{1}{5}$

32. $10\frac{7}{8}-9\frac{5}{6}$ $1\frac{1}{24}$

33. $4\frac{2}{5}-3\frac{4}{7}$ $\frac{29}{35}$

34. $3\frac{3}{4}+8\frac{11}{12}$ $12\frac{2}{3}$

35. $10\frac{7}{8}+12\frac{1}{6}$ $23\frac{1}{24}$

36. $15\frac{6}{13}-12\frac{17}{26}$ $2\frac{21}{26}$

37. An artist is putting cord around the edge of a rectangular picture frame. The dimensions are $7\frac{3}{8}$ in. by $5\frac{1}{4}$ in. Find the perimeter. $25\frac{1}{4}$ in.

1. Which fraction is equal to $9\frac{8}{17}$? D

   A $\frac{89}{17}$ B $\frac{72}{17}$ C $\frac{8}{153}$ D $\frac{161}{17}$

2. Find $11\frac{1}{12}-2\frac{1}{3}$. Which is (are) the correct difference(s)? A, D

   A $8\frac{3}{4}$ B $9\frac{1}{12}$ C $\frac{109}{12}$ D $\frac{35}{4}$

Colonial Currency

The Situation   See the Resource Book for a detailed discussion of this Extended Exploration.

Before the American Revolution, the Spanish dollar was the principal coin used in colonial America. At the same time, merchants used the British money system of *pounds* (£), *shillings* (s), and *pence* (d)—the plural of *penny*—for keeping financial records in the colonies.

$$1£ = 20s \qquad 1s = 12d$$

Since *all* coins were in short supply, many colonies printed their own paper money as well, like the Massachusetts Bay note shown. Each bill usually represented some fraction of a Spanish dollar that was easy to convert to British shillings and pence.

The Problem

Design a system of colonial paper money. Each bill should be less than or equal to a Spanish dollar.
Check students' work.

Something to Think About

*   Use the Massachusetts Bay note to find the value of a Spanish dollar in pence. 72d

*   In colonial times a pair of shoes cost $1, a pen cost 2 bits, a turkey cost $\$\frac{1}{4}$, and a chair cost $\$5\frac{7}{8}$ in Spanish coins.

    What is a reasonable number of paper bills to use to buy these items, if they were also priced in British money?
    Answers may vary. Sample Response: 12 paper bills

*   What information should you print on each of your paper bills? Sample Response: how much each bill is worth in British money and Spanish dollars

Present Your Results

Write a letter to a colonial governor explaining why your system of paper money should be used in the colony. You may want to make a sketch showing your design of the paper money.

IN THIS SECTION

EXPLORATION 1
♦ Decimal Place Values

EXPLORATION 2
♦ Integer Exponents

EXPLORATION 3
♦ Scientific Notation

Bright Ideas

1. a. addition;
   12.68 + 1.59
  b. 12 + 1 = 13, 6 + 5 = 11; 8 + 9 = 17; take one group of 10 from 17 and add 1 to 11 to get 12; take one group of 10 from 12 and add 1 to 13 to get 14; Sample Response:

$$
\begin{array}{r}
1\ 1\\
12.68\\
\underline{1.59}\\
14.27
\end{array}
$$

2. 29 ⓪ 5 ① 8 ② 7 ③

3. a.
$$
\begin{array}{r}
2 ⓪ 7 ① 8 ②\\
\underline{5 ⓪ 4 ① 2 ②}\\
7 ⓪ 11 ① 10 ②\\
7 ⓪ 12 ① 0 ②\\
8 ⓪ 2 ① 0 ②
\end{array}
$$

b. Students may trade to the tenths then to the hundredths, or to the hundredths then to the tenths. The second method is shown.

Setting the Stage

Some people think that adding and subtracting fractions is difficult. The mathematician Simon Stevin certainly felt this way! In 1585, he published *De Thiende* ("The Tenth"), a book designed to teach everyone "how to perform with an ease, unheard of, all computations . . . by integers without fractions."

Stevin might have used an example like the one at the right to explain his method. Can you decode it?

$$
\begin{array}{r}
12⓪\ 6①\ 8②\\
\underline{1⓪\ 5①\ 9②}\\
13⓪\ 11①\ 17②\\
13⓪\ 12①\ 7②\\
14⓪\ 2①\ 7②
\end{array}
$$

Think About It

1 Look at the example shown above.

  a. What problem is solved? How would you write the problem?

  b. Explain what happens at each step in Stevin's solution. How would you show these steps?

2 How would Stevin have written the number 29.587?

3 Use Stevin's method to find each sum or difference.

  a. 2⓪ 7① 8② + 5⓪ 4① 2②

$$
\begin{array}{r}
5 ⓪ 4 ① 2 ②\\
\underline{2 ⓪ 7 ① 8 ②}
\end{array}
\longrightarrow
\begin{array}{r}
5 ⓪ 3 ① 12 ②\\
\underline{2 ⓪ 7 ① 8 ②}
\end{array}
\longrightarrow
$$

  b. 5⓪ 4① 2② – 2⓪ 7① 8②

$$
\begin{array}{r}
4 ⓪ 13 ① 12 ②\\
\underline{2 ⓪ 7 ① 8 ②}\\
2 ⓪ 6 ① 4 ②
\end{array}
$$

D.e.c.i.m.a.l Place Values

GOAL

LEARN HOW TO...
- compare numbers using the decimal place value system
- write a decimal as a fraction

AS YOU...
- play a game with number squares

KEY TERM
- decimal place

SET UP   *Work in a group. You will need 10 cards numbered 0 through 9.*

▶ Simon Stevin's ideas for writing decimal fractions and calculating with them helped inspire the universal *decimal place value system*. In the decimal system, the value of a number is expressed by writing digits in certain positions called **decimal places**.

← place values

In words:

← three thousand eight hundred two and two hundred sixty-three thousandths

← five hundred twenty-five and nine hundredths

← nineteen and five tenths

whole number   fraction

4   **Try This as a Class**   Look at the chart above.

   a. What is the purpose of the decimal point?
   to separate the whole number and the fractional part of the number

   b. What happens to the value of each place as you move one place to its left? two places to its left?
   The value is multiplied by 10; The value is multiplied by 100.

   c. What is the place value of the seventh decimal place to the left of the decimal point?   millions

   d. What happens to the value of each place as you move one place to its right?   The value is divided by 10.

   e. What is the place value of the sixth decimal place to the right of the decimal point?   millionths

5   In 32.67159, the 7 is in the hundredths place, so its value is 7 • 0.01 or 0.07. In words, its value is "seven hundredths." Write the value of each digit in 32.67159 as a decimal and in words.

5. 30, three tens (or thirty); 2, two ones (or two); 0.6, six tenths; .07, seven hundredths; 0.001, one thousandth; 0.0005, five ten-thousandths; 0.00009, nine hundred-thousandths

6. **a.** 6.58
   b. twelve and fifty-six thousandths
   c. 100.3
   d. one thousand thirty-seven ten-thousandths

6 ✔ **CHECKPOINT** For each number written in words, write the decimal form. For each number written in decimal form, write its value in words.

a. six and fifty-eight hundredths   **b.** 12.056

c. one hundred and three tenths   **d.** 0.1037

▶ **Writing Decimals as Fractions** To write a decimal as a fraction, you may want to first identify the decimal's value in words.

EXAMPLE

1.25 means one and twenty-five hundredths.

$$1.25 = 1\frac{25}{100} = 1\frac{1}{4}$$

Hundredths means the denominator is 100.

7 Write each decimal as a fraction or mixed number in lowest terms.

a. 0.0009 $\frac{9}{10,000}$ **b.** 0.67 $\frac{67}{100}$ **c.** 56.2 $56\frac{1}{5}$ **d.** 1.375 $1\frac{3}{8}$

▶ **Comparing Decimals** You can use place value to help you compare and order decimals.

8 To review comparing decimal numbers, play the game *Where's the Best Place?* with your group a few times. Check students' work.

Where's the Best Place?

The object of the game is to build the greatest number possible.

◆ Each player makes a number chart as shown.   Game 1 $\boxed{0}$. $\boxed{\ }\boxed{\ }\boxed{\ }\boxed{\ }$

◆ Use ten cards numbered 0 through 9. Shuffle the cards and place them face down in a pile.

◆ One player draws a digit from the pile. Each player must decide where to write that digit in his or her number chart.

◆ After a digit is written, it cannot be erased. Once a digit is drawn, it cannot be used again in that game.

◆ The game is over when all places on each number chart are filled. The player with the greatest number wins the game.

9 Answer the questions relating to the game *Where's the Best Place?*

a. Suppose 9 is chosen first. Where is the best place to put the 9? Explain your choice.
in the tenths place; It has the greatest value.

b. Suppose 0 is chosen first. Where is the best place to put the 0? Explain your choice.
in the ten-thousandths place; It has the least value.

c. How would your game strategy in parts (a) and (b) be different if 0 were not always in the ones place? Put the 9 in the ones place, but still put the 0 in the ten-thousandths place.

10 The number charts of four students playing *Where's the Best Place?* are shown.

Christine [0] . [5] [6] [?] [4]   Julius [0] . [5] [4] [?] [6]

Marcus [0] . [5] [6] [4] [?]   Delia [0] . [5] [4] [6] [?]

a. Can Delia win the game? Explain.

b. Can Christine win the game? Explain.

c. Suppose "3" is chosen next. Who will win the game? Explain.

10. a. No; She has the same number of tenths as Christine and Marcus but fewer hundredths.
b. Yes; If a digit greater than 4 is drawn she will win
c. Marcus; 0.5643 > 0.5634

EXAMPLE

You can compare two decimals by comparing digits with the same place value, beginning at the left.

The **ones digits** are equal.

5.7 __?__ 5.69

Compare the **tenths digits**: 7 > 6.   **So, 5.7 > 5.69.**

---

11 Marcus argues that 5.69 > 5.7 because 69 > 7. Explain to Marcus why this is not correct. Since 7 tenths is equivalent to 70 hundredths, 69 hundredths is less than 7 tenths.

12 ✔ **CHECKPOINT** Replace each __?__ with >, <, or =.

a. 0.663 __?__ 0.671 <   **b.** 1.37 __?__ 1.365 >   **c.** 15.3 __?__ 2.68 >

d. 0.96 __?__ 0.960 =   **e.** 0.509 __?__ 0.51 <   **f.** 19.6 __?__ 1.96 >

✔ **QUESTION 12**

...checks that you can compare decimals.

HOMEWORK EXERCISES ▶ See Exs. 1–30 on pp. 199–200.

myriad
↓
10,000

INTEGER Exponents

SET UP *You will need: • Labsheet 4A*
• calculator

Archimedes, a Greek scientist and mathematician (287–212 B.C.), loved a challenge. One day he decided to find out the number of grains of sand it would take to fill the known universe! Unfortunately, the largest number the ancient Greeks had a name for was a *myriad* or 10,000. Archimedes knew this was not large enough.

16. a. To find each entry in the table, multiply the preceding one by 10; 10,000; 100,000; 1,000,000.
b. The exponent gives the number of zeros to write after the 1.

13 Discussion We have names for numbers greater than 10,000— million, billion, trillion. Why do you think the ancient Greeks did not? Sample Response: Quantities that large may not have been part of their experience.

▶ **Archimedes had the idea to name a number greater than a myriad by multiplying a myriad by a myriad — a *myriad of myriads*. He developed the idea of exponents by continuing this pattern.**

FOR◀HELP
with *exponents*, see
MODULE 1, p. 20

14 In exponential form, 10,000 is written as 10^4. Name the base and the exponent. base: 10; exponent: 4

15 Archimedes used a myriad of myriads, or 10,000 • 10,000, to name numbers. Write the value of 10,000 • 10,000 in each form.

  a. exponential form using 10,000 as the base $10,000^2$

  b. standard form 100,000,000

  c. exponential form using 10 as the base 10^8

According to some accounts, Archimedes may have worked out problems in the sand. ▶

Use Labsheet 4A for Questions 16–19.

16 Discussion A number that can be written using an exponent and a base is a **power**. For example, $1000 = 10 • 10 • 10 = 10^3$, so 1000 is "the third power of 10" or "10 to the third power." See above.

  a. Describe how multiplication can be used to complete the *Positive Powers of 10 Table* on Labsheet 4A. Complete the table.

  b. What is the relationship between the exponent and the standard form of a positive power of 10?

17 Describe how division can be used to complete the *Integer Powers of 10 Table*. Then complete the table.

17. Divide each decimal number or fraction by 10 to get the next number; 1, 1; 0.1; $\frac{1}{100}$; 0.001, $\frac{1}{1000}$

18 Look at the fraction forms of 10^{-1}, 10^{-2}, and 10^{-3} in the *Integer Powers of 10 Table*.

$$10^{-4} = \frac{1}{10,000} = \frac{1}{10^4} \text{ since } 10,000 = 10^4$$

a. Rewrite the fraction forms of 10^{-1}, 10^{-2}, and 10^{-3} so that the denominators are powers of 10. $\frac{1}{10^1}, \frac{1}{10^2}, \frac{1}{10^3}$

b. How are the exponents in the denominators related to the original exponents? They are opposites.

c. Write 10^{-5} as a decimal, as a fraction, and as a fraction with its denominator in exponential form. $0.00001, \frac{1}{100,000}, \frac{1}{10^5}$

19 Calculator You can use a calculator to evaluate powers. For example, to find 7^4 you can use this key sequence:

[7] [y^x] [4] [=]

a. Complete the *Powers of 2 Table* on Labsheet 4A.

b. How are the exponents in the denominators of the fractions related to the original exponents? They are opposites.

19. a. 32, 16, 4, 2, 1, 0.5, 0.125, 0.0625, 0.03125; 32, 16, 4, 2, 1, $\frac{1}{2}$, $\frac{1}{8}$, $\frac{1}{16}$, $\frac{1}{32}$; $\frac{1}{2^1}$, $\frac{1}{2^3}$, $\frac{1}{2^4}$, $\frac{1}{2^5}$

20. a. First, write a fraction with 1 as the numerator and the base raised to the opposite of the original power as the denominator. Then, simplify the fraction; $3^{-4} = \frac{1}{3^4} = \frac{1}{81}$.

20 **Try This as a Class** Think about your work with powers.

a. Explain how to find the value of an expression where the base is a positive integer and the exponent is a negative integer. Give an example.

b. What is the value of 2^0? of 10^0? of any nonzero base to the 0 power? 1; 1; 1

21 **Discussion** Archimedes calculated 10^{63} grains of sand would fill the universe, but he knew there were greater numbers. See Additional Answers.

a. Describe how numbers greater than 10^{63} can be written. Is there a greatest positive number? Explain.

b. How can exponents be used to write very small positive numbers? Is there a least positive number? Explain.

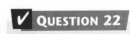

22 ✔ **CHECKPOINT** Write each number as a fraction with its denominator in exponential form.

a. 10^{-1} $\frac{1}{10^1}$ **b.** 5^{-3} $\frac{1}{5^3}$ **c.** 10^{-6} $\frac{1}{10^6}$

✔ **QUESTION 22**

...checks that you can rewrite expressions with negative exponents.

HOMEWORK EXERCISES ▶ See Exs. 31–55 on pp. 200–201.

Exploration 3

Scientific Notation

SET UP *You will need:* • *Labsheet 4B*
• *calculator*

▶ The number of digits a calculator can display is limited, but calculations with large (or small) numbers are still possible. A universal method is used to represent large and small numbers.

23 Try This as a Class For parts (a) and (b), describe how the results are displayed on a calculator as the steps are carried out.

a. Clear the calculator and then enter 10. Multiply by 10 and look at the result. Continue multiplying by 10 and looking at the result at least 20 times. Check students' work.

b. Clear the calculator and then enter 10. Divide by 10 and look at the result. Continue dividing by 10 and looking at the result at least 20 times. Check students' work.

c. What did the calculator display after completing part (a)? part (b)? Why does this happen?
1 E21, 1 E–19; The number of digits the calculator screen can display is limited.

24 Discussion Most calculators have a special way to display large and small numbers. Three displays for the same number are shown.

1E15	1e+15	1 15

a. What number is represented by the displays? one quadrillion

b. Write this number in standard form. 1,000,000,000,000,000

c. Why is the number not displayed in standard form?
It is too long to fit on the calculator screen.

▶ **Products and Quotients with Powers of 10** Suppose a calculator displays 1.23456e+13. This is the same as $1.23456 \cdot 10^{13}$, a decimal number multiplied by a power of ten.

25. $235 \cdot 1000 = 235,000$; $235 \cdot 10 = 2350$; $235 \cdot 1 = 235$; $235 \cdot 0.1 = 23.5$; $235 \cdot 0.01 = 2.35$; 0.235

Use Labsheet 4B for Questions 25 and 26.

25 Follow the directions on Labsheet 4B to complete the *Product Table*.

26 Discussion Look at your completed *Product Table*. Describe how to multiply a decimal by a positive power of 10. Then describe how to multiply a decimal by a negative power of 10.

Use Labsheet 4B for Questions 27 and 28.

27 Follow the directions on Labsheet 4B to complete the *Quotient Table*. $2300 \div 1000 = 2.3$; $2300 \div 10 = 230$; $2300 \div 1 = 2300$; $23,000$; $2300 \div 0.01 = 230,000$; $2300 \div 0.001 = 2,300,000$

28 Discussion Look at your completed *Quotient Table*. Describe how to divide a decimal by a positive power of 10. Then describe how to divide a decimal by a negative power of 10.

29 ✔ **CHECKPOINT** Find each product or quotient without using a calculator.

    a. $11.634 \cdot 10^3$ **b.** $11.634 \cdot 10^0$ **c.** $11.634 \cdot 10^{-1}$

    d. $9.75 \div 10^3$ **e.** $9.75 \div 10^0$ **f.** $9.75 \div 10^{-1}$

30 If 1.23456e+13 represents $1.23456 \cdot 10^{13}$, write the number represented by 2.376e–8 in standard form. 0.00000002376

31 Discussion Find each missing exponent. Explain your method.

    a. $0.00036 = 3.6 \cdot 10^?$ **b.** $3,600,000 = 3.6 \cdot 10^?$

▶ When a calculator displays a number as the product of a decimal and a power of 10, the decimal number is greater than or equal to 1 and less than 10. Numbers written this way are written in **scientific notation**

EXAMPLE

standard form		scientific notation
$12,345,000 = 1.2345 \cdot 10,000,000$	$=$	$1.2345 \cdot 10^7$
$0.0058 = 5.8 \cdot 0.001$	$=$	$5.8 \cdot 10^{-3}$

32 ✔ **CHECKPOINT** Write each number in scientific notation.

    a. 257,034   **b.** 0.0000727   **c.** 126.935

     $2.57034 \cdot 10^5$ $7.27 \cdot 10^{-5}$ $1.26935 \cdot 10^2$

HOMEWORK EXERCISES ▶ See Exs. 56–79 on pp. 201–202.

---

26. Sample Response: Move the decimal point right x places, where x is the power of 10; Move the decimal point left x places, where x is the opposite of the power of 10.

28. Sample Response: Move the decimal point left x places, where x is the power of 10; Move the decimal point right x places, where x is the opposite of the power of 10.

✔ **QUESTION 29**

...checks that you can multiply or divide a decimal by a power of 10.

29. a. 11,634
   b. 11.634
   c. 1.1634
   d. 0.00975
   e. 9.75
   f. 97.5

31. a. –4; The decimal point was moved left 4 places.
   b. 6; The decimal point was moved right 6 places.

✔ **QUESTION 32**

...checks that you can write numbers in scientific notation.

Key Terms

decimal place

Decimal Place Values (pp. 191–193)

In the decimal place value system, the positions of the digits in a number determine their values. To compare decimals, you need to compare place values.

Thousands	Hundreds	Tens	Ones	.	Tenths	Hundredths	Thousandths
		1	6	.	0	5	3

place values

sixteen and fifty-three thousandths = $16\frac{53}{1000}$

Example Compare 2.335 and 2.34.

2.335
2.34

The **ones** and **tenths** digits are equal. Compare the **hundredths** digits: **3 < 4**.

So, 2.335 < 2.34.

Integer Exponents (pp. 194–195)

Positive and negative integers and zero can be used as exponents. A number that can be written in exponential form is a power of the base.

Examples

the 4th power of 5

$$5^4 = 5 \cdot 5 \cdot 5 \cdot 5 = 625$$

$$4^{-3} = \frac{1}{4^3} = \frac{1}{4 \cdot 4 \cdot 4} = \frac{1}{64}$$

4 to the negative third power

The 0 power of any nonzero number is 1.

$$36^0 = 1$$

33 **Key Concepts Question** Write each expression in standard form.

a. 10^{-8}
0.00000001

b. 12^0 1

c. $3.98 \cdot 10^4$
39,800

d. $0.04 \div 0.1$ 0.4

Key Concepts

Multiplying and Dividing by Powers of Ten (pp. 196–197)

When multiplying and dividing by powers of ten, the exponent can help you decide where to place the decimal point.

Examples

$25.34 \cdot 10^3 = 25{,}340$ The decimal point **moves right 3** places.
$25.34 \div 10^4 = 0.002534$ The decimal point **moves left 4** places.
$25.34 \cdot 10^{-2} = 0.2534$ The decimal point **moves left 2** places.
$25.34 \div 10^{-1} = 253.4$ The decimal point moves right 1 place.

Scientific notation is a method for writing large and small numbers.

scientific notation

Examples Write 5261 and 0.013 in scientific notation.

a number between 1 and 10

$5261 = 5.261 \cdot 1000 = 5.261 \cdot 10^3$ a power of 10
$0.013 = \quad 1.3 \cdot 0.01 = 1.3 \quad \cdot 10^{-2}$

34 Key Concepts Question Find each product.

a. $213.24 \cdot 10^{-4}$ 0.021324
b. $149.7 \cdot 10^{-5}$ 0.001497
c. $0.0049 \cdot 10^{-3}$ 0.0000049
d. $0.01735 \cdot 10^6$ 17,350

Section 4
Practice & Application Exercises

Write each number in words.

1. 2523.12   **2.** 0.987   **3.** 43.065   **4.** 1.00198

Write each number as a fraction or a mixed number.

5. 0.98 $\frac{98}{100}$ or $\frac{49}{50}$ **6.** 23.7 $23\frac{7}{10}$ **7.** 0.208   **8.** 0.0059 $\frac{59}{10,000}$

9. 1.0019 $1\frac{19}{10,000}$ **10.** 3.24054 $3\frac{24,054}{100,000}$ or $3\frac{12,027}{50,000}$ **11.** 10.085421 $10\frac{85,421}{1,000,000}$ **12.** 15.06005 $15\frac{6005}{100,000}$ or $15\frac{1201}{20,000}$

1. two thousand five hundred twenty-three and twelve hundredths

2. nine hundred eighty-seven thousandths

3. forty-three and sixty-five thousandths

4. one and one hundred ninety-eight hundred-thousandths

7. $\frac{208}{1000}$ or $\frac{26}{125}$

▲ Barbara Sampson used her knowledge of telecommunications to start her own business in 1986.

13. In 1992 women-owned businesses in the United States numbered 6.4 million and employed 13.2 million people. Why do you think these values are written this way? Write each value in standard form. easier to read; 6,400,000; 13,200,000

Replace each ? with > , < , or =.

14. 0.24 ? 0.240 = **15.** 1.873 ? 1.875 <

16. 12.64 ? 11.65 > **17.** 0.13 ? 0.126 >

18. 28.1 ? 2.81 > **19.** 0.004 ? 0.040 <

Match each number with a point on the number line below.

20. 0.666 D **21.** 1.0 C **22.** 0.6 A **23.** 0.9059 F

24. 0.95 B **25.** 0.09 H **26.** 0.500 E **27.** 0.0075 G

28. Open-ended Write three decimal numbers with corresponding points located between points *E* and *F* on the number line above.
  Possible answers: any number between 0.5 and 0.9059

29. History The Chinese used decimal fractions and place values as early as the third century A.D. A measurement of 3.142 *tshun* (Chinese inches) would have been expressed as 3 *tshun*, 1 *fen*, 4 *li*, 2 *hao*. What do you think the words *fen*, *li*, and *hao* mean?
  tenths; hundredths; thousandths

30. Library Science Books are arranged on shelves in some libraries according to the *Dewey Decimal System*. List these Dewey decimal numbers in order from least to greatest: 513.01, 510.006, 510.42, 500.95, 510.4, 510.024, 513.52, 500.522, 510, 510.78.
  500.522, 500.95, 510, 510.006, 510.024, 510.4, 510.42, 510.78, 513.01, 513.52

Write each power of ten in standard form.

31. 10^2 100 **32.** 10^7 10,000,000 **33.** 10^1 10 **34.** 10^0 1

35. 10^{-1} 0.1 **36.** 10^{-3} 0.001 **37.** 10^{-4} 0.0001 **38.** 10^{-6} 0.000001

Write each power as a fraction with its denominator in standard form.

39. 2^{-4} $\frac{1}{16}$ **40.** 3^{-2} $\frac{1}{9}$ **41.** 6^{-3} $\frac{1}{216}$ **42.** 2^{-8} $\frac{1}{256}$

43. 5^{-4} $\frac{1}{625}$ **44.** 8^{-3} $\frac{1}{512}$ **45.** 12^{-2} $\frac{1}{144}$ **46.** 20^{-3} $\frac{1}{8000}$

Write each number in exponential form with base 10.

47. 1,000,000 10^6 **48.** 0.01 10^{-2} **49.** 10 10^1

50. 0.0001 10^{-4} **51.** 0.000001 10^{-6} **52.** 1 10^0

Atoms Use the information below for Exercises 53–55.

The hydrogen atom is the lightest atom. It has a diameter of 0.00000001 cm and a mass of $17 \cdot 10^{-25}$ g. It is so small that a drop of water contains 10^{21} hydrogen atoms.

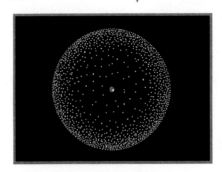

53. Write the diameter in exponential form with base 10. 10^{-8} cm

54. Write the mass as a fraction with its denominator in exponential form. $\frac{17}{10^{25}}$ g

▲ Computer-generated image of hydrogen atom

55. Write 10^{21} in standard form.
1,000,000,000,000,000,000,000

Write each product or quotient in standard form.

56. $3.6 \cdot 10^5$
360,000

57. $12.25 \cdot 10^{-3}$
0.01225

58. $15.3612 \cdot 10^2$
1536.12

59. $13.024 \cdot 10^4$
130,240

60. $101.397 \cdot 10^{-1}$
10.1397

61. $0.139 \cdot 0.0001$
0.0000139

62. $0.2385 \cdot 1000$
238.5

63. $436 \div 10,000$
0.0436

64. $58 \div 0.00001$
5,800,000

65. $5437 \div 10^3$
5.437

66. $0.0138 \div 10^{-4}$
138

67. $1.205 \div 10^2$
0.01205

Write each number in scientific notation.

68. 32,405
$3.2405 \cdot 10^4$

69. 120,684
$1.20684 \cdot 10^5$

70. 98.335
$9.8335 \cdot 10^1$

71. 229.0098
$2.290098 \cdot 10^2$

72. 0.0052
$5.2 \cdot 10^{-3}$

73. 0.000075
$7.5 \cdot 10^{-5}$

Challenge Write each product or quotient as a decimal.

74. $\dfrac{2.8 \cdot 10^4}{7 \cdot 10^5}$ 0.04

75. $(6 \cdot 10^3)(9 \cdot 10^{-5})$ 0.54

Mars

Astronomy Use the table.

76. Write the distance of each moon from the planet it orbits. Use scientific notation. $2.3 \cdot 10^4$, $9 \cdot 10^3$, $1.29 \cdot 10^5$, $1.1094 \cdot 10^7$, $2.12 \cdot 10^7$

77. Write the mass of each moon in standard form. See below.

78. List the moons by mass from least to greatest.
Deimos, Leda, Phobos, Adrastea, Ananke

Jupiter

Five Moons in the Solar System			
Moon	Planet	Distance from planet (km)	Mass (kg)
Deimos	Mars	23,000	$2.00 \cdot 10^{15}$
Phobos	Mars	9,000	$1.08 \cdot 10^{16}$
Adrastea	Jupiter	129,000	$1.91 \cdot 10^{16}$
Leda	Jupiter	11,094,000	$5.68 \cdot 10^{15}$
Ananke	Jupiter	21,200,000	$3.82 \cdot 10^{16}$

77. 2,000,000,000,000,000;
10,800,000,000,000,000;
19,100,000,000,000,000;
5,680,000,000,000,000;
38,200,000,000,000,000

Journal

Exercise 79 checks that you can relate place values and exponents.

Reflecting ‣ on the Section

Write your response to Exercise 79 in your journal.

79. Simon Stevin would have written 12.368 as 12⓪3①6②8③. Explain how the circled numbers he used in his notation are related to place values and exponents.

The circled zero represents the decimal point or the place value of the 12, which is 10^0, or 1. If x is a number in another circle, the place value of the number to the left of the circle is 10^{-x}.

Spiral ‣ Review

Find each sum or difference. (Module 3, p. 183)

80. $2\frac{1}{4} + \frac{1}{8}$ $2\frac{3}{8}$ 81. $3\frac{2}{3} - 1\frac{1}{9}$ $2\frac{5}{9}$ 82. $\frac{1}{8} + 1\frac{2}{5}$ $1\frac{21}{40}$ 83. $4\frac{3}{5} - 2\frac{2}{15}$ $2\frac{7}{15}$

Find the volume of a cube with each side length. (Module 1, p. 21)

84. 5 in. 125 in.³ 85. 10 ft 1000 ft³ 86. 1 m 1 m³ 87. 5 cm 125 cm³

Estimate each length or height using the unit in parentheses.
(Toolbox, pp. 582–583) Sample responses are given.

88. a bed (feet)
about 6 ft

89. a door (inches)
about 75 in.

90. a flag pole (yards)
about 10 yd

Extension ▶▶

Products and Quotients of Powers

When two numbers in exponential form have the same base, the exponents can help you find their product or quotient.

91. Find each product or quotient. Then find the missing exponent.

a. $10^3 \cdot 10^1 = 10^?$ b. $2^5 \cdot 2^3 = 2^?$ c. $4^0 \cdot 4^3 = 4^?$

d. $2^{-5} \cdot 2^{-3} = 2^?$ e. $10^{-5} \cdot 10^2 = 10^?$ f. $9^3 \cdot 9^{-2} = 9^?$

g. $10^3 \div 10^1 = 10^?$ h. $2^5 \div 2^3 = 2^?$ i. $5^2 \div 5^3 = 5^?$

j. $4^0 \div 4^3 = 4^?$ k. $10^{-5} \div 10^2 = 10^?$ l. $9^3 \div 9^{-2} = 9^?$

91. a. 10,000; 10^4
b. 256; 2^8
c. 64; 4^3
d. $\frac{1}{256}$; 2^{-8}
e. 0.001; 10^{-3}
f. 9; 9^1
g. 100; 10^2
h. 4; 2^2
i. $\frac{1}{5}$; 5^{-1}
j. $\frac{1}{64}$; 4^{-3}
k. $\frac{1}{10,000,000}$; 10^{-7}
l. 59,049; 9^5

92. Compare the exponents in each multiplication or division problem in Exercise 91 with the exponent in its answer. What pattern do you notice for the multiplication problems? for the division problems? The exponents are added; the exponents are subtracted.

93. Write rules for multiplying and dividing powers with the same base. To multiply, add the exponents. To divide, subtract the exponents.

Write each number as a fraction or mixed number in lowest terms.

1. 0.005 $\frac{1}{200}$
2. 0.14 $\frac{7}{50}$
3. 12.8 $12\frac{4}{5}$
4. 1.225 $1\frac{9}{40}$

Replace each ? with >, <, or =.

5. 0.342 _?_ 0.345 <
6. 1.84 _?_ 1.837 >
7. 12.2 _?_ 10.29 >
8. 0.091 _?_ 0.0910 =
9. 0.18 _?_ 0.175 >
10. 13.6 _?_ 1.36 >

Write each power of ten in standard form.

11. 10^3
12. 10^{-2}
13. 10^0
14. 10^4
15. 10^6
16. 10^{-7}
17. 10^5
18. 10^{-5}
19. 10^8
20. 10^1

11. 1000
12. 0.01
13. 1
14. 10,000
15. 1,000,000
16. 0.0000001
17. 100,000
18. 0.00001
19. 100,000,000
20. 10

Write each power as a fraction with its denominator in standard form.

21. 2^{-3} $\frac{1}{8}$
22. 4^{-2} $\frac{1}{16}$
23. 2^{-5} $\frac{1}{32}$
24. 6^{-2} $\frac{1}{36}$
25. 8^{-4} $\frac{1}{4096}$
26. 7^{-2} $\frac{1}{49}$
27. 3^{-4} $\frac{1}{81}$
28. 5^{-1} $\frac{1}{5}$
29. 1^{-7} $\frac{1}{1}$
30. 2^{-6} $\frac{1}{64}$

Write each product or quotient in standard form.

31. $2.45 \cdot 0.001$ 0.00245
32. $10^2 \cdot 0.0488$ 4.88
33. $129{,}723 \cdot 10^{-5}$ 1.29723
34. $10^{-3} \cdot 98.05$ 0.09805
35. $104.6 \div 10^2$ 1.046
36. $6825 \div 10^{-4}$ 68,250,000
37. $305.908 \div 10^{-3}$ 305,908
38. $0.004 \div 10^{-6}$ 4000
39. $0.312 \div 10^2$ 0.00312

Write each number in scientific notation.

40. 1255 $1.255 \cdot 10^3$ ✓
41. 0.0061 $6.1 \cdot 10^{-3}$
42. 36,040 $3.604 \cdot 10^4$ ✓
43. 184,536 $1.84536 \cdot 10^5$ ✓
44. 0.00089 $8.9 \cdot 10^{-4}$
45. 1017.70 $1.0177 \cdot 10^3$ ✓
46. 0.836271 $8.36271 \cdot 10^{-1}$
47. 905.33 $9.0533 \cdot 10^2$ ✓
48. 0.061 $6.1 \cdot 10^{-2}$

Standardized Testing ◀▶ Multiple Choice

1. Which is the greatest number? D

   A. $\frac{127}{4}$
   B. 40^{-3}
   C. 31.75
   D. $3.18 \cdot 10^1$

2. Which number is the quotient $6.3 \div 10^2$? B

   A. 630
   B. 0.063
   C. 10^{-2}
   D. 0.21

Section 5 Metric Units of Length

IN THIS SECTION

EXPLORATION 1
◆ Metric Conversions

EXPLORATION 2
◆ Metric Length Benchmarks

WARM-UP EXERCISES

Write each power in standard form.
1. 10^4 10,000
2. 10^{-2} 0.01
3. 10^1 10

Write each number using powers of ten.
4. 0.0001 10^{-4}
5. 10,000,000 10^7
6. 1 10^0

A Winning Measure

‹‹‹*Setting the Stage*

SET UP   *Work in a group. You will need:* • *string* • *chalk or masking tape* • *scissors*

In the past, measurements were not universal. Many old systems of measure were based on lengths of parts of the body.

A span was the distance between the tips of the thumb and the little finger when the hand was spread open. What would happen in an Olympic competition if the lengths of standing jumps were measured using spans?

Make a starting line with tape or chalk. Take turns jumping as far as you can from a standing position. Have someone mark your ending position. Cut a piece of string the length of your jump.

Think About It

1 Look at the span of your own hand. Estimate the length of your jump in spans.
  Answers will vary.

2 Measure the string using your span and compare it with your estimate. Make a table with two columns labeled *Student's name* and *Length of jump (in spans)*. In your table, record your name and the length of your jump in spans. **Check students' work.**

3 In your table, record the measures for your group.
  Check students' work.

4 Were all the jump measures in your group a whole number of spans? If not, how were parts of a span recorded?
Sample Response: No; as fractions

5 Using only the results in your table, can you determine the longest jump in your group? Explain.
Sample Response: No; The lengths of the spans probably differ.

6 How many different spans do you think were used to measure the jumps of students in your class? Answers will vary.

Exploration 1

Metric Conversions

GOAL

LEARN HOW TO...
◆ convert from one metric unit to another

AS YOU...
◆ look at long jump results

KEY TERMS
◆ meter (m)
◆ millimeter (mm)
◆ centimeter (cm)
◆ kilometer (km)

SET UP *Work in a group. You will need:* • *strings from the Setting the Stage* • *meter stick or metric measuring tape*

▶ **The creation of the metric system ended the confusion caused by using many different local systems of measure. Metric measures of length are based on the meter (m). The ruler below shows some parts of a meter.**

The distance between the shortest marks is a **millimeter (mm)**.

Ten millimeters is one **centimeter (cm)**.

Ten centimeters is one decimeter (dm).
Ten decimeters is one meter (m).

7 Use the diagram.

   a. How many centimeters are in a meter? 100

   b. How many millimeters are in a meter? 1000

▶ **Longer units of length are also based on the meter.**
10 meters = 1 dekameter (dam)
10 dam = 1 hectometer (hm)
10 hm = 1 kilometer (km)

8 A **kilometer (km)** is a metric unit used to measure longer distances, such as highway distances. How many meters are in one kilometer?
1000

9 **a.** How many kilometers are there in 1345 m? Explain.
1.345; Divide 1345 by 1000.

b. How many centimeters are there in 9 km? Explain.
900,000; Multiply 9 by 1000 to get meters and then by 100 to get centimeters.

▶ **Converting Units** The conversion chart shows the relationship between metric units of length.

Conversion Chart for Metric Measurements

× 10	× 10	× 10	× 10	× 10	× 10
km	hm	dam	m	dm	cm	mm
÷ 10	÷ 10	÷ 10	÷ 10	÷ 10	÷ 10

▶ Metric measurements can be changed from one unit of measure to another by multiplying or dividing by powers of ten.

EXAMPLE

4.5 m = __?__ cm
× **100**
4.5 m = 450 cm

__?__ m = 500 cm
5 m = 500 cm
÷ **100**

10 ✔ **CHECKPOINT** Use the conversion chart to decide whether you multiply or divide by a power of ten in each case.

a. to convert from a longer unit of measure, such as kilometers, to a shorter unit of measure, such as centimeters multiply

b. to convert from a shorter unit of measure, such as millimeters, to a longer unit of measure, such as meters divide

...checks that you know which operations to use when converting metric units.

▶ **The most commonly used units of measure for metric length are the kilometer, meter, centimeter, and millimeter.**

11 What power of ten is used to convert between the given units?

    a. millimeters and centimeters   **b.** centimeters and meters
         10^1 or 10^{-1} 10^2 or 10^{-2}
    c. millimeters and meters   **d.** meters and kilometers
         10^3 or 10^{-3} 10^{-3} or 10^3

12 ✔ **CHECKPOINT** Replace each ? with the correct measure.

    a. 3.1 km = __?__ m   3100   **b.** 0.9 cm = __?__ m   0.009

    c. 1.28 cm = __?__ mm   12.8   **d.** 0.62 m = __?__ mm   620

✔ **QUESTION 12**

...checks that you can convert metric units of length.

13   **a.** Measure, to the nearest half of a centimeter, the string that represents the length of the jump you made in the *Setting the Stage.*   Answers will vary.

    b. Make a table with four columns, labeled *Student's name, Centimeters, Millimeters, Meters.* Record your name and the length of your jump in centimeters.   Check students' work.

    c. Collect the results of part (a) from the other members in your group. Record their results in your table.   Check students' work.

    d. Use powers of ten to complete the *Millimeters* and *Meters* columns in your table.   Check students' work.

14 Which member(s) of your group jumped farther than 0.5 m, but less than 175 cm?   Answers may vary.

15 Besides ending the confusion caused by using many different systems of measurement, what are some other advantages of the metric system?   Sample Response: It is easy to convert from one unit to another and to measure very small lengths.

HOMEWORK EXERCISES ▶ See Exs. 1–20 on pp. 211–212.

LEARN HOW TO...
- recognize metric benchmarks
- use benchmarks to estimate lengths in metric units

AS YOU...
- estimate and measure lengths in your classroom

KEY TERM
- benchmark

Exploration 2

Metric Length Benchmarks

SET UP | You will need: • meter stick or metric tape measure • metric ruler

▶ You can use something whose measure you know as a **benchmark** to estimate lengths. The best benchmarks are ones that can be easily used in a variety of situations. Below are some items that could be used as benchmarks.

16 Discussion Look at the benchmarks.

a. What is an advantage of using your arm length as a benchmark? What is a disadvantage? Sample Responses: It's always available; It is not equal to a metric unit of length.

b. Is the width of a little finger a good benchmark for everyone to use for 1 cm? Explain. No; The width varies from person to person and also depends on where on the little finger the measurement is taken.

17 Use a meter stick or a metric tape measure.

a. Hold the meter stick alongside you with one end touching the floor. About how far up does it reach? Sample Response: to my waist

b. The measurement in part (a) can serve as a benchmark for 1 m. Find examples of objects or distances in your classroom that represent about 1 m in length. Sample Response: the distance from the floor to a doorknob, the height of a bookcase

c. Explain why each item you found in part (b) would or would not make a good benchmark. Sample Response: The heights of doorknobs are pretty standard, so that would make a good benchmark. Heights of bookcases vary too much to make a good benchmark.

18 ✔ **CHECKPOINT** Estimate each measurement in the table in meters. Then measure the length in meters, record the measure, and compare your estimate with the actual measure.
See Additional Answers.

✔ **QUESTION 18**

...checks that you can use benchmarks to estimate lengths.

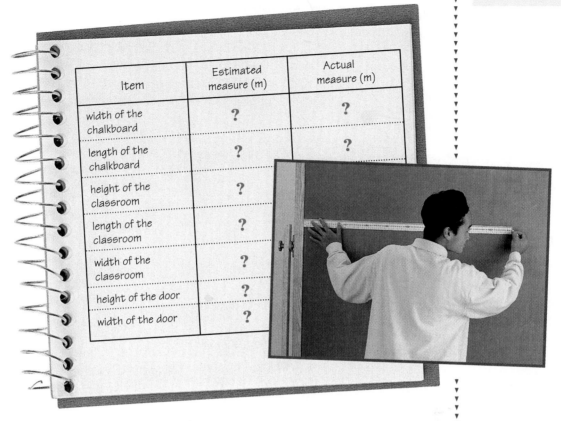

Item	Estimated measure (m)	Actual measure (m)
width of the chalkboard	?	?
length of the chalkboard	?	?
height of the classroom	?	
length of the classroom	?	
width of the classroom	?	
height of the door	?	
width of the door	?	

19 Find a convenient benchmark for each length.

    a. 1 cm   **b.** 5 cm   **c.** 10 cm   **d.** 20 cm

20 **a.** Use your benchmarks from Question 19 to estimate the length of each segment in centimeters.

       A ____ *B*

       C _____ *D*

       E _____ *F*

       G _____ *H*

  b. Measure each segment to the nearest tenth of a centimeter. Compare the measurement with your estimates in part (a).

19. Sample Response:
   a. width of my small fingernail,
   b. width of 2 quarters,
   c. length of "THE UNITED STATES OF AMERICA" on a dollar bill,
   d. length of a mousepad

20. a. Sample Response: about 1 cm, 6 cm, 3 cm, 10 cm
   b. 0.7 cm, 5.6 cm, 2.9 cm, 8.5 cm; Sample Response: The estimates were too high.

HOMEWORK EXERCISES ▶ See Exs. 21–40 on pp. 212–213.

Key Terms

meter (m)

centimeter (cm)

millimeter (mm)

kilometer (km)

Metric System (pp. 205–207)

The most commonly used metric units of length are related as follows:

1 meter (m) = 0.001 km, 100 cm, or 1000 mm
1 centimeter (cm) = 0.01 m or 10 mm
1 millimeter (mm) = 0.001 m or 0.1 cm
1 kilometer (km) = 1000 m

You can use these relationships to convert among units.

Example Convert 378 mm to centimeters.

You **divide** to convert from a smaller unit to a larger unit.

378 mm ÷ 10 = 37.8 cm   **10** mm = 1 cm

Example Convert 2.4 km to meters.

You **multiply** to convert from a larger unit to a smaller unit.

2.4 km • 1000 = 2400 m   **1000** m = 1 km

Benchmarks (pp. 208–209)

benchmark

The best benchmarks are ones that can be easily and conveniently used in a variety of situations.

Example Suzanne uses the length of her shoe as a benchmark for a measure of 25 cm. She estimates the width of a doorway as 4 shoe lengths, which is about 100 cm or 1 m.

CLOSURE QUESTION

State the four most commonly used metric units of length and describe how they are related to each other.

Answer: millimeter, centimeter, meter, and kilometer: A centimeter is 10 millimeters, a meter is 100 centimeters, and a kilometer is 1000 meters.

21 **Key Concepts Question** Explain how you can use the relationships between the metric units of length to find out how many millimeters there are in a kilometer.

Since 1 km = 1000 m and 1 m = 1000 mm, 1 km = 1000 • 1000 mm = 1,000,000 mm.

Section 5

Practice & Application Exercises ➤➤➤➤➤➤➤

1. Running competitions may use a course that is 3 km, 5 km, or 10 km long.

   a. Write the length, in meters, of each course. 3000 m; 5000 m; 10,000 m

   b. For an average person, 1 m is about two walking steps. About how many steps would it take an average person to walk each course? about 6000; about 10,000; about 20,000

   c. Suppose k represents a distance in kilometers and d represents the same distance in meters. Write a formula for converting from kilometers to meters. $d = 1000k$

Replace each ? with the correct measure.

2. 200 cm = __?__ m 2

3. 1.8 km = __?__ m 1800

4. 8.75 cm = __?__ mm 87.5

5. 400 m = __?__ km 0.4

6. 3.2 km = __?__ cm 320,000

7. 68.04 mm = __?__ m 0.06804

8. 5.06 cm = __?__ km 0.0000506

9. 600 km = __?__ mm 600,000,000

Replace each ? with > , < , or = .

10. 0.023 km __?__ 2.3 m >

11. 4050 mm __?__ 4.05 m =

12. 8 cm __?__ 10 mm >

13. 12.4 cm __?__ 56.2 m <

14. 9.05 cm __?__ 12 km <

15. 3.8 mm __?__ 38 km <

Animal Jump Records The world record jumps of several animals are described using an inappropriate metric unit. Change the metric unit to one that gives a better idea of the distance each animal jumped.

16. A dog named Bang jumped 914 cm while chasing a hare.

17. A South African sharp-nosed frog averaged 3400 mm for each jump in a triple-jump competition.

18. In an experiment done in 1910, a common flea jumped 0.00033 km.

19. In Australia, a female red kangaroo jumped 12,800 mm in the midst of a chase.

16. Sample Response: Change cm to m.

17. Sample Response: Change mm to m.

18. Sample Response: Change km to cm.

19. Sample Response: Change mm to m.

20. Challenge A decimeter is equal to ten centimeters and a hectometer is equal to ten thousand centimeters. What is the relationship between a decimeter and a hectometer? How many decimeters are in a hectometer? *1 decimeter = 0.001 hectometer; 1000*

Estimation Use benchmarks to estimate and draw a segment with each length. Then check your estimates with a metric ruler. *Check students' drawings.*

21. 3 cm   **22.** 15 cm   **23.** 21 cm   **24.** 40 mm

25. 4 cm   **26.** 105 mm   **27.** 0.15 m   **28.** 0.2 m

29. Writing Look at your answers to Exercises 24 and 25. Which measurement is more accurate? Explain.

29. Sample Response: Both show the same accuracy; Since 40 mm = 4 cm, I used the same benchmark for the two measurements.

Copy each measure. Then place a decimal point in the number so that the measure is reasonable for the object or animal shown.

30. length: 170 cm   *17.0 cm*

31. height: 0.9 mm   *90 mm*

32. width: 250 mm
25.0 mm

33. height: 125 m   *1.25 m*

34. length: 0.03 cm   *3 cm*

Writing Tell if each measure is *reasonable* or *unreasonable*. Compare the measures with others you have already estimated to support your answers. If a measure is unreasonable, give a better estimate.

Example: length of a bed: 1 m   Unreasonable. Since most adults are between 1 m and 2 m tall, the length of a bed is about 2 m.

35. distance from floor to door knob: 2 m

35. unreasonable; Sample Response: A doorknob comes about to my waist and the distance from the floor to my waist is about 1 m.

36. length of a car: 5 m

36. reasonable; Sample Response: I am about 1.5 m tall and you could fit 3 of me alongside a car.

37. distance from kitchen to living room: 90 m

37. unreasonable; Sample Response: The length of our classroom is about 7 m, so the length of a room in a house would be about 5 m.

38. height of a backyard fence: 9 m

38. unreasonable; Sample Response: My father is about 1.8 m tall, so the height of a fence would be about 2 m.

39. length of a city swimming pool: 15 m

39. reasonable; Sample Response: Since two of my classrooms could probably fit along the edge of a pool and my classroom is about 7 m long, 15 m is reasonable.

Reflecting ▶ on the Section

Be prepared to discuss your response to Exercise 40 in class.

40. The United States uses the inch, foot, yard, and mile as its customary units of length.

   a. Use a customary ruler and a meter stick to compare the length of a yard with that of a meter. Which is longer? Can you use the same benchmark for both a meter and a yard? Explain.

   b. Suppose the length of a race is 5 mi, or about 8 km, and you want to express that distance in smaller units. Using mental math, is it easier to convert the length of the race from miles to yards or from kilometers to meters? (1760 yd = 1 mi) Why?

Discussion

Exercise 40 checks that you can apply and compare measurements.

40. **a.** the meter stick; Yes, but the longer the actual measurement, the greater the error.
   b. kilometers to meters; Multiplying 8×1000 is easier than multiplying 5×1760.

Spiral ▶ Review

Write each number in exponential form with base 10. (Module 3, p. 198)

41. 1000 10^3 42. 0.001 10^{-3} 43. 10 10^1 44. 1 10^0

Interpreting Data In 1994 Alvin Straight, a 73-year-old man from Laurens, Iowa, rode his lawn mower to southwestern Wisconsin to visit his brother. Use the graph to answer the questions. (Module 1, p. 7)

45. About how long did it take Alvin Straight to travel 25 mi? 10 mi?
    about 5 h; about 2 h

46. About how far did Alvin Straight travel in $1\frac{1}{2}$ h? in $3\frac{1}{2}$ h?
    about 7.5 mi; about 17.5 mi

Alvin Straight's Lawn Mower Trip

Solve each equation. Then check each solution. (Module 2, p. 137)

47. $20 = n - 5$ 25   48. $n + 17 = 44$ 27   49. $n - 11 = 35$ 46

50. $-8 + n = 22$ 30   51. $5 + n = -7$ –12   52. $49 = n - 100$ 149

Working on the Module Project

Secret Codes

Understanding the Problem Suppose you came across a cash register receipt like the one shown below. You probably would not think it was a secret message, but it is! Each of the numbers 23 23 5 19 30 26 33 26 26 29 15 represents a letter.

 7 Describe strategies that you can use to try to break the code.
See Additional Answers.

The code used on the receipt is similar to the Caesar shift code described on page 160, but each letter of the message is shifted by a different amount, and different numbers can represent the same letter.

The code phrase THANK YOU determines how much each letter is shifted. Each letter in THANK YOU is given a number based on the letter's position in the alphabet (A = 1, B = 2, and so on).

 8 The table shows how the message can be decoded. Copy the table and complete the first two columns by writing the numbers on the receipt and the letters of the code phrase THANK YOU.

Thank You!
$23.23
 5.19
30.26
33.26
26.29
15.00

Code number	Code letter	Code letter's position in the alphabet	Decoded letter's position in the alphabet	Decoded letter
23	T	20	3	C
23	H	8	15	O
5	A	1	4	D

The third letter of the message was shifted 1 place. 4 + 1 = 5

 9 The equation $c - s = p$ can be used to decode the message.
See Additional Answers.
   a. What do you think c, s, and p represent?

   b. How can you find the value of s?

   c. Use the equation to find the fourth letter of the message.

 10 **a.** Complete the table and decode the message. (At the ninth letter of the message, start over with the first letter of the code phrase.) Codes are fun.

   b. What was used to end the message? 00

 11 **a.** Use a code word or phrase to write a message to a partner. Answers will vary.

   b. Can you decode your partner's secret message without the code word or phrase? Answers will vary.

Section 5
Extra Skill Practice

Replace each _?_ with the correct measure.

1. 482 m = _?_ cm 48,200
2. 125 mm = _?_ cm 12.5
3. 5 km = _?_ mm 5,000,000
4. 300 m = _?_ km 0.3
5. 32 mm = _?_ m 0.032
6. 7.01 cm = _?_ m 0.0701
7. 39.6 km = _?_ cm 3,960,000
8. 1.85 m = _?_ mm 1850
9. 500.8 mm = _?_ m 0.5008
10. 3.24 km = _?_ mm 3,240,000

Replace each _?_ with > , < , or = .

11. 43 mm _?_ 12 cm <
12. 2.4 km _?_ 2400 mm >
13. 88,000 m _?_ 88 km =
14. 14 cm _?_ 8 km <
15. 75 cm _?_ 0.3 m >
16. 13 mm _?_ 1300 m <
17. 5.1 cm _?_ 634 mm <
18. 33 m _?_ 3300 cm =
19. 427.99 km _?_ 500,000 cm >
20. 654.2 cm _?_ 70,000 m <

Copy each measure. Then place a decimal point in the number so that the measure is reasonable.

21. thickness of a dictionary: 600 mm 60.0
22. height of a table: 70 m 0.7
23. length of a pen: 1450 cm 14.5
24. length of a school bus: 115 m 11.5
25. width of a door: 0.8 cm 80
26. length of an eraser (not on a pencil): 5000 mm 50.00

Standardized Testing ◀▶ Open-ended

Think of something that would make a good benchmark for estimating each measure. Explain how you would use each benchmark and why it is convenient in that situation. Check students' work.

a. the width of a bedroom
b. the length of a goldfish
c. the height of a tree
d. the length of a street
e. the height of a cat
f. the distance around a finger

Section ⑥ Triangles and Equations

Symbols of the People

WARM-UP EXERCISES

State the operation that undoes the given operation.

1. addition
   subtraction
2. subtraction
   addition
3. multiplication
   division
4. division
   multiplication
5. State two properties of triangles.
   Sample Response: They have 3 sides; They have 3 angles; The sum of their angle measures is 180°.

◄◄◄ Setting the Stage

People have been sending messages using shapes and symbols for hundreds of years. Flags and banners can express ideas and communicate information without words. The designs of many of these flags are based on geometric concepts.

Navigation	Humanitarian Services	Sports

▲ This flag shows the *International Code of Signals* symbol for "person overboard."

▲ In many countries of the world this *Flag of Healing* is the sign of emergency medical assistance.

▲ Flags such as this checkered flag are used in some sports to signal the referee or the participants.

Think About It

1 Find an example of each geometric figure on one of the flags.

    a. a rectangle **b.** a triangle **c.** an acute angle **d.** a right angle

    e. a pair of triangles that are the same size and shape

2 a. What is the checkered flag used for?

    b. What fraction of the checkered flag is black? $\frac{18}{35}$

1. a. Sample Response: a square on the checkered flag
b. one of the halves formed by the diagonal in the first flag
c. the angles formed by the diagonal of the navigation flag
d. Sample Response: one of the corners of the middle flag
e. the two triangles formed by the diagonal in the first flag

2. a. Sample Response: to signal a car has crossed the finish line in a car race

Constructing
TRI△NGLES

SET UP *You will need:* • *Labsheet 6A* • *metric ruler* • *compass*

Many nations around the world have a national flag to symbolize their country. Some of these flags contain triangles.

Use Labsheet 6A for Questions 3–5.

3 Follow the directions on the labsheet to measure and group the triangles on the *Flags with Triangles*. **See Additional Answers.**

4 Discussion One way to classify triangles is by the lengths of their sides. Two segments that are equal in length are **congruent**. Did anyone in your class group the triangles using 0, 2, and 3 congruent sides? What other groupings were used?
Sample Response: Yes; all sides about 27 mm long, two sides less than 27 mm long, at least one side more than 27 mm long

▶ Some of the triangles you measured on Labsheet 6A had at least two congruent sides. These triangles are **isosceles**. Triangles with three congruent sides are **equilateral**. If all its sides are different lengths, a triangle is **scalene**.

5 a. Classify each triangle you measured as *isosceles*, *equilateral*, or *scalene*.

b. Which triangles can be classified more than one way? Why?

6 ✔ CHECKPOINT Classify the triangle with each set of side lengths as *isosceles*, *equilateral*, or *scalene*. Be as specific as possible.

a. 7 in., 5 in., 3 in.   **b.** 1 m, 1 m, 1 m   **c.** 2 cm, 4 cm, 4 cm
scalene   equilateral and isosceles   isosceles

7 Use your ruler to draw each triangle and label the side lengths.

a. isosceles triangle that is not equilateral   **b.** equilateral triangle
Samples are given.
c. scalene triangle with 5 cm, 8 cm, and 9 cm sides
Check students' drawings.

▶ Some triangles are more difficult to draw than others. A compass is one tool that can make the job easier if you know how to use it.

GOAL

LEARN HOW TO...
◆ classify triangles by side length
◆ construct triangles and circles
◆ determine which side lengths will form a triangle

AS YOU...
◆ examine flags

KEY TERMS
◆ congruent
◆ isosceles
◆ equilateral
◆ scalene
◆ circle
◆ center
◆ radius
◆ chord
◆ diameter
◆ arc
◆ construction

5. a. isosceles triangles: Philippines, Bahamas, Sudan, Equatorial Guinea; equilateral triangles: Philippines; scalene triangles: Tanzania, Trinidad and Tobago
b. equilateral triangles; Triangles with 3 congruent sides are equilateral. Since they contain at least 2 congruent sides, they are also isosceles.

✔ QUESTION 6

...checks that you can classify triangles.

7. a.

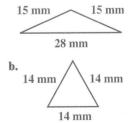

Compasses and Circles

You can use a compass to construct a *circle*.

To construct a circle, mark the *center C* of the circle. Place the tip of the compass on *C* and make a complete rotation.

A **circle** is the set of all points in a plane that are the same distance from a given point called the **center**.

A segment such as $\overline{CD}$ whose endpoints are the center and any point on the circle is a **radius** of the circle. The length of any radius is called *the* radius.

A segment such as $\overline{AB}$ whose endpoints are both on the circle is a **chord**.

Any chord such as $\overline{EF}$ that passes through the center of a circle is a **diameter** of the circle. The length of any diameter is called *the* diameter.

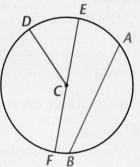

8 Construct a triangle with sides of length 4 cm, 6 cm, and 8 cm.
   Check students' drawings.

An **arc** is part of a circle.

Step 1 Draw an 8 cm segment with endpoints *A* and *B*.

Step 2 Open your compass to a radius of 6 cm. Place the tip on *A*. Draw an *arc* below $\overline{AB}$.

Step 3 Open your compass to a radius of 4 cm. Place the tip on *B*. Draw an arc that intersects the first arc.

Step 4 Label the intersection point *C*. Draw segments $\overline{AC}$ and $\overline{BC}$ to complete the triangle.

▶ You can draw some figures using just a straightedge and a compass. Drawings made this way are called **constructions**.

9 If possible, construct a triangle with the side lengths given. If not, explain why not. Label the sides with their lengths.

a. 1 cm, 3 cm, 6 cm   **b.** 2 cm, 3 cm, 4 cm

10 **a. Try This as a Class** What relationship must exist among the lengths of three segments for them to form a triangle?
The sum of the lengths of any 2 sides must be greater than the third side.

b. Change one side length in a set of three side lengths in Question 9 so that they will form a triangle.

Sample Response: Change the 1 cm side to 4 cm.

11 ✓ CHECKPOINT Tell whether segments with the given lengths *can* or *cannot* form a triangle. If they can, construct the triangle.

a. 2 cm, 3 cm, 8 cm
cannot

b. 5 cm, 7 cm, 9 cm
can; Check students' drawings.

HOMEWORK EXERCISES ▶ See Exs. 1–10 on p. 224.

9. **a.** not possible; It is impossible to make the sides intersect.
b. possible; Check students' drawings.

✓ **QUESTION 11**

…checks that you can tell whether 3 segments form a triangle, and that you can construct a triangle.

Exploration 2

Multiplication and **D**ivision **Equations**

SET UP *You will need a metric ruler.*

GOAL

LEARN HOW TO…
◆ write and solve multiplication and division equations

AS YOU…
◆ explore size relationships in flag designs

A country's flag may come in different sizes, but the relationships between the shapes in the design must stay the same.

12 The state flag of Spain is shown.

a. Measure the widths of the stripes to the nearest centimeter.

b. Describe the relationship between the widths.

12. **a.** 1 cm, 2 cm, 1 cm
b. Possible answers: The width of the yellow stripe is twice the width of a red stripe. The width of a red stripe is $\frac{1}{2}$ the width of the yellow stripe.

13 Copy the table. Use the relationship you described in Question 12(b) on page 219 to complete the table.

Spain's State Flag in Different Sizes						
Width of yellow stripe (cm)	10	14	**?**	18	**?**	15
Width of each red stripe (cm)	**?**	**?**	6	**?**	5.5	**?**

12; 11

5   7   9   7.5

14 Sometimes a relationship can be described by different equations. In each equation, *y* is the width of the yellow stripe and *r* is the width of one red stripe on Spain's state flag. Choose the letters of the equations that correctly describe the relationship between *y* and *r*. B, D, F

A. $2y = r$ **B.** $y = 2r$ **C.** $\frac{r}{2} = y$

D. $\frac{y}{2} = r$ **E.** $y = \frac{1}{2}r$ **F.** $r = \frac{1}{2}y$

▶ Since flags come in different sizes, mathematical language is often used to describe the flags so the designs will be made with the correct dimensions. In *Flags of the World*, by E. M. C. Barraclough, a description of the flag of Denmark includes the following lines.

" . . . the width of the cross is one seventh the hoist, the rectangles at the hoist are squares with sides three sevenths of the hoist, and the length of the rectangles in the fly is half as much again as that of the squares. "

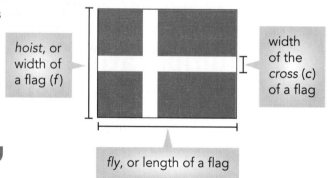

hoist, or width of a flag (*f*)

width of the cross (*c*) of a flag

fly, or length of a flag

▶ A verbal description can be used to write an equation.

Description in Words	Equation
The width of the cross is one seventh the hoist.	$c = \frac{1}{7}f$, where *c* = width of cross, and *f* = width of flag (hoist).

15 Write an equation for this description of Denmark's flag. *The width of the flag is seven times the width of the cross.*

$f = 7c$, where *f* = width of the flag and *c* = width of the cross.

16 ✔ **CHECKPOINT** Write an equation to describe each relationship. Identify any variables you use.

a. The width of Jamaica's flag is half the length of the flag.

◄ Each color on Jamaica's flag is a symbol—green for hope, black for hardships, and gold for sunlight.

b. The width of India's flag is three times the width of one of the stripes.

◄ The wheel at the center of India's flag is the *Dharma Chakra*, or Wheel of Law.

17 The relationship between the width of the cross on Denmark's flag and the width of the flag itself can be written in two ways.

Description in words	Equation
The width of the cross c is one seventh the width of the flag f.	$c = \frac{1}{7}f$
The width of the flag f is seven times the width of the cross c.	$7c = f$

a. Use one of the equations to find the width of the cross when the width of the flag is 21 in.   3 in.

$c = \frac{1}{7}f$; The equation gives the width of the cross in terms of the width of the flag.

b. Which equation did you use? Why?

18 **Discussion** Inverse operations can help you see how the equations above are related.

$$7c = f$$

Step 1 $\frac{7c}{7} = \frac{f}{7}$

Dividing by 7 is the same as multiplying by $\frac{1}{7}$.

Step 2 $c = \frac{f}{7}$, or $c = \frac{1}{7}f$

a. In Step 1, what is the result of dividing $7c$ by 7? Why?

b. Why is f divided by 7 in Step 1?

▶ **You can use the method above to solve equations. Look at the example on the next page.**

✔ **QUESTION 16**

...checks that you can write an equation to describe a relationship.

16. a. $w = \frac{1}{2}l$ or $w = \frac{l}{2}$, where w = width of the flag and l = length of the flag.

   b. $f = 3s$, where s = width of a stripe and f = width of the flag.

18. a. c; Division undoes multiplication. 7 divided by 7 is 1 and 1 times c is c.

   b. Whatever is done to one side of an equation must also be done to the other side to keep the equation balanced.

Use the equation $7c = f$ to find the width of the cross (c) when the width of the flag (f) is 17.5 in.

$7c = f$ — Substitute **17.5** for f.

$7c = \textbf{17.5}$

$\dfrac{7c}{7} = \dfrac{17.5}{7}$ — Divide both sides of the equation by **7**.

$c = 2.5$

Check:

$7c = 17.5$

$7(\textbf{2.5}) \overset{?}{=} 17.5$

$17.5 = 17.5$ ✔

The width of the cross is 2.5 in.

✔ **QUESTION 19**

...checks that you can solve equations by dividing.

19 ✔ **CHECKPOINT** Solve. Check each solution.

a. $3x = 24$ 8

b. $40 = 5x$ 8

c. $4x = 72$ 18

20 **Try This as a Class** Suppose the cross on a flag of Denmark is 4 in. wide. The equation $c = \dfrac{f}{7}$ can be used to find the width of the flag. Write an explanation to replace each _?_ in boxes (a) and (b). Then answer the questions in box (c).

20. a. Substitute 4 for c.
b. Multiply both sides of the equation by 7 to undo the division.

c. $f, 7 \cdot \dfrac{1}{7} = 1$

$c = \dfrac{f}{7}$

a. _?_ $4 = \dfrac{f}{7}$

$7 \cdot 4 = 7 \cdot \dfrac{f}{7}$ **b.** _?_

$28 = f$

c. What is the result of multiplying $\dfrac{f}{7}$ by 7? Why?

Check: $c = \dfrac{f}{7}$

$4 \overset{?}{=} \dfrac{28}{7}$

$4 = 4$ ✔

✔ **QUESTION 21**

...checks that you can solve equations by multiplying.

21 ✔ **CHECKPOINT** Solve. Check each answer.

a. $\dfrac{y}{2} = 49$ 98

b. $113 = \dfrac{1}{3}x$ 339

c. $\dfrac{z}{5} = 2021$ 10,105

22 Use the equations you wrote in Question 16.

a. If the width of a Jamaican flag is 24 in., what is the length?   48 in.

b. If the width of an Indian flag is 27 in., what is the width of one of its stripes?   9 in.

HOMEWORK EXERCISES ▶ See Exs. 11–24 on pp. 224–225.

Key Concepts

Key Concepts

Key Terms

Classifying and Constructing Triangles (pp. 217–219)

at least two congruent sides → isosceles

three congruent sides → equilateral

no congruent sides → scalene

congruent

isosceles

equilateral

scalene

construction

circle
  center
  radius
  chord
  diameter
  arc

A triangle can be constructed if the sum of the lengths of any two sides is greater than the length of the third side.

Example A triangle cannot be formed since $2 + 1 < 4$.

1 in. 2 in. 4 in.

Multiplication and Division Equations (pp. 219–222)

Multiplication and division can be used to solve equations.

Example

$3x = 54$

Divide both sides by **3**.

$$\frac{3x}{3} = \frac{54}{3}$$

$x = 18$

Check: $3x = 54$

$3 \cdot 18 \overset{?}{=} 54$

$54 = 54$ ✓

Example

$$\frac{y}{2} = 37$$

Multiply both sides by **2**.

$$2 \cdot \frac{y}{2} = 2 \cdot 37$$

$y = 74$

Check: $\dfrac{y}{2} = 37$

$$\frac{74}{2} \overset{?}{=} 37$$

$37 = 37$ ✓

CLOSURE QUESTION

Explain how you can classify triangles by the lengths of their sides. Then explain how you can use multiplication and division to solve equations.

Sample Response: Triangles can have 0, 2, or 3 sides that are equal in length. If no sides are equal in length, then the triangle is scalene. If 2 sides are equal in length, then the triangle is isosceles. If 3 sides are equal in length, then the triangle is equilateral (and isosceles). To solve equations that contain multiplication, divide to undo the multiplication. To solve equations that contain division, multiply to undo the division.

23 Key Concepts Question The lengths of two sides of a triangle are 3 in. and 7 in.

a. What whole-inch lengths will work for the third side?
5 in., 6 in., 7 in., 8 in., 9 in.

b. Which lengths from part (a) will make the triangle isosceles? scalene? 7 in.; 5 in., 6 in., 8 in., 9 in.

c. Suppose that twice the length x of the third side is equal to the sum of the lengths of the other two sides. Find x. 5 in.

YOU WILL NEED

For Exs. 1–3, 10:
◆ compass
◆ ruler

Use a compass and a ruler to construct each triangle. Label the sides with their lengths.

1. an isosceles triangle with sides of length 4 in., 4 in., and 5 in.
   Check students' drawings.

2. a scalene triangle with sides of length 2 in., 3 in., and 4 in.
   Check students' drawings.

3. an equilateral triangle with sides of length $3\frac{1}{2}$ in.
   Check students' drawings.

Tell whether each set of side lengths *can* or *cannot* form a triangle. If a triangle can be formed, tell whether the triangle is *isosceles*, *equilateral*, or *scalene*.

4. 3 in., 3 in., 5 in.   5. 2 km, 4 km, 6 km   6. 9 cm, 9 cm, 9 cm
   can; isosceles   cannot   can; equilateral and isosceles

7. 3.2 m, 4.1 m, 7 m   8. 7 m, 12 m, 23 m   9. $7\frac{1}{2}$ in., 8 in., 15 in.
   can; scalene   cannot   can; scalene

10. **Create Your Own** Use a compass and a ruler. Answers will vary.

    a. Design a rectangular flag. Include one or more triangles in your design.

    b. Give the side lengths of each triangle and classify each triangle as either *isosceles*, *equilateral*, or *scalene*.

    c. What are the dimensions of your flag? Find its area.

    d. What other geometric shapes are part of your flag design?

FOR ▶ HELP

with finding the
area of a rectangle,
see
TOOLBOX, p. 593

Solve. Check each answer.

11. $3w = 27$ 9   12. $12y = 36$ 3   13. $\frac{z}{3} = 6$ 18   14. $5x = 25$ 5

15. $15y = 300$ 20 16. $9 = \frac{1}{3}x$ 27   17. $\frac{r}{50} = 8$ 400   18. $128 = 4z$ 32

19. $n = 3l$, where n = the number of volunteers this year and l = the number of volunteers last year; 36 volunteers

20. $c = 2e$, where c = the current population and e = the population 8 years ago; 24,000 people

21. $c = 5p$, where c = the number of chickens and p = the number pigs; 30 chickens

22. $e = 8w$ where e = the width of the enlargement and w = original width; 24 in.

Write a multiplication equation to model each situation. Then solve each equation.

19. There are 3 times as many volunteers this year as last year. Last year there were 12 volunteers.

20. A population has doubled in 8 years. Eight years ago the population was 12,000.

21. A farm has 5 times as many chickens as pigs. The farm has 6 pigs.

22. The width of an enlarged photograph was 8 times its original size of 3 in. × 5 in.

23. Jen volunteers at the school store. This year she sold 4 times as many pens as last year. **See below.**

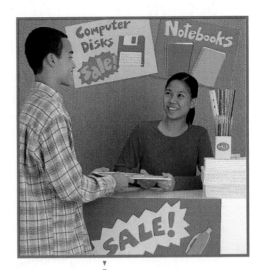

a. Write an equation using two variables to describe the relationship between the numbers of pens sold this year and last year. Identify the variables you use.

b. Use the same variables as in part (a) to write a different equation describing the same relationship.

c. If Jen sold 76 pens this year, how many did she sell last year? **19 pens**

Reflecting ▶ **on the Section**

Be prepared to discuss your response to Exercise 24 in class.

Discussion

Exercise 24 checks that you can apply ideas about triangles.

24. a. The side lengths of three equilateral triangles are x, y, and z. Length y is three times length x and twice length z. Write an equation that shows the relationship between x and y. $y = 3x$

b. Suppose the value of x is 4 in. Find the value of y. **12 in.**

c. What is the value of z when x is 4 in.? Explain.

6 in.; If $x = 4$, $y = 3 \cdot 4 = 12$. Since y is twice z, $z = \frac{y}{2} = \frac{12}{2} = 6$.

23. a. $t = 4l$, where t = the number of pens sold this year and l = the number of pens sold last year

b. $l = \frac{t}{4}$, where l = the number of pens sold last year and t = the number of pens sold this year

Spiral ▶ **Review**

Replace each ? with the correct measure. (Module 3, p. 210)

25. 300 cm = _?_ m **3**

26. 4.6 km = _?_ m **4600**

27. 9.75 cm = _?_ mm **97.5**

28. 10.84 cm = _?_ km **0.0001084**

29. The temperature is −28°F at 7 P.M. It falls 15°F that night, then rises x°F to a temperature of −34°F by noon the next day. (Module 2, p. 109)

a. Write an equation involving x to describe the situation. $-43 + x = -34$

b. Solve the equation to find the value of x. **9**

Find the perimeter of a rectangle with each length l and width w. (Toolbox, p. 593)

30. $l = 4$ cm, $w = 6$ cm **20 cm**

31. $l = 2$ in., $w = 18$ in. **40 in.**

32. $l = 15$ m, $w = 20$ m **70 m**

33. $l = 2$ ft, $w = 3\frac{1}{2}$ ft **11 ft**

Tell whether each set of side lengths *can* or *cannot* form a triangle. If they can, tell whether the triangle is *isosceles*, *equilateral*, or *scalene*.

1. 8 cm, 9 cm, 14 cm   can; scalene

2. 23 in., 23 in., 16 in.   can; isosceles

3. 7 km, 16 km, 25 km   cannot

4. 16 in., 16 in., 20 in.   can; isosceles

5. 4.7 m, 4.7 m, 4.7 m   can; isosceles and equilateral

6. 7.2 in., 9.8 in., 17 in.   cannot

7. 32 ft, 42 ft, 52 ft   can; scalene

8. 3.2 ft, 3.4 ft, 4.2 ft   can; scalene

9. 12 mm, 12 mm, 28 mm   cannot

10. $8\frac{1}{2}$ yd, $11\frac{3}{4}$ yd, 3 yd   cannot

Solve. Check each answer.

11. $\frac{x}{4} = 9$ 36

12. $7q = 56$ 8

13. $2 = \frac{y}{5}$ 10

14. $430 = 10k$ 43

15. $11 = \frac{y}{9}$ 99

16. $\frac{x}{3} = 60$ 180

17. $8x = 120$ 15

18. $12y = 60$ 5

19. $\frac{z}{25} = 3$ 75

20. $6h = 132$ 22

21. $56 = 4y$ 14

22. $1 = \frac{x}{12}$ 12

Write a multiplication or division equation to model each situation. Then solve each equation.

23. There were twice as many students in the chorus this year as last year. Last year there were 39 students in the chorus.

    23. $t = 2l$, where t = the number of students in chorus this year and l = the number of students in chorus last year; 78 students

24. John saved 5 times as much money for the trip as Steve did. John saved $60. $s = \frac{j}{5}$ where s = the amount of money Steve saved and j = the amount of money John saved; $12

1. Use a compass and a metric ruler to draw an example of each type of triangle that has a 7 cm long side and a 3 cm long side. Label the side lengths.   Check students' drawings.

   a. isosceles triangle

   b. scalene triangle

2. One banner is 3 times as long as a second banner. The first banner is $8\frac{1}{2}$ ft long. Write a multiplication equation to model the situation. Then solve the equation. $f = 3s$, where f = the length of the first banner and s = the length of the second banner; $2\frac{5}{6}$ ft

Completing the Module Project

Secret Codes

SET UP *Work with a partner.*

In this module, you explored several types of secret codes and some of the techniques used to create them. Now you are ready to create your own.

12 Design a secret code. Your secret code must: Answers will vary.

 * include a code key

 * represent every letter of the alphabet and include spaces between words

 * be different in some way from the codes you have learned about in this module

13 To test your code, do the following: Check students' work.

 * With your partner, choose who will be the sender and who will be the receiver. Have the sender write a short message without revealing it to the receiver and use the key to code the message. The receiver will have a copy of the code key.

 * Work with another group, who will act as eavesdroppers. The sender will "transmit" the coded message. See whether the receiver can decode the message using the code key. Also see if the eavesdroppers are able to decode your message.

14 Write a short description of your test. Check students' work.

 a. Could the receiver decode the message correctly?

 b. Could the eavesdroppers break your code?

Find the prime factorization of each number. (Sec. 1, Explor. 1)

1. 12
$2 \cdot 2 \cdot 3$

2. 21
$3 \cdot 7$

3. 24
$2 \cdot 2 \cdot 2 \cdot 3$

4. 42
$2 \cdot 3 \cdot 7$

5. 68
$2 \cdot 2 \cdot 17$

Find the greatest common factor (GCF) and the least common multiple (LCM) of each group of numbers. (Sec. 1, Explors. 2–3)

6. 6, 8 2; 24

7. 36, 90 18; 180

8. 25, 30, 75 5; 150

9. 20, 42, 280 2; 840

Replace each ? with >, <, or =. (Sec. 2, Explor. 1)

10. $\frac{3}{20}$ _?_ $\frac{4}{25}$ <

11. $\frac{2}{9}$ _?_ $\frac{1}{4}$ <

12. $\frac{5}{7}$ _?_ $\frac{3}{5}$ >

13. $\frac{4}{21}$ _?_ $\frac{12}{63}$ =

14. Suppose a coin is tossed 3 times in a row and the results of the tosses are recorded in order. (Sec. 2, Explor. 3)

 a. Draw a tree diagram to represent all the possible outcomes. See Additional Answers.

 b. What is the probability that the second toss is a head? $\frac{1}{2}$

Find each sum or difference. (Sec. 2, Explor. 2; and Sec. 3, Explors. 1 and 2)

15. $2\frac{4}{9} + 3\frac{1}{3}$ $5\frac{7}{9}$

16. $1\frac{7}{8} - 1\frac{1}{6}$ $\frac{17}{24}$

17. $8\frac{3}{5} - 4\frac{9}{10}$ $3\frac{7}{10}$

18. $14 + 3\frac{12}{25}$ $17\frac{12}{25}$

Write each number as a fraction or a mixed number in lowest terms. (Sec. 4, Explor. 1)

19. 0.075 $\frac{3}{40}$

20. 12.25 $12\frac{1}{4}$

21. 87.00340 $87\frac{17}{5000}$

22. 0.100005 $\frac{20,001}{200,000}$

23. 3.00528 $3\frac{33}{6250}$

24. Write two decimal numbers that are between 2.815 and 2.82. (Sec. 4, Explor. 1) Sample Response: 2.8151 and 2.81512

Replace each ? with >, <, or =. (Sec. 4, Explor. 1)

25. 0.87 _?_ 0.8695 >

26. 3.05 _?_ 3.10 <

27. 6.8 _?_ 6.800 =

Write each number as a fraction with its denominator in standard form. (Sec. 4, Explor. 2)

28. 10^{-5} $\frac{1}{100,000}$

29. 5^{-3} $\frac{1}{125}$

30. 1^{-9} $\frac{1}{1}$

31. 6^{-1} $\frac{1}{6}$

32. 11^{-2} $\frac{1}{121}$

Write each product or quotient in standard form. (Sec. 4, Explor. 3)

33. $25.32 \cdot 10^5$ 2,532,000

34. $25.32 \cdot 0.001$ 0.02532

35. $25.32 \div 10,000$ 0.002532

36. $25.32 \div 0.01$ 2532

Write each number in scientific notation. (Sec. 4, Explor. 3)

37. 8,900,000,000
$8.9 \cdot 10^9$

38. 342,000
$3.42 \cdot 10^5$

39. 0.00038
$3.8 \cdot 10^{-4}$

40. 12.0056
$1.20056 \cdot 10^1$

Replace each ? with the correct measure. (Sec. 5, Explor. 1)

41. 35 cm = __?__ mm 350   **42.** 3 m = __?__ cm 300   **43.** 440 m = __?__ km 0.440

Tell whether each measure is *reasonable* or *unreasonable*. Explain your choice. (Sec. 5, Explor. 2)

44. the height of a desk from the floor to the desk top: 90 cm

unreasonable; My waist is about 100 cm above the floor and the top of a desk is about 30 cm below my waist.

45. the length of a jump rope: 0.002 km

reasonable; The length of a jump rope is about 2 m, or 0.002 km.

Tell whether segments with the given side lengths *can* or *cannot* form a triangle. If they can, classify the triangle as *isosceles*, *equilateral*, or *scalene*. (Sec. 6, Explor. 1)

46. 3 km, 5 km, 4 km   **47.** 2 cm, 10 cm, 13 cm   **48.** 1 ft, 1 ft, 1 ft

can; scalene   cannot   can; isosceles and equilateral

Solve. Check each answer. (Sec. 6, Explor. 2)

49. $6x = 216$ 36   **50.** $\frac{y}{2} = 14$ 28   **51.** $51 = 3m$ 17   **52.** $22 = \frac{n}{6}$ 132

53. Look at the checkered flag. (Sec. 6, Explor. 2)

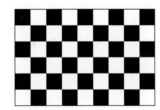

a. Write an equation that shows how the total area of the black squares in the flag is related to the area of the flag. Be sure to identify any variables you use. Let b = total area of black squares. Let f = area of flag. $b = \frac{1}{2}f$

b. Use your equation to find the total area of the black squares if the area of the flag is 60 in.^{2}. 30 in.^{2}

c. Use your equation to find the area of the flag if the total area of the black squares is 24 in.^{2}. 48 in.^{2}

Reflecting ◀▶on the Module

54. Writing Explain how mathematics is a universal language. To make your point, give examples using at least two of the mathematical ideas you have learned in this module. Check students' work.

THE ART OF
MOTION

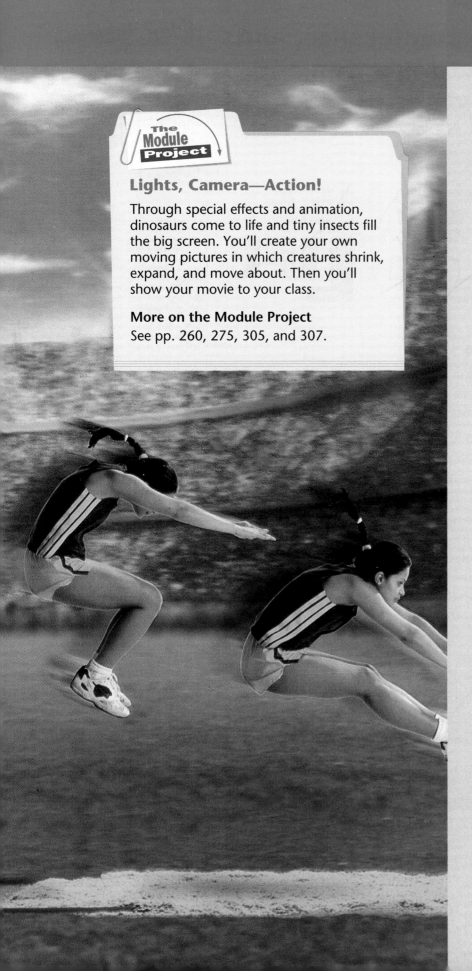

The Module Project

Lights, Camera—Action!

Through special effects and animation, dinosaurs come to life and tiny insects fill the big screen. You'll create your own moving pictures in which creatures shrink, expand, and move about. Then you'll show your movie to your class.

More on the Module Project

See pp. 260, 275, 305, and 307.

MODULE 4   SECTION OVERVIEW

1 Circumference, and Multiplication and Division of Fractions

As you make and use a simple moving picture machine:

◆ Find the circumference of a circle
◆ Multiply and divide fractions

2 Decimal Multiplication and Division

As you examine photos of motion too fast for the eye to see:

◆ Multiply and divide decimals
◆ Write quotients as terminating and repeating decimals
◆ Interpret division with zero

3 Rotations and Reflections

As you explore patterns that create a sense of motion in art:

◆ Describe a rotation
◆ Identify a reflection and lines of symmetry

4 Multiplication and Division of Integers

As you learn about special effects in movies, such as reverse motion:

◆ Multiply and divide integers
◆ Evaluate expressions with fractions, decimals, or integers

5 Translations, Similarity, and Two-Step Equations

As you explore animation:

◆ Use coordinates to describe translations
◆ Identify similar figures
◆ Solve two-step equations

INTERNET
To learn more about the theme:
http://www.mlmath.com

231

Section ① Circumference, and Multiplication and Division of Fractions

IN THIS SECTION

EXPLORATION 1
◆ Circumference of a Zoetrope

EXPLORATION 2
◆ Multiplying Fractions

EXPLORATION 3
◆ Dividing Fractions

The WHEEL of LIFE

WARM-UP EXERCISES

1. In the circle, which segment is a diameter of the circle? Explain how you know.

a; It is a segment that goes from one point on the circle to another point on the circle and passes through the center

2. Round each number to the indicated place value.
   a. 4293; tens   4290
   b. 23,845; thousands   24,000
   c. 738,103,032; millions   738,000,000

◄◄◄ Setting the Stage

Life is always in motion. One way artists capture the feeling of life in their work is to create a sense of motion. In this module you'll explore how mathematics can be used to add motion to art.

One art form that captures the art of motion is motion pictures. One of the first moving picture machines was called a *zoetrope* (zō′ ē trōp′), which means "wheel of life" in Greek.

A zoetrope is a large open cylinder. To use a zoetrope, you place a long strip of paper inside it. The strip has a drawing that is repeated over and over, each time with a slight change. When the zoetrope is spun, the drawing appears to come to life.

Think About It

1 What shapes are needed to build the base and the wall of a zoetrope? **a circle and a rectangle**

2 Suppose you spin the zoetrope shown above. What do you think you will see? **a figure walking**

GOAL

LEARN HOW TO...
- find the circumference of a circle

AS YOU...
- build a zoetrope

KEY TERM
- circumference

Circumference of a ZOETROPE

SET UP *Work in a group. You will need:* • *2 copies of Labsheet 1A* • *Labsheet 1B* • *compass* • *ruler* • *sheet of white paper* • *large sheet of dark poster board* • *scissors* • *glue* • *several circular objects* • *string* • *calculator* • *push pin* • *tape* • *small cardboard box or eraser*

▸ **Your group will use geometry and measurement to build a zoetrope.**

3 Follow Steps 1 and 2 to make the base of the zoetrope.
Check students' work.

Step 1 Use a compass and a ruler to draw a circle with a $3\frac{1}{2}$ in. radius on a sheet of white paper.

Step 2 Glue the sheet of paper onto a corner of the poster board. Then cut out the circle.

center

▸ **In Question 1, you may have noticed that the wall of the zoetrope can be made from a rectangle. The length of the rectangle must be equal to the distance around the zoetrope's circular base, or its circumference.**

4 Use your ruler to estimate the circumference of the zoetrope base to the nearest inch. Describe your method. **Sample Response: about 22 in.; I put a string around the zoetrope base and then measured the string with a ruler.**

▸ **When you know the diameter of a circle, another way to find its circumference is to use the relationship between the circle's circumference and its diameter.**

5 a. Use string and a ruler to measure the circumference and the diameter of 3 or 4 circular objects. Record your results.
Answers will vary. Check students' work.

b. The circumference of each object is about how many times its diameter? Sample Response: about 3 times

c. How can you estimate the circumference of a circle if you know its diameter? Estimate the circumference of your zoetrope base.
Sample Response: Multiply the diameter by 3; about 21 in.

▶ The exact relationship between the circumference (C) of a circle and its diameter (d) is given by the equation:

You read π as "pi." $$\pi = \frac{C}{d} \quad \text{or} \quad C = \pi d$$

diameter

circumference

 Calculator **Use a calculator to answer Question 6.**

6 a. Press the π key on your calculator. What value is displayed? How does it compare with your estimate in Question 5(b)?
3.141592654; The value shown on the calculator is more precise.

b. Will the actual circumference of the zoetrope base be *greater than* or *less than* your estimate in Question 5(c)? Explain.

c. Use the π key on your calculator to find the circumference of the zoetrope base. Round your answer to the nearest inch. 22 in.

d. You round decimals the same way you round whole numbers. Look at the value of π from part (a). Rounded to the nearest hundredth, π is 3.14. Explain why.

6. b. greater than; Since π > 3, the product of π and the diameter will be greater than the product of 3 and the diameter.
d. The digit in the place to the right of the hundredths place is less than 5. So, the digit in the hundredths place remains the same.

✔ **QUESTION 7**

...checks that you can find the circumference of a circle when you know its diameter.

7 ✔ **CHECKPOINT** Use 3.14 or the π key to find the circumference of a circle with each measure. Round each answer to the nearest hundredth. See below.

a. diameter = 6 in. **b.** diameter = 13 ft **c.** radius = 8 cm
18.84 in. or 18.85 in.   40.82 ft or 40.84 ft   50.24 cm or 50.27 cm

8 Use two copies of Labsheet 1A. Follow Steps 3–5 to make the wall of the zoetrope. Check students' work.

7. When two answers are given for calculations involving π, the first answer is found by using 3.14. The second is found by using the π key.

Step 3 On poster board, draw a rectangle that has a width of $3\frac{1}{2}$ in. and a length equal to the circumference you found in Question 6(c). Cut out the rectangle.

Step 4 Cut out the four *Zoetrope Side Strips* from two copies of Labsheet 1A. Glue the strips to the rectangle. Cut out the shaded slots.

Step 5 Gently curve the wall until the ends meet. Tape the ends together.

9 Follow Steps 6 and 7 to put together the zoetrope. Check students' work.

Step 6 Line up the unslotted edge of the wall with the base. Then tape them together.

Step 7 Put a push pin through the center of the base and into the cardboard box or eraser.

10 **Use Labsheet 1B.** Follow the directions below to make the *Animation Strip* and spin it in your zoetrope. Check students' work.

> **First** Cut out the four sections of the *Animation Strip.* Tape them together in order, F1, F2, and so on, with no overlap.

> **Next** Place the *Animation Strip* in your zoetrope so that each frame is centered under a cutout slot.

> **Then** Hold the cardboard box or eraser on a level surface so the zoetrope is at eye level. You may need to kneel down. Spin the zoetrope and look through the slots.

11 Describe what you see when you spin the zoetrope forward (counterclockwise) and backward (clockwise). a horse that is galloping forward; a horse that is galloping backward

12 **Discussion** Suppose you make the rectangular wall of a zoetrope before you make the circular base. Explain how you can use the length of the wall to find the diameter of the base. Divide the length of the wall by π.

HOMEWORK EXERCISES ▶ See Exs. 1–5 on pp. 242–243.

LEARN HOW TO...
♦ multiply fractions and mixed numbers
♦ use the distributive property
♦ find reciprocals

AS YOU...
♦ begin to create a zoetrope strip

KEY TERMS
♦ distributive property
♦ reciprocals

Exploration 2

Multiplying FRACTIONS

SET UP *You will need: • Labsheet 1C • ruler • fraction calculator (optional)*

▶ **Use Labsheet 1C for Questions 13 and 15 as you begin to make an interesting animation strip that uses rectangles.**

FOR ▶ HELP

with *reading a customary ruler*, see
TOOLBOX, p. 591

13 For the first four frames of the *Animated Rectangle,* the height of each rectangle will be half the height of the rectangle in the previous frame. The length of the base of each rectangle will be the same.

    a. Measure the height of the rectangle in Frame 1 (F1) to the nearest $\frac{1}{16}$ in. $1\frac{8}{16}$ in. or $1\frac{1}{2}$ in.

    b. Use paper-folding or your ruler to find half of the height of the rectangle in F1. This will be the height of the rectangle in Frame 2 (F2). $\frac{3}{4}$ in.

    c. Draw the rectangle in F2. Use the segment in F2 for the base. Check students' drawings on Labsheet 1C.

14 Fraction Calculator Because $\frac{1}{2}$ of $1\frac{1}{2}$ means $\frac{1}{2} \cdot 1\frac{1}{2}$, or $\frac{1}{2} \cdot \frac{3}{2}$, a fraction calculator can be used to find the product. Enter the key sequence below on your calculator. Does the calculator display agree with your answer in Question 13(b)? Yes.

15 a. Copy and complete the table to find the heights of the rectangles in F2, F3, and F4 of the *Animated Rectangle.* See table.

    b. Draw the rectangles in F3 and F4. Use the segment in each frame for the base of the rectangle. Check students' drawings on Labsheet 1C.

Frame	Height of rectangle (in.)	
F1	$1\frac{1}{2}$ or $\frac{3}{2}$	
F2	$\frac{1}{2}$ of $\frac{3}{2} = ?$	$\frac{3}{4}$
F3	$\frac{1}{2}$ of $? = ?$	$\frac{3}{4}; \frac{3}{8}$
F4	$\frac{1}{2}$ of $? = ?$	$\frac{3}{8}; \frac{3}{16}$

16 Discussion Look at the results in your table from Question 15.

a. Write multiplication equations that show how you found the heights of the rectangles in F2, F3, and F4.

b. Look for a pattern in the multiplication equations you wrote in part (a). How can you find the products without using a ruler, paper-folding, or a calculator?

c. What would be the height of the rectangle in F2 if the height of the rectangle in F1 were $1\frac{3}{4}$ in.? $\frac{5}{8}$ in.? Use a ruler to check.

▶ **Writing Products in Lowest Terms** Sometimes it is easier to divide by common factors in the numerator and denominator before you multiply fractions.

EXAMPLE

Find $\frac{6}{7} \cdot \frac{5}{18}$ in lowest terms.

Divide by 6.

Notice that a numerator and a denominator share the **common factor 6**.

$$\frac{\overset{1}{\cancel{6}}}{7} \cdot \frac{5}{\underset{3}{\cancel{18}}} = \frac{1}{7} \cdot \frac{5}{3} = \frac{5}{21}$$

Divide by 6.

17 Discussion In the Example, the numerator and the denominator also share the common factor 2. If you divide by the common factor 2, will you get a product in lowest terms? Explain.

No; The numerator and denominator of the product will still have a common factor of 3.

18 Use the method in the Example to evaluate $\frac{9}{20} \cdot \frac{14}{27}$. Which common factor(s) did you divide by before you multiplied?

$\frac{7}{30}$; Possible Answers: 3, 9, 2

▶ When you multiply a mixed number by a whole number or a fraction, it is sometimes easiest to use the **distributive property** to multiply each part of the mixed number separately.

EXAMPLE

$$3 \cdot 2\frac{2}{3} = 3\left(2 + \frac{2}{3}\right) = (3 \cdot 2) + \left(3 \cdot \frac{2}{3}\right) = 6 + 2 = 8$$

19 Suppose the height of the rectangle in F1 of a zoetrope strip is $1\frac{3}{8}$ in. and you want to double its height from F1 to F2. Use the distributive property to find the height of the rectangle in F2. $2\frac{3}{4}$ in.

20 How can you use the distributive property to evaluate $\frac{1}{2} \cdot 10\frac{2}{3}$?

✔ **QUESTION 21**

...checks that you can multiply fractions and mixed numbers.

20. $\left(\frac{1}{2} \cdot 10\right) + \left(\frac{1}{2} \cdot \frac{2}{3}\right) =$
$5 + \frac{1}{3} = 5\frac{1}{3}$

21 ✔ **CHECKPOINT** Find each product. Write each answer in lowest terms.

a. $\frac{5}{7} \cdot \frac{2}{3}$ $\frac{10}{21}$ **b.** $\frac{1}{6} \cdot 4\frac{2}{3}$ **c.** $\frac{5}{6} \cdot \frac{18}{35}$ $\frac{3}{7}$

d. $10 \cdot 7\frac{2}{5}$ 74   **e.** $\frac{5}{8} \cdot 2\frac{2}{5}$ $1\frac{1}{2}$ **f.** $1\frac{1}{2} \cdot 2\frac{2}{3}$ 4

22 The first two frames of two zoetrope strips are shown below. Replace each **?** with the fraction you must multiply by to change the height in F1 to the height in F2.

a.

$4 \cdot \underline{\ \ ?\ \ } = 1\frac{1}{4}$

b.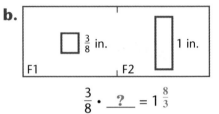

$\frac{3}{8} \cdot \underline{\ \ ?\ \ } = 1\frac{8}{3}$

▶ The products in Question 22 were both 1. **Two numbers whose product is 1 are reciprocals of each other.**

> **EXAMPLE**
>
> $\frac{4}{7} \cdot \frac{7}{4} = \frac{28}{28} = 1$ $\frac{1}{3} \cdot 3 = \frac{1}{3} \cdot \frac{3}{1} = \frac{3}{3} = 1$
>
> $\frac{4}{7}$ and $\frac{7}{4}$ are reciprocals. $\frac{1}{3}$ and 3 are reciprocals.

23. a. Switch the numerator and denominator in the original fraction; Use 1 as the numerator and the whole number as the denominator; First, write the mixed number as a fraction. Then, switch the numerator and denominator.

23 **Discussion** Look at the Examples and your answers to Question 22.

a. Describe a way to find the reciprocal of a fraction, a nonzero whole number, and a mixed number.

b. Does the number 0 have a reciprocal? Explain.
No; There is no number by which 0 can be multiplied to get 1.

✔ **QUESTION 24**

...checks that you can find the reciprocal of a number.

24 ✔ **CHECKPOINT** Replace each **?** with the number that makes the multiplication equation true.

a. $\frac{1}{2} \cdot \underline{\ \ ?\ \ } = 1$ 2   **b.** $5 \cdot \underline{\ \ ?\ \ } = 1$ $\frac{1}{5}$ **c.** $3\frac{3}{4} \cdot \underline{\ \ ?\ \ } = 1$ $\frac{4}{15}$

HOMEWORK EXERCISES ▶ See Exs. 6–27 on pp. 243–244.

Dividing
FRACTIONS

SET UP *You will need:* • *Labsheet 1C with completed Frames 1–4* • *ruler* • *scissors* • *tape* • *colored pencils* • *zoetrope*

▸ **To complete the last three frames of the *Animated Rectangle*, you'll divide the height of the rectangle in each previous frame by $\frac{1}{2}$. One way to divide is to separate into equal-sized parts.**

EXAMPLE

To find $4 \div \frac{1}{2}$, think about how many $\frac{1}{2}$-inch segments there are in 4 in.

By looking at a ruler, you can see that there are eight $\frac{1}{2}$-inch segments in 4 in., so

$$4 \div \frac{1}{2} = 8$$

25 Use a ruler or draw a picture to find each quotient.

    a. $3 \div \frac{1}{2}$ 6   **b.** $3 \div \frac{1}{4}$ 12   **c.** $3 \div 1\frac{1}{2}$ 2   **d.** $3 \div \frac{3}{4}$ 4

26 a. Look for a pattern in your answers to Question 25. For each expression, find the number you can multiply 3 by to get the same answer. $2, 4, \frac{2}{3}, \frac{4}{3}$

    b. It is not always possible to find a quotient using a ruler. Why would $3 \div \frac{5}{6}$ be difficult to evaluate with a ruler? How can you use multiplication to find the quotient $3 \div \frac{5}{6}$?

    Neither a centimeter ruler nor an inch ruler is divided into sixths; Multiply 3 by the reciprocal of $\frac{5}{6}$.

27 **Discussion** Explain a method you can use to divide fractions without using a ruler. *Multiply the dividend by the reciprocal of the divisor.*

28 Find each quotient using your method from Question 27. Then use a ruler to check your results. Does your method work? If not, how can you modify it so that it does work?

a. $\frac{7}{8} \div \frac{1}{16}$ 14   b. $4 \div \frac{1}{4}$ 16   c. $1\frac{1}{4} \div \frac{1}{8}$ 10   d. $5\frac{1}{4} \div 1\frac{3}{4}$ 3

✔ QUESTION 29

...checks that you can divide fractions and mixed numbers.

29 ✔ **CHECKPOINT** Find each quotient.

a. $2 \div \frac{2}{3}$ 3   b. $\frac{2}{3} \div 2$ $\frac{1}{3}$ c. $6\frac{7}{10} \div \frac{3}{10}$ $22\frac{1}{3}$ d. $3\frac{1}{2} \div 1\frac{4}{5}$ $1\frac{17}{18}$

▶ **Use Labsheet 1C for Questions 30 and 31. You should have completed Frames 1–4 in Exploration 2.**

30 You can find the height of each rectangle in Frames 6–8 of the *Animated Rectangle* by dividing the height of the previous rectangle by $\frac{1}{2}$.

Frame	Height of rectangle (in.)
F5	$\frac{3}{16}$
F6	$? \div ? = ?$ $\frac{3}{16} \div \frac{1}{2} = \frac{3}{8}$
F7	$? \div ? = ?$ $\frac{3}{8} \div \frac{1}{2} = \frac{3}{4}$
F8	$? \div ? = ?$ $\frac{3}{4} \div \frac{1}{2} = \frac{3}{2}$

a. The height of the rectangle in Frame 5 (F5) is $\frac{3}{16}$ in. Write a division expression for the height of the rectangle in F6. $\frac{3}{16} \div \frac{1}{2}$

b. Copy and complete the table to find the heights of the rectangles in F6, F7, and F8. *See table.*

c. Draw the rectangles in F6, F7, and F8. Use the segment in each frame for the base of the rectangle. *Check students' drawings on Labsheet 1C.*

31 To view the *Animated Rectangle,* follow the directions below. Then describe what you see. You may want to add your own visual effects to make the animation more interesting.

First Cut out the four strips and tape them together so the frames are in order, with no overlap.

Next Use one color to shade the interior of the rectangles in Frames 1–8.

Then Place the completed strip in the zoetrope so the frames are centered under the slots. Spin the zoetrope. *If spun clockwise, the size of the rectangle increases, and then the size decreases.*

HOMEWORK EXERCISES ▶ See Exs. 28–43 on pp. 244–245.

Section 1
Key Concepts ▶▶▶▶▶▶▶▶▶▶▶▶▶▶▶▶▶▶▶▶▶▶▶

Key Terms

Circumference (pp. 233–235)
Circumference is the distance around a circle. The relationship between a circle's circumference (C) and its diameter (d) is given by:

$\boxed{\pi \text{ is about } 3.14.}$ ▶ $\pi = \dfrac{C}{d}$ or $C = \pi d$

diameter

circumference

circumference

Rounding Decimals (p. 234)
You round decimals the same way you round whole numbers.

Example To the nearest hundredth, 0.23874 is 0.24.

hundredths place ↗ ↑ $8 \geq 5$, so round the 3 up to 4.

Multiplying Fractions (pp. 236–238)
To multiply fractions, you first multiply the numerators. Then you multiply the denominators.

Sometimes it is easier to divide by all the common factors *before* you multiply to get a product in lowest terms.

Example

Divide by 8. ▶

Divide by 3. ▶

$\dfrac{\overset{1}{\cancel{8}}}{\underset{3}{\cancel{9}}} \cdot \dfrac{\overset{5}{\cancel{15}}}{\underset{2}{\cancel{16}}} = \dfrac{1}{3} \cdot \dfrac{5}{2} = \dfrac{5}{6}$

You can use the distributive property to multiply a mixed number. (p. 237)

Example $\dfrac{1}{3} \cdot 6\dfrac{1}{4} = \dfrac{1}{3}\left(6 + \dfrac{1}{4}\right) = \left(\dfrac{1}{3} \cdot 6\right) + \left(\dfrac{1}{3} \cdot \dfrac{1}{4}\right) = 2 + \dfrac{1}{12} = 2\dfrac{1}{12}$

distributive property

Reciprocals (p. 238)
Two numbers whose product is 1, such as 5 and $\dfrac{1}{5}$, are reciprocals.

reciprocals

---

33. First, rewrite 6 as $\dfrac{6}{1}$ and $2\dfrac{1}{9}$ as $\dfrac{19}{9}$. Next, divide 6 and 9 by their common factor, 3. Multiply the numerators, and then multiply the denominators. Finally, simplify the answer. So, $6 \cdot 2\dfrac{1}{9} =$ $\dfrac{6}{1} \cdot \dfrac{19}{9} = \dfrac{6 \div 3}{1} \cdot \dfrac{19}{9 \div 3} =$ $\dfrac{2}{1} \cdot \dfrac{19}{3} = \dfrac{2 \cdot 19}{3 \cdot 1} = \dfrac{38}{3} =$ $12\dfrac{2}{3}$. Or, use the Distributive Property as follows: $6 \cdot 2\dfrac{1}{9} = 6 \cdot \left(2 + \dfrac{1}{9}\right) =$ $(6 \cdot 2) + \left(6 \cdot \dfrac{1}{9}\right) =$ $12 + \dfrac{6}{9} = 12\dfrac{6}{9} = 12\dfrac{2}{3}$.

Key Concepts Questions

32 Find the circumference of a circle with a diameter of 4 in. 12.56 in. or 12.57 in.

33 Explain two ways to find $6 \cdot 2\dfrac{1}{9}$. See above.

Continued on next page ▼

Section 1

Key Concepts

◀ ◀ ◀ ◀ ◀ ◀ ◀ ◀ ◀

Dividing Fractions (pp. 239–240)

To divide a number by a fraction, you multiply the number by the reciprocal of the fraction.

Example To find $3\frac{2}{3} \div \frac{5}{9}$, multiply $3\frac{2}{3}$ by $\frac{9}{5}$.

$$3\frac{2}{3} \div \frac{5}{9} = \frac{11}{3} \div \frac{5}{9} = \frac{11}{3} \cdot \frac{9}{5} = \frac{11}{\cancel{3}} \cdot \frac{\cancel{9}^{3}}{5} = \frac{11}{1} \cdot \frac{3}{5} = \frac{33}{5} = 6\frac{3}{5}$$

The **reciprocal** of $\frac{5}{9}$ is $\frac{9}{5}$.

34 **Key Concepts Question** Find $4\frac{1}{3} \div \frac{5}{6}$ in lowest terms. $5\frac{1}{5}$

Section 1

Practice & Application Exercises

◀ ◀ ◀ ◀ ◀ ◀ ◀ ◀

Sequoias, or redwood trees, are among the largest and oldest living things. They may be over 300 ft tall, over 10 ft in diameter, and several thousand years old.

▼

For Exercises 1–5, use 3.14 or the $\boxed{\pi}$ key on a calculator. If necessary, round each answer to the nearest hundredth.

Find the circumference of each circle.

1. diameter = 19 ft
59.66 ft or 59.69 ft

2. radius = 7 m
43.96 m or 43.98 m

3. diameter = 1 in.
3.14 in.

4. Forestry Suppose you want to estimate an uncut tree's diameter.

   a. How can you use the circumference of a tree's trunk to estimate its diameter? Divide the circumference by 3.

   b. Use your method from part (a) to estimate each diameter.
   Sample Responses are given in table.

Tree	giant sequoia	American elm	black willow	sugar maple
Circumference (ft)	83	26	33	19
Diameter (ft)	? $27\frac{2}{3}$ ft	? $8\frac{2}{3}$ ft	? 11 ft	? $6\frac{1}{3}$ ft

5. **Native American Tepees** Tepees made from poles covered with animal skin or tree bark served as homes for some tribes of the North American Great Plains. The poles used to build the frame of a tepee must be at least 4 ft longer than the diameter of the circular base of a tepee to allow for tying them together. Suppose a tepee has a base circumference of 35 ft. Estimate the height of its poles.
Sample Response: about 16 ft

Find each product. Write each answer in lowest terms.

6. $\frac{5}{9} \cdot \frac{1}{6}$ $\frac{5}{54}$

7. $\frac{7}{8} \cdot 4$ $3\frac{1}{2}$

8. $\frac{5}{9} \cdot \frac{3}{35}$ $\frac{1}{21}$

9. $4 \cdot 2\frac{3}{8}$ $9\frac{1}{2}$

10. $2\frac{7}{15} \cdot \frac{5}{11}$ $1\frac{4}{33}$

11. $2\frac{1}{4} \cdot 1\frac{1}{6}$ $2\frac{5}{8}$

12. $\frac{4}{7} \cdot \frac{14}{15} \cdot \frac{5}{12}$ $\frac{2}{9}$

13. $\frac{7}{8} \cdot 6 \cdot 3\frac{1}{2}$ $18\frac{3}{8}$

14. $4\frac{2}{3} \cdot 1\frac{5}{7} \cdot \frac{3}{4}$ 6

15. How could you have used the distributive property to find some of the products in Exercises 6–14? Which ones?

16. **Ikebana** In the Sogetsu school of Japanese floral arranging, the heights of the main stems, called the *shin*, *soe*, and *hikae*, depend on the diameter and the height of the vase. For a large arrangement, the heights should be as follows.

15. Rewrite the mixed number in the problem as the sum of a whole number and a fraction. Multiply each part of the sum by the other factor in the problem; 9, 10, 13

* The height of the *shin* must be twice the sum of the diameter of the vase and the height of the vase.

* The height of the *soe* must be three-quarters the height of the *shin*.

* The height of the *hikae* must be half the height of the *soe*.

Suppose a florist uses a vase that has a $7\frac{1}{2}$ in. diameter and is 3 in. tall. How tall must each main stem be?

a. *shin* 21 in.

b. *soe* $15\frac{3}{4}$ in.

c. *hikae* $7\frac{7}{8}$ in.

Estimation Use compatible numbers to estimate each product.

Example: $\frac{1}{4} \cdot 17 \longrightarrow \frac{1}{4} \cdot 16 = \frac{1}{4} \cdot \frac{16}{1} = 4$

$\frac{1}{4} \cdot 17$ is a little more than 4.

16 is close to 17 and it is divisible by 4.

17. $\frac{1}{3} \cdot 13$
a little more than 4

18. $23 \cdot \frac{1}{6}$
a little less than 4

19. $\frac{1}{5} \cdot 32$
a little more than 6

20. $61 \cdot \frac{1}{4}$
a little more than 15

Number of Animal Species at Three Major Public Zoos, 1996

= 160 species

Audubon (New Orleans)

Chicago

Denver

21. **Interpreting Data** Look at the graph.

a. How many symbols are used to represent the number of animal species at the Audubon Zoological Park? $2\frac{1}{4}$

b. Use your result from part (a) to find the number of animal species at the Audubon Zoological Park. 360

c. How many animal species are there at the Chicago Zoological Park? at the Denver Zoological Park? 400; 600

22. Suppose you want to cover a floor that is $4\frac{1}{4}$ ft wide and $8\frac{1}{2}$ ft long with tiles that are 1 ft by 1 ft. How many tiles will you need?
You need to buy 37 tiles, since it takes $36\frac{1}{8}$ tiles to cover the floor.

Find the reciprocal of each number.

23. $\frac{3}{7}$ $\frac{7}{3}$

24. 12 $\frac{1}{12}$

25. $\frac{25}{8}$ $\frac{8}{25}$

26. $2\frac{4}{5}$ $\frac{5}{14}$

27. **Challenge** Replace each ? below with one of the digits 2, 4, 6, or 8 to create an expression for each product. Do not repeat digits.

a. the greatest product

b. the least product

$\boxed{?}\ \boxed{?}$

$\boxed{?}\ \boxed{?}$

a. Possible answers: $\frac{8}{2}\cdot\frac{6}{4},\frac{8}{4}\cdot\frac{6}{2}$

b. Possible answers: $\frac{2}{8}\cdot\frac{4}{6},\frac{2}{6}\cdot\frac{4}{8}$

c. the product that is closest to 1 Possible answers: $\frac{8}{6}\cdot\frac{2}{4},\frac{8}{4}\cdot\frac{2}{6}$

Find each quotient. Write each answer in lowest terms.

28. $\frac{2}{3}\div\frac{4}{9}$ $1\frac{1}{2}$

29. $1\div\frac{2}{7}$ $3\frac{1}{2}$

30. $\frac{5}{8}\div\frac{5}{8}$ 1

31. $4\div1\frac{1}{5}$ $3\frac{1}{3}$

32. $\frac{7}{9}\div\frac{5}{12}$ $1\frac{13}{15}$

33. $6\div\frac{1}{8}$ 48

34. $\frac{4}{5}\div\frac{3}{7}$ $1\frac{13}{15}$

35. $\frac{6}{11}\div4$ $\frac{3}{22}$

36. $2\frac{4}{7}\div\frac{2}{3}$ $3\frac{6}{7}$

37. $1\frac{4}{5}\div1\frac{1}{2}$ $1\frac{1}{5}$

38. $\frac{5}{6}\div7\frac{1}{3}$ $\frac{5}{44}$

39. $2\frac{5}{8}\div1\frac{1}{6}$ $2\frac{1}{4}$

40. **Carpentry** "Penny" is the unit used for the size of a nail. An 8-penny nail is twice the length of a 3-penny nail. An 8-penny nail is $2\frac{1}{2}$ in. long. What is the length of a 3-penny nail? $1\frac{1}{4}$ in.

41. **Writing** Answer without actually doing the division. Do you expect the quotient $\frac{2}{3}\div\frac{4}{5}$ to be *greater than* or *less than* 1?

greater than or *less than* $\frac{2}{3}$? Explain how you know.

Sample Response: Since $\frac{4}{5}>\frac{2}{3}$, I would expect the quotient to be less than one. In division, as the divisor decreases, the quotient increases. Since $\frac{2}{3}\div1=\frac{2}{3}$ and $\frac{4}{5}<1,\frac{2}{3}\div\frac{4}{5}>\frac{2}{3}$.

42. Theater Northern Illinois University has a collection of scale models of stage sets for scenes from operas performed on campus. The models are built $\frac{1}{48}$ actual size. The model shown is a public square in nineteenth century Bohemia, a region of the Czech Republic.

a. A door on one of the buildings in the model is $\frac{11}{16}$ in. wide and $1\frac{3}{4}$ in. tall. Find the actual dimensions of the door. **33 in. wide and 84 in. tall**

b. The red-and-white striped pole in the model is $4\frac{5}{8}$ in. high. How many of these scale-model poles can be cut from a 1 ft long dowel? **2**

c. **Open-ended** Use facts about the scale model. Write and solve a word problem that involves fraction multiplication. Then write and solve a word problem that involves fraction division. **See below.**

Reflecting ◀▷ on the Section

Be prepared to discuss your response to Exercise 43 in class.

43. Suppose F1 of a zoetrope strip shows a person. To make the person appear taller, which of the following can be done to the person's height? Give an example to justify each choice.

A. multiply by $\frac{1}{2}$ B. divide by $\frac{1}{2}$ C. multiply by $\frac{4}{3}$ D. divide by $\frac{4}{3}$

 B and C; $2 \div \frac{1}{2} = 4$, $2 \cdot \frac{4}{3} = 2\frac{2}{3}$

Spiral ◀▷ Review

Tell whether each combination of side lengths can form a triangle. (Module 3, p. 223)

44. 15 cm, 6 cm, 7 cm **cannot**   45. 20 in., 9 in., 12 in. **can**

Evaluate each expression. (Module 1, p. 65)

46. $15 - 3 \cdot 2$ **9**   47. $26 + (14 - 8)$ **32**   48. $56 \div 7 \cdot 5$ **40**

Replace each __?__ with the correct power of 10. (Module 3, p. 199)

49. $2.7 \cdot$ __?__ $= 270$ **10^2**   50. $0.043 \div$ __?__ $= 4.3$ **10^{-2}**

51. $31 \div$ __?__ $= 3100$ **10^{-2}**   52. $9.6 \cdot$ __?__ $= 0.0096$ **10^{-3}**

Discussion

Exercise 43 checks that you understand the effects of multiplying and dividing by fractions.

42. c. Sample Response: A door on one of the buildings in a model is $\frac{11}{16}$ in. wide and $1\frac{3}{4}$ in. tall. Find the area of the door in the model.; $1\frac{13}{64}$ in.^{2}; The red-and-white striped pole in a model of a public square is $4\frac{5}{8}$ in. high. The model is built $\frac{1}{48}$ actual size. Find the actual height of the pole.; 222 in., or $18\frac{1}{2}$ ft

Extra Skill Practice

For Exercises 1–5, use 3.14 or the 🔲 π key on a calculator. Find the circumference of each circle with the given diameter. Round each answer to the nearest hundredth. For Exercises 1–5, the first answer is found by using 3.14. The second is found by using π.

1. 5 m   2. 32 cm   3. 24 ft   4. 15 in.   5. 10.5 cm 32.97 or 32.99 cm
15.7 or 15.71 m   100.48 or 100.53 cm   75.36 or 75.40 ft   47.1 or 47.12 in.

Find each product. Write each answer in lowest terms.

6. $\frac{1}{7} \cdot \frac{2}{9}$ $\frac{2}{63}$

7. $\frac{5}{11} \cdot \frac{3}{10}$ $\frac{3}{22}$

8. $16 \cdot \frac{3}{8}$ 6

9. $\frac{10}{13} \cdot 26$ 20

10. $\frac{7}{12} \cdot \frac{2}{21}$ $\frac{1}{18}$

11. $18 \cdot \frac{7}{9}$ 14

12. $\frac{5}{9} \cdot 2\frac{7}{10}$ $1\frac{1}{2}$

13. $5\frac{1}{3} \cdot 1\frac{1}{8}$ 6

14. $4\frac{1}{2} \cdot \frac{8}{9}$ 4

15. $10 \cdot 7\frac{3}{5}$ 76

16. $\frac{2}{3} \cdot \frac{18}{25} \cdot \frac{3}{8}$ $\frac{9}{50}$

17. $4 \cdot 2\frac{1}{2} \cdot \frac{6}{7}$ $8\frac{4}{7}$

Find the reciprocal of each number.

18. $7\frac{1}{7}$

19. $\frac{8}{11}$ $\frac{11}{8}$

20. $\frac{19}{5}$ $\frac{5}{19}$

21. $4\frac{1}{3}$ $\frac{3}{13}$

22. 45 $\frac{1}{45}$

Find each quotient. Write each answer in lowest terms.

23. $\frac{5}{6} \div \frac{1}{12}$ 10

24. $\frac{3}{7} \div \frac{6}{11}$ $\frac{11}{14}$

25. $\frac{2}{3} \div \frac{4}{9}$ $1\frac{1}{2}$

26. $\frac{10}{13} \div \frac{25}{26}$ $\frac{4}{5}$

27. $8 \div \frac{4}{7}$ 14

28. $\frac{5}{9} \div 10$ $\frac{1}{18}$

29. $2\frac{4}{7} \div \frac{3}{4}$ $3\frac{3}{7}$

30. $5\frac{1}{4} \div 1\frac{2}{5}$ $3\frac{3}{4}$

31. $5\frac{1}{2} \div 3\frac{1}{6}$ $1\frac{14}{19}$

32. $\frac{5}{6} \div 7\frac{1}{2}$ $\frac{1}{9}$

33. $6 \div 2\frac{4}{5}$ $2\frac{1}{7}$

34. $\frac{41}{84} \div 3$ $\frac{41}{252}$

Study Skills ◀▶ Listening

To become an active listener, you need to give your full attention to what is being said. While you are listening, ask yourself whether you understand everything, and make connections between ideas. Try to picture in your mind what the speaker is talking about.

1. Have a partner read aloud the *Setting the Stage* on page 232. Practice being an active listener while your partner is reading.

2. After you have listened to the reading, write down the ideas you remember. Include any questions you thought of while listening.
   Check students' work.

Section ② Decimal Multiplication and Division

IN THIS SECTION

EXPLORATION 1
◆ Multiplying Decimals

EXPLORATION 2
◆ Dividing Decimals

EXPLORATION 3
◆ Repeating Decimals

THROUGH THE CAMERA'S EYE

Setting the Stage ▸

The world of things too small or too fast for the eye to see can be captured through the art of photography. A tiny flying insect called a *green lacewing* is shown here in the first stages of a backward loop.

The lacewing's movement has been made more visible by freezing the action for short time intervals and enlarging the size of the image.

Think About It

1 The actual body length of a green lacewing is only about 1.4 cm. Which phrase do you think describes the relationship between the size of the image in the photo and the insect's actual size? Explain.

A. 10^2 times actual size

B. 0.099 times actual size

C. 1.5 times actual size

D. 1.05 times actual size

E. 11.9 times actual size

F. $6\frac{1}{5}$ times actual size

1. C; Sample Response: The photograph of the body is about 2 cm, which is about 1.5 times the actual size.

GOAL

LEARN HOW TO...
◆ estimate decimal products
◆ multiply decimals

AS YOU...
◆ examine the lacewing photo

Exploration 1

Multiplying
DECIMALS

SET UP *Work with a partner. You will need a calculator.*

▶ **To find how much the image in the photo is enlarged, you can estimate the product of 1.4 and each choice in Question 1 on page 247. One way to estimate decimal products is to use powers of 10.**

FOR ◄ HELP

with *multiplying by powers of 10,* see
MODULE 3, p. 199

EXAMPLE

Suppose you guessed that the lacewing in the photo is 0.099 times its actual size. To check your guess, you can estimate the product (1.4)(0.099) by substituting a power of 10 for 0.099.

$$(1.4)(0.099) \approx (1.4)(0.1)$$

"is approximately equal to" ⟶ ≈ 0.14

0.099 is between 0.1 and 0.01, but is closer to 0.1.

2 a. Will the exact product (1.4)(0.099) be *greater than* or *less than* the estimate of 0.14 in the Example? How can you tell without multiplying 1.4 and 0.099? less than; Since 0.099 < 0.1, 1.4(0.099) < 1.4(0.1).

b. If the guess in the Example is correct, then the image of the lacewing's body in the photo should be about 0.14 cm long. Do you think 0.14 cm is a reasonable estimate? Explain.
No; The body in the photo would be smaller than the actual body.

3 Suppose you guessed that the image in the photo is 11.9 times actual size. Estimate the product (1.4)(11.9) by substituting a power of 10 for 11.9. Is the guess reasonable? Explain.
about 14; No; The width of the entire photograph is less than 12 cm.

 QUESTION 4

...checks that you can use powers of 10 to estimate decimal products.

4 ✔ **CHECKPOINT** Copy each problem. Use estimation with powers of 10 to place the decimal point in each product.

a. (0.36)(9.6) = 3456
(0.36)(9.6) = 3.456

b. (348.7)(0.22) = 76714
(348.7)(0.22) = 76.714

c. (52.14)(0.89) = 464046
(52.14)(0.89) = 46.4046

d. (0.092)(96.85) = 891020
(0.092)(96.85) = 8.91020

5 **Try This as a Class** Look at your results from Question 4.

    a. How were the digits in each product determined**?**

    b. How is the number of decimal places in each product related to the number of decimal places in the two factors**?**

    c. To find (0.12)(0.4), you must use a zero as a placeholder after you multiply the digits. Which is correct: *0.480* or *0.048***?** Why**?**

6 **✔ CHECKPOINT** Find each product.

    a. (4.57)(0.9)   **b.** (189.5)(6.4)   **c.** (0.012)(7.75)
       4.113   1212.8   0.093

▶ **This game can help you find other strategies for estimating decimals.**

HIT THE TARGET

◆ The first player enters the starting number on a calculator.

◆ Then players alternate turns entering ✕ , a decimal number, and = .

◆ The first player to get a number on the calculator display that is within the given target range (including the endpoints) is the winner.

Sample   Starting number: 200   Target range: 114 to 124   **Display**

Player 1 enters   **2** **0** **0** **✕** **·** **5** **=**   100.

Player 2 enters   **✕** **1** **·** **1** **=**   110.

Player 1 enters   **✕** **1** **·** **0** **5** **=**   115.5

> Since 115.5 is between 114 and 124, Player 1 wins!

7 Calculator Play the game *Hit the Target* with each number and range. **Check students' work.**

    a. 350, range: 767 to 777   **b.** 475, range: 350 to 360

8 **Discussion** Predict whether each product will be *greater than*, *less than*, or *equal to* the number in red. Explain how you know.

    a. (**3.6**)(1)   **b.** (**4.75**)(0.92)   **c.** (**57.97**)(1.007)

9 Describe the product when a positive number is multiplied by 0, by a number between 0 and 1, and by a number greater than 1.

10 Find the actual change in size in Question 1 on page 247. The body length of the image in the photo is 2.15 cm.
    The image in the photo is about 1.5 times the actual size.

HOMEWORK EXERCISES ▶ See Exs. 1–12 on p. 257.

GOAL

LEARN HOW TO...
◆ estimate decimal quotients
◆ divide decimals

AS YOU...
◆ investigate the flight of a golf ball

Exploration 2

Dividing DECIMALS

The photo shows a golf club striking a golf ball. Each image of the club and the ball follows the previous one by 0.001 seconds.

0 seconds   0.001 seconds   0.002 seconds   0.003 seconds   0.004 seconds

FOR◄HELP

with *dividing by powers of 10,* see **MODULE 3, p. 199**

11 Try This as a Class By looking at the printing on the ball, you can see that the ball spins. It spins about one half of a revolution in 0.004 s. Suppose it continues to spin at the same rate.

a. About how long does it take the ball to make one revolution? 0.008 s

b. The entire flight of the golf ball lasts about 6 s. Write a division problem that can be used to find how many revolutions the ball will make during its flight. 6 ÷ 0.008

c. How can you use a power of 10 to estimate the quotient from part (b)? Estimate the quotient. Find $6 \div 10^{-2}$; about 600

✔ QUESTION 12

... checks that you can use powers of 10 to estimate quotients of decimals.

12 ✔ CHECKPOINT Use powers of 10 to estimate each quotient.

a. 9.62 ÷ 1.1
about 9.62

b. 46.75 ÷ 0.091
about 467.5

c. 0.5 ÷ 11.2
about 0.05

13 Copy each problem. Use estimation to place the decimal point in each quotient.

a. $98\overline{)24.50}$ .25

b. $8\overline{)108.0}$ 13.5

c. $116\overline{)8386.8}$ 72.3

14 **Try This as a Class** Look at your results from Question 13.

 a. How were the digits in each quotient determined?
 by using the usual process for division

 b. How is the position of the decimal point in each quotient related to the position of the decimal point in the dividend?
 The decimal point in the quotient is directly above the decimal point in the dividend.

 c. Find the quotient $68\overline{)138.04}$.
 2.03

15 **Discussion** Look at these division problems.

$$8\overline{)72} \qquad 80\overline{)720} \qquad 88\overline{)792} \qquad 800\overline{)7200}$$

 a. How are the divisors and dividends in the last three problems related to the divisor and the dividend in the first problem?
 The divisor and dividend in the first problem are multiplied by the same number.

 b. Find all four quotients. What do you notice about them?
 9; The quotients are the same.

 c. What happens to the quotient when you multiply the dividend and the divisor by the same number?
 The quotient remains the same.

▶ **Dividing by a Decimal** In Question 14, you explained how to divide a decimal by a whole number. You can use this skill and the pattern you found in Question 15 to divide by a decimal.

16 In Question 11(c), you estimated the number of revolutions the golf ball makes in 6 s by using the quotient $0.008\overline{)6}$.

 a. By what power of 10 can you multiply the divisor 0.008 to make it a whole number? What must you do to the dividend to keep the quotient the same? 1000; Multiply the quotient by 1000.

 b. Use part (a) to rewrite the problem $0.008\overline{)6}$. Then find the quotient and compare it with your estimate in Question 11(c).
 $8\overline{)6000}$; 750; They are similar.

17 Find the quotients $1.648 \div 0.8$ and $0.00578 \div 0.17$. 2.06; 0.034

▶ **Remainders** When division has a remainder, you have to write a zero at the end of the dividend to continue to divide.

EXAMPLE

18 Discussion Look at the Example on page 251.

   a. The dividend changed from 54 to 54.0 and then to 54.00. How is 54 related to 54.0 and 54.00?

   b. How are the quotients in each stage of the division different?

   c. How do you know when the division is complete?

19 Find the quotient 3.4)‾50.49‾. **14.85**

20 ✔ **CHECKPOINT** Find each quotient. Use estimation to check.

   a. 48.6 ÷ 22.5 **2.16** **b.** 0.315 ÷ 0.005 **63** **c.** 14.7 ÷ 2.4 **6.125**

HOMEWORK EXERCISES ▶ See Exs. 13–26 on pp. 257–258.

QUESTION 20

...checks that you can divide decimals.

GOAL

LEARN HOW TO...
- find quotients that repeat
- write a fraction as a decimal
- interpret division with zero

AS YOU...
- analyze a photo of a drop of milk

KEY TERMS
- repeating decimal
- terminating decimal

Exploration 3

Repeating DECIMALS

SET UP *You will need a calculator.*

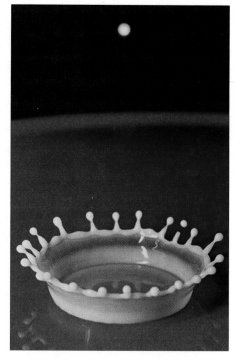

▶ **The photo shows a drop of milk falling onto a plate of milk.**

21 **Try This as a Class** The actual diameter of the drop is 0.09 cm.

   a. Write a division problem to answer this question: The drop in the photo is about 0.35 cm wide. About how many times as wide as the actual drop is it?
     0.35 ÷ 0.09; about 4 times as wide

   b. Find the quotient for the division problem from part (a). How is this division problem different from the ones in Exploration 2?
     3.8888...; The remainder will never be 0.

   c. The quotient in part (b) is a **repeating decimal**. It is written as 3.8̄. What do you think the bar over the 8 means? The 8 repeats.

▶ When remainders begin to repeat in a division problem, you can tell that the quotient will be a repeating decimal.

EXAMPLE

$1.9 \div 1.1 \longrightarrow$

$$
\begin{array}{r}
1.7272 \\
11\overline{)19.0000} \\
\underline{11} \\
80 \\
\underline{77} \\
30 \\
\underline{22} \\
80 \\
\underline{77} \\
30
\end{array}
$$

Remainders begin to repeat.

The digits 7 and 2 repeat.

$1.9 \div 1.1 = 1.\overline{72}$

▶ **Writing a Fraction as a Decimal** You can write the decimal equivalent of a fraction by dividing the numerator by the denominator. For example, $\frac{6}{11} = 6 \div 11 = 0.545454 \ldots = 0.\overline{54}$.

22 Write each decimal carried out to 6 decimal places.

   a. $0.5\overline{45}$ 0.545454   **b.** $0.5\overline{4}$ 0.544444   **c.** $0.\overline{545}$ 0.545545

23 Order $0.5\overline{45}$, $0.5\overline{4}$, and $0.\overline{545}$ from least to greatest. $0.5\overline{4}, 0.\overline{545}, 0.5\overline{45}$

24 ✔ **CHECKPOINT** Find each quotient.

   a. $0.9\overline{)12.1}$ $13.\overline{4}$ **b.** $0.56 \div 3.3$ $0.1\overline{69}$ **c.** $7.89 \div 1$ 7.89

   d. $\frac{5}{6}$ $0.8\overline{3}$ **e.** $0.12\overline{)0.9456}$ 7.88   **f.** $0.45 \div 2.7$ $0.1\overline{6}$

✔ **QUESTION 24**

…checks that you can find and write quotients that are repeating decimals.

25 The quotients in Question 24(c) and 24(e) are examples of **terminating decimals**. Why do you think they are called terminating decimals? The decimals terminate or end.

26 Suppose you want to round a quotient to the nearest hundredth. How far should you carry out the division? Why? Round the quotient $6.73 \div 0.49$ to the nearest hundredth.

26. to the thousandths place; to find the digit to the right of the place to be rounded; 13.73

27 **Discussion** Look at your results from Question 24. What can you say about the quotient when a positive number is divided by 1? by a number greater than 1? by a number between 0 and 1?

27. The quotient will be the number itself; The quotient will be less than the number; The quotient will be greater than the number.

28 Predict whether each quotient will be *greater than*, *less than*, or *equal to* the number in red. Explain how you know.

   a. $8.7 \div 1$
   equal to;
   The divisor is 1.

   b. $13.12 \div 1.2$
   less than; The divisor
   is greater than 1.

   c. $\frac{69.3}{0.99}$
   greater than;
   The divisor is
   between 0 and 1.

▶ **Division and Zero** You know that the product of any number and zero is always zero. Now you'll explore what happens when a division problem involves zero.

29 🖩 Calculator Use a calculator to answer the following questions. Be sure to try more than one example.

   a. What happens when you divide zero by any number besides zero? The answer is 0.

   b. Predict what will happen when you divide a non-zero number by zero. You will get an error message.

   c. Check your prediction in part (b). What answer appears on your calculator display? Sample Response: ERR: DIVIDE BY 0

▶ Your calculator might have displayed an error message when you tried to divide a number by zero because division by zero is *undefined*. To understand why, you can explore some division equations involving zero.

30. a. 0; 0 · x = 12; undefined; 0 · x = 0; any number
b. No; 12 ÷ 0 and 0 ÷ 0; The related multiplication equations have no solution or more than one solution.
c. Sample Response: Yes
d. Division by zero is undefined because there is either no quotient that can be found or there is more than one quotient that can be found.

30 **Try This as a Class** One way to find a quotient is to solve a related multiplication equation, as in the first row of the table below.

   a. Copy and complete the table. For each division equation, write a related multiplication equation. If possible, find the value of *x* that makes the equation true. Otherwise, write *undefined*.

Division equation	Related multiplication equation	Value of *x*
12 ÷ 3 = x	3 · x = 12	4
0 ÷ 3 = x	3 · x = 0	?
12 ÷ 0 = x	?	?
0 ÷ 0 = x	?	?

   b. Does each division equation have a quotient? If not, which ones do not? Why?

   c. Do the results in your table agree with your answers to Question 29?

   d. Use your results from parts (a)–(c) to explain why division by zero is undefined.

HOMEWORK EXERCISES ▶ See Exs. 27–46 on pp. 258–259.

Multiplying Decimals (pp. 248–249)

To multiply decimal numbers, you first multiply them as whole numbers. Then the number of decimal places in the product is the sum of the numbers of decimal places in the factors.

You can use powers of 10 and estimation to check whether a product of decimals is reasonable.

Example   2 places   2 places

$$(66.25)(0.82) = 54.3250 \longleftarrow 2 + 2 = 4 \text{ decimal places}$$

Check: The factor 0.82 is a little less than 1, so the product will be a little less than 66.25. Therefore, 54.325 is a reasonable answer.

Dividing Decimals (pp. 250–251)

To divide decimal numbers, you first multiply the divisor and the dividend by a power of 10 that will make the divisor a whole number. Then you divide. You may have to write zeros at the end of the dividend.

Example $16.2 \div 7.5$

$$7.5 \overline{) 16.2}$$
$$\times 10 \quad \times 10$$

$$
\begin{array}{r}
2.16 \\
75 \overline{) 162.00} \\
150 \\
\hline
120 \\
75 \\
\hline
450 \\
450 \\
\hline
0
\end{array}
$$

You place the decimal point in the quotient above the decimal point in the dividend.

Check: The quotient 2.16 is reasonable, because $16.2 \div 7.5 \approx 16 \div 8 = 2$.

---

31 Key Concepts Question Estimate each product or quotient. Tell whether your estimate is *greater than* or *less than* the exact answer. Then find the exact answer.

a. $(7.8)(0.995)$ **b.** $720 \div 0.08$ **c.** $(6.05)(2.2)$

Continued on next page

31. Sample responses are given.
a. about 7.8; greater than; 7.761
b. about 7,200; less than; 9000
c. about 12; less than; 13.31

Key Terms

repeating decimal

terminating decimal

Repeating and Terminating Decimals (pp. 252–253)

A decimal in which a digit or a sequence of digits keeps repeating is a repeating decimal. The bar indicates which digits repeat.
A decimal that stops is a terminating decimal.

You can write the decimal equivalent of a fraction by dividing the numerator by the denominator. (p. 253)

Examples

repeating decimal

terminating decimal

$$\frac{4}{15} = 4 \div 15 = 0.2666\ldots = 0.2\overline{6} \qquad \frac{7}{8} = 7 \div 8 = 0.875$$

The digit 6 repeats.

Division with Zero (p. 254)

Zero divided by any non-zero number is always zero, because the product of zero and any non-zero number is always zero.

Example $0 \div 9 = 0$, because $0 \cdot 9 = 0$.

Division by zero is undefined, because there is no number by which you can multiply zero to produce a non-zero product.

Example $9 \div 0$ is undefined, because there is no number that makes $0 \cdot ? = 9$ a true statement.

CLOSURE QUESTION

Explain how to place the decimal point in an answer when you are multiplying decimals and when you are dividing decimals. Then explain why division by zero is undefined.

Sample Response:
For multiplication, the number of decimal places in the product is the sum of the number of decimal places in the factors. For division, multiply the dividend and the divisor by a power of 10 that makes the divisor a whole number, then place the decimal point in the quotient above the decimal point in the dividend. Division by zero is undefined because you can't find any number that when multiplied by zero produces a non-zero product.

32 Key Concepts Question Predict whether each quotient will be *greater than*, *less than*, or *equal to* the number in red. Then find the exact quotient to check each prediction.

a. $4.5 \div 1$
equal to; 4.5

b. $0.64 \div 0.015$
greater than; $42.\overline{6}$

c. $\dfrac{0.8}{1.1}$
less than; $0.\overline{72}$

Practice & Application Exercises

Copy each problem. Use estimation to place the decimal point in each product.

1. (0.09)(7.2) = 648 0.648

2. (215.4)(0.3) = 6462 64.62

3. (4.78)(0.652) = 311656 3.11656

4. (591.6)(3.87) = 2289492
   2289.492

Find each product. Show your work.

5. (25.9)(9.78)
   253.302

6. (0.09)(3.6)
   0.324

7. (102.1)(0.7)
   71.47

8. (415.2)(0.89)
   369.528

9. (32.76)(0.025)
   0.819

10. (0.48)(0.15)
    0.072

Estimation For Exercises 11 and 12, use estimation. Explain your method. Then tell whether the exact answer will be *greater than* or *less than* your estimate.

11. Carlos placed a bunch of grapes on a scale at a fruit stand. The bunch weighed 2.7 lb. Grapes are on sale for $1.59 per pound. Suppose Carlos has a $5 bill. Does he have enough money to buy the grapes? Explain.   Yes; Sample Response:
    3 · $1.60 = $4.80; less than; 2.7 < 3 and $1.59 < $1.60

12. Electricity usage is measured in kilowatt-hours (kW • h). The bill shows the amount of electricity used for the month of February, along with the price per kW • h. Estimate the cost of the electricity for February.   about $24.40;
    Sample Response: 244 · 10^{-1} = 24.4; greater than

--- *Electricity Bill* ---

Dates: 2/1/97 through 2/28/97

Number of kW • h		Price per unit
244	×	$0.12647

Copy each problem. Use estimation with powers of 10 to place the decimal point in each quotient.

13. 23.4 ÷ 0.08 = 2925 292.5

14. 4.41 ÷ 0.12 = 3675 36.75

15. 115 ÷ 9.2 = 125 12.5

16. 49.7 ÷ 1.4 = 355 35.5

17. A student took the quiz shown. Without doing the problems, find two errors. Explain how you identified each error.

    Problems 2 and 5 are incorrect;
    Since the divisors in both
    problems are less than 1, the
    quotients should be greater than
    the dividend.

    Exploration 2 Quiz

    1. 92.4 ÷ 77 = 1.2

    2. 1.3 ÷ 0.25 = 0.52

    3. 344.1 ÷ 9.25 = 37.2

    4. 57.5 ÷ 0.08 = 718.75

    5. 39.6 ÷ 0.11 = 36

Find each quotient. Show your work.

18. $27 \div 4.5$ 6   **19.** $0.34 \div 0.04$ 8.5   **20.** $1.8\overline{)10.08}$ 5.6

21. $1.74 \div 0.3$ 5.8   **22.** $0.005\overline{)90}$ 18,000   **23.** $0.87 \div 1.2$ 0.725

24. **Geometry Connection** Suppose a circle has a circumference of 157 cm. Find the diameter of the circle. Use 3.14 for π. Do not use a calculator. 50 cm

25. Carmen finds a picture of a grasshopper in a science magazine. The picture caption reads, "Picture is 0.8 of actual size."

  a. Is the picture *larger* or *smaller* than the actual grasshopper? smaller

  b. Suppose the actual grasshopper is 5.2 cm long. How long is the picture? 4.16 cm

  c. Suppose the picture is 36 mm long. How long is the actual grasshopper? 45 mm

26. Brenda's solution to the problem $34.56 \div 0.72$ is shown. Is she correct? Do you think her method will always work? Explain.
Yes; Yes; Brenda is just using a fast way to multiply both the divisor and the dividend by 100.

Write each decimal carried out to six decimal places.

27. $0.\overline{315}$ **28.** $6.3\overline{6}$ **29.** $0.02\overline{7}$ **30.** $101.\overline{81}$
0.315315   6.363636   0.027777   101.818181

Find each quotient. Show your work.

31. $0.47 \div 0.6$ $0.78\overline{3}$ **32.** $0.45\overline{)13.6}$ $30.\overline{2}$ **33.** $1.4 \div 2.7$ $0.5\overline{18}$

34. $\dfrac{1.2}{9}$ $0.1\overline{3}$ **35.** $56.12 \div 0$ **36.** $0.11\overline{)67.5}$ $613.\overline{63}$
                                                    undefined

Write each fraction as a decimal rounded to the nearest hundredth.

37. $\dfrac{5}{8}$ 0.63   **38.** $\dfrac{2}{3}$ 0.67   **39.** $\dfrac{7}{12}$ 0.58   **40.** $\dfrac{3}{7}$ 0.43

Predict whether each quotient will be *greater than*, *less than*, or *equal to* the number in red. Explain how you know.

41. **14.67** $\div$ 9.1   **42.** $\dfrac{\mathbf{30.1}}{0.86}$ **43.** **5.825** $\div \dfrac{102}{101}$

less than;
The divisor is
greater than 1.

greater than; The
divisor is between 0
and 1.

less than;
The divisor is
greater than 1.

44. Graphic Design Graphic designers often need to reduce photos to fit in a small space. A graphic designer for an art book needs to include a photo of a sculpture in the book. In the photo, the sculpture is 18.7 cm high. In the book, the sculpture must be 5.5 cm high.

   a. About how much does the designer need to reduce the photo?

   b. Find the reduction that will make the photo fit perfectly into the book's space. Explain the method you used.

45. Challenge Replace each ? with one of the digits 1, 3, 5, or 9 to create an expression for each quotient. ? · ? ÷ ? · ?

   a. the least quotient $1 \cdot 3 \div 9 \cdot 5$ b. the greatest quotient
   $9 \cdot 5 \div 1 \cdot 3$

Reflecting on the Section

Write your response to Exercise 46 in your journal.

46. Margo works part-time at a clothing store. She is paid monthly. Part of her earnings statement for the month of May is shown.

May Earnings		
Hourly rate	Hours worked	Gross earnings
$9.88	53.75	$351.05

   a. Use estimation with powers of 10 to check whether Margo's earnings statement is accurate.

   b. Write and solve an equation to find out whether the earnings statement is accurate.

   c. Which method is better, part (a) or part (b)? Why?

Spiral Review

Evaluate each expression. (Module 4, pp. 241–242)

47. $\frac{3}{8} \cdot \frac{4}{11}$ $\frac{3}{22}$ 48. $4 \div \frac{2}{5}$ 10   49. $2\frac{1}{4} \cdot 8$ 18

50. $3\frac{1}{3} \div \frac{5}{6}$ 4   51. $2\frac{1}{5} \cdot \frac{5}{12}$ $\frac{11}{12}$ 52. $5\frac{2}{5} \div \frac{3}{10}$ 18

53. Val lives 11 blocks due east of Cora. Cora lives 4 blocks due west of Amy. Where does Amy live in relation to Val? (Module 1, p. 44)
   7 blocks due west

Draw an angle with each measure. Then classify each angle as *acute,* *obtuse, right,* **or** *straight.* (Module 2, p. 83)

54. 60°   55. 145°   56. 22°   57. 174°

---

*Side notes:*

44. a. to about $\frac{1}{3}$ its actual size
b. about 0.294; $5.5 \div 18.7 \approx 0.294$

Journal

Exercise 46 checks that you can estimate with decimals in real-life situations.

46. a. Since $53.75 \text{ h} \cdot \frac{\$10}{1 \text{ h}} = \$537.50$, the statement is not accurate.
b. Sample Response: $9.88x = 351.05$; Since the solution to the equation is about 35.5, Margo was paid for only 35.5 hours.
c. Sample Response: the one in part (b); The second method can identify where the error was made.

54.
60°
acute

55.
145°
obtuse

56.
22°
acute

57.
174°
obtuse

Lights, Camera—Action!

You'll explore several mathematical concepts that can be used to create special animated effects to use in your zoetrope. To complete the project, you'll work as a group to create and set up a viewing station featuring several animation strips that use the special effects of your choice.

SET UP

You will need:
- *Project Labsheet A*
- *scissors*
- *tape*
- *compass*
- *ruler*
- *colored pencils or markers (optional)*

Estimation Use your estimation skills to create a shrinking effect.

 1 You can use a copying machine to reduce the size of a figure that is too difficult to redraw. For example, a 75% reduction will result in a figure 0.75 times its actual size. Suppose you want to use a copying machine to shorten the figure in Frame 1 (F1) by about 6 mm in each frame from F2 to F4.

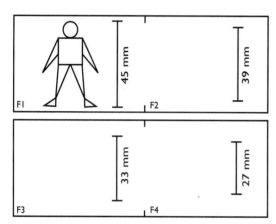

a. Estimate the height of the figure needed for F2 in relation to the height of the original figure in F1. What percent reduction should you use to create the figure for F2 on a copying machine?
   F2 is about 0.9 times F1; 90%

b. Estimate the percent reduction you should use on the original figure in F1 to create the figures for F3 and F4. about 75%, about 60%

 2 **Use Project Labsheet A.** Check students' work.

a. Cut out the pieces of *Blank Zoetrope Strip A* and tape them together in order.

b. Draw a rectangle with a base length of 5 cm and a height of 1.5 cm in the center of F1. Complete F2–F8 by reducing each previous base length by 0.5 cm and increasing the height by 0.5 cm. Color the interior of each rectangle.

c. Place your strip in the zoetrope with the frames centered under the slots. Spin the zoetrope. Describe what happens.

Section 2

Extra Skill Practice

You will need: • graph paper or 150 pennies (optional) (Exs. 37–40)

Find each product. Estimate to check that answers are reasonable.

1. (5.3)(2.6)
   13.78
2. (17)(3.9)
   66.3
3. (6.32)(0.87)
   5.4984
4. (65)(0.12)
   7.8
5. (4.58)(0.034)
   0.15572
6. (13.8)(9.5)
   131.1
7. (0.009)(289.6)
   2.6064
8. (0.56)(0.7)
   0.392
9. (237.1)(19.4)
   4599.74
10. (0.019)(0.27)
    0.00513
11. (48)(25.31)
    1214.88
12. (0.84)(0.39)
    0.3276

Predict whether each product will be *greater than, less than,* **or** *equal to* **the number in red. Explain how you know.** equal to; Any number multiplied by 1 is the number itself.

13. **(45.8)(0.23)**
    less than; 0 < 0.23 < 1
14. (1.76)**(931.2)**
    greater than; 1.76 > 1
15. **(642.9)**(1)
16. (0.089)**(0.51)**
    less than; 0 < 0.089 < 1

Find each quotient. Estimate to check that answers are reasonable.

17. 72)0.216
    0.003; 0.210 ÷ 70 = 0.003
18. 21.28 ÷ 0.56
    38; 20 ÷ 0.5 = 40
19. 1.6)10.384
    6.49; 10 ÷ 2 = 5
20. $\frac{9}{11}$
    0.81; 11 ÷ 11 = 1
21. 0.35)2.1
    6; 2 ÷ 0.5 = 4
22. 378.92 ÷ 0
    undefined
23. $\frac{2.4}{21.6}$
    0.1; 2 ÷ 20 = 0.1
24. 46.3 ÷ 0.09
    514.4; 50 ÷ 0.1 = 500
25. 0.076)17.48
    230; 17 ÷ 0.1 = 170
26. $\frac{15}{22}$
    0.681; 15 ÷ 20 = 0.75
27. 48.02 ÷ 49
    0.98; 49 ÷ 49 = 1
28. 0 ÷ 0.281
    0; The quotient of 0 divided by any number except 0 is 0.

Predict whether each quotient will be *greater than, less than,* **or** *equal to* **the number in red. Explain how you know.**

29. **24.32** ÷ 0.38
    greater than; 0 < 0.38 < 1
30. 185)**82.14**
    less than; 185 > 1
31. **537.4** ÷ 1
    equal to; The divisor is 1.
32. **74.25** ÷ 0.99
    greater than; 0 < 0.99 < 1
33. **562** ÷ 3488
    less than; 3488 > 1
34. **87** ÷ 87.3
    less than; 87.3 > 1
35. **484** ÷ 0.8
    greater than; 0 < 0.8 < 1
36. **0.732** ÷ 5
    less than; 5 > 1

Visual Thinking **For Exercises 37–40, draw and shade 10 × 10 grids or use pennies to represent and find each product or quotient.** Check students' work.

37. (6)(0.15)
    0.9
38. (12)(0.09)
    1.08
39. 1.5 ÷ 6
    0.25
40. 1.36 ÷ 4
    0.34
41. **Open-ended** For each of Exercises 37–40, describe a real-world situation that can be represented using the given expression. See below.

Standardized Testing ▶ Multiple Choice

1. Use estimation with powers of 10 to choose the product (0.033)(401.52). A

   A 13.25016   **B** 132.5016   **C** 1.325016   **D** 1325.016

2. Which is the quotient 0.09 ÷ 1.1? D

   A 0.082   **B** 0.081   **C** 0.81   **D** 0.0$\overline{81}$

---

41. Sample Responses: Janet bought six small shells for 15¢ each. What was the total cost?; Leroy bought 12 stickers for 9¢ each. What was the total cost?; Hal cut a piece of wire 1.5 ft long into six pieces. How long was each piece?; Celine cut a piece of string 1.36 m long into four pieces. How long was each piece?

IN THIS SECTION

EXPLORATION 1
♦ Rotations and Symmetry

EXPLORATION 2
♦ Reflections and Symmetry

The MATH of MOTION

◄···**Setting the Stage**

A sense of motion is sometimes created in artworks by the clever use of patterns, as in these Native American designs.

▲ This "whirlwind" design was woven into an Apache basket tray.

▲ A metalworker of the Fox tribe stamped and scribed this ornate pattern on a silver pin.

▲ Tiny colored beads were used to create this design for a Fox belt. The pattern combines the styles of both Plains and Woodlands tribes.

Think About It

1 Choose two of the artworks above. Explain how you think each design creates a sense of motion.

2 Look for designs on objects in your classroom such as clothing, backpacks, posters, and so on, that create a sense of motion. Explain how each design achieves this effect. Check students' work.

ROTATIONS and SYMMETRY

GOAL

LEARN HOW TO...
- rotate a figure
- describe a rotation
- identify rotational symmetries

AS YOU...
- study designs used in artwork

KEY TERMS
- rotation
- center of rotation
- image
- rotational symmetry
- rotational symmetries

SET UP *You will need:* • *Labsheets 3A and 3B* • *scissors* • *tape* • *tracing paper* • *zoetrope* • *protractor*

3 Use Labsheet 3A. Each frame of the *Jewelry Design Zoetrope Strip* contains part of the petal design used on the Fox silver pin shown on page 262.

a. Cut out the pieces of the zoetrope strip and tape them together. Place the strip in the zoetrope so that each frame is centered under a slot. Check students' work.

b. What do you think will happen when the zoetrope is spun?
Sample Response: The design will spin.

c. Spin the zoetrope clockwise and observe what happens. Describe what you see. The design spins clockwise.

d. Now spin the zoetrope counterclockwise. Is the result the same as in part (c)? Explain. No; The design spins counterclockwise.

4 Use Labsheet 3B. Follow the directions on Labsheet 3B to investigate how the *Stick Figure* can be rotated from one position to another. a–d. Check students' work. e. 42°; Sample Response: I measured ∠YPZ. **f.** 318°; 360° − 42° = 318°

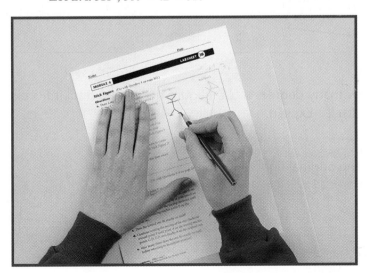

► A **rotation** turns a figure about a fixed point—the **center of rotation**—a certain amount in one direction, either clockwise or counterclockwise. The new figure is the **image** of the original figure. In this book, the image for any transformation is shown in red.

EXAMPLE

The rotation shown can be described in two ways.

Clockwise Rotation

The image is a **90° clockwise rotation** of the original figure about point *P*.

Counterclockwise Rotation

The image is a **270° counterclockwise** rotation of the original figure about point *P*.

center of rotation

5 Find the number of degrees each figure must be rotated in the opposite direction to obtain the same result as each indicated rotation.

a. 180° clockwise rotation 180°

b. 135° counterclockwise rotation 225°

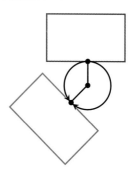

6 How many degrees must a figure be rotated until it fits exactly on itself? Explain. 360°; The figure must rotate a complete circle, and a circle contains 360°.

✔ **QUESTION 7**

...checks that you can describe a rotation.

7 ✔ **CHECKPOINT** Describe the rotation of the original figure in two ways.
108° counterclockwise, 252° clockwise

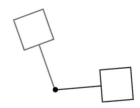

▶ You have explored rotations about a point outside a figure. Now you'll investigate rotations about a point that is inside a figure.

Use Labsheet 3B for Questions 8 and 9.

8 Follow the directions on Labsheet 3B to investigate what happens when you rotate the *Six-Pointed Star* about its center.
a, b. Check students' work. c. Yes. d. Check students' work. e. 5 times

▶ A figure that fits exactly on itself after a rotation of less than 360° about a point has **rotational symmetry**.

A. **B.** **C.** **D.**

These figures have rotational symmetry.

These figures do not have rotational symmetry.

▶ The amounts of rotation that fit a figure exactly on itself are the **rotational symmetries** of the figure.

9 **Discussion** *The Six-Pointed Star* on Labsheet 3B has rotational symmetries of 60°, 120°, 180°, 240°, and 300°. How do you think these angles were determined?

10 Look at figures A and B above that have rotational symmetry.

a. How many rotational symmetries does each figure have? 4, 2

b. Describe all the rotational symmetries of each figure.
72°, 144°, 216°, and 288°; 120° and 240°

11 ✔ **CHECKPOINT** Find all rotational symmetries of each figure.

a.

72°, 144°, 216°, and 288°

b.

90°, 180°, and 270°

c.

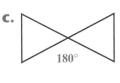

180°

12 Look at the designs shown on page 262.

a. Which designs appear to have rotational symmetry?

b. Estimate the rotational symmetries for each design in part (a).

┃ **HOMEWORK EXERCISES** ▶ See Exs. 1–13 on pp. 271–272.

9. The measures of the angles are multiples of 60°, which is the number of degrees through which one point must be rotated to fit exactly on the adjacent point.

✔ **QUESTION 11**

...checks that you can identify all the rotational symmetries of a figure.

12. a. the designs on the Apache basket and Fox pin
b. Apache basket: 72°, 144°, 216°, 288°; Fox pin: 45°, 90°, 135°, 180°, 225°, 270°, 315°

GOAL

LEARN HOW TO...
◆ identify a reflection
◆ identify lines of symmetry

AS YOU...
◆ explore mirror images in art

KEY TERMS
◆ vertex of a triangle
◆ congruent
◆ reflection
◆ line of reflection
◆ line symmetry
◆ line of symmetry

13. The right hand of the image is raised; The image appears to move closer to the surface of the mirror; The image appears to move farther away from the mirror.

Exploration 2

REFLECTIONS and SYMMETRY

SET UP *You will need:* • *Labsheet 3C* • *ruler* • *2 sheets of tracing paper* • *mirror, polyester film, or MIRA®*

▶ **Artworks with patterns that contain mirror images can also create a sense of motion.**

13 Discussion Imagine that you are looking at yourself in a mirror. What happens to your reflection when you raise your left hand? when you move closer to the mirror? when you move farther away from the mirror?

14 Follow Steps 1–3 to investigate mirror images. Check students' work.

Step 1
Fold a sheet of tracing paper in half. Then draw a triangle with a dark pencil or pen.

Step 3
Unfold your paper. Label the *vertices* of your original triangle *A, B,* and *C.*

Step 2
Turn over your folded paper and trace the triangle you drew in Step 1.

Each point where two sides of the triangle meet is a **vertex.**

15 The triangle with vertices *A, B,* and *C* is called "triangle *ABC*" and written △*ABC*. Place a MIRA® on the fold so you can see the reflection of △*ABC*. See Additional Answers.

a. Describe the reflection of △*ABC*. How is the reflection of △*ABC* related to the triangle on the right side of the fold?

b. What do you think will happen to the reflection of △*ABC* when the MIRA® is moved closer to △*ABC*? farther away from △*ABC*?

16 Place the MIRA® on the fold again. Use *A′*, read as "*A* prime," to label the image of point *A*. Use *B′* and *C′* to label the images of points *B* and *C*. **See below.**

▶ **Two figures that are the same shape and the same size are congruent.**

> The figures are congruent.

17 Make another tracing of △*ABC*. Use the tracing to show that △*ABC* and △*A′B′C′* are congruent. What did you have to do to the tracing in order to show that the triangles are congruent?
flip the tracing over

16. Sample Response:

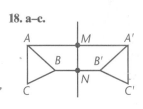

A ⋮ *A′*
B ⋮ *B′*
C ⋮ *C′*

▶ △*A′B′C′* is the *reflection* of △*ABC* across the fold. **A reflection is a flip across a line. The line is the line of reflection. The result is a mirror image of the original figure.**

EXAMPLE

Each image is a reflection of the original figure across the line shown.

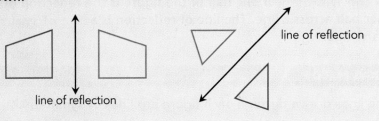

line of reflection

line of reflection

---

18 Use your drawing from Question 14 to investigate some of the properties of reflections.

18. a–c.

A | *M* | *A′*
B | *B′*
C | *N* | *C′*

a. Draw a segment along the fold to represent the line of reflection.

b. Draw a segment connecting *A* and its image, *A′*. This segment is written as $\overline{AA'}$. Now draw $\overline{BB'}$.

c. Use *M* to label the point of intersection of $\overline{AA'}$ and the line of reflection. Use *N* to label the point of intersection of $\overline{BB'}$ and the line of reflection.

d. Look at the four angles formed where $\overline{AA'}$ intersects the line of reflection. What do you notice? **Each angle is a right angle.**

e. Measure the distance from *A* to *M* and the distance from *A′* to *M*. How do the two distances compare? **The two distances are the same.**

f. Measure the distance from *B* to *N*. Without measuring, predict the distance from *B′* to *N*. Then check your prediction.

18. f. The distance from *B* to *N* will be the same as the distance from *B′* to *N*; The distances are the same.

...checks that you
can identify a
reflection.

19. a. No; The figures are
not the same size.
b. Yes; The figures are
the same size and shape
and corresponding parts
of the figures are directly
across the line of
reflection.
c. No; Corresponding
parts of the figures are
not directly across the
line of reflection.

19 ✔ **CHECKPOINT** Tell whether each image is a reflection of
the original figure across the line between them. For any that are
not reflections, explain why they are not.

a. **b.** **c.**

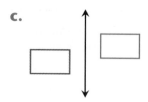

20 **Use Labsheet 3C.** Look at the *Congruent Butterflies*.
See Additional Answers.
  a. How can you find a line of reflection that will reflect the top
butterfly so that it fits exactly on the bottom butterfly?

  b. Use your method from part (a) to locate and draw the line of
reflection.

▶ **Symmetry in Designs** The use of reflections in an artwork often
results in a design that contains figures with *line symmetry*. A figure
has **line symmetry** if one half of the figure is the reflection of the
other half across a line. The line of reflection is a **line of symmetry**
for the figure.

Line symmetry is
common in nature. A
black fly, shown here
greatly enlarged, has
a vertical line of
symmetry.
▼

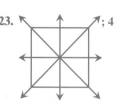

EXAMPLE

The lines drawn through each figure are lines of symmetry.

Some figures have
more than one line
of symmetry.

23. ; 4

21 **Use Labsheet 3C.** Draw all the lines of symmetry on each
portion of the *Fox Belt Design*. Check students' work.

22 **Create Your Own** Draw a shape that has at least two lines of
symmetry. Check students' drawings.

23 ✔ **CHECKPOINT** Draw a square. Then draw all its lines of
symmetry. How many lines of symmetry does a square have?

...checks that you
can identify lines of
symmetry.

HOMEWORK EXERCISES See Exs. 14–31 on pp. 272–274.

You can use computer drawing software to create a shape with two lines of symmetry for Question 22 on page 268.

Step 1 Choose the auto grid option to show a grid on your screen. From any point on a grid line, draw a continuous line or shape.

> You can also draw intersecting horizontal and vertical lines.

Step 2 Duplicate your figure. Then flip the copy horizontally or vertically. Drag the copy so that it meets the original figure.

The shape has one line of symmetry.

Step 3 To create a second line of symmetry, first group the two images to form one object. Next duplicate the object and flip the copy horizontally or vertically. Then drag the copy so that it meets the original object.

The shape has vertical and horizontal lines of symmetry.

Key Concepts

rotation

image

center of
rotation

rotational
symmetry

rotational
symmetries

reflection

line of reflection

congruent

vertex of a
triangle

Rotations (p. 264)

A rotation turns a figure about a point a certain number of degrees either clockwise or counter-clockwise. The new figure is the image of the original figure.

P is the center of rotation.

Example The figure shows a 60° clockwise or 300° counter-clockwise rotation around point P.

Rotational Symmetry
(p. 265)

A figure that fits exactly on itself after being rotated less than 360° about a point has rotational symmetry.

Example This figure has rotational symmetries of 72°, 144°, 216°, and 288°.

Reflections (p. 267)

A reflection flips a figure across a line.

Each point on the original figure and its image are the same distance from the line of reflection.

If you connect a point and its image with a segment, the segment will intersect the line of reflection at a right angle.

The original figure and its image are congruent, since they are the same size and shape.

Example

line of reflection

24. The rotational symmetries of O are infinite, and the rotational symmetry of X and of S is 180°. B and E do not have rotational symmetry.

24 Key Concepts Question Tell whether each letter has rotational symmetry. If so, find all its rotational symmetries.

B O X E S

Section 3

Key Concepts

Line Symmetry (p. 268)

If one half of a figure is a reflection of the other half, the figure has line symmetry.

line symmetry

line of symmetry

Example

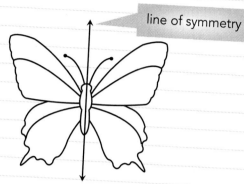

line of symmetry

CLOSURE QUESTION

State two types of symmetry and describe each type.

Sample Response:
Rotational symmetry and line symmetry; Rotational symmetry is when a figure can be turned less than 360° about a point and fit exactly on itself. Line symmetry is when half of a figure can be flipped across a line and fit exactly on the other half.

25 Key Concepts Question Tell whether each letter in Question 24 has line symmetry. If so, copy the letter and draw all its lines of symmetry. **All the letters except the letter S have line symmetry. The letter O has an infinite number of lines symmetry.** ◄B► ◄|► ◄E►

Section 3

Practice & Application Exercises

YOU WILL NEED

For Exs. 1–2:
♦ protractor

For Exs. 4, 8–11, 28–30:
♦ protractor
♦ ruler

For Exs. 5–7:
♦ tracing paper

For Exs. 45–46:
♦ Labsheet 3D
♦ tracing paper
♦ ruler
♦ protractor

For each clockwise rotation of the original figure in Exercises 1 and 2:

a. ~~Estimation~~ Estimate the amount of rotation.

b. Find the actual amount of rotation.

c. Describe another rotation that results in the same image.

1. a. Sample Response: about 100° clockwise
   b. 105° clockwise
   c. 255° counterclockwise

2. a. Sample Response: about 30° counterclockwise
   b. 30° counterclockwise
   c. 330° clockwise

3. How many degrees does the minute hand of a clock rotate in 5 min? in 12 min? 30°; 72°

4. Open-ended Draw a scalene triangle with a right angle. Mark and label a point below the triangle to use as the center of rotation. Then draw the image of the triangle after a 60° counterclockwise rotation.

Trace each shape below. Then use your tracing to determine whether the shape has rotational symmetry. For each shape that has rotational symmetry, find all its rotational symmetries.

5. 180°

6. 120° and 240°

7. 60°, 120°, 180°, 240°, and 300°

8. Create Your Own The Fox pin design shown on page 262 has rotational symmetry. Create your own pin design that has rotational symmetry. Check students' drawings.

Diatoms are one-celled or colonial algae that live under water. ▶

Biology The microscopic organisms shown below, called *diatoms*, have rotational symmetry. Find all the rotational symmetries of each diatom.

9. 180°

10. 72°, 144°, 216°, and 288°

11. 120° and 240°

12. Challenge Draw a figure that has rotational symmetries of 90°, 180°, and 270°.

13. Writing Several angles of rotation can be used to create designs with rotational symmetry. How can you use the prime factorization of 360 to make a list of possible rotational symmetries?

Tell whether each diagram shows a reflection of the original figure across the given line. If not, explain why not.

14.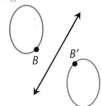

No; Corresponding points of the figures are not the same distance from the line of reflection.

15. No; The figures are not the same size.

16. No; $\overline{BB'}$ does not intersect the line of reflection at a right angle.

Tell whether the figures in each pair are congruent.

17. Yes. 18. No. 19. No.

For each figure, tell whether the line shown is a line of symmetry. If it is not, explain why not.

20. 21. 22.

Yes.

20. No; One half of the figure is not a reflection of the other half.

22. No; One half of the figure is not reflected across the line onto the other half.

Native American Designs Many Native American peoples enhanced the beauty of everyday objects with elaborate decorations. The rug shown below was made by the Navajo people.

◄ This Navajo rug was woven about 1940.

23. Tell whether the design on the rug shown above has rotational symmetry. Explain. Yes; 180°

24. Tell whether the design shown above has line symmetry. Explain.
   Yes; there are vertical and horizontal lines of symmetry.

25. **Writing** Explain how reflections were used in the rug design.

25. A vertical line of symmetry could be drawn through the middle of the design, and a horizontal line of symmetry could also be drawn through the middle of the design. Both lines of symmetry could be used to reflect the design.

26. *Palindromes* are words or numbers that look the same whether they are written from left to right or from right to left. For example, the name ANNA and the number 525 are both palindromes.

   a. Some palindromes have line symmetry. Identify the line of symmetry in the word MOM. a vertical line through the middle of the letter O

   b. Find two other examples of word or number palindromes that have line symmetry. Sample Response: HAH, 8008

28. Sample Response:

29. Sample Response:

RESEARCH

Exercise 31 checks that you can recognize rotations and reflections.

30. Sample Response:

38. a. $\frac{12}{40}$, or $\frac{3}{10}$; $\frac{15}{40}$, or $\frac{3}{8}$

---

27. Visual Thinking Think of two objects in nature that have line symmetry. Make a sketch of each object. *Check students' work.*

Challenge **For each description, draw a figure that fits the description.**

28. has both line symmetry and rotational symmetry

29. has rotational symmetry but not line symmetry

30. has line symmetry but not rotational symmetry *See below.*

Reflecting ▶on the Section

31. A logo is a symbol that identifies a company, a sports team, or some other organization. Look through newspapers, magazines, catalogs, and other sources to find logos that use a rotation, a reflection, or possibly both in their designs. Cut out or copy the logo to share with the class. *Check students' work.*

Spiral ◀▶Review

Find each product or quotient. (Module 4, pp. 255–256)

32. (30.4)(0.07) 2.128 **33.** 0.3)‾9‾7‾.‾5‾6 325.2 **34.** (51.8)(2.3) 119.14

35. $\frac{4.8}{11}$ 0.4$\overline{36}$ **36.** (0.089)(0.06) **37.** 38.6 ÷ 0.4 96.5
0.00534

Event	Total
blue	15
red	12
green	13

38. Suppose the spinner was spun 40 times. Use the results in the table to answer parts (a) and (b). (Module 1, p. 33)

   a. What is the experimental probability that the spinner stops on red? on blue?

   b. Suppose the spinner is spun 120 times. About how many times do you expect the spinner to stop on red? on blue?
36; 45

Find each sum or difference. (Module 2, p. 109)

39. –16 + 7 –9 **40.** 26 – (–13) 39 **41.** –54 + 54 0

42. –38 – (–5) –33 **43.** –9 + (–25) + 6 –28 **44.** –42 – 11 – (–7) –46

Finding the Center of Rotation

Use Labsheet 3D for Exercises 45 and 46.

45. Follow the directions to explore how to find the center of rotation for the *Rotated Stick Figure*.
    See Additional Answers.

46. Use the center of rotation you found in Exercise 45. Draw the image of the Stick Figure after a 50° counter-clockwise rotation. Check students' work.

Working on the Module Project ▼

Lights, Camera—Action!

SET UP   *You will need: • Project Labsheet A • scissors • tape • protractor • zoetrope*

3–5. Check students' work.

 3 **Use another copy of Project Labsheet A.** Cut out the pieces of *Blank Zoetrope Strip A* and tape them together.

 4 a. Mark a point in the center of each frame of the zoetrope strip to use as a center of rotation.

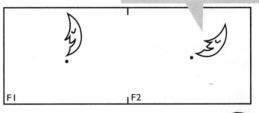

45° clockwise rotation of the figure in F1.

   b. Draw a small figure centered in the upper half of Frame 1 (F1) above the point you marked in part (a). Then draw the image of the figure after the rotation of your choice in F2.

   c. What angle of rotation did you use? Why?

   d. Complete F3–F8 by rotating the image in the previous frame by the same number of degrees you used in part (b).

 5 Place your strip in the zoetrope so the frames are centered under the slots. Then spin the zoetrope. Describe what you see.

You will need: • *protractor* (Ex. 1) • *ruler* (Ex. 1)

1. Draw a triangle. Mark and label a point below the triangle to use as the center of rotation. Then draw the image of the triangle after a 130° clockwise rotation.   **Sample Response:**

Determine whether each shape has rotational symmetry. For each shape that has rotational symmetry, find all its rotational symmetries.

2.   Yes; 180°

3.   No.

4.   Yes; 90°, 180°, and 270°

5. No.

Tell whether each diagram shows a reflection of the original figure across the line.

6.   No.

7. S   Yes.

8.   Yes.

Tell whether the figures in each pair are congruent.

9.   Yes.

10.   No.

11.   Yes.

Standardized Testing ◀▶ Free Response

One figure in each pair is the image of the other after one or two transformations. Name the type(s) of transformation(s) that was (were) used to produce each image from the original figure.   Sample Responses are given.

1.

a 90° rotation counterclockwise followed by a reflection

2.

a 180° rotation

3.

a 180° rotation followed by a reflection

FOR ASSESSMENT AND PORTFOLIOS

Congruent Snowflakes

SET UP *You will need: • white paper • scissors*

The Situation See the Resource Book for a detailed discussion of this Extended Exploration.

You can create snowflake designs by folding a piece of white paper and cutting out different shapes.

The Problem

Create the paper snowflake shown below.
Check students' work.

Something to Think About

♦ How can you use rotational symmetry and line symmetry to help solve the problem? Draw the lines of symmetry to find the basic pattern that is repeated by rotation.

Present Your Results

Write a summary that clearly explains how you solved the problem. Include any drawings or other representations that will help make your explanation clear to others. See below.

Answers will vary:
Sample Response: I used a compass to draw a circle and cut it out. I folded the circle into eighths and cut off the arc. I cut off the tip to create the square. I cut half of the other shapes on the edges and then I unfolded the paper.

WARM-UP EXERCISES

Multiply.
1. 56 • 23   1288
2. 398 • 47   18,706
3. 46.52 • 32.4
                    1507.248

Divide.
4. 625 ÷ 25   25
5. 13,203 ÷ 27   489
6. 17.5908 ÷ 3.21 5.48

Special EFFECTS

◄‹‹‹**Setting the Stage**

order frames were viewed

order frames were filmed

One of the first special effects used by moviemakers was *reverse motion*, which was created by running film backward.

The 1922 silent film *Payday* contains a famous reverse motion scene. Charlie Chaplin plays a construction worker forced to catch bricks tossed up by co-workers on the ground.

Chaplin, standing on a high open framework, catches the bricks any way he can—with his feet, his chin, etc. Amazingly, he catches them all without falling!

Charlie Chaplin™ © Roy Export Company Establishment 1997 Represented by Bliss House, Inc., West Springfield, MA 01089

Think About It

1 a. How do you think reverse motion was used to create the scene from the movie *Payday* shown above? Charlie Chaplin actually was throwing the bricks to construction workers. The scene was filmed and then reversed.

b. What are some other interesting visual effects that might be created using reverse motion?

1. b. Sample Response: food appearing on a plate while it is being eaten, a broken dish being made whole again

Multiplying and Dividing INTEGERS

GOAL

LEARN HOW TO...
◆ multiply and divide integers

AS YOU...
◆ experiment with reverse motion

KEY TERMS
◆ commutative property of multiplication
◆ associative property of multiplication

SET UP *Work in a group. You will need:* • *Labsheets 4A–4C* • *zoetrope* • *scissors* • *tape*

▶ **You can use your zoetrope to experiment with the effects created by reverse motion.**

Use Labsheets 4A–4C for Questions 2–4.

2 a. Cut out the pieces of the zoetrope strip of *A Person Walking Forward* and tape them together. Place the strip in your zoetrope so that each frame is centered under a slot.
   Check students' work.

b. Predict what will happen to the image when you spin the zoetrope forward (counterclockwise) and backward (clockwise). Record your predictions in the *Walking Person Table*.
   person walks forward; person walks backward

c. Spin the zoetrope forward and backward and observe what happens to the image. Record your findings in the *Walking Person Table*.
   person walks forward; person walks backward

3 Repeat parts (a)–(c) of Question 2 for the zoetrope strip of *A Person Walking Backward*. Record your predictions and results in the *Walking Person Table*.

4 Look at your completed *Walking Person Table*.

   a. Which results were most surprising? Why?

   b. What patterns do you see in the table? Explain.

3. a. Check students' work.
b. person walks backward; person walks forward.
c. person walks backward; person walks forward.

4. a. Sample Response: none; In Section 3 I learned about the effects of spinning a zoetrope clockwise or counterclockwise.
b. Spinning the zoetrope clockwise gives the opposite effect of spinning it counterclockwise.

▶ **You saw that there is a pattern in the different effects created by opposite motions in a zoetrope. In this exploration, you'll see how a similar pattern can be used to multiply and divide integers.**

▶ **Multiplication can be shown as movement on a number line, using repeated addition.**

EXAMPLE

Find the product 2 · (–3).

2 · (–3) means, "Add negative three 2 times."

Start at –3.   Face the positive direction.   Move backward 3 units.

–3   +   (–3)

-7 -6 -5 -4 -3 -2 -1 0 1

So, 2 · (–3) = –6.

5 **Discussion** How can you show 3 · (–2) on a number line? Start at –2. Face the positive direction. Move backward 2 units and then 2 more.

6 Find each product by writing the multiplication as a repeated addition and finding the sum.

a. 3 · 4 $4 + 4 + 4 = 12$ **b.** 3 · 0 $0 + 0 + 0 = 0$ **c.** 3 · (–4)
$(-4) + (-4) + (-4) = -12$

Use Labsheet 4C for Questions 7 and 8.

7.

×	3	2	1	0	–1	–2	–3
3	9	6	3	0	–3	–6	–9
2	6	4	2	0	–2	–4	–6
1	3	2	1	0	–1	–2	–3
0	0	0	0	0	0	0	0
–1	–3	–2	–1	0	1	2	3
–2	–6	–4	–2	0	2	4	6
–3	–9	–6	–3	0	3	6	9

7 Follow the directions to complete the *Multiplication Table*.

8 **Discussion** You can use your results from Question 7 to help discover rules for multiplying integers.

8. a. negative
b. positive
c. Multiply the factors as if both were whole numbers. Then make the product negative if the signs of the integers are opposite or make the product positive if the signs of the integers are the same.

a. Is the product of a positive integer and a negative integer *positive* or *negative*?

b. Is the product of two negative integers *positive* or *negative*?

c. How can you find the products in parts (a) and (b)?

…checks that you can multiply integers.

9 ✔ **CHECKPOINT** Find each product. (*Note:* 3(–7) = 3 · (–7).)

a. 3(–7) –21   **b.** (–4)(–12) 48 **c.** –9(8) –72   **d.** (–1)(–1) 1

10 How do the expressions (–5)(–9) and (–9)(–5) compare? How do their products compare? The factors are the same but are written in a different order; They are the same.

11 How do the expressions (–2)(3 · 4) and (–2 · 3)4 compare? How do their products compare? The factors are the same but are grouped differently; They are the same.

▶ **Properties of Multiplication** The **commutative property of multiplication** says that you can change the order of numbers in a multiplication problem and still get the same product. The **associative property of multiplication** says that you can change the grouping when you multiply numbers and still get the same product.

12 **Mental Math** Use the properties of multiplication and mental math to find the product $(-5)(25)(-6)(-4)$. -3000

▶ **Dividing Integers** You used patterns to help discover how to multiply integers. Now you'll use these patterns to divide integers.

13 **Try This as a Class** For every division problem, there is a related multiplication problem. For example, consider the division $12 \div 6 = 2$. The related multiplication is $6 \cdot 2 = 12$.

   a. Think about the division equation $-20 \div 5 = x$. Write the related multiplication equation. $5x = -20$

   b. What number must x equal to make the multiplication equation you wrote in part (a) true? -4

   c. What is the quotient $-20 \div 5$? -4

14 Write and solve a multiplication equation to find each quotient.

   a. $30 \div (-6) = x$ **b.** $-14 \div 2 = x$ **c.** $-9 \div (-3) = x$
   $-6x = 30; -5$ $2x = -14; -7$ $-3x = -9; 3$

   d. $-17 \div 17 = x$ **e.** $45 \div (-15) = x$ **f.** $-32 \div 4 = x$
   $17x = -17; -1$ $-15x = 45; -3$ $4x = -32; -8$

15 **Discussion** Think about your results from Question 14.
   See above.
   a. Consider the division $180 \div (-5)$. Will the quotient be *positive* or *negative*? How do you know?

   b. Write your own rule for dividing integers.

16 ✔ **CHECKPOINT** Find each quotient.

   a. $-18 \div (-3)$ **b.** $\dfrac{35}{-7}$ -5 **c.** $-150 \div 5$ **d.** $\dfrac{-48}{-6}$ 8
        6 -30

17 Is division associative? commutative? Support each answer with examples. No, $(100 \div (-10)) \div (-2) = 5$, $100 \div ((-10) \div (-2)) = 20$;
   No, $(-5) \div (-10) = 0.5$, $(-10) \div (-5) = 2$

18 **Discussion** Describe how the effects you saw in the zoetrope with the person walking forward and backward are related to the rules for multiplying and dividing integers. See above.

▌ **HOMEWORK EXERCISES** ▶ See Exs. 1–26 on pp. 285–286.

15. a. negative;
$(-5)(-36) = 180$
b. If the signs of the divisor and dividend are the same, the quotient is positive. If the signs are different, the quotient is negative.

18. (forward spin) of (strip of a person walking forward) shows (a person walking foward),
$(+)(+) = (+)$; (forward spin) of (strip of a person walking backward) shows (a person walking backward), $(+)(-) = (-)$; (backward spin) of (strip of a person walking forward) shows (a person walking backward), $(-)(+) = (-)$; (backward spin) of (strip of a person walking backward) shows (a person walking forward), $(-)(-) = (+)$

✔ **QUESTION 16**

...checks that you can divide integers.

Exploration 2

E Evaluating XPRESSIONS

In the early days of moviemaking, a close-up was considered a special effect. Because the camera did not move, the actors had to walk toward the camera.

Have you ever taken a close-up photo of a friend that came out blurry? To get a sharp picture in a close-up, the distance between the lens and the film must be increased. To focus close-ups, early moviemakers used extension tubes.

EXAMPLE

Suppose a 12.5 mm extension tube was added to a 25 mm lens for a close-up shot. Use the formula below to find the amount the lens opening setting had to be decreased in this situation.

$$\text{decrease in setting} = \frac{\text{lens size (mm)} + \text{extension length (mm)}}{\text{lens size (mm)}}$$

Remember, you must follow the order of operations.

$$= \frac{25 + 12.5}{25}$$

$$= \frac{37.5}{25}$$

$$= 1.5$$

The lens opening setting must be decreased by 1.5.

19. The fraction bar is a grouping symbol like parenthesis.

FOR◄HELP
with *order of operations*, see
MODULE 1, p. 65

19 Why was the addition operation performed before the division operation in the Example above**?**

20 Suppose a 20.5 mm extension tube is added to the lens in the Example for a different close-up shot. Find the amount the lens opening setting must be decreased. 1.82

21 For each expression, choose the letter of the correct value.

a. $3 \cdot 5\frac{2}{3} - 7$ C

b. $-36 \div (-2 + 11)$ B

c. $\dfrac{21}{0.3 + 0.4}$ A

> **A.** 30   **B.** −4
> **C.** 10   **D.** −2

22 Copy each number sentence and add grouping symbols to make each a true statement.

a. $-5 - 2 \cdot 7 + (-3) = -13$ **b.** $\frac{2}{3} \cdot 1\frac{3}{4} + \frac{5}{8} = 1\frac{7}{12}$

23 ✔ **CHECKPOINT** Evaluate each expression.

a. $5\frac{3}{4} - 2\frac{1}{2} \cdot \frac{3}{8}$ $4\frac{13}{16}$ **b.** $3.4 \cdot (7 - 2.9) + 11$ 24.94   **c.** $-42 \div 8 + 5^2$ 19.75

24 Suppose afternoon ticket prices at a movie theater are $3 for children under 16 and $5 for adults. Evening ticket prices are $4.50 for children under 16 and $7.75 for adults.

a. Choose variables for the number of children's tickets and the number of adults' tickets sold. Write an expression for the income in dollars from afternoon ticket sales each day.

b. Suppose 234 children's tickets and 127 adults' tickets were sold one afternoon. Use the expression you wrote in part (a) to find the income from afternoon ticket sales.

c. Write an expression for the income from evening ticket sales.

d. Look at the table. Use the expressions you wrote in parts (a) and (c) to determine whether the total income from ticket sales in dollars is correct. If not, find the correct total.

Motion Theater Ticket Sales			
Number of afternoon tickets sold		Number of evening tickets sold	
Children under 16	346	Children under 16	293
Adults	177	Adults	314
Total income from ticket sales in dollars			$5657.25

25 Evaluate each expression when $x = -6$.

a. $18.2 - x \cdot 4$ 42.2   **b.** $6x + \frac{1}{2}$ $-35\frac{1}{2}$ **c.** $54 \div (3 - x)$ 6

d. $\frac{1}{2}x + 7.2$ 4.2   **e.** $-12 - (x + 4)$ −10   **f.** $\frac{2x + 1}{5}$ $-\frac{11}{5}$, or $-2\frac{1}{5}$

HOMEWORK EXERCISES ▶ See Exs. 27–52 on pp. 286–287.

---

22. a. $-5 - [2 \cdot (7 + (-3))]$
$= -13$
b. $\frac{2}{3} \cdot \left(1\frac{3}{4} + \frac{5}{8}\right) = 1\frac{7}{12}$

✔ **QUESTION 23**

…checks that you can evaluate expressions that contain fractions, decimals, or integers.

24. a. Let c = the number of child tickets and a = the number of adult tickets; $3c + 5a$
b. $1337
c. $4.50c + 7.75a$
d. The total is incorrect; $5675

Section 4
Key Concepts

Multiplying and Dividing Integers (pp. 280–281)

The product or quotient of two integers:
- is positive when both integers are positive or both are negative.
- is negative when one integer is positive and the other is negative.

Examples
$$-3(-8) = -3 \cdot (-8) = 24 \qquad -24 \div (-8) = 3$$
$$3(-8) = 3 \cdot (-8) = -24 \qquad -24 \div 3 = -8$$

Reordering or regrouping can help you find products of more than two numbers using mental math. (p. 281)

Evaluating Expressions (pp. 282–283)

You evaluate expressions containing fractions, decimals, or integers the same way you evaluate whole number expressions. Follow the order of operations and evaluate expressions inside grouping symbols first.

Example

$$\frac{(-7) \cdot 8^2 - 3}{-6 - (-1)} = \frac{(-7) \cdot 64 - 3}{-6 - (-1)}$$

First evaluate the numerator.

$$= \frac{-448 - 3}{-6 - (-1)}$$

$$= \frac{-451}{-6 - (-1)}$$

Then evaluate the denominator.

$$= \frac{-451}{-6 + 1} = \frac{-451}{-5} = 90\frac{1}{5}$$

properties of
multiplication
commutative
associative

CLOSURE QUESTION

How is multiplication of positive and negative integers like multiplication of only positive integers? How is it different?

Sample Response: When multiplying positive and negative integers, you first multiply the integers as if they were positive, and then you determine the sign of the product. When you are multiplying only positive integers, you do not need to determine the sign of the product.

Key Concepts Questions

26 What can you tell about two integers if their product is positive? if it is negative? The integers are either both positive or both negative; The integers have opposite signs.

27 Evaluate each expression.

a. $-13 + 4 \div (-2)$ -15

b. $2\frac{5}{6} - 1\frac{1}{3} \cdot \frac{1}{4}$ $2\frac{1}{2}$

Section 4

Practice & Application Exercises ▸▸▸▸▸▸▸

YOU WILL NEED

For Ex. 60:
◆ graph paper
◆ ruler

For Exs. 61–66:
◆ algebra tiles

Find each product.

1. (–6)(5) –30   2. 15(–4) –60   3. 7(–6) –42   4. (–5)(–8) 40

5. (–9)(–4) 36   6. (22)(–11) –242   7. (–3)(12) –36   8. 30(–9) –270

Find each quotient.

9. –24 ÷ 6 –4   10. $\frac{72}{-9}$ –8   11. –45 ÷ (–9) 5   12. $\frac{-63}{9}$ –7

13. $\frac{-77}{-7}$ 11   14. 136 ÷ (–2) –68   15. $\frac{200}{-4}$ –50   16. 96 ÷ (–4) –24

Find each product.

17. (–2)(–3)(–8) –48   18. (3)(–10)(–1)4 120   19. 3(3)(–2)(4) –72

20. (–5)(–7)(–2)(–8) 560   21. (–7)(–8)(3) 168   22. 6(–25)(–2)(–4)(–5) 6000

23. Look at your answers to Exercises 17–22. Think about the number of positive and negative factors in each expression. When is the product of a set of integers positive? When is it negative? ·

23. when all the factors are positive or when there are an even number of negative factors; when there are an odd number of negative factors

24. **Golf** In golf, *par* is the number of strokes considered necessary to complete a hole in expert play. A *birdie* is a score of one stroke under par, and a *bogey* is a score of one stroke over par.

   a. Use integers to represent par, a birdie, and a bogey. 0, –1, 1

   b. Jamal and Craig finished a round of 18 holes with the given numbers of pars, birdies, and bogeys. What integer represents each golfer's final score as a number of strokes over, under, or at par? –2 for Jamal, 1 for Craig

Jamal

10 pars
5 birdies
3 bogeys

Final Score: _?_

Craig

11 pars
3 birdies
4 bogeys

Final Score: _?_

25. The chart shows the net gain or loss of a small company over the first three quarters of its start-up year. Suppose each quarter lasts 90 days.

Financial Report (in dollars)	1st Quarter	2nd Quarter	3rd Quarter
Net sales			
Bicycles	$12,560	$18,944	$21,490
Parts	5,800	2,500	7,820
Service	788	651	560
	19,148	22,095	29,870
Costs and expenses			
Building operation	12,400	10,790	12,095
Employee wages	13,048	10,495	12,375
	25,448	21,285	24,470
Net gain (loss)	(6,300)	810	5,400

Parentheses indicate a loss, or negative amount.

a. Find the mean loss per day during the first quarter. −70

b. Find the mean gain per day during the second quarter. 9

c. Find the mean loss or gain per day over all three quarters. −1

26. a. (−5)(−5)(−5), (−5)(−5)(−5)(−5)
b. −125, 625
c. negative; positive; (−5)(−5)(−5) = 25(−5) = −125, (−5)(−5)(−5)(−5) = (25)(25) = 625
d. If the exponent is an odd number, the product is negative. If the exponent is an even number, the product is positive.

26. Challenge Think about the expressions $(-5)^3$ and $(-5)^4$.

a. Write $(-5)^3$ and $(-5)^4$ as multiplication expressions.

b. Evaluate each multiplication expression you wrote in part (a).
$(-5)^3 = $? and $(-5)^4 = $? .

c. Is $(-5)^3$ *positive* or *negative*? Is $(-5)^4$ *positive* or *negative*? Explain how you decided.

d. Use your results from parts (a)–(c) to write a rule for evaluating powers of negative integers.

Evaluate each expression.

27. $4.5 \cdot 7 - 12$ 19.5   28. $\left(\frac{2}{7} + \frac{4}{21}\right) \div 5$ $\frac{2}{21}$ 29. $-11 + 2^3 (-3)$ −35

30. $2\frac{2}{5} \div 4 + \frac{2}{3}$ $1\frac{4}{15}$ 31. $-64 \div (-9 - 7)$ 4   32. $26.79 - 0.31 \cdot 8$ 24.31

33. $-2(13 - (-6))$ −38   34. $0.49 \div 0.7 - 3$ −2.3 35. $-18 \div 3^2 + 5(-6)$ −32

Evaluate each expression when $e = 5$, $f = 7.2$, and $g = 0.4$.

36. $3g$ 1.2   37. $\frac{f}{e}$ 1.44   38. $21.8 - f$ 14.6 39. $(e + f) \cdot g$ 4.88

40. **Telephone Rates** Suppose a phone company charges $2.30 for the first minute and $.87 for each additional minute for a long-distance call from Los Angeles, California, to Sydney, Australia. The length of each call is rounded up to the nearest minute.

Sydney

Los Angeles

a. Let x = the number of additional minutes after the first minute. Write an expression that represents the total cost of the call for any number of minutes. $2.3 + 0.87x$

b. How much will a 12 min call cost? $11.87

Evaluate each expression when $a = -6$ and $b = -2$.

41. $15 - b$ 17   42. $8b$ –16   43. $\dfrac{42}{a}$ –7   44. $3b + 7$ 1

Evaluate each expression when $x = \dfrac{3}{4}$, $y = 6$, and $z = 1\dfrac{1}{3}$.

45. $5x$ $3\dfrac{3}{4}$ 46. $7 - z$ $5\dfrac{2}{3}$ 47. $y \div \dfrac{4}{5}$ $7\dfrac{1}{2}$ 48. $9z + y$ 18

49. **Open-ended** Write a word problem that can be solved by evaluating the expression $4x + 10$ when $x = -6$. Then solve the problem. See above.

50. **Temperature** To convert a Celsius temperature to the equivalent Fahrenheit temperature, you can use the expression $1.8C + 32$, where C is the temperature in °C. What is the Fahrenheit temperature equivalent to 14°C?   57.2°F

51. **Snowy Tree Crickets** You can use the expression $\dfrac{5}{9}(n + 8)$ to estimate the temperature in degrees Celsius, where n is the number of times a snowy tree cricket chirps in 15 seconds. Suppose a snowy tree cricket chirps 34 times in 15 seconds. Estimate the Celsius temperature to the nearest degree.   about 23°C

Reflecting ◀▶on the Section

Write your response to Exercise 52 in your journal.

52. Can you tell whether the product or quotient of two integers is *greater than* or *less than* either integer when both are negative? when one is positive and one is negative? Explain. See above.

Journal

Exercise 52 checks that you understand multiplication and division with integers.

Tell whether each figure has *line symmetry*, *rotational symmetry*, **or** *both*. (Module 4, pp. 270–271)

53. both

54. line symmetry

55. rotational symmetry

Solve each equation. Check each answer. (Module 3, p. 223)

56. $6x = 42$ 7   57. $\frac{y}{4} = 36$ 144   58. $9s = 81$ 9   59. $\frac{r}{13} = 52$ 676

60. a–b.

a trapezoid

60. a. Graph the ordered pairs (1, 4), (4, 1), (–6, 1), and (–4, 4) in a coordinate plane. (Module 2, p. 95)

   b. Draw segments to connect the points in the order listed in part (a). Connect the last point to the first point. Name the polygon that is formed.

Extension ▶ ▶

Simplifying Variable Expressions Using Algebra Tiles

Algebra tiles can help you see how to simplify an expression with more than one term.

Follow the steps below to simplify each expression. Let the ▬ tile represent the variable *x* and the ◼ tile represent the number 1.

First — Model the expression using algebra tiles.

Then — Simplify the expression by grouping like tiles.

2x + 3   +   **x + 1**   =   **3x + 4**

61. $3x + 1 + 2x$
    $5x + 1$

62. $4x + 2x$
    $6x$

63. $5 + 3x + 4$
    $3x + 9$

64. $2x + 7x + 5$
    $9x + 5$

65. $6 + 3x + 4x$
    $7x + 6$

66. $3x + 3x + 2x$
    $8x$

Extra Skill Practice

Find each product or quotient.

1. $(-7)(4)$ –28

2. $12(-4)$ –48

3. $-27 \div (-3)$ 9

4. $7(-6)$ –42

5. $(-8)(-6)$ 48

6. $-42 \div 6$ –7

7. $\dfrac{-45}{-9}$ 5

8. $(32)(-11)$ –352

9. $98 \div (-7)$ –14

10. $\dfrac{63}{-9}$ –7

11. $(-4)(-8)(-2)$ –64

12. $140 \div (-4)$ –35

Evaluate each expression.

13. $-15 + 2^3(-7)$ –71

14. $\left(\dfrac{1}{6} + \dfrac{7}{18}\right) \div \dfrac{5}{8}$ $\dfrac{8}{9}$

15. $(1.4)(8) - 3.6$ 7.6

16. $4\dfrac{3}{4} \cdot \dfrac{5}{6} + 11$ $14\dfrac{23}{24}$

17. $-124 \div (-2 - 6)$ 15.5

18. $5^2 \cdot (37.9 - 4.31)$ 839.75

Evaluate each expression when $a = \dfrac{3}{4}$, $b = 6$, and $c = 1\dfrac{1}{3}$.

19. $7 \div c$ $5\dfrac{1}{4}$

20. ab $4\dfrac{1}{2}$

21. $2a + b$ $7\dfrac{1}{2}$

22. $9 - ac$ 8

Evaluate each expression when $q = 2.4$, $r = 0.7$, and $s = 8$.

23. $3r$ 2.1

24. $q \div s$ 0.3

25. $(q - r) \cdot s$ 13.6

26. $9r + q$ 8.7

Evaluate each expression when $x = -3$, $y = 9$, and $z = -5$.

27. $27 - z$ 32

28. $12x$ –36

29. $y + z \cdot x$ 24

30. $(-42 - y) \div x$ 17

Standardized Testing ◄► Performance Task

Roger Jones bought 16 pens priced at $.23 each. As he was leaving the store, he noticed a sign that read, "All pens on sale for 2 cents off." So he went back to the checkout counter and explained that he did not receive the discount on his purchase. "You owe me the difference between $.23 and $.02, multiplied by 16," he explained. To which the cashier replied, "If that is true, then *you owe me* $3.36!"

Explain to the cashier and Roger Jones what, if any, mistakes in mathematics each made and how to correct them. Use integers to represent the numbers in the problem.

Sample Response: Roger Jones incorectly stated the discount as $(23 - 2) \cdot 16 = 336$, or $3.36. This is his cost, and the discount is $2 \cdot 16 = 32$¢. The cashier incorrectly calculated the discount as $(2 - 23) \cdot 16 = -336$, or –$3.36, which would mean Roger Jones owed him that amount. The cashier subtracted incorrectly by subtracting the cost from the discount instead of the discount from the cost.

IN THIS SECTION

EXPLORATION 1
◆ Translations

EXPLORATION 2
◆ Changing Size and Shape

EXPLORATION 3
◆ Solving Two-Step Equations

ANIMATION

◄◄◄ *Setting the Stage*

WARM-UP EXERCISES

Decide whether each pair of figures is congruent. Explain your reasoning.

1.

No; the figures are not the same shape.

2.

Yes; the figures are the same size and shape.

3.

No; the figures are the same shape but are not the same size.

Use mental math to solve.

4. $-7 + x = 4$ 11
5. $p + 13 = 42$ 29
6. $12 + m = 8$ −4

When animated cartoons first replaced the zoetrope, artists still had to draw every frame much as you have done in this module. Today, to use computer animation to show a character parachuting to the ground, artists need to draw only the first, middle, and last frames—a computer draws all the frames in between!

Think About It

1 Suppose you were shown only the hand-drawn sketches of the computer animation sequence above. Do you think you would be able to tell what was happening in the sequence? Explain.
Yes; the parachutist was descending.

2 Sketch the first, the middle, and the last drawing of a simple computer animation sequence of your own. **Check students' work.**

TRAN**S**lations

GOAL

LEARN HOW TO...
◆ use coordinates to describe translations
◆ locate the image from a translation on a coordinate plane

AS YOU...
◆ explore ways to create animations

KEY TERMS
◆ transformation
◆ translation
◆ x-axis
◆ y-axis

SET UP   *You will need: • Labsheet 5A • tracing paper • graph paper*

▶ Computer animators used *transformations* to parachute the character on page 290 to the ground. A **transformation** is a change in a figure's shape, position, or size. The reflections and rotations you learned about in Section 3 are two types of transformations.

3   A **translation**, or slide, is another type of transformation. Each image below is a translation of the original figure.

a. Trace one of the original figures shown. Then slide the tracing along the arrows until it fits exactly on the image.
     Check students' work.
b. Did you have to flip or turn the tracing in order to make it fit exactly on the image? No

c. Are the original figure and its image congruent? Explain.
     Yes; the two figures are the same shape and size.
d. Use the directions *up* or *down* and *right* or *left* to describe the movement shown by each translation.   right; left and down

4 **Discussion** The transformations below are not translations.

a. How does each transformation differ from the translations shown in Question 3?   The first image has been rotated. The second image is larger than the original.

b. How would you define a translation?
     Sample Response: a change in a figure's position without a change in shape, size, or orientation

► The transformations used to move figures on a computer screen are described using the coordinates of points on the figures. Image 1 and Image 2 below are the results of two different translations of △ABC.

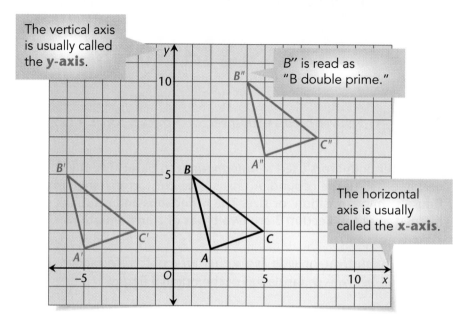

The vertical axis is usually called the **y-axis**.

B″ is read as "B double prime."

The horizontal axis is usually called the **x-axis**.

5 Describe the translation of △ABC that results in the image △A′B′C′.
a translation of 7 units to the left

6 Copy and complete the table. Record the coordinates of the vertices of △ABC and the vertices of its two images.

	Vertex	Coordinates	Vertex	Coordinates	Vertex	Coordinates
△ABC	A	(2,1)	B	? (1, 5)	C	? (5, 2)
△A′B′C′	A′	? (−5, 1)	B′	? (−6, 5)	C′	? (−2, 2)
△A″B″C″	A″	? (5, 6)	B″	? (4, 10)	C″	? (8, 7)

7 **Discussion** Look at your completed table from Question 6.

a. How are the coordinates of the vertices of △A′B′C′ related to the coordinates of the vertices of △ABC?
Each x-coordinate is 7 less and each y-coordinate is the same.

b. How does the relationship you found in part (a) describe the movement on the coordinate plane shown by the translation?
The image is 7 units to the left of the original.

c. Repeat parts (a) and (b) for △A″B″C″ and △ABC. Each x-coordinate is 3 more and each y-coordinate is 5 more. The image is 3 units to the right and 5 units above the original.

8 Suppose a third translation of △ABC subtracts 5 from the y-coordinate of each vertex of △ABC. Describe the location of the image of △ABC produced by this translation. 5 units below the original

► In Questions 6–8 on page 292, you saw that a translation can be defined by describing how the coordinates of the points of the original figure are changed. The notation (x + 1, y – 2) means add 1 to each x-coordinate and subtract 2 from each y-coordinate.

9 **Use Labsheet 5A.** Follow the directions on Labsheet 5A for *Translating a Figure* with the translation (x + 1, y – 2).

10 Use coordinates to describe each translation.

a. 2 units to the right
(x + 2, y)

b. 1 unit to the left, 3 units up
(x – 1, y + 3)

11 ✔ **CHECKPOINT** Suppose you want to translate a triangle 3 units to the left and 4 units down.

a. Use coordinates to describe the translation. (x – 3, y – 4)

b. Draw a triangle with vertices (–2, 2), (3, 5), and (4, 1) on a coordinate plane. Then draw its image after the translation. Label the coordinates of the vertices of the image.

12 **Discussion** Help! The character shown has lost its image. Its image is the result of the translation (x – 10, y + 1).

a. Use the directions *right* or *left* and *up* or *down* to describe how the translation moves a figure. **10 units left and 1 unit up**

b. Use coordinates to describe the translation that will make the image move back so it fits exactly on the original figure.
(x + 10, y – 1)

c. Suppose the tip of the left foot of the image is at (11, 5). Find the coordinates of the tip of the left foot of the original figure.
(21, 4)

HOMEWORK EXERCISES ► See Exs. 1–13 on pp. 300–301.

9. a. The translation is 1 unit to the right and 2 units down.
b. Original figure: W(1,2); X(3,4); Y(4,1); Z(2,1); Image: W'(2, 0); X'(4, 2); Y'(5, –1); Z'(3, –1)
c.

d. It is the same.

✔ **QUESTION 11**

…checks that you can use coordinates to describe a translation and locate an image.

11. b.

LEARN HOW TO...
- stretch or squash a figure on a coordinate plane
- identify similar figures

AS YOU...
- explore ways to make animation more realistic

KEY TERM
- similar

15. b. $(3x, y)$: $A'(-6, 0)$, $B'(-6, 1)$, $C'(0, 2)$, $D'(6, 1)$, $E'(6, 0)$; $(x, 3y)$: $A''(-2, 0)$, $B''(-2, 3)$, $C''(0, 6)$, $D''(2, 3)$, $E''(2, 0)$; $(3x, 3y)$: $A'''(-6, 0)$, $B'''(-6, 3)$, $C'''(0, 6)$, $D'''(6, 3)$, $E'''(6, 0)$
c. Check students' drawings. Vertices should be those listed in part (b).
d. Transformation 1: horizontal stretch; Transformation 2: vertical stretch; Transformation 3: both horizontal and vertical stretch. Both the image and the original figure are pentagons.

16. a. 2 units, 4 units; Transformation 1: 2 units, 12 units; Transformation 2: 6 units, 4 units; Transformation 3: 6 units, 12 units
b. The first transformation results in a horizontal stretch, the second in a vertical stretch, and the third in a horizontal and vertical stretch by the same amount.

Exploration 2

CHANGING SIZE *and* SHAPE

SET UP *Work in a group of three. You will need:* • *Labsheet 5B* • *graph paper* • *ruler*

▶ To make movement appear smoother and more realistic, animators often use *stretch* and *squash* effects, as shown in this animation sequence of a bouncing ball.

13 In which drawings is the ball squashed or stretched? 5 to 9

14 a. Which of the drawings are translations of drawing 1? In drawings 2, 3, 4, and 10 the ball has been both translated and rotated.
b. How can you tell that the other drawings are not translations of drawing 1? They do not have the same size and shape as drawing 1.

▶ Squashing and stretching transformations can be described with coordinates.

Use Labsheet 5B for Questions 15–17.

15 Follow the directions on Labsheet 5B to explore how different transformations can be used in *Stretching and Squashing a Figure*.

16 Discussion Use the image you drew on Labsheet 5B.

a. Find the height and the width of figure *ABCDE* and the height and the width of the image you drew.

b. Does the image you drew show a stretch in both the height and the width of the original figure? Explain.

▶ Figures are **similar** if they have the same shape, but not necessarily the same size.

EXAMPLE

These are similar triangles.   These are *not* similar triangles.

Congruent figures are similar.

17 Look at the images the members of your group drew on Labsheet 5B.   *See above.*

   a. Which images look similar to figure *ABCDE*? Why?

   b. Find the lengths of the sides of each image you listed in part (a).

   c. How do the lengths of the sides you found in part (b) compare with the lengths of the sides of figure *ABCDE*? How do your findings relate to the transformation?

18 a. Copy △*EFG* on graph paper.   **Check students' work.**

   b. Predict whether each transformation below will result in an image that is similar to △*EFG*.

   A. $\left(\frac{1}{2}x, y\right)$ No.   **B.** $\left(x, \frac{1}{2}y\right)$ No.   **C.** $\left(\frac{1}{2}x, \frac{1}{2}y\right)$ Yes.

   c. Each member of your group should graph the image of △*EFG* after one of the transformations A, B, or C in part (b).   See above.

   d. Determine whether each image is similar to △*EFG*. Explain your reasoning.
   A: No, horizontal squashing only; B: No, vertical squashing only;
   C: Yes, horizontal and vertical squashing by the same amount

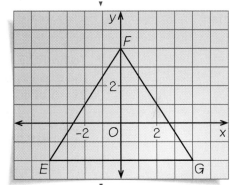

19 ✔ **CHECKPOINT** Tell whether each transformation will result in an image that is similar to the original figure. Explain.

   a. (*x*, 2*y*) See above.   **b.** (3*x*, 3*y*) See above.   **c.** $\left(\frac{1}{4}x, \frac{1}{2}y\right)$ See below.

20 Discussion Suppose △*Q'R'S'* is the image of △*QRS* after the transformation (*x*, 2*y*). The coordinates of *R'* are (−3, 8). How can you use the coordinates of *R'* to find the coordinates of *R*?
   Use the same *x*-coordinate, but divide the *y*-coordinate of *R'* by 2.

HOMEWORK EXERCISES ▶ See Exs. 14–21 on pp. 301–302.

---

17. a. the image from the third transformation; It has the same shape as the original figure.
b. $\overline{A'''E'''}$ is 12 units long, $\overline{A'''B'''}$ and $\overline{D'''E'''}$ are both 3 units long, $\overline{B'''C'''}$ and $\overline{D'''C'''}$ are about $6\frac{3}{4}$ units long
c. Each side is 3 times as long; Size has been changed, but not the position or shape.

18. c. Check students' drawings. Vertices are as follows. Transformation A: *E'*(−2, −2), *F'*(0, 4), *G'*(2, −2);
Transformation B: *E'*(−4, −1), *F'*(0, 2), *G'*(4, −1);
Transformation C: *E'*(−2, −1), *F'*(0, 2), *G'*(2, −1)

19. a. No; vertical stretching only
b. Yes; both horizontal and vertical stretching by some amount

✔ **QUESTION 19**

...checks that you can use coordinates to find whether a transformation produces a similar image.

19. c. No; horizontal and vertical squashing, but by different amounts

Exploration 3

Solving TWO-STEP EQUATIONS

SET UP *You will need Labsheet 5C.*

▶ **Sometimes computer animators need to change the shape of a figure *and* move it across the screen. For this type of transformation, they use multiplication and division with addition and subtraction.**

21. The image will be stretched 2 times horizontally and 3 times vertically. It will be moved 3 units to the right and 4 units below the original.

21 **Discussion** How do you think the transformation $(2x + 3, 3y - 4)$ will change the shape and the location of the flag shown?

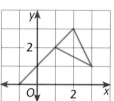

22 **Use Labsheet 5C.** Follow the directions to examine the effects of the transformation $(2x + 3, 3y - 4)$ on the flag.
a. $A'(1, -4), B'(5, 2), C'(7, 5), D'(9, -1)$; **b.** Check students' drawings. Vertices should be as listed in part (a).

▶ **To find the *x*-coordinate of point *A'* (the image of *A*), you evaluated the expression $2x + 3$ for $x = -1$. Substituting –1 for *x* in the expression $2x + 3$ gives $2(-1) + 3$.**

23 **Discussion** When you evaluate the expression $2(-1) + 3$, which operation do you perform first? Why?
multiplication; In the order of operations, multiplication is done before addition.

▶ **The order of operations tells you how to evaluate an expression.**

FOR ◄ HELP

with *order of operations*, see
MODULE 1, p. 65

EXAMPLE

Evaluate the expression $2x + 3$ when $x = 4$.

$2x + 3$	Add 3.	$8 + 3 = 11$
$2x$	Multiply by 2.	$2 \cdot 4 = 8$
x	Start with the number.	4

24 **Use Labsheet 5C.** Mark the point (7, 2) on the image you
drew of the flag. Predict the coordinates of the point on the
original figure that was transformed to (7, 2). (2, 2)

▶ **Sometimes you want to find the coordinates of a point when you
know the coordinates of its image. To find the *x*-coordinate, first write
an equation using the expressions for the *x*-coordinate from the
transformation and from the image.**

Transformation   Image

$(2x + 3, 3y - 4)$ $(7, 2)$

$2x + 3 = 7$

▶ **Then you need to find a value for *x* that makes the equation true.**

25 **Discussion** Examine the diagram below that shows the steps for
solving the equation $2x + 3 = 7$.

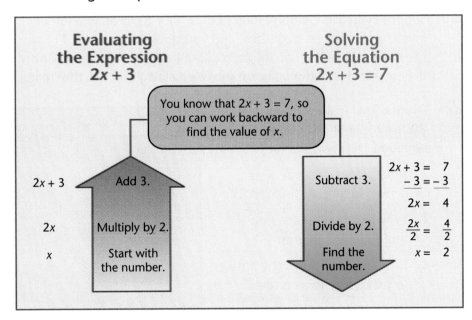

Evaluating
the Expression
$2x + 3$

Solving
the Equation
$2x + 3 = 7$

You know that $2x + 3 = 7$, so
you can work backward to
find the value of *x*.

$2x + 3$ Add 3.   Subtract 3.

$2x$ Multiply by 2.   Divide by 2.

x Start with
the number.   Find the
number.

$2x + 3 = 7$
$- 3 = -3$
$2x = 4$

$\dfrac{2x}{2} = \dfrac{4}{2}$

$x = 2$

a. What inverse operation is used to undo the multiplication $2x$?
division by 2
b. Why do you *subtract 3* before you *divide by 2*?
Otherwise, you would have to divide 3 by 2, 7 by 2, and subtract the quotients.
c. How do you know in what order to use the inverse operations
to solve an equation?
Do addition or subtraction first. Then, multiplication or division. That is,
reverse the order of operations.

26 a. To find the *y*-coordinate of the point whose image is (7, 2) after the transformation (2*x* + 3, 3*y* – 4), use the diagram below to solve the equation 3*y* – 4 = 2. 2

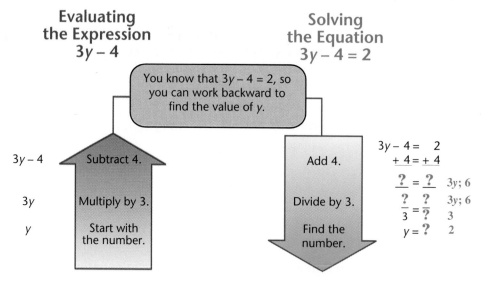

b. How do the coordinates you found in part (a) and in Question 25 compare with your prediction from Question 24?
They are the same.

27 Suppose you use the translation (3*x* – 2, 2*y* + 5) to draw another image of the flag on page 296, and you label the point (4, 11) on the image. Solve the equations 3*x* – 2 = 4 and 2*y* + 5 = 11 to find the coordinates of the point on the original flag that has this image. (2, 3)

28 Discussion A student wrote this example of how to solve an equation with two operations.

a. What inverse operation is shown in Step 1? in Step 3?
addition of 4, multiplication by 2

b. Why did the student not multiply by 2 in Step 1?
It's less complicated to do addition or subtraction first.

c. How can you check the answer to make sure it is correct?
Substitute 18 for *y* in the original equation, and see if the resulting sentence is true.

✔ **QUESTION 29**

...checks that you can solve two-step equations.

29 ✔ **CHECKPOINT** Solve each equation. Check each solution.

a. 9*x* – 6 = 21 3   **b.** $\frac{y}{3}$ + 2 = 14 36   **c.** –2*x* + 7 = 15 –4

HOMEWORK EXERCISES ▷ See Exs. 22–39 on pp. 303–304.

Section 5
Key Concepts

Key Terms

Transformations and Translations (pp. 291–293)

A transformation is a change in a figure's shape, size, or location. Transformations can be described using coordinates.

transformation

A translation is a transformation that slides a figure to a new location. The image is congruent to the original figure.

translation

Example The original trapezoid is translated 4 units to the right and 2 units up.

Original: (x, y)
Image: $(x + 4, y + 2)$

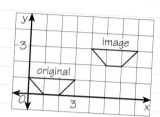

x-axis

y-axis

Transformations that Stretch or Squash (pp. 294–295)

You can stretch or squash a figure horizontally by multiplying the x-coordinates of all its points by the same factor, or vertically by multiplying the y-coordinates of all its points by the same factor. A factor greater than one stretches. A factor between zero and one squashes.

When you stretch or squash a figure horizontally and vertically by the same factor, the image is similar to the original figure. Figures are similar if they are the same shape, but not necessarily the same size.

similar

Examples

horizontal stretch   vertical squash   similar to original

  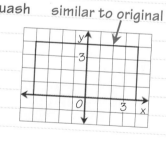

30 **Key Concepts Question** Choose the letters of the transformations that result in an image similar to the original figure. Explain.

A. $\left(\frac{1}{5}x, \frac{1}{5}y\right)$ B. $(x + 3, y - 1)$ C. $(4x, 3y)$

30. A: The figure is squashed vertically and horizontally the same amount. B: Only the position of the original figure is changed.

Continued on next page

Section ⑤

Key Concepts

Solving Two-Step Equations (pp. 297–298)

You solve two-step equations by working backward through the order of operations using inverse operations.

Example Solve the equation $3n - 8 = 13$ and check your solution.

$$3n - 8 = 13$$
$$3n - 8 + 8 = 13 + 8 \qquad \text{Step 1: Add 8 to both sides.}$$
$$3n = 21 \qquad \text{Step 2: Simplify.}$$
$$\frac{3n}{3} = \frac{21}{3} \qquad \text{Step 3: Divide both sides by 3.}$$
$$n = 7 \qquad \text{Step 4: Simplify.}$$

Check: $3(7) - 8 = 21 - 8 = 13$ ✔

CLOSURE QUESTION

How are translations like stretches or squashes? How are they different.

Sample Response: Both are types of transformations that change a figure in some way. A translation slides a figure to a different location without rotating or reflecting it. Also, a translation does not change the size or shape of a figure, so its image is congruent to the original figure. A stretch or squash changes a figure's size and sometimes its shape, so the image is not congruent to the original figure. Also, a stretch or squash does not slide, rotate, or reflect a figure.

31 Key Concepts Question The coordinates of the image of a point after the transformation $\left(2x + 17, \frac{y}{2} + 4\right)$ are (19, 9). Find the coordinates of the original point. (1, 10)

Section ⑤

Practice & Application Exercises

YOU WILL NEED

For Exs. 12–13 and 16:
♦ graph paper

For Ex. 37:
♦ calculator

Tell whether each diagram shows a translation of the original figure. If not, explain why not.

1.

No; The figure has been rotated.

2.

No; The figure has been turned over.

3.

Yes.

Describe each translation using coordinates.

4. 9 units to the left $(x - 9, y)$

5. 5 units down $(x, y - 5)$

6. 12 units up $(x, y + 12)$

7. 3 units to the right $(x + 3, y)$

8. 6 units to the right and 7 units up $(x + 6, y + 7)$

9. 2 units to the left and 4 units down $(x - 2, y - 4)$

10. **African Patterns** Many traditional African patterns were created by translating a design. Use coordinates to describe how the design shown was translated to create the pattern. $(x + 4, y + 2)$

◄ The *Namba*, or knot, fabric pattern was created by the Kuba people of the Congo. It has its origin in the knotting of string to make fishnets.

11. **Research** Look through clothing catalogs or newspapers to find two examples of patterns that were created by translating a figure. Cut them out to show in class.
Check students' work.

Draw a rectangle on a coordinate plane. Then draw its image after each translation.

12. $(x + 3, y - 4)$

13. $(x - 2, y - 5)$

12. Answers will vary. However, the image of the rectangle should be 3 units to the right and 4 units below the original.

13. Answers will vary. However, the image of the rectangle should be 2 units to the left and 5 units below the original.

For Exercises 14 and 15, tell which figures in each set are similar.

14. A   B
B and D
C   D

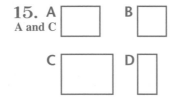

15. A   B
A and C
C   D

16. See Additional Answers.

16. a. Copy rectangle *WXYZ* on graph paper.

b. For each transformation, predict how the size, shape, or location of the image of rectangle *WXYZ* will differ from that of the original figure.

Transformation A: $(3x, y)$

Transformation B: $(x - 2, y)$

Transformation C: $\left(x, \dfrac{y}{4}\right)$

Transformation D: $(3x, 3y)$

c. Draw each image. Tell whether the image is similar to rectangle *WXYZ*. Explain your reasoning.

Computer Graphics With most computer drawing software, you can stretch or squash a graphic by dragging one of the *handles* of its *boundary box*. Choose the letter of the transformation that describes each stretched image of the graphic at the right.

boundary box

handle

17. c

18. A

19. B

A. (2x, 2y) B. (2x, y) C. (x, 2y)

20. Suppose a computer animator wants to use the transformation (5x, y) to stretch the figure shown.

a. Make a sketch of how you think the figure will look after the transformation.

b. What transformation of the image you drew in part (a) will undo the stretch and result in an image that is the same size and shape as the original figure? $\left(\frac{1}{5}x, y\right)$

21. a. The figure at the right shows the image of △ABC after a reflection across the y-axis. Write the coordinates of the vertices of △ABC and the vertices of its image.

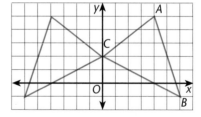

b. By what numbers can you multiply the coordinates of a point to reflect it across the x-axis? the y-axis?

c. Write the coordinates of the image of each point after a reflection across the indicated axis. (3, –7), (–4, 0), (5, –8), (–4, –9)

Q(3, 7), x-axis

R(4, 0), y-axis

S(–5, –8), y-axis

T(–4, 9), x-axis

Solve each equation. Check each solution.

22. $2t + 9 = 17$ 4

23. $\frac{n}{3} - 6 = 4$ 30

24. $12 + 4y = -32$ –11

25. $5m - 4.5 = 7$ 2.3

26. $2 + \frac{x}{4} = 2$ 0

27. $-9b + 6 = 21$ $-1\frac{2}{3}$

28. $\frac{p}{6} - 11 = 37$ 288

29. $12h + 45 = 72$ $2\frac{1}{4}$

30. $\frac{k}{7} + 0.6 = 5.7$ 35.7

For Exercises 31–33, write an equation to represent each statement. Then solve the equation and check your solution.

31. Seven more than twice a number is thirty-one. $2n + 7 = 31;\ 12$

32. A number divided by three and then decreased by eight is five.
$\frac{n}{3} - 8 = 5;\ 39$

33. Four increased by the product of a number and six is eighteen.
$4 + 6n = 18;\ 2\frac{1}{3}$

34. A bike rental store charges a flat fee of $15 plus $3 per day to rent a mountain bike.

   a. Let x = the number of days a mountain bike is rented. Write an equation to show the cost of renting a mountain bike.
   Let c = the rental cost. So, $c = 15 + 3x$

   b. Suppose a person was charged $63 for renting a mountain bike. For how many days did the person rent the bike? 16 days

35. Open-ended Write a word problem that can be answered by solving the equation $4x - 15 = 33$. Then solve the problem.
Sample Response: Erik received $15 off the price of 4 CD's. If his bill was $33, what was the original price of a CD?; $12

36. Firefighting To calculate how far a water stream from a fire hose with a $\frac{3}{4}$ in. diameter nozzle will reach, firefighters use this formula:

$$S = \frac{n}{2} + 26$$

n = nozzle pressure in pounds per square inch

   a. Suppose the end of a fire hose with a $\frac{3}{4}$ in. diameter nozzle is positioned about 60 ft from a fire for safety reasons. Use the formula to find the amount of nozzle pressure needed for the water stream to reach the fire.
68 pounds per square inch

   b. Challenge For every $\frac{1}{8}$ in. increase in nozzle diameter, the water stream reaches another 5 ft. Suppose the nozzle of the fire hose used in part (a) had a 1 in. diameter. What nozzle pressure would be needed to reach the fire? 48 pounds per square inch

S = horizontal reach of the water stream in feet

37. 📟 Calculator Describe a key sequence that you can use to solve the equation $\frac{x}{7} - 12 = 5$ on a calculator. Then use your key sequence to solve the equation. Check your solution.
See Additional Answers.

38. $\triangle R'S'T'$ is the image of $\triangle RST$ after the transformation $\left(3x - 2, \frac{y}{2}\right)$.

The coordinates of the vertices of $\triangle R'S'T'$ are $R'(-5, 1)$, $S'(-2, 2)$, and $T'(1,1)$. Find the coordinates of the vertices of $\triangle RST$.
$R(-1, 2), S(0, 4), T(1, 2)$

Journal

Exercise 39 checks that you can solve two-step equations.

Reflecting ◀▶ on the Section

Write your response to Exercise 39 in your journal.

39. Examine Owen's solution to the equation $2x + 7 = 18$ and his teacher's comment. Where did Owen make an error? What should he have done instead?

In the second step, Owen should have also divided 7 by 2. Or, he could have subtracted 7 from both sides of the equation first, and then divided both sides by 2.

$2x + 7 = 18$

$\frac{2x}{2} + 7 = \frac{18}{2}$

$x + 7 = 9$

$x + 7 - 7 = 9 - 7$

$x = 2$

Owen, please review and redo your work. If $2x + 7 = 18$ and $x = 2$, then $2 \cdot 2 + 7$ should equal 18, but it does not.

Spiral ◀▶ Review

Evaluate each expression. (Module 4, p. 284)

40. $(4.6 + 7.2) \cdot 5$ 59
41. $-9 - 28 \div 7$ -13
42. $\frac{4}{9} \cdot (-12) + 3$ $-2\frac{1}{3}$

43. $11 + 6 \cdot 3\frac{3}{8}$ $31\frac{1}{4}$
44. $0.32 \div 0.8 \cdot 1.2$ 0.48
45. $-68 \div 2 + (-54)$ -88

Replace each ? **with the number that makes the statement true.**
(Table of Measures, p. 597)

46. $3 \text{ h} = \underline{?} \text{ min}$ 180
47. $25 \text{ min} = \underline{?} \text{ s}$ 1500
48. $90 \text{ min} = \underline{?} \text{ h}$ $1\frac{1}{2}$

Replace each ? **with >, <, or =.** (Module 3, p. 170)

49. $\frac{7}{24} \underline{\quad?\quad} \frac{5}{12}$ $<$
50. $\frac{3}{27} \underline{\quad?\quad} \frac{2}{9}$ $<$
51. $\frac{4}{16} \underline{\quad?\quad} \frac{7}{48}$ $>$

Animator: Karen Kiser

Frame	1	3	6	10
Size	1	0.3	1.4	1

Karen Kiser uses a table like the one above to show computer commands that animate squashes and stretches. For example, a command of *size 2* multiplies the *y*-coordinate by 2 and divides the *x*-coordinate by 2.

52. Use coordinates to describe the change in size in each frame.

$(x, y); \left(\frac{1}{0.3}x, 0.3y\right); \left(\frac{1}{1.4}x, 1.4y\right); (x, y)$

Working on the Module Project

Lights, Camera—Action!

Transformations Use transformations to create your own animation strip.

 6 **Use Project Labsheet B.** Each frame of *Blank Zoetrope Strip B* represents the first quadrant of a coordinate plane. Check students' work.

a. Cut out the zoetrope strip pieces and tape them together.

b. Draw a simple figure in Frame 1 of the strip. Mark several points on the figure and record their coordinates.

c. Decide how to move the figure from frame to frame. Then use coordinates to describe your transformation.

d. Complete F2–F3 by drawing the image of the figure in the previous frame after your transformation from part (c).

 7 Place your animation strip in the zoetrope so the frames are centered under the slots. Spin the zoetrope. What do you see? Check students' work.

Section ⑤

Tell whether each diagram shows a translation of the original figure. If not, explain why not.

1. No; The figure has been rotated or reflected.

2. Yes.

3.   No; The figure has been rotated or reflected.

For Exercises 4–6, describe each translation using coordinates.

4. 3 units to the left and 6 units down $(x - 3, y - 6)$

5. 1 unit to the left and 5 units up $(x - 1, y + 5)$

6. 8 units to the right and 2 units down $(x + 8, y - 2)$

7. Draw a triangle on a coordinate plane. Then draw its image after the translation $(x - 2, y + 3)$. Check students' work. The image of the rectangle will be 2 units to the left and 3 units above the original.

Tell whether each transformation will result in an image that is similar to the original figure. Explain your reasoning.

8. $\left(\frac{1}{2}x, 2y\right)$ No; The figure is squashed horizontally and stretched vertically

9. $(4x, y)$ No; There is only horizontal stretching.

10. $\left(\frac{1}{5}x, \frac{1}{5}y\right)$ Yes; The figure is squashed the same amount horizontally and vertically.

11. Suppose a computer animator wants to use the transformation $\left(x, \frac{1}{4}y\right)$ to squash the figure at the right. Make a sketch to show how the car will look after the transformation. See Additional Answers.

Solve each equation. Check each solution.

12. $2y + 8 = 42$ 17

13. $9x - 17 = 19$ 4

14. $\frac{s}{4} + 11 = 20$ 36

15. $21n - 7 = 35$ 2

16. $6z - 7 = 13$ $3\frac{1}{3}$

17. $\frac{q}{8} - 5 = 7$ 96

18. $35 + 4r = 15$ –5

19. $\frac{f}{9} - 12 = 3$ 135

Standardized Testing ◀▶ **Open-ended**

Sketch a small, simple design on a coordinate plane. Next, describe how the transformation $(2x + 2, \frac{3}{4}y)$ would change your design.

Then, sketch the image of your design for that transformation. Locate a point on the image and find the coordinates of the corresponding point on the original figure.

Check students' drawings. The transformation is a horizontal stretch by a factor of 2 followed by a horizontal translation 2 units right, and a vertical squash by a factor of $\frac{3}{4}$.

Completing the Module Project

Lights, Camera—Action!

In this module you have been using mathematics to create special animated effects with your zoetrope strips. To complete the project, you'll work as a group to create and set up a viewing station featuring several animation strips that use the special effects of your choice.

8–11. Check students' work.

 8 Choose your favorite animation strip from the ones you have already made, or create a new one by applying the techniques you have learned. Be sure that each group member contributes at least one strip for the viewing station.

 9 Create a sign for your viewing station. Include the title of each animation strip, a brief description of the mathematical ideas that were used to create it, and the animator's name.

Some of the mathematical ideas you have explored are:

- ◆ fraction multiplication and division

- ◆ decimal estimation

- ◆ integer multiplication and division

- ◆ transformations: rotations, reflections, translations, stretches and squashes

- ◆ solving equations

 10 Set up your viewing station. Be sure your sign is clearly visible.

 11 Now it's showtime! With your group, visit each viewing station and view the animation strips.

SET UP

Work in a group.

You will need:

- *Project Labsheets A and B*
- *zoetrope*
- *poster paper*
- *scissors*
- *tape*
- *ruler*
- *protractor*

Review and Assessment

You will need: • *calculator* (Exs. 1–3) • *protractor* (Ex. 29)
• *tracing paper* (Ex. 30) • *graph paper* (Ex. 42)

Use 3.14 or the π key on a calculator. **Find the circumference of a circle with each measure. If necessary, round each answer to the nearest hundredth.** (Sec. 1, Explor. 1) **1–3.** Answers are given using the π key.

1. diameter = 12 cm
   37.70 cm
2. radius = 4 ft 25.13 ft
3. diameter = 23 ft 72.26 ft

Find the reciprocal of each number. (Sec. 1, Explor. 2)

4. 1 1
5. $\frac{5}{8}$ $\frac{8}{5}$
6. $1\frac{1}{3}$ $\frac{3}{4}$
7. 9 $\frac{1}{9}$

Find each product or quotient. Write each answer in lowest terms.
(Sec. 1, Explors. 2 and 3)

8. $\frac{5}{8} \cdot \frac{4}{9}$ $\frac{5}{18}$
9. $\frac{3}{10} \div \frac{2}{5}$ $\frac{3}{4}$
10. $7\frac{1}{2} \cdot 3$ $22\frac{1}{2}$
11. $\frac{8}{9} \div \frac{2}{3}$ $1\frac{1}{3}$

12. $3 \div \frac{5}{6}$ $3\frac{3}{5}$
13. $4\frac{2}{5} \cdot 2\frac{5}{6}$ $12\frac{7}{15}$
14. $8\frac{4}{7} \div \frac{1}{3}$ $25\frac{5}{7}$
15. $\frac{8}{11} \cdot 2\frac{3}{4}$ 2

Estimate each product or quotient. Tell whether each estimate will be *greater than* or *less than* the exact answer. Then find the exact answer.
(Sec. 2, Explors. 1 and 2)

16. (3.2)(0.09)
    0.32, greater than, 0.288
17. 3.2 ÷ 0.9
    4, greater than, 3.$\overline{5}$
18. (4)(0.103)
    0.4, less than, 0.412
19. 47 ÷ 0.011
    4700, greater than, 4272.72

20. 2.5 ÷ 8
    0.3, less than, 0.3125
21. (7.9)(1.25)
    10, greater than, 9.875
22. (38)(0.07)
    2.8, greater than, 2.66
23. 28.96 ÷ 0.24
    100, less than, 120.$\overline{6}$

Write each fraction as a decimal. (Sec. 2, Explor. 3)

24. $\frac{3}{8}$ 0.375
25. $\frac{5}{6}$ 0.8$\overline{3}$
26. $\frac{2}{9}$ 0.$\overline{2}$
27. $\frac{8}{5}$ 1.6

28. **Which quotients in Exercises 24–27 are terminating? Which are repeating?** (Sec. 2, Explor. 3) $\frac{3}{8}$ and $\frac{8}{5}$; $\frac{5}{6}$ and $\frac{2}{9}$

29. **Tell whether the top part of the windmill shown at the right has rotational symmetry. If so, find all its rotational symmetries.** (Sec. 3, Explor. 1)
    Yes; 20°; 40°; 60°; 80°; 100°; 120°; 140°; 160°; 180°; 200°; 220°; 240°; 260°; 280°; 300°; 320°; 340°

◄ This windmill is in Southern Utah.

30. Tell whether the diagram shows a reflection of the original figure across the given line. If not, explain why not. (Sec. 3, Explor. 2)
No; The distance from *A* to the line of symmetry is not the same as the distance from *A'* to the line of symmetry.

Find each product or quotient. (Sec. 4, Explor. 1)

31. 9(–7) –63   **32.** 28 ÷ (–4) –7   **33.** (–12)(–6) 72   **34.** –36 ÷ 6 –6

35. –104 ÷ (–8) 13   **36.** (–2)(–13)(–1) –26   **37.** $-\frac{12}{3}$ –4   **38.** 7(–4)(3)(–5) 420

Evaluate each expression. (Sec. 4, Explor. 2)

39. $6.2 \div (2.1 + 1) \cdot 14.7$ 29.4   **40.** $2\frac{5}{8} \cdot 1\frac{1}{2} - 3\frac{15}{16}$ **41.** $\frac{3^3 + 5(-3)}{-7 - (-4)}$ –4

For Exercises 42 and 43, use △ABC shown at the right.

42. a. Suppose you want to move △ABC 3 units to the left and 1 unit down. Describe the transformation using coordinates. (Sec. 5, Explor. 1) $(x - 3, y - 1)$

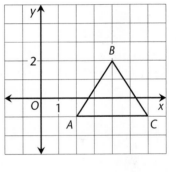

  b. Draw △ABC on graph paper. Then draw its image after the translation in part (a).
  Check students' drawings. Vertices are A′(–1, –2), B′(1, 1), C′(3, –2).

43. Use transformations I, II, and III. (Sec. 5, Explor. 2)

I: $\left(2x, \frac{y}{2}\right)$ II: $\left(2x, 2y\right)$ III: $\left(\frac{x}{2}, y\right)$

  a. For each transformation of △ABC, predict how the size, the shape, or the location of the image of △ABC will be different from that of the original figure.

  b. Draw each image and tell whether it is similar to △ABC.

43. a. I: The image will be twice as wide and half as high; II: The image will be twice as wide and twice as high; III: The image will be half as wide, but the same height.
b. Check students' drawings. Vertices are:
I: $A'\left(4, -\frac{1}{2}\right)$, $B'(8, 1)$, $C'\left(12, -\frac{1}{2}\right)$;
II: $A'(4, -2)$, $B'(8, 4)$, $C'(12, -2)$;
III: $A'(1, -1)$, $B'(2, 2)$, $C'(3, -1)$;
Only transformation II results in a similar triangle.

Solve each equation. Check each solution. (Sec. 5, Explor. 3)

44. $2x + 4 = 28$ 12   **45.** $3n - 7 = 29$ 12   **46.** $\frac{y}{4} + 15 = 17$ 8

Reflecting ◀▶ on the Module

47. Writing Describe how rotations, reflections, and translations are alike and how they are different. Give examples and draw sketches to support your answer. **See Additional Answers.**

The Module Project

May I Ask You a Few Questions?

How many ways are there to have fun? You'll gather and organize data about the ways students in your school spend their free time. You'll use percents and a visual display to present the results of your survey.

More on the Module Project
See pp. 342, 356, and 373.

1 Ratios and Data Displays

As you examine running speeds:

- Find unit rates
- Set up proportions
- Make stem-and-leaf plots
- Interpret histograms

2 Proportions and Plots

As you explore some unusual, thrilling, or daring pastimes:

- Solve proportions using cross products
- Make a scatter plot
- Fit a line to a scatter plot
- Interpret box-and-whisker plots

3 Percent

As you analyze movie ratings:

- Estimate and find percents
- Find a missing part or whole

4 Percent and Probability

As you study sports statistics:

- Write a fraction as a decimal or a percent
- Use percents to make predictions
- Find theoretical probabilities when two or more events occur one after the other

INTERNET
To learn more about the theme:
http://www.mlmath.com

Section ① Ratios and Data Displays

IN THIS SECTION

EXPLORATION 1
♦ Ratios and Proportions

EXPLORATION 2
♦ Stem-and-Leaf Plots

EXPLORATION 3
♦ Histograms

Run for Your Life

- - - **Setting the Stage**

How do you spend your free time? In this module, you'll explore some of the ways young people enjoy their free time today.

One popular leisure activity is running. In the book *Zanboomer*, a high school student named Zan Hagen decides to take up cross-country running. Her coach, Rinehart, helps her train for a three-mile race.

Zanboomer by R.R. Knudson

Rinehart's stopwatch clicked go. I leaped along the course. He would meet me at the one-mile mark by crossing the meadow in Monk's car. He would meet me again at the two-mile mark by short-cutting on foot through woods. At both points he'd call my times.

…

"Five minutes flat, too fast," Rinehart shouted at our first checkpoint.

The second mile I saved too much by tripping into a water hazard. "Meathead," I called myself.

"Ten minutes, fifty seconds," Rinehart blared. His math was right, my pace wrong.

Think About It

1 Zan's goal was to run each mile of the three-mile race in 5 minutes, 10 seconds. How did her times at the one-mile and two-mile marks compare with that goal? *10 s too fast, 30 s too slow*

2 Zan finished her three-mile training run in 16 minutes. How long did it take her to run the last mile? *5 min 10 s*

Ratios AND Proportions

GOAL

LEARN HOW TO...
- ◆ find unit rates
- ◆ set up proportions

AS YOU...
- ◆ explore running times

KEY TERMS
- ◆ ratio
- ◆ rate
- ◆ unit rate
- ◆ proportion

Runners often try to establish a steady running pace. Zan ran the last two miles of her three-mile training run in 11 min.

▸ **Zan's pace, the number of minutes compared to the number of miles, can be expressed as a *ratio*. A ratio is a comparison of two quantities by division and can be written in any of the three forms below.**

> **The ratio that expresses Zan's pace can be written in three ways.**
>
> 11 min to 2 mi   11 min : 2 mi $\dfrac{11 \text{ min}}{2 \text{ mi}}$

3 Zan ran the first mile in 5 min. Write the ratio "5 min to 1 mi" in two other ways. $5 \text{ min} : 1 \text{ mi}, \dfrac{5 \text{ min}}{1 \text{ mi}}$

▸ **Since the ratios that describe Zan's run compare minutes to miles, they are *rates*. A rate is a ratio that compares quantities measured in different units.**

4 Suppose Zan walked 1 mi after every 3 mi run. Write a ratio that compares the number of miles she walked to the number of miles she ran. Is this ratio a rate? Explain. $1 \text{ mi} : 3 \text{ mi};$ No; The units of the quantities being compared are the same.

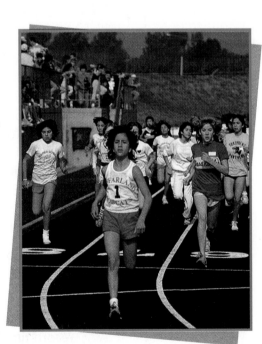

▸ **You can use *unit rates* to compare rates. A unit rate is the rate for one unit of a given quantity.**

5 Which of Zan's rates, *5 min to 1 mi* or *11 min to 2 mi*, is a unit rate? Which rate do you think is faster? Explain. 5 min to 1 mi; 5 min to 1 mi; At 5 min/mi, she would run 2 mi in 10 min, which is less than 11 min.

6 **Discussion** Is the ratio $\dfrac{1 \text{ min}}{0.5 \text{ mi}}$ a unit rate? Explain why or why not. No; The rate given is not for 1 mi.

▶ Suppose it takes Raisheen 85 min to run 10 mi. You can use *proportions* to find her unit rate. A **proportion** is an equation stating that two ratios are equivalent.

EXAMPLE

Raisheen's rate is $\frac{85 \text{ min}}{10 \text{ mi}}$. What is her unit rate?

SAMPLE RESPONSE

	Rate		Unit rate
	$\frac{85 \text{ min}}{10 \text{ mi}}$	=	$\frac{x \text{ min}}{1 \text{ mi}}$

What number must you divide the numerator and denominator by to change 10 mi to 1 mi?

$$\frac{85 \text{ min} \div 10}{10 \text{ mi} \div 10} = \frac{x \text{ min}}{1 \text{ mi}}$$

$$\frac{8.5 \text{ min}}{1 \text{ mi}} = \frac{x \text{ min}}{1 \text{ mi}}$$

Raisheen's unit rate is 8.5 min/mi.

7 Discussion What other method can you use to find a unit rate?
Sample Response: Divide the rate's numerator by its denominator.

8 Jenna's running pace is 63 min for 7 mi. Write this as a unit rate. Did *Jenna* or *Raisheen* run faster? Explain.   9 min/mi; Raisheen; It took her 0.5 min less to run 1 mi.

9 ✔ **CHECKPOINT** Write each rate as a unit rate.

a. $\frac{120 \text{ min}}{15 \text{ mi}}$ 8 min/mi   **b.** $\frac{129 \text{ mi}}{3 \text{ h}}$ 43 mi/h   **c.** $\frac{\$20}{8 \text{ lb}}$ $2.50/lb

✔ **QUESTION 9**

...checks that you can determine unit rates.

10 Suppose Chi can maintain a pace of 7.5 min/mi for a distance of 13 mi. How long will it take her to run 13 mi?
97.5 min, or 1 h 37.5 min

	Unit rate		Rate for 13 mi
time →	$\frac{7.5 \text{ min}}{1 \text{ mi}}$	=	$\frac{? \text{ min}}{13 \text{ mi}}$
distance →			

11 Sharon is training for the Boston Marathon, a 26.2 mi race.

a. Use a proportion like the one in Question 10 to find how long it will take Sharon to finish the race at a pace of 6 min/mi.
157.2 min, or 2 h 37.2 min

b. The women's record time for the 1994 Boston Marathon was approximately 142 min. If Sharon hopes to finish in the record time, what should her unit rate be during the run?
about 5.4 min/mi

HOMEWORK EXERCISES ▶ See Exs. 1–13 on pp. 321–322.

Stem-and-Leaf Plots

GOAL

LEARN HOW TO...
♦ interpret and make stem-and-leaf plots

AS YOU...
♦ examine race results

KEY TERMS
♦ median
♦ mode
♦ stem-and-leaf plot
♦ range

Every year there are hundreds of benefit races throughout the United States. The Seattle Pratt and Chew Classic is a 4 mi race that benefits an emergency feeding program for the homeless. The finishing times for the 16-and-under age group in the 1995 Classic are shown.

For Questions 12–13, use the results shown at the right.

12 **Discussion** Suppose a middle school student finished the Pratt and Chew Classic with a time of 35 min. Based on the results shown at the right, do you think that time is *fast*, *slow*, or *average*? Explain.

Sample Response: average; Most of the finishing times are in the 30s.

▶ **One way to answer Question 12 is to find an average or typical finishing time.**

Name	Time (min)
Dan	31
Alesa	42
Elizabeth	39
Eben	34
Stephanie	36
Fong	31
David	39
Megan	57
Ryan	31
David	42
Randy	39
Laura	31
Andrew	40

Name	Time (min)
Michael	24
Matthew	37
Loreen	57
Jacquie	81
Patrick	31
Garrett	25
Shannon	43
Shelby	39
Zachariah	33
Tyler	40
Ilsa	34
Graham	65
Greer	50

13 **a.** Find the mean of the finishing times for the 16-and-under age group. Round your answer to the nearest tenth. 40.7 min

b. The **median** is the middle item when you order a data set from least to greatest. When there are an even number of data items, the median is the mean of the two middle numbers. Find the median of the finishing times for the 16-and-under age group. 39 min

c. The **mode** is the item or the items that appear most often in a data set. Find the mode of the finishing times for the 16-and-under age group. 31 min and 39 min

14 **a.** Suppose 81 had not been included in the data set. How would that affect each average you found in Question 13?
See above.

b. **Discussion** Which average in Question 13 do you think best represents the running data? Explain.

14. a. The modes and median would be the same, but the mean would be lowered to 39.0 min.

FOR ▶ HELP
with *mean*, see
TOOLBOX, p. 595

b. Median; Sample Response: I would not use the mean because the 81 min time is unusually slow in comparison to the other times and this affects the mean more than the median or mode. The mode is seldom used as the average for numerical data, and in this case there are two modes.

When data values are spread over a wide range, a graph may describe the data more effectively than an average value. One type of graph you can use is a **stem-and-leaf plot**. The stem-and-leaf plot below shows the finishing times from the table on page 315.

title ▶

**Seattle Pratt and Chew Classic
16-and-under Age Group, 1995**

The stems are ordered vertically from least to greatest.

```
2 | 4 5
3 | 1 1 1 1 3 4 4 6 7 7 9 9 9 9
4 | 0 0 2 2 3
5 | 0 7 7
6 | 5
7 |
8 | 1
```

6|5 represents 65 min

The leaves of a stem are ordered horizontally from least to greatest.

key

15 Compare the data in the table with the stem-and-leaf plot.

a. Why do you think the numbers 2 through 8 were chosen as the stems for the running data?
They are the first digits in the lowest and highest data values.

b. Why are there no leaves for the stem 7?
The data contains no numbers in the 70s.

c. What do the stems represent?   the first digits in the data values

d. What do the leaves represent?   the second digits in the data values

e. What finishing time is represented by 4|3?   43 min

f. How are two or more identical finishing times shown in the stem-and-leaf plot? Give an example to support your answer.

16 a. The slowest finishing time for the 16-and-under age group was 81 min. What was the fastest finishing time?   24 min

b. The **range** of a data set is the difference between the greatest data value and the least data value. What is the range of the finishing times for the 16-and-under age group?   57 min

17 Discussion Use the stem-and-leaf plot shown above.
Sample Responses are given.

a. A *cluster* in a data set is a group of data values that are close in value. One cluster appears around the value 39. Where else do you see a cluster in the data?   around the value 33

b. A *gap* in a data set is a place where there is a "jump" between data values. One gap occurs between 57 and 65. Where else do you see a gap in the data set?   between the values 65 and 81

c. How could you use the stem-and-leaf plot to group the data values into fast, slow, and average times?

15. f. repeated leaves for a given stem;
Possible Answers:
3|1 1 1 1;
3|4 4;
3|7 7;
3|9 9 9 9;
4|0 0;
4|2 2;
5|7 7

17. c. Data values within 5 min of the median could be considered average times, those times below this set of data, fast times, and those above it, slow times.

▶ Suppose you wanted to find out how the finishing times of teachers compare with the finishing times of students 16-and-under who ran in the 1995 Seattle Pratt and Chew Classic.

The finishing times of all the teachers who ran in the race are listed at the right. All times have been rounded to the nearest minute.

Name	Time (min)
Maxwell	26
Julie	44
Marcia	35
Charles	28
Candy	31
Debra	36
Ron	31
Wayne	25
Karen	28
Jeff	28
Erin	41
Eric	38
Brendan	23

Name	Time (min)
	30
	42
	35
	39
	26
	37
	25
	38
	38
	26
	28
	31
	29

18 ✔ **CHECKPOINT** Complete parts (a)–(d) to make a stem-and-leaf plot of the teachers' finishing times in the 1995 Pratt and Chew Classic.

a. Use the running times to choose the stems. List each stem in a column from least to greatest. Draw a vertical segment to separate the stems from the leaves.

b. Use each data value to create a leaf to the right of a stem. Be sure the leaves are listed in order from least to greatest.

c. Include a key that identifies one of the values represented by the stem-and-leaf plot.

d. Write a title for your stem-and-leaf plot.

19 **Discussion** Use the stem-and-leaf plot you made in Question 18 showing the teachers' race results.

a. Find the median, mode, and range of the running times.

b. Where do you see gaps or clusters in the data? Look back at Question 17.

c. Suppose a teacher finished the Pratt and Chew Classic with a time of 35 min. Explain whether you would consider that time *fast*, *slow*, or *average*.

d. How do your answers in parts (a)–(c) compare with the answers in Questions 13, 16, and 17 for the students?

HOMEWORK EXERCISES ▶ See Exs. 14–16 on pp. 322–323.

✔ **QUESTION 18**

…checks that you can make a stem-and-leaf plot.

18. a–d.
Finishing Times (min);
Seattle, Pratt and Chew Classic;
Teachers' Group; 1995

2 | 3 5 5 6 6 6 8 8 8 9
3 | 0 1 1 1 5 5 6 7 8 8 9
4 | 1 2 4

4 | 1 represents 41 min

19. a. 31 min, 28 min, 21 min
b. Sample Response: a gap between the values 31 and 35; a cluster around the value 37
c. Sample Response: Average, because 35 is close to the median of 31.
d. The median, mode, and range were all lower for the teachers. There were no significant data gaps, and the clusters were closer together.

GOAL

LEARN HOW TO...
- interpret histograms

AS YOU...
- examine the results of a 5K race

KEY TERM
- histogram

Exploration 3

Histograms

▶ In Exploration 2, you saw running times displayed with a stem-and-leaf plot. Sometimes another type of data display is more convenient.

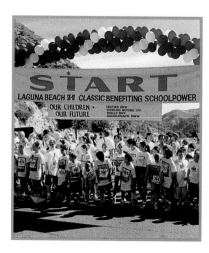

The Schoolpower Laguna Beach Classic is run along the Pacific coast and through a scenic canyon. In 1996, runners aged 3–78 helped raise money to aid local schools.

20 Discussion Nearly 1000 people ran in the 5 km, or 5K, race of the 1996 Schoolpower Laguna Beach Classic. Their times ranged from the winning time of 15 min 36 s to times slightly over an hour.

a. Estimate the range of the running times in the 5K race.
about 45 min

b. Suppose you had a list of all the individual running times for the 5K race. Why would it be difficult to use a stem-and-leaf plot to display the data? There is too much data spread over too large a range.

▶ The frequency table below shows how many runners finished the 1996 Schoolpower 5K race in each of the time intervals listed. The *histogram* below displays the same data.

1996 Schoolpower Laguna Beach Classic Finishing Times	
Interval (min:s)	Frequency
15:00–24:59	168
25:00–34:59	462
35:00–44:59	218
45:00–54:59	121
55:00–64:59	21

A **histogram** is a bar graph with no spaces between the bars.

21 a. Why does the first time interval start at 15 rather than at 0?
There are no data values less than 15.

b. In which time interval did most of the runners finish the race?
25:00 – 34:59

c. How many runners finished in the 45:00–54:59 time interval?
121 runners

22 Discussion Can you use the frequency table or histogram to find the slowest finishing time? Explain.
No; No individual data values are given.

23 Suppose a runner finishes a 5K race with a time of 35 min. Do you think this time is *fast, slow,* or *average*, based on the results in the histogram? Explain. Sample Response: slow; Of 990 runners, 630 had a faster time.

HOMEWORK EXERCISES See Exs. 17–18 on pp. 323–324.

Section ① Key Concepts

Key Terms

Ratios, Rates, and Proportions (pp. 313–314)

A ratio is a comparison of two quantities by division. A rate is a ratio that compares two quantities measured in different units.

ratio

rate

Examples

$\dfrac{36 \text{ in.}}{12 \text{ in.}}$ Since this ratio compares inches to inches, it is not a rate.

$\dfrac{\$4.75}{5 \text{ blank tapes}}$ This ratio is a rate.

A proportion is an equation stating that two ratios are equivalent.

proportion

Example

$\dfrac{\$4.75}{5 \text{ blank tapes}} = \dfrac{\$0.95}{1 \text{ blank tape}}$ A unit rate is the rate for one unit of a given quantity.

unit rate

24 Key Concepts Question Suppose a female runner can run at a constant rate of 7 min/mi. Using this rate, determine how long it would take her to finish the Boston Marathon (26.2 mi).

183.4 min, or 3 h 3.4 min   Continued on next page

Key Terms

stem-and-leaf plot

median

mode

range

histogram

Displays of Data (pp. 315–319)

Stem-and-leaf plots, frequency tables, and histograms can be used to organize and display data. Stem-and-leaf plots show each data item.

1972–1996 Boston Marathon Women's Championship Times
(All times were rounded to the nearest minute.)

```
14 | 2 3 4 4 5 5 5 5 5 5 5 7 7 9
15 | 0 4 4 5
16 | 2 5 7 7 9
17 |
18 | 6 9
```

The **mode** is the data item that appears most often.

The **median** is the middle data value of an ordered data set.

16|7 represents 167 min

The range of a set of data is the difference between the greatest data value and the least data value. The range of the data set above is 189 min − 142 min = 47 min.

Frequency tables and histograms display frequencies in given intervals.

1972–1996 Boston Marathon Women's Championship Times

Time (min)	Frequency
140–149	14
150–159	4
160–169	5
170–179	0
180–189	2

A histogram is a special type of bar graph. The bars of a histogram touch each other.

CLOSURE QUESTION

What are some ways to represent data? How do these ways compare?

Sample Response: Give the range, the mean, the median, and the mode, or draw a histogram or a stem-and-leaf plot. The range, the mean, the median, and the mode are numbers, whereas the histogram and the stem-and-leaf plot are a visual representation.

25 Key Concepts Question Was the runner in Question 24 on page 319 fast enough to win the Boston Marathon in any year from 1972 to 1996? Use both graphs above to find how many marathons she would have won. Which graph was easier to use?

Yes; 2 marathons, the stem-and-leaf plot

Section ① Practice & Application Exercises ▸▸▸▸▸▸▸▸

Write each rate as a unit rate.

1. $\dfrac{39 \text{ min}}{6 \text{ mi}}$ **6.5 min/mi**

2. $\dfrac{152 \text{ mi}}{8 \text{ gal}}$ **19 mi/gal**

3. $\dfrac{\$16.50}{3 \text{ lb}}$ **$5.50/lb**

4. $\dfrac{24 \text{ servings}}{4 \text{ pans}}$ **6 servings/pan**

5. $\dfrac{18\cent}{3 \text{ min}}$ **6¢/min**

6. $\dfrac{\$1.89}{2 \text{ bunches}}$ **$.95/bunch**

7. **Whales** A single blue whale may eat 4.5 tons of krill, a type of small shrimp, per day. Copy and complete the proportion below to show how many tons of krill a blue whale may eat in one week.

$$\frac{4.5 \text{ tons}}{1 \text{ day}} = \frac{? \text{ tons}}{7 \text{ days}} \quad \textbf{31.5}$$

8. **Weather** For a rainstorm to be defined as a cloudburst, rain must fall at a rate of at least 4 in. per hour. Suppose it rains 5.7 in. in 1.5 h. Could that be described as a cloudburst? **No.**

9. **Ultra-Marathons** Helen Klein holds many of the records in the 65–69-year-old age group for ultra-marathoners, athletes who run races much longer than marathons. In 1991 she ran 100 mi in about 21 h. Represent Helen Klein's running pace as a unit rate. Round your answer to the nearest tenth. **4.8 mi/h**

In 1995, at the age of 72, Helen Klein completed the Eco-Challenge competition in Utah. The Eco-Challenge includes hiking, orienteering, and rock climbing. ◄

10. **Population** The total area of the Marshall Islands is 70 mi². The total population of the Marshall Islands is about 61,000 people. Find the *population density,* or unit rate of people per square mile, for the Marshall Islands. **about 871 people/mi²**

11. **Race-Walking** To receive the Presidential Sports Award for race-walking, a person must race-walk a total of 200 mi at an average rate no slower than 12 min/mi.

   a. Copy and complete the table below to show the distance covered and race-walking times for a rate of 12 min/mi.

Time (min)	? **6**	12	? **60**	120	? **2400**
Distance (mi)	0.5	1	5	? **10**	200

   b. How many hours would it take to race-walk a total of 200 mi at a rate of 12 min/mi? **40 h**

12. Fuel Efficiency The cruise ship *Queen Elizabeth 2* moves only about 60 ft for each gallon of diesel fuel that it burns. About how many gallons of fuel are used when the ship travels one mile?

about 88 gal

13. Suppose Toni walks at the rates shown in the table below.

Time (s)	1	5	20	30	50
Distance (ft)	5	25	100	150	250

a. How far would you expect Toni to walk in 25 s? 125 ft

b. Challenge This data can be graphed to create a picture of Toni's walking rate. Draw a coordinate plane with seconds along the horizontal axis and feet along the vertical axis. Then use the numbers in the table to graph Toni's walking rate. Draw segments to connect the points in order.

c. Use the graph to find how far you would expect Toni to walk in 25 s. Compare this answer with your answer in part (a).

125 ft; It is the same.

13. b.

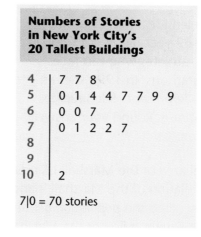

14. Skyscrapers The stem-and-leaf plot below shows the numbers of stories in the 20 tallest buildings in New York City.

▲ One Worldwide Plaza is on a former site of Madison Square Garden.

Numbers of Stories in New York City's 20 Tallest Buildings

```
 4 | 7 7 8
 5 | 0 1 4 4 7 7 9 9
 6 | 0 0 7
 7 | 0 1 2 2 7
 8 |
 9 |
10 | 2
```

7|0 = 70 stories

▲ Carnegie Hall Tower towers over Carnegie Hall, a famous concert hall built in 1891.

a. Do you notice any gaps or clusters in the data? Explain.

Sample Response: a gap between 77 and 102, a cluster around 60

b. What is the range of the data on the stem-and-leaf plot? 55

c. Based on the data in the stem-and-leaf plot, how many stories do you think the tallest building in New York City has? 102

d. Writing The 47-story *One Worldwide Plaza* in New York City is 778 ft tall, while the 60-story *Carnegie Hall Tower* in New York City is only 757 ft tall. Explain how this can be true.

14. d. Sample Response: The height of a story in *One Worldwide Plaza* is greater than that of a story in *Carnegie Hall Tower*.

15. **History** The stem-and-leaf plot at the right gives the approximate age at which each king or queen of England since 1154 was crowned.

   a. What is the range of the ages shown on the stem-and-leaf plot? **63 years**

   b. Find the median and the mode of the data.
      28 years; 18 years and 25 years

   c. Suppose the next English monarch is 60 years old when crowned. How does this number affect the median of the data set? the mode of the data set?
      The median changes to 29. The mode is unaffected.

Ages of English Monarchs when Crowned, since 1154

```
0 | 1 9 9
1 | 0 2 4 7 8 8 8
2 | 1 2 3 4 5 5 5 6 8
3 | 0 1 1 3 3 6 7 7 8
4 | 0 1 3 4
5 | 1 4 7 9
6 | 4
```

3|0 = 30 years old

16. The table at the left shows the top 10 prize-winning horses as of 1996, and the number of races they won.

   a. Make a stem-and-leaf plot to show the number of races won by each of the horses. Be sure to include a title and a key for your plot.

   b. Use the stem-and-leaf plot to find the range, the mean, the median, and the mode of the number of wins.

   c. What would you consider an average number of wins for this group of horses? Explain.

Top Ten Prize-Winning Horses, 1996

Horse	Wins	Earnings
Cigar	19	$9,999,815
Alysheba	11	$6,679,242
John Henry	39	$6,597,947
Best Pal	18	$5,129,645
Sunday Silence	9	$4,968,554
Easy Goer	14	$4,873,770
Unbridled	8	$4,489,475
Spend A Buck	10	$4,220,689
Creme Fraiche	17	$4,024,727
Devil His Due	11	$3,920,405

16. a. Frequency of Wins of Leading Prize-Winning Horses

```
0 | 8 9
1 | 0 1 1 4 7 8 9
2 |
3 | 9
```

1 | 7 represents 17 wins

b. 31 wins, 15.6 wins, 12.5 wins, 11 wins
c. Sample Response: 12.5 wins; The mean is too high. The mode, 11, is reasonable as well.

17. **Marathons** The histogram shows the number of women in each age group who completed the 1995 Seattle Marathon in a time of less than 3.5 h. Use the histogram to answer each question.

   a. How many different ages are included in each interval? **5 ages**

   b. About how many women aged 40 years and older finished the marathon in less than 3.5 h? **6 women**

   c. Why might the statement, "The oldest woman to finish the marathon in less than 3.5 hours was 59 years old," be incorrect?
      From the histogram, we know only that the woman was between 55 and 59 years old.

Female Runners Who Completed the 1995 Seattle Marathon in Under 3.5 Hours

Visual
THINKING
Exercise 18 checks
your understanding
of data displays.

Reflecting on the Section

18. Use the stem-and-leaf plot and the histogram showing the results of the 1995 Seattle Pratt and Chew Classic for students in the 16-and-under age group.

**Seattle Pratt and Chew Classic
16-and-Under Age Group, 1995**

```
2 | 4 5
3 | 1 1 1 1 3 4 4 6 7 7 9 9 9 9
4 | 0 0 2 2 3
5 | 0 7 7
6 | 5
7 |
8 | 1          6|5 represents 65 min
```

a. Copy the stem-and-leaf plot and turn it sideways. Compare it with the histogram. What do you notice about the shapes of the two displays? Why do you think this happens?

b. Will a histogram and a stem-and-leaf plot made from the same data set always show the same relationship that you saw in part (a)? Explain.

18. a. They are the same; In one row of the stem-and-leaf plot, 5 entries, for example, take up 5 units of space. In one bar of the histogram, a frequency of 5 takes up 5 units of space also.
b. No; The intervals used in the histogram must correspond to the range of the data values within 1 row of the stem-and-leaf plot.

Spiral Review

Solve each equation. Check each solution. (Module 4, p. 300)

19. $4n + 17 = 50$ $8\frac{1}{4}$ 20. $\frac{y}{3} + 4 = 92$ 264   21. $\frac{x}{4} - 3 = -15$ –48

Use mental math to find a reasonable estimate for the cost of each purchase. (Toolbox, pp. 582–583)   Accept reasonable estimates.

22. 5 packages of gum at $0.39 per package   about $2.00

23. 3 sandwiches at $2.48 per sandwich   about $7.50

24. 5 lb of potatoes at $3.98 for 10 lb   about $2.00

Write each fraction in lowest terms. (Module 3, p. 170)

25. $\frac{11}{33}$ $\frac{1}{3}$ 26. $\frac{12}{60}$ $\frac{1}{5}$ 27. $\frac{19}{38}$ $\frac{1}{2}$

28. $\frac{30}{150}$ $\frac{1}{5}$ 29. $\frac{8}{20}$ $\frac{2}{5}$ 30. $\frac{40}{48}$ $\frac{5}{6}$

Write each rate as a unit rate.

1. $\dfrac{\$43}{4\text{ h}}$ $10.75/h

2. $\dfrac{127\text{ km}}{8\text{ L}}$ 15.875 km/L

3. $\dfrac{672\text{ noodles}}{3\text{ boxes}}$ 224 noodles/box

4. $\dfrac{40\text{ gal}}{9\text{ min}}$ $4\frac{4}{9}$ gal/min

5. Pamela begins a 24-question math quiz at 1:16 P.M., answers every question, and hands in her paper at 1:32 P.M. Represent the pace at which she answered the questions as a unit rate. 1.5 questions/min

6. This list gives the heights, in inches, of the students in a seventh-grade math class: 64, 57, 62, 68, 54, 64, 59, 63, 64, 60, 59, 58, 65, 56, 58, 64, 60, 55, 66, 57, 61. Use these heights to make a stem-and-leaf plot, including a key and a title. State the range, the median, the mode, and the mean of the data. What would you consider to be an average height for this group of students? Explain your choice(s).

   Heights in a 7th Grade Math Class
   5 | 4 5 6 7 7 8 8 9 9
   6 | 0 0 1 2 3 4 4 4 4 5 6 8

   5 | 4 represents 54 in.

   See below.

7. Use the histogram at the right. Is the number of students who read 6 or more books *greater than, equal to,* or *less than* the number of students who read fewer than 6 books? greater than

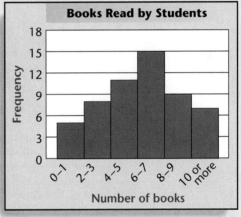

Books Read by Students

Study Skills ◀▶ Creating a Test

To reinforce what you have learned, it may be helpful to create your own test and then solve it. To create a test, you need to think about the important ideas taught and about which questions show how well you understand these ideas.

1. a. Look back through Section 1. Identify the important ideas.

   b. Create a test based on these ideas and then solve your test to make a solution key. Answers will vary. Check students' work.

2. a. Ask a classmate to complete your test. Use your solution key to grade the test. Check students' work.

   b. Ask the student who took the test for suggestions about how the test could be improved. Revise the test and solution key based on these suggestions. Check students' work.

1. a. Sample Response: writing and simplifying ratios, rates, and proportions; interpreting and creating stem–and–leaf plots, frequency tables, and histograms; finding the mean, mode, median, and range of a set of data values

6. range: 14; median: 60; mode: 64; mean: about 61; 60 in. or 61 in.; Both averages are at about the center of the data set. The mode is too high.

FOR ASSESSMENT AND PORTFOLIOS

What's for Lunch?

The Situation See the Resource Book for a detailed discussion of this Extended Exploration.

You have been hired to lead tours at the zoo shown on the map below.

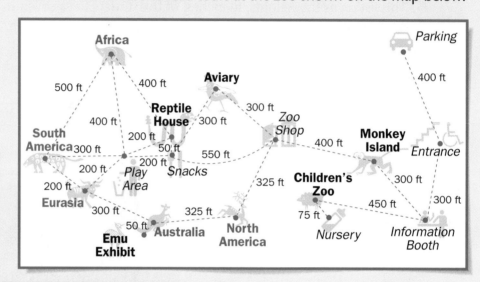

Feeding Times at the Zoo		
Animal	**Starting time**	**Location in the zoo**
chimpanzee	11:30 A.M.	Africa
hippopotamus	10:00 A.M.	Africa
kangaroo	9:30 A.M.	Australia
Japanese macaque	9:00 A.M.	Eurasia
Siberian tiger	11:00 A.M.	Eurasia
sea lion	10:00 A.M.	North America
polar bear	11:30 A.M.	North America
jaguar	11:00 A.M.	South America
llama	9:30 A.M.	South America

The Problem

Design a tour that starts at the Play Area and visits as many of the animal feedings and exhibits as possible while keeping walking distance to a minimum. (*Note:* Feedings last approximately 20 min.). Spend at least 30 min at each of the five major areas of the zoo, labeled in red on the map. The tour can start as early as 8:30 A.M. but must end by 12 noon. Answers will vary. Check students' work.

Present Your Results

Describe your tour. Include data on the total time spent on the tour, the exhibits and animal feedings visited, and the total distance walked. Explain the decisions and assumptions you made to solve this problem.

Section ② Proportions and Plots

IN THIS SECTION

EXPLORATION 1
♦ Cross Products

EXPLORATION 2
♦ Scatter Plots

EXPLORATION 3
♦ Box-and-Whisker Plots

Just for Fun

Setting the Stage ▸▸▸▸▸▸▸▸▸▸▸▸▸▸▸▸▸▸▸▸▸▸▸▸▸▸▸▸▸

For many of us, a great way to spend an afternoon might include going to the movies, playing a sport, or going for a bike ride. For Ashrita Furman, an afternoon off means time to ride on a pogo stick. For Eddy McDonald, it might be time to spend testing his yo-yo skills. And Richard Rodriguez could use the time to get ready for his next roller-coaster marathon.

Think About It

1 Record-holder Ashrita Furman covered a distance of 16 mi on a pogo stick in 6 h 40 min. Estimate his speed in miles per hour (mi/h). **about 2.4 mi/h**

2 Eddy McDonald completed 8437 yo-yo loops in 1 h and 21,663 yo-yo loops in 3 h. Which is the faster rate? **8437 yo-yo loops in 1 h**

3 Richard Rodriguez set a world record by riding the Big Dipper roller coaster at Blackpool Pleasure Beach in England for 549 h! For how many days did he ride the Big Dipper? **about 23 days**

WARM-UP EXERCISES

Complete each proportion.

1. $\dfrac{2}{1} = \dfrac{6}{?}$ 3

2. $\dfrac{?}{8} = \dfrac{3}{1}$ 24

3. $\dfrac{125}{30} = \dfrac{?}{6}$ 25

Write in lowest terms.

4. $\dfrac{39}{52}$ $\dfrac{3}{4}$

5. $\dfrac{21}{49}$ $\dfrac{3}{7}$

LEARN HOW TO...
- solve proportions using cross products

AS YOU...
- explore the riders' experience on a roller coaster

KEY TERM
- cross products

▶ **Exploration 1**

Cross Products

▶ **Many people enjoy the thrill of riding a roller coaster. The feelings of being pulled out of your seat and of being pushed back into it are due to changes in speed and direction of motion. The sensations you feel on a roller coaster are related to your weight, which depends on Earth's gravity, or 1 G. The diagram below explains more about what happens when you ride a roller coaster.**

When you plunge downhill, you are lifted out of your seat. You experience less than 1 G, so you feel lighter than normal.

When you change direction and speed uphill, you are pushed down into your seat. You experience more than 1 G, so you feel heavier than normal.

Normally, you experience 1 G, so you feel your actual weight.

▶ **If you weigh 100 lb and experience 2 G going up a hill on a roller coaster, you feel as if you weigh twice your weight, or 200 lb. You can use a proportion to show this relationship.**

actual weight ⟶ $\dfrac{100 \text{ lb}}{1 \text{ G}} = \dfrac{200 \text{ lb}}{2 \text{ G}}$ ⟵ apparent weight at 2 G

4 Use a proportion like the one above to find each value.

a. the apparent weight at 0.5 G of a person who actually weighs 215 lb *107.5 lb*

b. the actual weight of a person who has an apparent weight of 520 lb at 4 G *130 lb*

5 Discussion Suppose at liftoff an astronaut has an apparent weight of 531 lb at 4.5 G. The proportion below can be used to find the astronaut's apparent weight at 12 G. Why might it be difficult to solve this proportion using your method from Question 4? Sample Response: Neither of the rates is a unit rate.

apparent weight at liftoff

$$\frac{531 \text{ lb}}{4.5 \text{ G}} = \frac{x \text{ lb}}{12 \text{ G}}$$

apparent weight at 12 G

▶ Recall that a proportion is an equation stating that two ratios are equivalent. You can use this idea to discover another way of solving proportions.

6 For each pair of ratios, determine whether the ratios are equivalent. Explain the method you used.

a. $\frac{2}{6} \stackrel{?}{=} \frac{3}{9}$　　**b.** $\frac{6}{11} \stackrel{?}{=} \frac{4}{7}$　　**c.** $\frac{6}{8} \stackrel{?}{=} \frac{12}{16}$

d. $\frac{6}{9} \stackrel{?}{=} \frac{9}{12}$　　**e.** $\frac{3}{24} \stackrel{?}{=} \frac{4}{36}$　　**f.** $\frac{10}{15} \stackrel{?}{=} \frac{12}{18}$

▶ In the proportion below, the products 2 · 9 and 3 · 6 are cross products.

> **EXAMPLE**
>
> $$2 \cdot 9 = 18 \qquad \frac{2}{6} \times = \frac{3}{9} \qquad 3 \cdot 6 = 18$$

7 Evaluate the cross products for each pair of ratios in Question 6. What do you notice about the cross products when the ratios are equivalent? What do you notice when they are not equivalent?
The cross products are equivalent; The cross products are not equivalent.

8 Discussion Look at your results from Question 7. How can you use cross products to determine whether two ratios are equivalent?
If the cross products are equivalent, the ratios are equivalent.

9 For each pair of ratios, use cross products to determine whether the ratios are equivalent.

a. $\frac{8}{15} \stackrel{?}{=} \frac{5}{9}$　　**b.** $\frac{3}{12} \stackrel{?}{=} \frac{5}{20}$　　**c.** $\frac{3}{25} \stackrel{?}{=} \frac{1}{8}$　　**d.** $\frac{7}{21} \stackrel{?}{=} \frac{12}{39}$

not equivalent　　equivalent　　not equivalent　　not equivalent

▲ The first looping roller coaster in the United States, the Flip-Flap, opened in 1895 at Coney Island in Brooklyn, New York. Its riders experienced a whopping 12 G— more than twice what astronauts experience during liftoff!

6. Sample responses are given for the second part of each.
a. equivalent; Simplify the ratios.
b. not equivalent; Rewrite each ratio as a ratio with 77 as a denominator.
c. equivalent; Simplify the ratios.
d. not equivalent; Simplify the ratios.
e. not equivalent; Simplify the ratios.
f. equivalent; Simplify the ratios.

▶ In Question 10 you will explore why you can use cross products to find out whether two ratios are equivalent.

10 Try This as a Class Use the proportion $\frac{4}{6} = \frac{6}{9}$.

a. Rewrite the ratios using a common denominator equal to the product of the two denominators.

Original ratios	Product of denominators	Equivalent ratios
$\frac{4}{6} = \frac{6}{9}$	$6 \cdot 9 = 54$	$\frac{4 \cdot ?}{54} = \frac{6 \cdot ?}{54}$ 9; 6

b. Compare the products in the numerators of the equivalent ratios you wrote in part (a) with the cross products for the ratio pair. What do you notice? The products are the same.

11 a. Choose one pair of equivalent ratios from Question 6 on page 329. Repeat parts (a) and (b) of Question 10 for the ratios you chose. What do you notice about the products in the numerators? The products are the same.

b. Choose a pair of ratios from Question 6 that are not equivalent. Repeat parts (a) and (b) of Question 10 for this ratio pair. What do you notice about the products in the numerators? The products are not the same.

▶ You can use cross products to solve proportions with an unknown.

12 Try This as a Class In Question 5 on page 329 you examined this proportion.

$$\frac{531 \text{ lb}}{4.5 \text{ G}} = \frac{x \text{ lb}}{12 \text{ G}}$$

a. Use cross products to write an equation for the proportion.
$(531)(12) = 4.5x$

b. How would you solve the equation you wrote in part (a)?
Divide both sides of the equation by 4.5.

c. Solve the equation to find the rider's apparent weight at 12 G.
1416 lb

d. What is the rider's actual weight at 1 G? 118 lb

✔ QUESTION 13

...checks that you can solve a proportion.

13 ✔ **CHECKPOINT** Solve each proportion.

a. $\frac{68}{12} = \frac{51}{x}$ 9   **b.** $\frac{3}{5} = \frac{n}{16}$ 9.6   **c.** $\frac{5}{s} = \frac{8}{7}$ 4.375   **d.** $\frac{x}{24} = \frac{15}{180}$ 2

HOMEWORK EXERCISES ▶ See Exs. 1–11 on pp. 337–338.

Scatter Plots

GOAL

LEARN HOW TO...
- make a scatter plot
- fit a line to a scatter plot

AS YOU...
- examine how much a rubber band stretches

KEY TERMS
- scatter plot
- fitted line

SET UP *Work in a group of four or five. You will need:* • *Labsheet 2A*
• *rubber band* • *50 pennies* • *large paper clip*
• *small paper clip* • *tape* • *lined paper* • *metric ruler*
• *small plastic (sandwich) bag* • *strand of uncooked spaghetti*

A daredevil rides a hot air balloon 150 ft into the air and jumps out wearing a harness attached to 50 ft rubber bands called *bungee cords.* This is bungee jumping, an activity that is not for everyone. The greater the jumper's weight, the more bungee cords are needed to prevent the jumper from hitting the ground.

▶ **In this activity, you'll model bungee jumping and explore the relationship between weight and the stretch of a rubber band.**

14 Use Labsheet 2A. Follow the directions on Labsheet 2A to set up the *Rubber Band Stretch Experiment.*
Check students' work.

15 a. Add 5 pennies to the plastic bag. Check students' work.

b. When the bag stops moving, mark the location of the bottom edge of the rubber band. Write the number of pennies in the bag next to your mark.
Check students' work.

c. Repeat parts (a) and (b) seven times. Check students' work.

Number of pennies	Distance stretched (cm)
5	?
10	?
15	?
20	?
25	?
30	?
35	?
40	?

16 a. Take the pennies out of the bag, but do *not* remove the paper or rubber band apparatus from the wall.
Check students' work.

b. Measure the distance from the top edge of the paper to each 5-penny mark. Check students' work.

c. Copy and complete the table at the left. Answers will vary.

17 **a.** Plot the data points from your group's table and the other groups' tables on the *Rubber Band Stretch Graph*.
Answers will vary. Check students' graphs.
b. What do you notice about the points on the graph?
The points almost fit along a line.

▶ The graph you drew in Question 17(a) is a *scatter plot*. A **scatter plot** can be used to compare two sets of data. If the data points are close to a line, it may be possible to *fit a line* to the scatter plot to help make predictions.

18 **a.** Place a piece of spaghetti on the scatter plot so that the data points are close to the spaghetti and there are about the same number of points on one side of the spaghetti as on the other side. Check students' work.

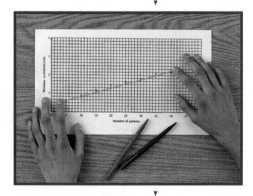

b. Draw a line segment along the piece of spaghetti. This is a **fitted line** for the scatter plot. Check students' work.

c. **Discussion** Do you think every person will draw the same line? Explain. No; The procedure for drawing the line is inexact.

d. Use the fitted line to predict the distance the rubber band will stretch with 27 pennies in the bag. Then predict how far it will stretch with 50 pennies in the bag. Answers will vary.

e. Place 27 pennies in the bag. Mark the point on the notebook paper that the bottom edge of the rubber band reaches. Then add enough pennies to the bag to total 50 and mark the paper. Check students' work.

f. Measure the two new distances. How close are these distances to the estimates you made in part (d)? Answers will vary.

✔ **QUESTION 19**

...checks that you can use a fitted line to make predictions.

19 ✔ **CHECKPOINT** Use the fitted line from Question 18(b) to predict the distance the rubber band will stretch with 32 pennies. Answers will vary.

20 **Discussion** A 100 ft bungee cord with a $\frac{5}{8}$ in. diameter will stretch to a maximum of 150 ft with a 140 lb load. A 300 lb load can increase the stretch to 200 ft. How do you think the stretch length was determined for different weights? Sample Response: in a manner similar to the rubber band experiment.

HOMEWORK EXERCISES ▶ See Exs. 12–15 on pp. 338–339.

You can use spreadsheet software or other graphing technology to make your scatter plot for Question 17 on page 332.

Step 1 Enter the data for the graph into the spreadsheet.

Enter the data for the horizontal axis in column A.

	A	B	C	D	E
1	Number of pennies	Distance (cm)			
2	5	0.5			
3	10	0.8			
4	15	1.2			
5	20	1.4			
6	25	1.5			

NUMBER OF PENNIES VS. DISTANCE

B6   × ✓   1.5

Enter the corresponding data for the vertical axis in column B.

Step 2 To make a graph, highlight the data you entered and choose the option that makes a chart. Then select the type of graph you want to make.

Options

Make Chart...

Protect Cells
Unprotect Cells

Add Page Break
Remove Page Break

Lock Title Position
Print Range...

Go To Cell...

Chart Options

Modify — Axis, Series, Labels, General

Gallery — Bar, Line, Scatter, Pie, Stacked Bar, X–Y Line, X–Y Scatter, Pictogram

Step 3 Experiment with the labels, grid lines, and scale until the graph appears the way you want it to. Be sure to include a title.

Number of Pennies vs. Distance

Step 4 You can print out the graph and draw a fitted line through your scatter plot as you did in Question 18 on page 332. Some graphing technology will also let you draw a fitted line or it will draw one for you.

LEARN HOW TO...
◆ interpret box-and-whisker plots

AS YOU...
◆ examine stone-skipping data

KEY TERM
◆ box-and-whisker plot

Exploration 3

Box-and-Whisker Plots

SET UP *You will need Labsheet 2B.*

An annual stone-skipping tournament is held every July 4 on Mackinac Island in Lake Huron in northern Michigan. Contestants pitch stones over the water. The winner is the person who makes a stone *skip,* or bounce off the surface, the most times before the stone sinks.

▶ **Suppose you want to know whether your stone skipping is good enough to win the tournament. To help decide, you could use a box-and-whisker plot to analyze the winning numbers of skips in past tournaments.**

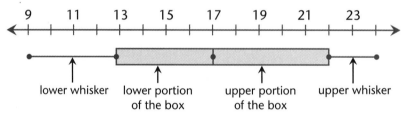

Winning Numbers of Skips: Mackinac Island Stone Skipping Tournament, 1969–1984*

lower whisker   lower portion of the box   upper portion of the box   upper whisker

*except 1981

▲ In 1996, Sarah Marx won the Mackinac Island Stone Skipping Tournament in the 12-years-and-under division.

Use Labsheet 2B for Questions 21–25.

21 To find out how the *Box-and-Whisker Plot* displays a set of data, record each winning number of skips on a line plot.
See Additional Answers.

22 Discussion In 1973 and 1975, records were set for the least and greatest numbers of skips. What were the record numbers? Where are they shown on the box-and-whisker plot?
9 skips, 24 skips; at the end of the whiskers

23 a. On the box-and-whisker plot, how many data points are represented by each whisker, including the endpoints? 4 data points

b. One whisker is longer than the other whisker. Does that mean that it represents more data points? Explain. No; It means the range of the 4 lowest data points is greater than the range of the four highest.

24 **a.** The vertical segment in the box is at 17. How many data points are greater than 17? less than 17? Do you think the vertical segment represents the *mean*, the *median*, or the *mode*?
                                                          7, 7; median
   b. A box-and-whisker plot divides a data set into four groups. About what percent of the total number of data values are in each of the four groups? about 25%

25 **Try This as a Class** The number of skips four people can make are given below. Use the box-and-whisker plot to find each person's chance of winning the tournament. Explain.

   a. 8 skips   **b.** 17 skips   **c.** 22 skips   **d.** 13 skips

25. a. about 0; The lowest number of skips a person won with in the years shown is 9. However, it is possible, though unlikely, that a person could win the tournament with as few as 8 skips.
b. about 50%; About half of the winning number of skips were 17 or less.
c. about 75%; About 75% of the winning number of skips were 22 or less.
d. about 25%; About 25% of the winning number of skips were 13 or less.

▶ **Box-and-whisker plots are useful for comparing two or more sets of data. The box-and-whisker plots below show how two stone-skipping rivals have performed in competition from 1992–1995.**

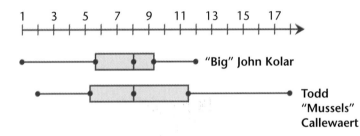

Numbers of Skips: Mackinac Island Stone Skipping Tournament, 1992–1995

26 ✔ **CHECKPOINT** Use the box-and-whisker plots above.

   a. Each year contestants make 6 throws. Each plot above shows 24 throws for the four years of competition. About how many data points are in each box? in each whisker? 12; 6

   b. Who had the most skips in 1992–1995 tournament play? Who had the fewest? How many skips was this for each?
   Callewaert; Kolar; 18 skips; 1 skip

   c. Compare the median number of skips made by each stone skipper during the four years of tournament play.
   They are the same.

   d. The best 25% of Todd Callewaert's throws from 1992–1995 made 11.5 skips or more. How does this compare with John Kolar's throws? The best 25% of Kolar's throws ranged from about 9.3 to 12 skips.

   e. Is it possible to tell who won most often in the years 1992–1995? Explain. No; The graphs do not indicate the year. For example, Callewaert's worst year may have been Kolar's best.

✔ **QUESTION 26**

...checks that you can interpret box-and-whisker plots.

▌ **HOMEWORK EXERCISES** ▶ See Exs. 16–18 on pp. 340–341.

Section 2

Key Concepts

Cross Products (pp. 328–330)

You can use cross products to solve a proportion.

Example Solve the proportion $\frac{3}{2} = \frac{x}{6}$.

$$\frac{3}{2} \diagup \frac{x}{6}$$

> Use cross products to write an equation. Then solve the equation.

$$3 \cdot 6 = 2x$$

> Divide both sides by 2.

$$\frac{18}{2} = \frac{2x}{2}$$

$$x = 9$$

Scatter Plots and Fitted Lines (pp. 331–333)

You can use a scatter plot to explore how two data sets are related. If the points are close to a line, you can use a fitted line to make predictions.

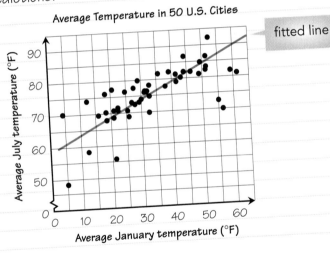

Average Temperature in 50 U.S. Cities

fitted line

Average July temperature (°F)

Average January temperature (°F)

Key Concepts Questions

27 Solve each proportion.

    a. $\frac{3}{4} = \frac{n}{18}$ 13.5   **b.** $\frac{2}{11} = \frac{y}{88}$ 16   **c.** $\frac{8}{70} = \frac{6}{t}$ 52.5

28 Use the scatter plot above to predict the temperature in July for a city that has an average January temperature of 40°F. about 80°F

Key Concepts

Box-and-Whisker Plots (pp. 334–335)

Sometimes you can use a box-and-whisker plot to display data.

Average January Temperature in 50 U.S. Cities

0   10   20   30   40   50   60   70

Temperature (°F)

The **lower whisker** contains about 25% of the data values.

The box contains about 50% of the data values.

The **upper whisker** contains about 25% of the data values.

CLOSURE QUESTION

Describe how you can use cross products.

Sample Response: Cross products can be used to solve a proportion. You can use the fact that in a true proportion the cross products are equal to find an equivalent equation that can then be solved using division.

29 **Key Concepts Question** Use the box-and-whisker plot shown above.

a. Estimate the maximum data value recorded.   about 62

b. About how many of the 50 cities had average January temperatures below 22°F? Explain. about 12 or 13; The lower whisker, containing about 25% of the data values, includes the data values less than or equal to 22.

Section ②

Practice & Application Exercises

YOU WILL NEED

For Exs. 14–15:
♦ graph paper
♦ ruler

1. **Zoos** Nine apes at the National Zoological Park in Washington, D.C., eat a combined total of 12 lb of oranges per day. How many pounds of oranges are needed per day to feed 15 apes?   20 lb

2. Japanese macaques (mə-kăks´) are short-tailed monkeys. Two Japanese macaques get 0.5 kg of biscuits each day. How much would seven macaques get each day?   1.75 kg

3. How many grams of protein are contained in 510 g of tuna if 85 g of tuna contain 24 g of protein?   144 g

4. The morning menu for one orangutan is shown below. Write a morning menu that can be used to feed 10 orangutans.

> **Morning Menu for One Orangutan**
>
> 1 apple   1/4 lb boiled meat
> 1/2 lb kale   1/3 lb green beans
> 1/2 orange   1/3 lb monkey biscuits
> 2 stalks celery

5. A giant panda eats 150 lb of bamboo every 5 days. How many pounds of bamboo would you expect it to eat in 30 days? 900 lb

6. Currency Exchange Suppose an American tourist in London exchanges 150 U.S. dollars and receives 100 British pounds. How many British pounds should the tourist receive for 600 U.S. dollars? 400 British pounds

Solve each proportion.

7. $\frac{2}{x} = \frac{14}{28}$ 4   **8.** $\frac{7}{10} = \frac{x}{3}$ 2.1   **9.** $\frac{6}{x} = \frac{9}{10.5}$ 7   **10.** $\frac{10}{16} = \frac{x}{24}$ 15

11. ▣ Calculator To solve the proportion $\frac{4.8}{2} = \frac{x}{5}$, Ang used the key sequence [4] [·] [8] [÷] [2] [×] [5] [=] .

a. Ang got an answer of 12. Is she correct? Yes.

b. Describe the method Ang used to solve the proportion.
   Ang simplified the left side of the proportion and then multiplied both sides by 5.

c. Describe another key sequence to solve the proportion.
   Sample Response: $5 \times 4.8 \div 2$

12. Choose the letter of the scatter plot that you think shows the better fitted line. Explain your choice.

    A. Lorna's scatter plot   **B.** Andrea's scatter plot

*Sidebar answers:*

4. 10 apples; $2\frac{1}{2}$ lb boiled meat; 5 lb kale; $3\frac{1}{3}$ lb green beans; 5 oranges; $3\frac{1}{3}$ lb monkey biscuits; 20 stalks celery

12. Sample Response: Neither line fits the data well. B is better than A because points are more evenly distributed above and below the line.

13. Use the scatter plot you chose in Exercise 12.

    a. About how many stories would you expect a 1200 ft skyscraper to have? *about 90 stories*

    b. **Writing** There are two skyscrapers with a height of 900 ft. One has 71 stories, while the other has 64 stories. Why do you think they have different numbers of stories?
The height of a story in the two buildings is not the same.

    c. **Challenge** About how many feet tall is an average story?
about 13.4 ft

14. The first two columns of the table below show the floor sizes of different tents and the number of sleepers each tent can hold.
See Additional Answers.

    a. Use the data in the first two columns of the table to make a scatter plot.

    b. Draw a fitted line for your scatter plot.

    c. Using your graph, predict the floor size of a tent that can sleep 12 people.

Tent Sizes and Prices		
Floor size (ft²)	Number of sleepers	Price
135	4	$162.99
140	6	$289.99
160	8	$309.99
200	10	$299.99
108	5	$159.99
110	6	$184.99
64	4	$99.99
81	5	$139.99
100	6	$199.99
109	6	$229.99
49	3	$89.99
60	3	$109.99

15. The last column of the table above shows the price of each tent.
See Additional Answers.

    a. Use the data in the last two columns to make a scatter plot.

    b. Draw a fitted line for your scatter plot.

    c. Using your graph, predict the price of a tent that can sleep 12 people.

16. **Automobile Racing** The Indianapolis 500 is an annual 500 mi race for automobiles. The box-and-whisker plots below show the winning times for selected years. All times have been rounded to the nearest minute.

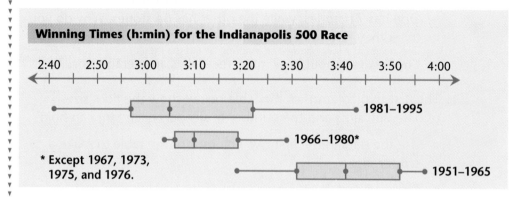

Winning Times (h:min) for the Indianapolis 500 Race

* Except 1967, 1973, 1975, and 1976.

16. c. 75% of the winning times for 1966–1980 were faster than the indicated times; At least 75% of the winning times for 1951–1965 were in the same interval as the indicated times or slower than the indicated times.
d. Sample Response: Nearly half the winning times for 1951–1965 were slower than the slowest winning time for 1981–1985. The median dropped by about 35 min.

17. C; The lowest data value, 12, and the highest data value, 63, are shown at the end of the whiskers in the stem-and-leaf plot in C.

a. In the 1951–1965 box-and-whisker plot, the slowest time was 3 h 57 min. Estimate the fastest winning time for those years.
about 3 h 18 min

b. Estimate the median winning time in the period 1966–1980.
about 3 h 10 min

c. About 25% of the winning times from 1981–1995 were between 3 h 22 min and 3 h 44 min. How do these times compare with those in the years 1966–1980? 1951–1965?

d. **Open-ended** Make two statements based on the plots for the periods 1981–1995 and 1951–1965.

17. **Chess** In 1995, Garry Kasparov successfully defended his world championship chess title against Anand Viswanathan in an 18-game match. The stem-and-leaf plot shows the number of moves in each of the 18 games. Choose the letter of the box-and-whisker plot below that represents the data shown in the stem-and-leaf plot. Explain how you know.

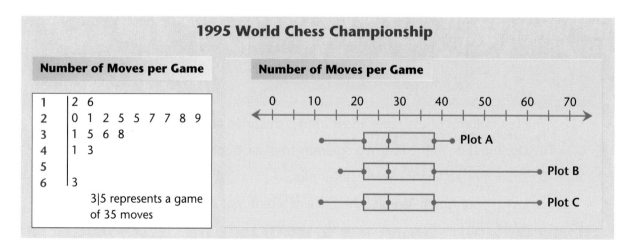

1995 World Chess Championship

Number of Moves per Game

1	2 6
2	0 1 2 5 5 7 7 8 9
3	1 5 6 8
4	1 3
5	
6	3

3|5 represents a game of 35 moves

Number of Moves per Game

18. Both graphs show temperature data for the same 50 cities.

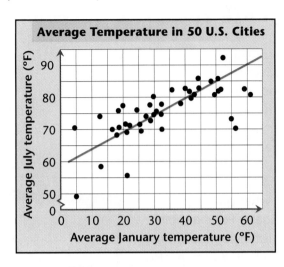

Average Temperature in 50 U.S. Cities

Average January Temperature
in 50 United States Cities (°F)

a. What was the lowest average temperature in January for the
50 cities? Which graph could you use to determine this?
about 5°F; either

b. About how many of the 50 cities are in the box portion of the
box-and-whisker plot? about 25 cities

c. Estimate the range of the average temperatures in July for the
cities that are in the box of the box-and-whisker plot.
about 15°F, or about 30°F if students include the data point at about (22, 56)

Spiral ◀▶ Review

Write each rate as a unit rate. (Module 5, p. 319)

19. $\dfrac{\$290}{40\ h}$ $7.25/h   20. $\dfrac{45\ min}{5\ mi}$ 9 min/mi   21. $\dfrac{\$13}{2\ lb}$ $6.50/lb

Write each product in exponential form. (Module 1, p. 20)

22. $5 \cdot 5$ 5^2 23. $4 \cdot 4 \cdot 4 \cdot 4$ 4^4 24. $3 \cdot 3 \cdot 3 \cdot 3 \cdot 3$ 3^5

Write each fraction as a decimal. (Module 4, p. 256)

25. $\dfrac{2}{5}$ 0.4   26. $\dfrac{5}{15}$ $0.\overline{3}$ 27. $\dfrac{9}{45}$ 0.2

Visu**a**l
T H I N K I N G

Exercise 18 checks
that you understand
box-and-whisker
and scatter plots.

May I Ask You a Few Questions?

Beginning the Module Project

A survey or opinion poll is a way to collect information about a group of people. For your module project, your class will work together to create a survey that investigates how the students in your school spend their free time. Next, you and your partner will interview students and collect information. Then, you will organize the data and decide how to present your findings.

SET UP

You will need:
* *clipboard or other writing surface*

Creating a Survey As a class, decide what question about free time your survey will investigate. For example, "How often do students at our school listen to music?" or "What types of music do students listen to?" You may also pick a general topic, such as "How do students spend their free time?" **1–2. Check students' work.**

 1
  a. Write 5 to 10 survey questions about your topic. Be sure to include questions that ask the age, the grade level, and the gender of the person answering the survey form.

  b. Review your questions. Will the people being surveyed understand each question? Do the questions provide enough information for your topic? Make any changes necessary.

Gathering Data In most schools it would be difficult to collect information from every student. It is easier to survey a *representative sample* of students. Because this sample must represent the entire school, you will survey people from each grade level. Your teacher will help you select an appropriate sample size.

Your sample must also be *random*. This means that each person in the population has an equal chance of being surveyed. For example, you could choose to survey every tenth person on a school roster.

 2 Describe how your class will choose your random representative sample. Then conduct your survey.

Section 2

Extra Skill Practice

Solve each proportion.

1. $\dfrac{8}{12} = \dfrac{r}{27}$ 18

2. $\dfrac{6}{t} = \dfrac{3}{18}$ 36

3. $\dfrac{24}{54} = \dfrac{20}{v}$ 45

4. $\dfrac{32.5}{x} = \dfrac{5}{14}$ 91

Use the data in the table.

5. Make a scatter plot of the data.
   See graph below.

6. Fit a line to the data.
   See graph below.

7. Using your fitted line, predict the average depth of a sea with an area of 500,000 mi^2. about 3800 ft

Use the box-and-whisker plot below.

8. Estimate the maximum and the minimum data values. about 52, about 89

9. Of the 30 games played, about how many had scores below 65?
   about 8

10. About how many games had scores above 78?
    about 8

Oceans and Seas		
Name	Area (mi^2)	Average depth (ft)
Okhotsk Sea	613,900	2818
Gulf of Mexico	595,800	4961
Bering Sea	889,600	5243
South China Sea	1,422,800	3478
Caribbean Sea	1,063,300	8173
Mediterranean Sea	971,400	4902
Japan Sea	377,600	5748
Andaman Sea	232,400	3596
Red Sea	173,700	1831

Women's National Basketball Association Team Scores, 1997

Houston Comets

Standardized Testing ▶ **Open-ended**

Create a 20-item data set that can be represented by the box-and-whisker plot. Copy the plot and add a title. Answers will vary.
Check students' work.

Section ③ Percent

IN THIS SECTION

EXPLORATION 1
◆ Estimating Percents

EXPLORATION 2
◆ Finding Percents

EXPLORATION 3
◆ Finding Parts or Wholes

WARM-UP EXERCISES

Convert each fraction to a percent.

1. $\frac{1}{4}$ 25%

2. $\frac{1}{10}$ 10%

3. $\frac{1}{2}$ 50%

Solve each proportion.

4. $\frac{x}{100} = \frac{14}{40}$ 35

5. $\frac{32}{100} = \frac{50}{x}$ 156.25

You Be the Critic

Setting the Stage

Going to the movies is a favorite pastime of many people. At any given time, many movies compete for your viewing attention. To decide which movies you want to see, you can use reviews and rating systems such as the one shown below.

FREE WILLY	STAR WARS SPECIAL EDITION
A troubled boy bonds with an orca whale confined in an aquarium.	George Lucas's first sci-fi thriller of Good versus Evil.
Audience Approval: 79% National Critics ★★★¹/₂	Audience Approval: 93% National Critics ★★★¹/₂

4 stars is the highest rating, and 1 star is the lowest. Half-stars may be given.

Audience Approval rating is the percent of people who gave the movie $3\frac{1}{2}$ or 4 stars.

Try This as a Class Choose two movies or television programs. Using 1–4 stars, have each student in your class rate the two choices. Make a frequency table to show the results.

Think About It

1 For each movie or program your class rated, write a ratio to compare the number of students who gave it $3\frac{1}{2}$ or 4 stars with the total number of students who rated the movie or television program. **Answers will vary. Check students' work.**

2 Is your class's Audience Approval rating for each movie or program rated *greater than 25%*? *greater than 50%*? *greater than 75%*? **Answers will vary. Check students' work.**

Estimating Percents

GOAL

LEARN HOW TO...
- estimate percents

AS YOU...
- analyze movie ratings

SET UP *You will need:* • *Labsheet 3A* • *the table from the Setting the Stage*

Suppose that 17 of the 30 students who saw a movie gave it a rating of $3\frac{1}{2}$ or 4 stars. You can use *"nice" fractions* to estimate the percent equivalent of $\frac{17}{30}$.

> "Nice" fractions are fractions such as $\frac{1}{5}$, $\frac{1}{2}$, $\frac{3}{4}$, and $\frac{7}{10}$ that can easily be converted to percents.
>
> $\frac{1}{5} = 20\%$ $\frac{1}{2} = 50\%$
>
> $\frac{3}{4} = 75\%$ $\frac{7}{10} = 70\%$

3 The ratio $\frac{17}{30}$ is close to the ratio $\frac{18}{30}$. Is $\frac{17}{30}$ *greater than* or *less than* $\frac{18}{30}$? How do you know**?**

4 a. What "nice" fraction is equivalent to $\frac{18}{30}$? $\frac{6}{10}$ or $\frac{3}{5}$

b. What is the percent equivalent of the fraction in part (a)**?** 60%

c. Estimate the percent equivalent of $\frac{17}{30}$. about 60%

▶ You can use a percent bar model to help visualize $\frac{17}{30}$ as a percent.

5 Use Labsheet 3A. You can also estimate the percent represented by $\frac{17}{30}$ using a percent bar.

▶ Some other "nice" fractions, and their percent equivalents, are given on page 346.

3. less than; Sample Response: 17 < 18 so 17 parts of a whole are less than 18 parts of a whole.

5. a.

b. $\frac{1}{5}$, $\frac{2}{5}$, $\frac{3}{5}$, $\frac{4}{5}$

c–e.

f. a little less than 60%

Halves

$\frac{1}{2} = 0.50 = 50\%$

Thirds

$\frac{1}{3} = 0.3\overline{3} = 33\frac{1}{3}\%$

$\frac{2}{3} = 0.6\overline{6} = 66\frac{2}{3}\%$

Fourths

$\frac{1}{4} = 0.25 = 25\%$

$\frac{2}{4} = 0.50 = 50\%$

$\frac{3}{4} = 0.75 = 75\%$

Fifths

$\frac{1}{5} = 0.20 = 20\%$

$\frac{2}{5} = 0.40 = 40\%$

$\frac{3}{5} = 0.60 = 60\%$

$\frac{4}{5} = 0.80 = 80\%$

6 Suppose 22 out of 28 students gave a movie a rating of $3\frac{1}{2}$ or 4 stars. **Sample responses are given.**

a. What "nice" fraction would you use to estimate the percent equivalent of $\frac{22}{28}$? $\frac{21}{28}$ or $\frac{3}{4}$

b. Use the fraction from part (a) to estimate the Audience Approval rating for this movie. **about 75%**

c. Discussion What other "nice" fractions can you use to estimate the percent? Which gives the best estimate?

7 Suppose 9 out of 24 students gave a movie a rating of $3\frac{1}{2}$ or 4 stars. Estimate the Audience Approval rating as a percent. Explain your reasoning. **Sample Response: about 36%; 9 out of 24 is about 9 out of 25, or 36 out of 100.**

6. c. $\frac{4}{5}, \frac{2}{3}$; By using a common denominator of 420, you can see that $\frac{4}{5}$ is the closest estimate.

8 ✔ **CHECKPOINT** Estimate the percent equivalent of each fraction.

a. $\frac{13}{18}$ **about 75%**   **b.** $\frac{8}{48}$ **about 16%**   **c.** $\frac{29}{104}$ **about 29%**
Sample Responses are given.

✔ **QUESTION 8**

…checks that you can estimate percents.

9 Try This as a Class Julia estimates $\frac{5}{24}$ with the nice fraction $\frac{6}{24}$. Yvonne uses the "nice" fraction $\frac{5}{25}$.

a. The percent equivalent of $\frac{5}{24}$ is about 21%. Whose estimate is closer to the percent equivalent? **Yvonne**

b. Which do you think changes a fraction more, adding 1 to the *numerator* or adding 1 to the *denominator*? **adding 1 to the numerator (provided the numerator is less than or equal to the denominator)**

Changing Numerator or Denominator to Estimate Percents

$$\frac{\text{numerator}}{\text{denominator}} \nearrow \frac{\text{numerator} + 1}{\text{denominator}}$$
$$\searrow \frac{\text{numerator}}{\text{denominator} + 1}$$

c. Is your answer to part (b) true when the numerator is greater than the denominator?

9. c. No; If the numerator is 1 more than the denominator, the amount of change is the same in either case. (For example, $\frac{3}{2} = 1\frac{1}{2}, \frac{4}{2} = 2, \frac{3}{3} = 1$, so the change is $\frac{1}{2}$ in both cases.) Otherwise, if the numerator is greater than the denominator, adding 1 to the denominator produces the greatest change. (For example, $\frac{100}{2} = 50$, $\frac{101}{2} = 50\frac{1}{2}, \frac{100}{3} = 33.\overline{3}$, so adding 1 to the denom-inator results in the greatest change.)

10 Estimate the Audience Approval rating for the two movies or programs rated by your class in the *Setting the Stage* on page 344. **Answers will vary. Check students' work.**

HOMEWORK EXERCISES ▶ See Exs. 1–7 on p. 353.

Exploration 2

Finding Percents

SET UP *You will need the frequency table from the* Setting the Stage *on page 344.*

11 a. Sample Response: about $66\frac{2}{3}\%$, about 60%; 19 out of 30 is about 20 out of 30, or about 2 out of 3. 15 out of 24 is about 15 out of 25.
b. Sample Response: No; Since the numerator was increased by 1, the audience approval rating for Movie A is less than the $66\frac{2}{3}\%$ estimate, and since the denominator was increased by 1 to estimate the rating for Movie B, the actual rating is greater than 60%. So we really can't tell which movie has the higher rating based on the estimates.

11 Try This as a Class Suppose a class gave two movies $3\frac{1}{2}$ or 4 stars as shown in the ratios below.

Movie A	Movie B
$\frac{19}{30}$	$\frac{15}{24}$

   a. Estimate the Audience Approval rating for each movie. Explain the reasoning you used.

   b. Using estimation, can you determine which movie had a higher Audience Approval rating? Explain.

▶ A percent bar model can help you see how to set up a proportion to find the exact percent equivalent for a ratio.

EXAMPLE

Set up a proportion to find the Audience Approval rating for Movie A, represented by the ratio $\frac{19}{30}$.

SAMPLE RESPONSE

Rotate the bar 90° so the parts are over the wholes.

The shaded part represents the students who liked the movie.

12 Solve the proportion in the Example on page 348 to find the Audience Approval rating for Movie A. Round your answer to the nearest whole percent. How does the answer compare with your estimate in Question 11? **63%; Sample Response: The answer is lower than the estimate.**

13 ✔ **CHECKPOINT** Set up and solve a proportion to write each ratio as a percent.

a. $\frac{27}{90}$ **30%**   b. 35 to 105 **$33\frac{1}{3}\%$**   c. $\frac{18}{63}$ **about 29%**

QUESTION 13

…checks that you can set up and solve a proportion to find a percent.

14 a. Set up and solve a proportion to find the Audience Approval rating for Movie B to the nearest whole percent. **$\frac{x}{100} = \frac{15}{24}$, 63%**

b. Which movie received a higher Audience Approval rating, Movie A or Movie B? **Using the rounded percents, the ratings were the same.**

c. Is $\frac{19}{30} = \frac{15}{24}$? Explain why rounding to the nearest whole percent may be misleading.

14. c. No; There is a difference between the percents, but it is lost when the numbers are rounded.

15 **Discussion** Sometimes rounding to the nearest whole percent may not give the best answer.

a. Find the Audience Approval rating for Movie B to the nearest tenth of a percent. **62.5%**

b. Does your answer in part (a) change your answer to Question 14(b)? Explain.

Yes; Since 63.3% > 62.5%, Movie A had the higher rating.

> Audience Approval rating for Movie A rounded to the nearest tenth of a percent
>
> $\frac{x}{100} = \frac{19}{30}$
>
> $30x = 1900$
>
> $x = \frac{1900}{30}$
>
> $\begin{array}{r} 63.\overline{3} \\ 30\overline{)1900.0} \\ \underline{180} \\ 100 \\ \underline{90} \\ 100 \end{array}$ ← about 63.3%

Write each ratio as a percent. Round to the nearest tenth.

16 $\frac{8}{35}$ and $\frac{22}{97}$ **22.9%, 22.7%**   **17** $\frac{14}{29}$ and $\frac{15}{35}$ **48.3%, 42.9%**   **18** $\frac{7}{35}$ and $\frac{8}{49}$ **20%, 16.3%**

19 **Try This as a Class** Use your class's star ratings from page 344. **Answers will vary. Check students' work.**

a. Set up and solve a proportion to find the Audience Approval rating for each movie or television program. Round each answer to the nearest tenth of a percent.

b. Which movie or program had a higher Audience Approval rating?

c. Find a fraction that has a percent equivalent within 0.5% of each class Audience Approval rating.

HOMEWORK EXERCISES ▶ See Exs. 8–14 on pp. 353–354.

Exploration 3

Finding Parts or Wholes

▶ Audience Approval ratings are based on exit polls of at least 300 filmgoers per movie. If you know the total number of people surveyed, you can use "nice" fractions to estimate how many people gave a movie $3\frac{1}{2}$ or 4 stars.

20 Suppose a survey of 300 people was used to determine the 79% Audience Approval rating for *Free Willy*. The percent bar below shows one way a "nice" fraction can be used to estimate how many people gave the movie $3\frac{1}{2}$ or 4 stars.

People 0 300

Percent 0% 20% 40% 60% 80% 100%

a. What "nice" fraction is equivalent to 20%? $\frac{1}{5}$ or $\frac{2}{10}$

b. Find 20% of 300. 60

c. What "nice" fraction is equivalent to 80%? $\frac{4}{5}$ or $\frac{8}{10}$

d. Use your answers from parts (a)–(c) to estimate 79% of 300. about 240

▲ In the late 1960s, an audience at the Rivoli Theater in South Fallsburg, New York, viewed a "3-D" movie through special glasses.

21 Discussion Set up and solve a proportion to find 79% of 300. (*Hint:* Think of rotating the percent bar.) How does the exact answer compare with your estimate in Question 20? 237; It is very close.

$$\text{part} \longrightarrow \frac{79}{100} = \frac{?}{?} \longleftarrow \text{part}$$
$$\text{whole} \qquad\qquad\qquad\qquad \longleftarrow \text{whole}$$

✔ **QUESTION 22**

...checks that you can find a percent of a number.

22 ✔ CHECKPOINT Suppose a survey of 400 people was used to determine the 76% Audience Approval rating for a movie.

a. Estimate 76% of 400 using a "nice" fraction. about 300

b. Find 76% of 400. 304

23 Suppose 350 people rated the movie *Star Wars—Special Edition*, which had an Audience Approval rating of 93%.

  a. Estimate the number of people who gave *Star Wars—Special Edition* $3\frac{1}{2}$ or 4 stars. Explain the method you used.

  b. Set up and solve a proportion to find 93% of 350. 326

23. a. Sample Response: about 315; Since 93% is about 90%, or $\frac{9}{10}$, multiply 350 by $\frac{9}{10}$.

▶ **You just used proportions to find the part when you know the whole. Sometimes you know the part and need to find the whole.**

24 **Discussion** Suppose a movie has an Audience Approval rating of 45% because 162 people gave it a rating of $3\frac{1}{2}$ or 4 stars.

  a. Is 162 the *part* or is it the *whole*? Explain.

  b. Estimate how many people rated the movie. Explain the method you used.

24. a. part; Out of the entire group interviewed, 162 gave a rating of $3\frac{1}{2}$ or 4 stars.
b. Sample Response: about 324; 45% is about 50% so $\frac{162}{whole}$ is about $\frac{1}{2}$ and the whole is about 324.

▶ **You can use a proportion to find the whole.**

EXAMPLE

45% of a number is 162. Set up a proportion to find the whole.

SAMPLE RESPONSE

	Percent		**People**	
part →	$\dfrac{45}{100}$	$=$	$\dfrac{162}{x}$	← part
whole →				← whole

---

25 Solve the proportion in the Example to find the total number of people who rated the movie in Question 24. How does your answer compare with your estimate in Question 24(b)?
360 people; Sample Response: The estimate was reasonable.

26 Suppose 9 people give a movie a rating of $3\frac{1}{2}$ or 4 stars, resulting in an Audience Approval rating of 36%. Set up and solve a proportion to find how many people rated the movie.
25 people

27 ✔ **CHECKPOINT** Suppose 27% of a number is 135. What is the number? Explain the method you used. 500; Sample Response: Use the proportion $\frac{27}{100} = \frac{135}{x}$.

✔ **QUESTION 27**

...checks that you can find the whole amount if you are given the percent.

HOMEWORK EXERCISES ▶ See Exs. 15–26 on pp. 354–355.

Percent Bar Model (pp. 345–347)

When solving problems involving percent, "nice" fractions can be used to help estimate solutions. "Nice" fractions can be converted to percents easily. The estimation can be shown on a percent bar model.

Example About what percent is 31 out of 40?

$\frac{31}{40}$ is close to the "nice" fraction $\frac{3}{4}$.

$\frac{3}{4} = 75\%$, so $\frac{31}{40}$ is a little more than 75%.

Proportions and Percents (pp. 348–351)

You can use proportions to find a missing part or whole.

Example

Suppose 65% of students surveyed say they prefer creamy peanut butter to chunky peanut butter. If 78 students preferred creamy, how many students were surveyed?

Since the total number of students surveyed is not known, the variable x represents the whole.

Solving the proportion gives x = 120, so 120 students were surveyed.

CLOSURE QUESTION

Explain how to estimate and how to find the exact value of the percent equivalent for a fraction.

Sample Response: To estimate the percent equivalent, change the numerator or denominator of the fraction slightly so that the result is equivalent to a "nice" fraction whose percent equivalent is known. For the exact percent equivalent, set up and solve the proportion that equates the fraction to $\frac{x}{100}$.

28 Key Concepts Question Find each missing part or whole.

a. 11% of a number is 44. 400   **b.** 73% of 124 is a number. 90.52

Section 3

Practice & Application Exercises

1. Suppose that 7 out of 12 commercials during a certain TV show are about food. Draw a percent bar and use it to estimate the percent of commercials that advertise food. **See Additional Answers.**

2. It is estimated that 1 out of 11 employed Americans works in a shopping center or a shopping mall. Estimate the percent of Americans who work in a shopping center or a mall. **about 10%**

3. In a movie survey, 5 out of every 16 people who responded gave a movie a rating of 9 or 10 on a scale of 1 to 10.
   Sample responses are given.
   a. What "nice" fraction can you use to estimate the percent of people who gave the movie a rating of 9 or 10? $\frac{1}{3}$

   b. Estimate the percent of people who gave a movie a rating of 9 or 10. **about $33\frac{1}{3}$%**

Estimate the percent equivalent of each ratio. **Sample responses are given.**

4. $\frac{7}{12}$ about 50%   5. $\frac{20}{24}$ about 80%   6. $\frac{9}{40}$ about 20%   7. $\frac{25}{33}$ about 75%

8. Set up and solve a proportion to find the actual percent for Exercises 1 and 2. Round each answer to the nearest percent.
$$\frac{7}{12} = \frac{x}{100}, \ 58\%; \ \frac{1}{11} = \frac{x}{100}, \ 9\%$$

Write each ratio as a percent. Round each answer to the nearest tenth.

9. $\frac{4}{12}$ 33.3%   10. $\frac{27}{135}$ 20%   11. $\frac{51}{68}$ 75%   12. $\frac{48}{750}$ 6.4%

13. **Entertainment Spending** In 1990, on average, each person under the age of 25 spent $833 on entertainment. Of that amount, $344 was spent on televisions, radios, and sound equipment. What percent of the entertainment money was spent on televisions, radios, and sound equipment? **about 41%**

14. **Publishing** Of the 46,738 new books published in 1990, 5172 were for juveniles. What percent of the books were for juveniles? **about 11%**

15. According to a Gallup poll, on any given day, 71% of the 250 million people in the United States read a newspaper and 36% read a magazine.

    a. Estimate the number of people in the United States who read a newspaper yesterday. **about 175 million Americans**

    b. Estimate the number of people in the United States who will read a magazine today. **about 83 million Americans**

16. **Television Viewing** The percent bar below shows 50% of the United States population.

People (millions) 0   250

Percent 0%   50%   100%

   a. According to a survey in *TV Guide*, 46% of people in the United States said they would not stop watching television for anything less than $1 million. Estimate the number who would not stop watching television for anything less than $1 million.
about 125 million Americans

   b. In the same survey, 25% said they would not give up television even if they were given $1 million. Estimate the number of people in the United States who would not stop watching television even if they were given $1 million. about 62.5 million Americans

17. Suppose 68% of students at a school do not like the dress code. If 374 students do not like the dress code, how many students are there in the school? Explain your reasoning. 550 students; $\frac{68}{100} = \frac{374}{x}$

Find each unknown number.

18. 15% of a number is 13.5. 90   19. 12 is 30% of a number. 40

20. 82% of a number is 533. 650   21. 62% of 25 is a number. 15.5

22. **Challenge** Teenagers from three schools estimated how much time they spent viewing or listening to each medium on a school day. Here are their combined results.

Medium	Time spent (min)	
	Mean	Median
television	136	120
radio	101	60
records/tapes	87	60
MTV	29	0

   a. The percent of the teenagers who did not watch MTV at all must be greater than what percent? How do you know?
50%; The median is 0.

   b. Suppose teenagers spent a mean of 29% of their free time listening to the radio. How long is their total free time? about 348 min

23. Suppose that when a math teacher eats in a restaurant, the teacher tips exactly 15% of the total bill. After enjoying a meal, the teacher leaves $2.40 on the table. How much did the meal cost? $16.00

24. a. Based on your own experience, estimate the number of minutes of free time a teenager has on a typical school day. Answers will vary. Check students' work.

b. Use your answer to part (a) and the mean time spent on each medium listed in Exercise 22 to estimate the percent of free time teenagers spent on each of the various media.
Answers will vary. Check students' work.

c. Do you think the percents for students in your school would be *higher, lower,* or *the same as* the results you found in part (b)? Explain your answer. Answers will vary. Check students' work.

25. Jo set up the proportion $\frac{100}{350} = \frac{x}{34}$ to find 34% of 350.

a. Is there anything wrong with Jo's proportion? Explain.
Yes; The ratios Jo has set up are not equivalent.

b. Set up a proportion that will give the correct answer, and solve it. $\frac{34}{100} = \frac{x}{350}$; 119

Reflecting ◀▷ on the Section

26. Find examples that show how percents are used in discounting prices. Describe the examples, and explain how you could use "nice" fractions to estimate or find the amount of each discount.
Answers will vary. Check students' work.

RESEARCH

Exercise 26 checks that you understand how to find a percent of a number.

Spiral ◀▷ Review

Solve each proportion. (Module 5, p. 336)

27. $\frac{3}{5} = \frac{x}{15}$ 9

28. $\frac{x}{9} = \frac{20}{180}$ 1

29. $\frac{8}{x} = \frac{32}{40}$ 10

Find the absolute value of each integer. (Module 2, p. 94)

30. –121 121

31. 43 43

32. –1 1

Write each fraction in lowest terms. (Module 3, p. 170)

33. $\frac{25}{30}$ $\frac{5}{6}$

34. $\frac{14}{49}$ $\frac{2}{7}$

35. $\frac{27}{81}$ $\frac{1}{3}$

The Interest Formula

To find the simple interest *I* paid on an amount, or *principal*, you can use this formula:

$$I = p \times r \times t$$

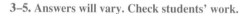

principal ↗   annual interest rate ↑   time in years ↖

Find the simple interest in each situation.

36. $p = \$1200$
    $r = 5\%$
    $t = 1$ year $60

37. $p = \$1800$
    $r = 7\%$
    $t = 4$ years $504

38. $p = \$1000$
    $r = 5.5\%$
    $t = 8$ months $36.67

39. **Challenge** Suppose in Exercise 37 the interest earned each year were left in the account, so that the principal increased each year.

   a. Find the total interest earned in 4 years. $559.44

   b. Compare your answers for part (a) and Exercise 37.   Answer to part (a) is greater.

May I Ask You a Few Questions?

Analyzing Data Each pair of students should report their results to the class. Then the class can organize and analyze all the data.

3–5. Answers will vary. Check students' work.

 3 How many students did you and your partner interview? Use fractions and percents to compare your sample size with that used by the entire class.

 4 Use fractions and percents to summarize the combined data. What did the survey reveal? Do the results vary by age? by grade level? by gender?

 5 How do the class results compare with the information you collected with your partner? Are the results what you expected? Did the different sample sizes affect your findings? Describe and explain any differences or similarities.

 6 Suppose you and your classmates surveyed only your friends. Why is this not a random sample? Why is it not a representative sample? See Additional Answers.

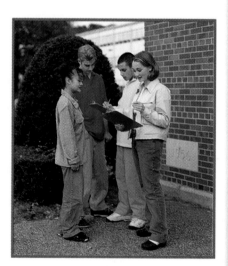

Section ③
Extra Skill Practice

Estimate the percent equivalent of each ratio.

1. $\frac{10}{18}$ about 55%   2. $\frac{23}{45}$ about 50%   3. $\frac{44}{198}$ about 22%   4. $\frac{21}{34}$ about 60%

5. $\frac{35}{125}$ 28%   6. $\frac{36}{81}$ about 44%   7. $\frac{73}{90}$ about 80%   8. $\frac{5}{18}$ about 25%

Write each ratio as a percent. Round to the nearest tenth.

9. $\frac{30}{120}$ 25%   10. $\frac{42}{210}$ 20%   11. $\frac{24}{36}$ 66.7%   12. $\frac{18}{54}$ 33.3%

13. $\frac{55}{90}$ 61.1%   14. $\frac{13}{70}$ 18.6%   15. $\frac{14}{20}$ 70%   16. $\frac{15}{75}$ 20%

Solve for each unknown number.

17. 11% of a number is 17.6.   160

18. A number is 23% of 16.   3.68

19. 65% of a number is 455.   700

20. A number is 90% of 180.   162

21. A number is 40% of 27.   10.8

22. 25% of a number is 48.   192

23. 21% of a number is 126.   600

24. A number is 17% of 20.   3.4

Standardized Testing ◀▶ Performance Task

Copy and complete the table. If necessary, round to the nearest tenth of a percent. Write a paragraph explaining what the table shows, and describe at least one conclusion that you can draw from the table.

Day	Students surveyed*	Good	OK	Not good	
Monday	28	21 (?%)	? (21.4%)	? (3.6%)	75; 6; 1
Tuesday	27	16 (?%)	7 (?%)	4 (?%)	59.3; 25.9; 14.8
Wednesday	25	? (32%)	? (52%)	4 (?%)	8; 13; 16
Thursday	24	6 (?%)	3 (?%)	? (?%)	25; 12.5; 15; 62.5
Friday	?	4 (20%)	2 (?%)	? (?%)	20; 10; 14; 70

* Students who were absent or brought lunches were not surveyed.

See Additional Answers.

IN THIS SECTION

EXPLORATION 1
♦ Fractions, Decimals, and Percents

EXPLORATION 2
♦ Predicting Using Percents

EXPLORATION 3
♦ Multistage Experiments

Make Every Shot Count

◀---·*Setting the Stage*

In 1996, over 127,000 cheering fans attended the 20-game tour of the USA Women's National Basketball Team. The "Dream Team" lived up to its name, winning every game against some of the nation's best college teams. The team scored an average of 96.4 points per game and won by an average of 46.2 points! The team also had an impressive record for foul shots, called *free throws*. The statistics for the top five free-throw shooters are shown below.

▲
The "Dream Team" was coached by Tara VanDerveer, shown above. Coaches usually choose the best free-throw shooter to attempt the free throw on a technical foul.

PLAYERS	FREE THROWS MADE (FTM)	FREE THROWS ATTEMPTED (FTA)
Sheryl Swoopes	27	33
Jennifer Azzi	58	64
Nikki McCray	28	35
Katy Steding	50	60
Teresa Edwards	13	15

Warm Up Exercises
See page 359.

Think About It

1 Suppose there are three seconds left on the clock and the score is tied when a technical foul is called on the other team. If you were head coach Tara VanDerveer, which player would you choose to attempt the free throw? Why? Sample Response: Jennifer Azzi; She has both the greatest percent and the greatest number of free throws made.

2 Suppose a player made 1 free throw out of 1 attempt. Would that player be the best choice for the free throw? Why? No; There is not enough data.

Exploration 1 ▸▸▸▸▸▸▸▸▸▸▸▸▸▸▸▸▸▸▸▸▸▸▸▸▸▸▸▸▸▸▸▸▸▸▸▸▸▸▸

Fractions, Decimals, and Percents

GOAL

LEARN HOW TO...
◆ write a fraction as a decimal or percent

AS YOU...
◆ test your free-throw ability

SET UP *Work in a group of four. You will need:* • *large paper cup* • *cotton balls* • *masking tape* • *ruler*

▸ The ratio of *free throws made* to *free throws attempted* tells how good a player is at the free-throw line. For example, Nikki McCray made 28 out of 35 free throws on the National Team's college tour. This ratio can be expressed in several ways.

Ratio	Fraction form	Decimal form	Percent form
28 to 35 or 28 : 35	$\frac{28}{35}$	0.8	80%

WARM-UP EXERCISES

Write the fraction as a decimal. Round answers to the nearest thousandth.

1. $\frac{3}{7}$ 0.429

2. $\frac{11}{51}$ 0.216

3. $\frac{67}{102}$ 0.657

Find the probability of each outcome when you roll a six-sided die.

4. 2 $\frac{1}{6}$

5. an even number $\frac{1}{2}$

3 Discussion Look at the different forms of the ratio shown in the table.

a. Explain how the decimal form of the ratio was found.
     by dividing the numerator by the denominator

b. How are the decimal and percent forms of the ratio related? Write the decimal 0.67 in percent form.
     The percent form is 100 times the decimal form; 67%

c. Describe an easy way to find the decimal form of a ratio if you know its percent form.
     Move the decimal point 2 places to the left.

4 Use the free-throw statistics in the *Setting the Stage*.
     See Additional Answers.

a. Represent the free-throw performance for each player on the USA Women's National Team in fraction, decimal, and percent form. Round each decimal to the nearest thousandth.

b. Which player had the best free-throw record? How does this compare with the player you chose in Question 1 on page 358?

c. Which form of the ratio makes comparing the statistics easiest?

▶ **Sometimes you can use mental math to write ratios as percents.**

EXAMPLE

Use mental math to write $\frac{15}{20}$ as a percent.

SAMPLE RESPONSE

Method 1: Use an equivalent fraction.

15 • ?

$$\frac{15}{20} = \frac{n}{100}$$

Since 20 • **5** = 100, $n = 15 • 5 = 75$.

20 • ?

$$\frac{15}{20} = \frac{75}{100} = 75\%$$

Method 2: Use a "nice" fraction.

$$\frac{15}{20} = \frac{3}{4}$$

Write $\frac{15}{20}$ as a "nice" fraction.

$\frac{3}{4} = 75\%$, so $\frac{15}{20} = 75\%$.

5 Mental Math Use mental math to write each ratio as a percent.

a. $\frac{8}{10}$ 80% **b.** $\frac{6}{24}$ 25% **c.** $\frac{12}{25}$ 48% **d.** $\frac{5}{15}$ $33\frac{1}{3}\%$

▶ **How good are you at the free-throw line? In the simulation in Question 6, you will find out.**

6. Answers will vary. Check students' work.

6 a. Place a paper cup on the floor. Use masking tape to make a free-throw line 1 m from the cup.

b. Take turns shooting "free throws" by tossing a cotton ball into the cup. First each player takes 8 shots, then 10, and then 15. Be sure your feet do not cross the free-throw line.

c. Record the numbers of free throws made (FTM) and free throws attempted (FTA).

✔ **QUESTION 7**

...checks that you can represent a ratio in fraction, decimal, and percent forms.

7 ✔ **CHECKPOINT** Use the data you recorded in Question 6 (c).

Answers will vary. Check students' work.

a. Find the fraction, decimal, and percent forms of the ratios of FTM to FTA for 8, 10, and 15 shots for each person in your group. Then find each person's overall ratio.

b. Does your percent increase if you have more chances? Explain.

HOMEWORK EXERCISES ▶ See Exs. 1–12 on pp. 368–369.

Exploration 2

Predicting Using Percents

SET UP *You will need your results from Question 6 on page 360.*

GOAL

LEARN HOW TO...
- estimate percents using "nice" fractions and mental math
- use percents to make predictions

AS YOU...
- examine basketball statistics

▶ On the team's college tour, the USA Women's National Team showed that they were great not only at free throws, but also at two- and three-point field goals from all over the court!

3-point goal line

8 Discussion On the college tour, the team's center, Rebecca Lobo, made 43 of the 99 field goals she attempted. How could you use mental math to estimate the percent of field goals she made?

Since 43 out of 99 is close to 43 out of 100, the percent is about 43%.

▶ Teresa Edwards made 11 out of the 23 three-point field goals she attempted during the tour. Two "nice" fractions that can be used to estimate her three-point percent are shown below.

Original Fraction	"Nice" Fractions	
$\frac{11}{23}$	$\frac{11}{22}$ and $\frac{12}{25}$	These fractions are approximations of the original fraction.

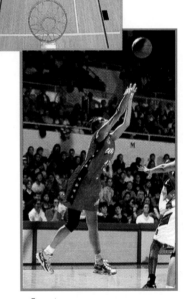

9 Discussion Think about the fractions $\frac{11}{23}$, $\frac{11}{22}$, and $\frac{12}{25}$.

a. The fraction $\frac{12}{25}$ is a "nice" fraction because the denominator is a factor of 100. Why is $\frac{11}{22}$ a "nice" fraction? $\frac{11}{22} = \frac{1}{2}$

b. Use mental math to estimate Edwards's three-point percent using the "nice" fraction $\frac{11}{22}$. Is the estimate *higher* or *lower* than the actual percent? about 50%; higher

c. Use mental math to estimate Edwards's three-point percent using the "nice" fraction $\frac{12}{25}$. 48%

d. The percent form of $\frac{11}{23}$ is about 47.8%. Which "nice" fraction, $\frac{11}{22}$ or $\frac{12}{25}$, is a better estimate for $\frac{11}{23}$? $\frac{12}{25}$

▲ A 3-point field goal is made from behind the 3-point line.

Section 4 Percent and Probability

361

10 ✔ **CHECKPOINT** Field goal statistics for individual players during the USA Women's National Team's 1996 college tour are shown below. Estimate the percent of field goals made by each player.

Player	Field goals made	Field goals attempted	
Sheryl Swoopes	103	198	about 50%
Dawn Staley	3	18	about 17%
Katy Steding	47	125	about 40%

▶ **Percents can be used to show the past performance of a basketball player. If you think of the percents as experimental probabilities, you can also predict a player's future performance.**

> ### EXAMPLE
>
> **Nikki McCray made about 30% of her three-point field goals during the college tour. Estimate the number of three-point field goals she might make in her next 50 attempts.**
>
> **SAMPLE RESPONSE**
>
> **Method 1:** Use fraction form.
>
> 30% of 50 = $\frac{3}{10}$ • 50 = 15
>
> **Method 2:** Use decimal form.
>
> 30% of 50 = 0.30 • 50 = 15
>
> **You can expect Nikki McCray to make about 15 of the next 50 three-point field goals that she attempts.**

11 Ruthie Bolton made about 80% of the free-throws she attempted during the 20-game tour. About how many free throws would you expect her to make in her next 25 attempts? about 20

12 ✔ **CHECKPOINT** On the tour, the USA Women's National Team made 112 of 336 three-point field goals attempted. Based on that record, tell how many three-point field goals you would expect the team to make in each number of attempts.

a. 60 about 20   **b.** 80 about 27   **c.** 45 about 15   **d.** 120 about 40

13 Use your results from Question 7 on page 360. Based on your free-throw results, find the number of free throws you would expect to make in 35 attempts. Explain your reasoning. Answers will vary.

▐ **HOMEWORK EXERCISES** ▶ See Exs. 13–17 on p. 369.

Multistage Experiments

GOAL

LEARN HOW TO...
- find theoretical probabilities for a multistage experiment

AS YOU...
- analyze repeated free throws

KEY TERM
- multistage experiment

SET UP *You will need graph paper.*

▶ A player fouled while shooting is allowed two free-throw attempts. You can use the player's past performance to find the theoretical probability that the player will make 2, 1, or 0 free throws.

Suppose Nikki McCray had been fouled while shooting. Since she made 28 out of 35 free throws during the National Team's college tour, the probability that she will make a free throw is $\frac{28}{35}$ or 80%.

14 a. How many of the 35 attempted free throws did Nikki McCray miss during the college tour? **7 free throws**

b. Find the probability that Nikki McCray will miss a free throw. Write your answer as a percent, a decimal, and a fraction. **20%, 0.2, $\frac{1}{5}$**

▶ The probabilities can be shown by a tree diagram.

First free throw

0.80 ——— S   S = scores

0.20 ——— M   M = misses

> She makes the free throw and scores.

15 a. What outcomes are shown in the tree diagram? **scores on the first free throw, misses on the first free throw**

b. How is the probability of each outcome shown? **as a decimal on the appropriate branch of the tree**

▶ Branches can be added to the tree to show all the possible outcomes when Nikki McCray attempts two free throws.

> Assume that her second outcome is not affected by the first one.

First free throw Second free throw Outcome

0.80 —— S
  0.80 —— S   S,S
  0.20 ? —— ? M   S,M
  0.80 ? —— ? S   ? M, S
0.20 —— M
  0.20 ? —— ? M   ? M, M

> She makes the first, and misses the second.

16 a. Copy and complete the tree diagram on page 363 showing all the possible outcomes for Nikki McCray's two free throws. Replace each question mark with the appropriate probability or outcome. **See tree diagram.**

b. What outcome does "M,S" represent? **miss the first free throw, score on the second**

c. Do you think the probability that Nikki McCray makes both free throws is *greater than*, *less than*, or *equal to* 0.80? Why?

▶ **You can use a 10 × 10 grid to determine the probability that Nikki McCray will make both.**

Start on the left and shade in complete **columns**.

Start at the top and shade in complete **rows**.

Shade 80% of the **columns** to show the probability that she makes her first free throw.

Shade 80% of the **rows** to show the probability that she makes her second free throw.

The part of the grid that is shaded twice represents the probability that she makes both free throws.

17 Which part of the second grid represents the probability that Nikki McCray will make both free throws? **the part that is shaded twice, which is 64 out of 100 squares, or 0.64**

18 Shade a 10 × 10 grid to show the probability that Nikki McCray will *miss* both free throws. What is that probability?

19 Discussion Think about the grid you shaded in Question 18 and the second grid shown above.

a. How are the two grids alike?

b. How could you have used the second shaded grid above to find the probability that she misses both free throws? **Count the squares that were not shaded at all and divide by 100.**

c. Explain how you can use your grid from Question 18 to find the probability that she makes the first free throw and misses the second. **Count the squares that were shaded the first time, but not the second.**

d. Describe how each outcome in the tree diagram on page 363 is displayed on the second grid above.

20 **Try This as a Class** In Question 17, the probability that Nikki McCray will make both free throws is 0.8 • 0.8 = 0.64.

   a. What do the factors 0.8 and 0.8 represent in this product?
     the probability on each try of making a single free throw

   b. How can these numbers be read from the tree diagram?
     They are on each branch of the tree that represents a score.

   c. Explain how the probability that she makes the first free throw and she misses the second free throw can be computed without using a grid.

   d. What is the probability that she makes at least one of the free throws attempted? 0.96

20. c. Multiply the probability of the first event happening by the probability of the second event happening, (0.8×0.2).

▶ **A situation like the repeated free throw attempts, which involves two or more events happening one after the other, is a multistage experiment.**

21 ✔ **CHECKPOINT** Suppose Jennifer Azzi is fouled while shooting. Overall, she made 58 of the 64 free throws she attempted.

   a. Make a tree diagram showing all possible outcomes for the free throws attempted. Label each branch with the probability.
     See Additional Answers.

   b. What is the probability that she makes exactly one free throw? 0.17

   c. What is the probability that she does not make either free throw? about 0.01

   d. What is the probability that she makes at least one free throw? about 0.99

✔ **QUESTION 21**

...checks that you can use a tree diagram to find probabilities in multistage experiments.

22 If a player who is not shooting is fouled after the opposing team has committed six fouls, she is allowed one free throw attempt. If she makes the free throw, she is allowed one more attempt. See Additional Answers.

   a. Draw a tree diagram showing all possible outcomes for Jennifer Azzi in this situation.

   b. What is the probability that Jennifer Azzi makes exactly one free throw? How does this probability compare with the probability you found in Question 21(b)? Explain.

HOMEWORK EXERCISES ▶ See Exs. 18–25 on pp. 370–371.

Section 4
Key Concepts

Fraction-Decimal-Percent Equivalents (pp. 359–360)

A ratio can be represented as a fraction, a decimal, or a percent.

Example The ratio of 39 out of 60 can be expressed in the following ways.

Ratio form	Fraction form	Decimal form	Percent form
39 to 60 or 39 : 60	$\frac{39}{60}$	0.65	65%

Predicting Using Percents (pp. 361–362)

You can use percents to predict future outcomes.

Example In 1992, Cal Ripken of the Baltimore Orioles baseball team got 160 hits out of 637 times at bat. How many hits do you expect Cal Ripken to get in 60 times at bat?

First write the ratio as a "nice" fraction or percent.

$$\frac{160}{637} \approx \frac{160}{640} \rightarrow \frac{160}{640} = \frac{16}{64} = \frac{1}{4} = 25\%, \text{ so } \frac{160}{637} \approx 25\%$$

Then use the fraction or decimal form to find the answer.

Fraction Form

$$\frac{1}{4} \cdot 60 = 15$$

Decimal Form

$$0.25 \cdot 60 = 15$$

In 60 times at bat, you can expect Cal Ripken to make about 15 hits.

---

23 **Key Concepts Question** On the college tour, Lisa Leslie made 135 of the 220 field goals she attempted.

a. Express the ratio 135:220 as a fraction, a decimal, and a percent. $\frac{135}{220}$ or $\frac{27}{44}$, 0.614, 61.4%

b. Based on her performance, how many field goals do you expect Lisa Leslie to make in her next 50 attempts? about 31 field goals

Section 4
Key Concepts

▶▶▶▶▶▶▶▶▶▶▶▶▶▶▶▶▶▶▶▶▶▶▶▶

Key Term

Probability and Multistage Experiments (pp. 363–365)

An experiment that consists of doing two or more things one after the other is a multistage experiment.

multistage experiment

The probabilities of the outcomes of a multistage experiment can often be found by shading a grid or constructing a tree diagram.

Example A bag contains three yellow chips and one blue chip. A chip is drawn from the bag, the color is noted, and then the chip is put back in the bag.

If this experiment is done twice, what is the probability that the first chip is yellow and the second is blue?

Shaded Grid

Shade $\frac{3}{4}$ of the grid to show the probability that the first chip is yellow.

Shade $\frac{1}{4}$ of the grid to show the probability that the second chip is blue.

Tree Diagram

first chip   second chip   outcome

$\frac{1}{4}$ B $\frac{1}{4}$ B   B,B

$\frac{3}{4}$ Y   B,Y

$\frac{3}{4}$ Y $\frac{1}{4}$ B   Y,B

$\frac{3}{4}$ Y   Y,Y

B = Blue
Y = Yellow

$P(\text{first Y, then B}) = \frac{3}{4} \cdot \frac{1}{4} = \frac{3}{16}$

The probability that the first chip is yellow and the second chip is blue is $\frac{3}{16}$.

24 **Key Concepts Question** Use the Example above.

a. What outcome is represented by each region on the grid—blue? yellow? white? **B, B; Y, Y; B, Y**

b. What is the probability of the outcome represented by each region described in part (a)? $\frac{1}{16}, \frac{9}{16}, \frac{3}{16}$

CLOSURE QUESTION

Explain how you can use percents to predict future outcomes.

Sample Response: Use past performance to write the ratio of desired outcomes to total outcomes. Convert this to a percent. Multiply this percent by the total number of future outcomes to find the predicted number of desired outcomes.

1. Holdsclaw: $\frac{6}{16}$, 0.375, 37.5%; Conklin: $\frac{5}{8}$, 0.625, 62.5%; Marciniak: $\frac{5}{13}$, 0.385, 38.5%; T. Johnson: $\frac{7}{10}$, 0.7, 70%.

1. Basketball In the 1996 NCAA women's college basketball championship game, Tennessee beat Georgia 83 to 65. The table shows some of the field-goal statistics for four Tennessee players from that game. Represent each player's field-goal performance in fraction, decimal, and percent forms. Round each decimal to the nearest thousandth.

Player	Field goals made	Field goals attempted
Holdsclaw	6	16
Conklin	5	8
Marciniak	5	13
T. Johnson	7	10

Baseball A player's batting average is the decimal form of the ratio of *number of hits* to *times at bat* rounded to the nearest thousandth. Find the 1992 batting average for each player.

2. David Justice (Braves): 124 for 484   0.256

3. Barry Larkin (Reds): 162 for 533   0.304

4. Frank Thomas (White Sox): 185 for 573   0.323

5. Kruk; Sample Response: Round the decimal forms of the ratios of *number of hits* to *times at bat* to the nearest ten–thousandth and compare the decimal numbers.

5. Bip Roberts of the Cincinnati Reds and Jon Kruk of the Philadelphia Phillies both had .323 batting averages in 1992, which were high enough for third and fourth place in the National League batting average race. Roberts had 172 hits in 532 times at bat. Kruk had 164 hits in 507 times at bat. Which player was in third place? How did you find your answer?

Luis Ulacia is shown rounding third base after hitting a home run in the first inning of the game against the United States. ▼

6. Olympics On July 28, 1996, the United States Olympic baseball team lost to the defending Olympic championship team from Cuba by a score of 10–8. Find the batting average for each player in the game whose batting results are shown in the table. Represent each average in fraction, decimal, and percent form.

Player	Hits	Times at bat	
Ulacia (Cuba)	2	5	$\frac{2}{5}$, 0.400, 40%
Paret (Cuba)	1	3	$\frac{1}{3}$, 0.333, 33.3%
Lee (U.S.A.)	3	4	$\frac{3}{4}$, 0.750, 75%
Glaus (U.S.A.)	1	4	$\frac{1}{4}$, 0.250, 25%

Write each ratio in percent form.

7. 9 : 50 *18%*

8. $\frac{1}{4}$ *25%*

9. 0.1 *10%*

10. 0.975 *97.5%*

11. $\frac{50}{80}$ *62.5%*

12. $\frac{162}{225}$ *72%*

13. Jewelry Eighteen-karat gold is 75% pure gold. Suppose a piece of 18-karat gold jewelry weighs 2 oz. Use mental math to determine how many ounces of pure gold the jewelry contains. *1.5 oz*

14. Interpreting Data If given the ability to travel through time, to become invisible, to fly, or to read minds, about 20% of 560 adults polled in a magazine would choose the ability to fly. Another 35% would choose the ability to travel through time. Suppose 2000 adults had been polled. How many of them would you expect to choose each ability listed below?

   a. fly like a bird *about 400 adults*

   b. travel through time *about 700 adults*

   c. become invisible or read minds *about 900 adults*

▲
The *Museo del Oro* (Gold Museum) in Bogotá, Colombia, preserves over 33,000 gold objects made by the native cultures before the arrival of Europeans.

15. Challenge Use the meaning of *batting average* given for Exercises 2–6. Brian Hunter of the Atlanta Braves had one hit in the 1992 World Series and had a .200 batting average. Sid Bream, also of the Braves, had the same average in 15 times at bat in the World Series.

   a. How many times did Brian Hunter bat in the World Series? *5 times*

   b. How many hits did Sid Bream have in the World Series? *3 hits*

16. Suppose Charisse is studying sleep patterns. She records the total amount she sleeps each night for one year. At the end of the year, she finds she has slept 2628 h out of the total 8760 h in the year.

   a. What percent of the year did Charisse spend sleeping? *30%*

   b. Estimate how long you can expect Charisse to sleep tonight. *about 7 h*

   c. Is it likely that she will sleep exactly the number of hours you found in part (b)? Explain. *No; 7 h is both an average and an estimate.*

17. About 26 million people in the United States wear contact lenses. Of that total, about 21% are between the ages of 18 and 25. Estimate the number of people aged 18 to 25 in the United States who wear contact lenses. *about 5 million*

Consider the experiment of flipping a coin and rolling an 8-sided die. Shade a grid to find the probability of each event.

18. heads and the number 6 $\frac{1}{16}$ or 6.25%

19. tails and a number less than 4 $\frac{3}{16}$ or 18.75%

20. tails and an odd number $\frac{1}{4}$ or 25%

21. heads and a number greater than 2 $\frac{3}{8}$ or 37.5%

22. Suppose this spinner is spun twice.

a. **Writing** Which of the grids below could you shade to find the probability that the first spin will be red and the second spin will be blue? Explain.

A. 10 × 10 grid

B. 3 × 3 grid

C. 3 × 6 grid

b. Copy the grid you chose in part (a). Shade it to find the probability that the first spin is red and the second is blue.

23. A box contains two red and three blue marbles. Three marbles are removed from the box one after another without looking. After each marble is removed, its color is recorded and the marble is put back into the box before the next marble is removed.

a. Copy and complete this tree diagram to show the outcomes of this experiment. Label each branch of the tree with the probability. See Additional Answers.

first marble

R

B

b. Use the tree diagram to find the probability of each event.

* removing three red marbles 0.064

* removing three blue marbles 0.216

* removing a blue, then a red, and then a blue marble 0.144

* removing a red, then a red, and then a blue marble 0.096

* removing exactly two red marbles 0.288

* removing at least one red marble 0.784

22. a. B or C; On either grid, you could shade $\frac{1}{3}$ of the columns red (to represent the fraction of the spinner that is red) and $\frac{2}{3}$ of the rows blue (to represent the fraction of the spinner that is blue). Grid B would be easier to work with.

b. Using the 3 × 3 grid, the first column should be shaded red. Then the first two rows should be shaded blue. 2 out of the 9 squares are shaded twice, so the probability is $\frac{2}{9}$. $\left(\frac{1}{3} \cdot \frac{2}{3} = \frac{2}{9}\right)$

24. Challenge Suppose three marbles are removed from the box in Exercise 23 one after another, but each marble is not replaced before the next marble is removed. Repeat parts (a) and (b) of Exercise 23 for this experiment. See Additional Answers.

Reflecting ◀▶ on the Section

Write your response to Exercise 25 in your journal.

25. During her previous basketball games this season, Alyssa made 20 free throws in 40 attempts. She calculated her free-throw percent to be 50%. In today's game, she made 10 free throws out of 10 attempts, or 100%. Alyssa thinks her free-throw percent is now 75%. Is she correct? Explain. No; Alyssa's free-throw ratio is $\frac{30}{50}$ or 60%.

> **Journal**
>
> Exercise 25 checks that you understand how to use percent to make predictions.

Spiral ◀▶ Review

Solve each proportion. (Module 5, p. 336)

26. $\frac{18}{12} = \frac{24}{x}$ 16   27. $\frac{3}{13} = \frac{x}{325}$ 75   28. $\frac{x}{100} = \frac{4}{5}$ 80   29. $\frac{5}{x} = \frac{2}{20}$ 50

Career ◾ Connection

Pharmacist: Kristi Melby

Kristi Melby's job as a pharmacist includes determining the proper amount, or dosage, of medicine, and mixing powdered medicine with a liquid to form a solution.

30. For children, the proper dosage of some medicines depends on body weight. For example, the children's dosage of penicillin is 15 milligrams (mg) for each kilogram of body weight. Write and solve a proportion to find how many milligrams of penicillin Kristi Melby should give a child who weighs 44 lb. (*Hint:* Use 5 kg as the equivalent of 11 lb.) $\frac{15 \text{ mg}}{1 \text{ kg}} = \frac{x \text{ mg}}{20 \text{ kg}}$; 300 mg

31. Every 5 milliliters (mL) of an oral solution of penicillin should contain 250 mg of penicillin powder.

   a. Express this information as a unit rate. 50 mg/mL

   b. Write and solve a proportion to find how many milliliters of solution Kristi Melby needs to make for 900 mg of penicillin. $\frac{50 \text{ mg}}{1 \text{ mL}} = \frac{900 \text{ mg}}{x \text{ mL}}$; 18 mL

▲ Kristi Melby serves Native American families on the Fond du Lac Reservation in Cloquet, Minnesota.

Write each ratio as a fraction, a decimal, and a percent.

1. 1:3 $\frac{1}{3}$, 0.3$\overline{3}$, 33$\frac{1}{3}$%

2. 15:30 $\frac{1}{2}$, 0.5, 50%

3. 16:20 $\frac{4}{5}$, 0.8, 80%

4. 7:25 $\frac{7}{25}$, 0.28, 28%

5. 12:18 $\frac{2}{3}$, 0.66$\overline{7}$, 66$\frac{2}{3}$%

6. 23:100 $\frac{23}{100}$, 0.23, 23%

7. 4.5:10 $\frac{9}{20}$, 0.45, 45%

8. 21:28 $\frac{3}{4}$, 0.75, 75%

9. 14:64 $\frac{7}{32}$, about 0.22, about 22%

Write each fraction as a percent using estimation or mental math. Sample estimates are given.

10. $\frac{111}{334}$ about 33%

11. $\frac{13}{25}$ 52%

12. $\frac{9}{26}$ about 33%

13. $\frac{2}{9}$ about 20%

14. $\frac{7}{20}$ 35%

15. $\frac{20}{27}$ about 75%

16. $\frac{24}{98}$ about 25%

17. $\frac{9.5}{50}$ 19%

18. $\frac{6}{21}$ about 30%

19. Suppose the probability that it will rain is $\frac{5}{7}$ each day for two consecutive days.

   a. What is the probability that it will not rain on a given day? $\frac{2}{7}$

   b. Make a tree diagram to find all the possible outcomes of rain on two consecutive days. R = rain, N = no rain

   c. Use a grid to show the probability of rain on two consecutive days. $\frac{25}{49} \approx 50\%$

   d. What is the probability that it will rain one day and will *not* rain the next day? $\frac{10}{49} \approx 20\%$

1. Choose the letter(s) of the ratio(s) that is (are) *not* equivalent to 13.5%. B, D

   A 0.135   B $\frac{5}{37}$ C 13.5 : 100   D $\frac{6}{36}$

2. A paper bag contains 4 plums and 12 nectarines. Without looking, Frida reaches into the bag and pulls out the first fruit she touches, which happens to be a plum. Then Pat takes a fruit from the bag in the same way. What is the probability that she will also get a plum? D

   A $\frac{1}{16}$ B 25%   C $\frac{3}{16}$ D 20%

Completing the Module Project

May I Ask You a Few Questions?

You have gathered and organized data about the free time of students in your school. In order for your survey to be useful, you must now share your findings. In this module you have learned several ways to present data. 7–11. **Check students' work.**

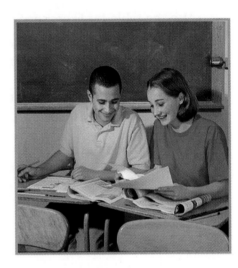

Choosing a Data Display Many magazines and newspapers display survey results in bar graphs, line plots, histograms, or tables. Often the data is in percent form. But no matter the form, the visual display of the data must be clear and informative.

 7 Summarize your class survey data in a table. Present the data using fractions, decimals, and percents.

 8 Make a general statement about the results shown in the table that you made in Project Question 7. Does the statement answer the topic question? Explain.

9 Decide what type of visual display, other than a table, would best organize your data. Create your display. Be sure to include a title.

Favorite Free-Time Activities

Survey Questions

Age? 12

Gender? male

Grade level? 7

How many hours of free time do you have each weekday? 5 hours

How many hours of free time do you have each weekend day? 8 hours

What is your favorite way to spend your free time? listen to music

How much time do you spend on this activity during a typical week? 28 hours

Do you play organized sports? If so, which ones? yes, soccer

Do you take any special lessons? If so, what kinds? no

 10 Explain your choice of visual display in Project Question 9. Why do you think your choice is a good way to show the data? Does it answer the topic question as well as the table in Project Question 7? Why or why not?

 11 If you were to organize another survey, what topic would you research? What would you do differently?

Review and Assessment

See Additional Answers for the graphs for Ex. 5 and 15.

You will need: • *Review and Assessment Labsheet* (Ex. 15)

Write each rate as a unit rate. (Sec. 1, Explor. 1)

1. $\dfrac{95 \text{ min}}{11 \text{ mi}}$ about 8.6 min/mi   2. $\dfrac{\$15}{4 \text{ lb}}$ $3.75/lb

3. $\dfrac{86 \text{ mi}}{3 \text{ gal}}$ about 28.7 mi/gal   4. $\dfrac{250 \text{ km}}{16 \text{ L}}$ 15.625 km/L

Areas of State Parks in 9 States	
State	Acres (in thousands)
Alabama	50
Arkansas	47
Georgia	57
Hawaii	25
Idaho	42
Maine	75
Montana	41
Rhode Island	9
Virginia	66

Use the table for Exercises 5–7. (Sec. 1, Explor. 2)

5. Make a stem-and-leaf plot of the data. Be sure to include a key and a title.

6. Find the range, the mean, the median, and the mode for the data.   range: 66 thousand; mean: about 45.8 thousand; median: 47 thousand; mode: none

7. Colorado has about 340,000 acres of state parkland. Suppose you include Colorado in the list. How would your stem-and-leaf plot change?   I would have to add 27 more stems (8–34) and one more leaf.

Use the histogram for Exercises 8–10. (Sec. 1, Explor. 3)

1995 Athens to Atlanta Skating Marathon

8. About how many skaters finished the marathon in less than 7 h?   Accept reasonable estimates; about 95 skaters

9. Can you tell the winning time of the marathon? Explain.   No; Individual times are not indicated.

10. For which two time intervals was the combined number of skaters about the same as the number of skaters who did not finish the race?   4:00–4:59 and 8:00–8:59

Solve each proportion. (Sec. 2, Explor. 1)

11. $\dfrac{20}{x} = \dfrac{10}{17}$ 34   12. $\dfrac{8}{9} = \dfrac{12}{x}$ 13.5   13. $\dfrac{x}{414} = \dfrac{31}{713}$ 18

14. A theater that shows large-format 3-D movies uses special film that runs through the projector at a rate of 5.5 ft/s. (Sec. 2, Explor. 1)

   a. How long will it take 30 ft of film to run through the projector?   about 5.5 s

   b. How many miles long is a film that runs through the projector in 40 min?   2.5 mi

15. Use the Review and Assessment Labsheet. Plot the points on the *Bridge Length Graph* and then answer the questions on the labsheet. (Sec. 2, Explor. 2) **a.** about 150 m **b.** about 3.3 ft

Use the box-and-whisker plot shown below. (Sec. 2, Explor. 3)

16. Estimate the median time for each race.

Race Results (min:s) for 13–14 Year Old Swimmers in Regina, Saskatchewan, January 1997

2:10 2:15 2:20 2:25 2:30 2:35 2:40 2:45 2:50 2:55 3:00

200 m Freestyle about 2:23

200 m Backstroke
about 2:44

Estimate the percent equivalent of each ratio. (Sec. 3, Explor. 1)

17. $\frac{4}{19}$ about 20% **18.** $\frac{19}{26}$ about 80% **19.** $\frac{43}{66}$ about 67% **20.** $\frac{28}{70}$ 40%

Write each fraction as a percent. Tell which fraction is greater.
(Sec. 3, Explor. 2)

21. $\frac{28}{56}$ and $\frac{32}{58}$ 50%, about 55%; $\frac{32}{58}$

22. $\frac{7}{9}$ and $\frac{63}{78}$ 77.$\overline{7}$%, about 81%; $\frac{63}{78}$

Find each unknown number. (Sec. 3, Explor. 3)

23. 27% of 502 is a number. 135.54

24. 6% of a number is 70. 1166.$\overline{6}$

25. A bag contains 3 red marbles and 2 blue marbles. One marble is taken out of the bag without looking. The color is recorded and the marble is returned to the bag. Then the process is repeated once more. (Sec. 4, Explors. 1–3)

First   Second
marble marble

0.6 R
0.6 R
0.4 B
0.6 R
0.4 B
0.4 B

a. Draw a tree diagram that shows all the possible outcomes of the experiment. What is the theoretical probability of getting two red marbles? Write the answer as a fraction, a decimal, and a percent. $\frac{9}{25}$, 0.36, 36%

b. Suppose the experiment is done 300 times. About how many times would you expect to get two red marbles? about 108 times

Reflecting ◀▶ on the Module

26. Journal Describe a situation in everyday life in which you could use one of the mathematical ideas from the module. Answers will vary.

FLIGHTS
of FANCY

MODULE 6 · SECTION OVERVIEW

The Module Project

Wild Wings

How do designers of planes improve their designs? In this project, you'll test and analyze two designs for gliders. Then you'll use geometry and measurement ideas to compare the designs and suggest ways to improve them.

More on the Module Project
See pp. 408, 433, and 451.

INTERNET
To learn more about the theme:
http://www.mlmath.com

Section ①

Inequalities, Polygons, and Probability

WARM-UP EXERCISES

Write each inequality in words.

1. $2s > 8$
   two times *s* is greater than 8

2. $b \le 14$
   b is less than or equal to 14

3. State the formula for the area of a square.
   $A = s^2$, where *s* is the length of a side of the square

4. State the formula for the area of a rectangle.
   $A = lw$, where *l* is the length and *w* is the width of the rectangle

Find each probability.

5. picking an even number from the numbers 0–9
   $\frac{1}{2}$

▲ Lilienthal also built biplane gliders.

6. selecting a red pen if there are 2 red pens, 2 blue pens, and 1 black pen in a container
   $\frac{2}{5}$

----‣ *Setting the Stage*

The history of flight is filled with daring and imaginative people, such as Otto Lilienthal.

MACHINES *by Robert O'Brien*

. . . Lilienthal became enthralled with flight while watching the storks of his native Pomerania soar over his house on their unwieldy wings. In 1891, at the age of 43, he began building and flying gliders—monoplanes with curved, ribbed batwings. In the next five years, he made more than 2,000 glides, many from a man-made hill shaped like a cone, so that he could take off downhill in any direction that the wind dictated.

Detailed drawing of a monoplane glider designed by Lilienthal in 1895 ▶

Think About It

1 What do you think a monoplane is? Sample Response: a plane with only one pair of wings

2 In the five years after he started building gliders, what was the average number of glides Lilienthal made each year? about 400 glides

GOAL

LEARN HOW TO...
◆ write and graph inequalities

AS YOU...
◆ investigate how wing design makes flight possible

KEY TERM
◆ inequality

INEQUALITIES

SET UP *You will need a 3 in. by 11 in. strip of paper.*

Otto Lilienthal studied birds to try to learn the secrets of flight. Like many of the pioneers of flight, he noticed that a bird's wings are curved and streamlined, not flat.

As a wing moves through a stream of air, some of the air passes over the top and some goes underneath. The two airstreams meet again behind the wing.

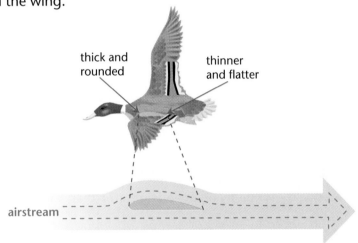

thick and rounded

thinner and flatter

airstream

3 You can use a strip of paper to investigate the effect of air moving over a wing. Hold the strip of paper along a short side.

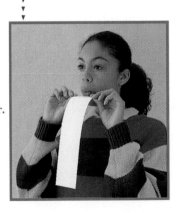

a. Air is pressing against all sides of the paper with equal force, so why does the paper droop?
Sample Response: There is a downward force because of the weight of the paper.

b. Blow across the top of the paper. Describe what happens.
The paper rises.

c. What happens if you blow harder, increasing the speed of the air? The paper rises higher.

d. What happens if the speed of the air is decreased?
The paper falls.

▶ **Daniel Bernoulli, an 18th century Swiss mathematician, discovered that when the speed of a liquid or gas such as air increases, the pressure that it exerts decreases. This is *Bernoulli's principle.***

4 Discussion When you blew across the paper in Question 3, the air above the paper moved faster than the air below it.

  a. According to Bernoulli's principle, explained on page 379, was the air pressure pressing down on the top of the paper *greater than* or *less than* the air pressure pushing up on the bottom of the paper? less than

  b. Use your answer to part (a) to explain why the paper rose when you blew across it.

Because a bird's or plane's wing is curved, the air passing over it moves faster than the air passing underneath it. The faster-moving air above the wing exerts less pressure on the wing than the air underneath. This difference in air pressure creates an upward force called *lift*.

5 Try This as a Class Birds must fly faster than 11 mi/h to create enough lift to overcome the downward pull of gravity.

  a. List several speeds greater than 11 mi/h.
     Sample Response: 11.2 mi/h, 12 mi/h, 15 mi/h, 16 mi/h
  b. Draw a number line and plot the points that represent the speeds you listed in part (a). Sample Response:

▶ There are many flying speeds that are greater than 11 mi/h. Instead of trying to list or plot them all, you can write an *inequality*. The symbols $>$, $<$, $\geq$, and $\leq$ are used to write **inequalities**.

EXAMPLE

Write an inequality for all flying speeds greater than 11 mi/h.

Let f be flying speed in miles per hour.

   Flying speed is greater than 11 mi/h.

The inequality is read, "f is greater than 11." $f > 11$

Graph the inequality on a number line to show all the possible solutions, that is, all the values of f that make the inequality a true statement.

The open circle means 11 is not included.   7 8 9 10 11 12 13 14 15 16 17 18   The shaded part of the number line shows the solutions.

---

6 a. Is 9.5 mi/h a solution of the inequality in the Example? Is 11.04 mi/h a solution? How does the graph show this?
     No; Yes; The point that corresponds to 11.04 is on the shaded part of the number line.
  b. What does the arrowhead on the right side of the graph mean?
     all the numbers to the right are solutions

7 The house sparrow is one of the slowest birds. Its flying speed is usually less than or equal to 19 mi/h. **a. c.** Let *s* = the flying speed of the house sparrow in miles per hour.

   a. Write an inequality to represent all flying speeds less than or equal to 19 mi/h. $s \leq 19$

   b. The graph of the inequality from part (a) is shown below. Why do you think the circle is filled in? The graph includes 19.

   c. The house sparrow's flying speed is usually greater than or equal to 16 mi/h. Write an inequality for this fact. Then sketch a number line and graph the inequality. $s \geq 16;$

▶ **Combining Inequalities** The information about a house sparrow's flying speed can be combined into one inequality.

EXAMPLE

Let *s* = house sparrow's flying speed in miles per hour.

s **is greater than or equal to** 16   and   *s* **is less than or equal to** 19.

↓   ↓

$s \geq 16$ and $s \leq 19$

$16 \leq s \leq 19$ This statement can be read as, "16 is less than or equal to *s* and *s* is less than or equal to 19."

---

8 a. Discussion How would you graph the inequality $16 \leq s \leq 19$?

   b. Graph the inequality $16 \leq s \leq 19$.

8. a. Shade the part of a number line between 16 and 19 and draw filled-in circles at 16 and 19.

9 ✔ **CHECKPOINT** Choose a variable to represent the speed of the bird or plane in each speed fact below. Use the variable to write an inequality for the fact, then graph the inequality.

   a. Spine-tailed swifts are among the fastest birds in the world. They have been clocked at flying speeds of up to 218 mi/h.

   b. The *Spirit of St. Louis*, the plane Charles Lindbergh flew on the first solo transatlantic flight in 1927, was designed to fly at speeds of at least 49 mi/h but below 125 mi/h.

✔ **QUESTION 9**

...checks that you can write and graph an inequality.

9. a. If *t* = the speed of the spine-tailed swift, then $t \leq 218$.

b. If *s* = the speed of the plane, then $49 \leq s < 125$.

HOMEWORK EXERCISES ▶ See Exs. 1–12 on pp. 389–390.

GOAL

LEARN HOW TO...
- find the areas of polygons

AS YOU...
- study the wing of an albatross

KEY TERMS
- polygon
- concave
- convex
- regular polygon
- parallelogram
- quadrilateral

Exploration 2

AREAS of POLYGONS

SET UP *Work with a partner. You will need:*
- *ruler* • *6–10 ice-cream sticks*

One factor to consider when designing a glider is how much weight its wings must carry. This is called the *wing loading* and is measured by dividing the glider's total weight by its total wing area.

To help decide how large the wings of their "flying machines" had to be, some early fliers studied the wing loading of birds—especially large soaring birds such as vultures and albatrosses.

▲ The wandering albatross is a large sea bird that can soar above the ocean for an hour or more without ever flapping its wings!

10. b. Sample Responses: In a convex polygon, the measure of each of the interior angles is less than 180°. A concave polygon has at least one interior angle that has a measure greater than 180°.

In a convex polygon, the segments joining any two nonadjacent vertices (the diagonals of the polygon) all lie in the interior of the polygon. In a concave polygon, part of a diagonal lies outside the polygon.

▶ **How can you estimate the area of a bird's wing?** One way is to use *polygons* to model its size and shape. In the drawing, an albatross's wing is modeled with three *polygons*.

10. a. Sample Response: The sides meet only at their endpoints; All the sides meet with no gaps.

10 A **polygon** is a simple, flat closed figure formed by segments.

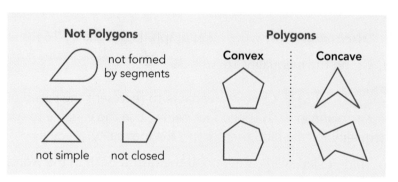

a. What does *simple* mean? What does *closed* mean? See above.

b. How are **concave** and **convex** polygons different?

c. In a **regular polygon**, all the segments are the same length and all the angles are equal in measure. Is a square a regular polygon? Explain. Yes; All the sides of a square have the same length and each angle measures 90°.

11 a. Tell whether each of the three polygons used to model the albatross wing is *concave* or *convex*. **Each is convex.**

   b. Is polygon *ABCDEFG* in the model *concave* or *convex*? Explain.
   concave; ∠B and ∠E point in.

▶ You can estimate the area of one wing of the albatross in the drawing by finding the sum of the areas of the three polygons used to model it.

12 Polygon *ABFG* at the right is a rectangle. Find its area and explain your method.

A   B
1.1 ft
G   1.3 ft   F

▶ Another type of polygon used in the wing model is a *parallelogram*. A **parallelogram** is a **quadrilateral** (a 4-sided polygon) in which both pairs of opposite sides are parallel.

FOR ▶ HELP
with *finding the area of a rectangle*, see
TOOLBOX, p. 593

12. 1.43 ft²; Sample Response: Multiply the length of the base, 1.3 ft, by the height, 1.1 ft.

13 Discussion Which of the polygons used to model the albatross wing on page 382 appear to be parallelograms? **ABFG, BCEF**

14 Try This as a Class Complete parts (a)–(d) to discover how to find the area of a parallelogram.

   a. Follow these steps to make a parallelogram. **Check students' work.**

Form a rectangle with your ice-cream sticks. Measure the length and width of the rectangle.

Place a ruler along the left side of the rectangle. Rotate the ruler to form a parallelogram by making the left and right sides longer.

   b. How does the area of the parallelogram you made in part (a) compare with the area of the original rectangle?
   The areas are the same.

   c. The length of the base *b* of a parallelogram and its height *h* are measured as shown on the notebook. How are the length of the base and the height of the ice-cream-stick parallelogram related to the length and width of the original rectangle? **They are the same.**

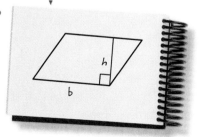

   d. Write a formula for finding the area *A* of a parallelogram if you know its height *h* and the length of its base *b*. **A = bh**

15 ✔ **CHECKPOINT** Quadrilateral *BCEF* in the model of the albatross wing on page 382 is a parallelogram. Its dimensions are shown at the right. What is its area? 1.65 ft²

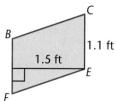

16 Try This as a Class The dimensions of △*CDE* in the model of the albatross wing are shown below. The figure shows how a triangle congruent to △*CDE* can be put together with △*CDE* to form a parallelogram.

a. How are the areas of the two triangles related? They are equal.

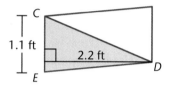

b. How are the length of the base and the height of △*CDE* related to the length of the base and the height of the parallelogram? They are the same.

c. If you know the area of the parallelogram, how can you find the area of one of the triangles? Multiply the area of the parallelogram by $\frac{1}{2}$.

d. Write an expression that can be used to find the area *A* of a triangle if you know its height *h* and the length of its base *b*. $A = \frac{1}{2}bh$

e. What is the area of △*CDE*? 1.21 ft²

17 a. Use your results from Questions 12, 15, and 16(e) to find the area of one wing of the albatross shown on page 382. 4.29 ft²

b. Assume both wings of the albatross have the same area. What is the total wing area? 8.58 ft²

18 a. Suppose the albatross in the drawing on page 382 weighs 20 lb. Use the total wing area in Question 17(b) and the formula below to find the wing loading of the albatross in pounds per square foot. Round your answer to the nearest hundredth. 2.33 lb/ft²

$$\text{wing loading} = \frac{\text{total weight}}{\text{total wing area}}$$

combined area of both wings

b. One of Otto Lilienthal's gliders had a total wing area of 150.7 ft². Without the pilot, the glider weighed 44 lb. Suppose the pilot weighed 170 lb. To the nearest hundredth, what was the wing loading of the glider? How does its wing loading compare with the wing loading of the albatross?

1.42 lb/ft²; It is less.

HOMEWORK EXERCISES ▶ See Exs. 13–18 on p. 391.

GEOMETRIC PROBABILITY

GOAL

LEARN HOW TO...
◆ use areas to find theoretical probabilities
◆ find the probabilities of complementary events

AS YOU...
◆ simulate a skydiving competition

KEY TERMS
◆ complementary events
◆ geometric probability

SET UP *Work with a partner. You will need:* • *tape* • *ruler* • *3 in. by 5 in. index card* • *scissors* • *construction paper*

One of the first recorded attempts at human flight occurred in A.D. 852 in Cordoba, Spain. Someone leaped from a tower, but instead of flying, fell to earth. Fortunately, this foolhardy person's cloak caught enough air to prevent any serious injury, turning this impossible attempt at flight into a parachute jump!

▶ Since that "flight," parachutes have become so advanced that skydivers compete to land in small target areas. You will simulate a skydiving competition by launching an autogyro over a landing area.

19 Make an autogyro. **Check students' work.**

Step 1

5 in.

$1\frac{1}{2}$ in.

Cut a $1\frac{1}{2}$ in. by 5 in. rectangle from the index card, and fold it into three $\frac{1}{2}$ in. by 5 in. rectangles.

Step 2

stem

2 in.

Make a 2 in. cut along each fold.

Step 3

Fold the rectangles together to form a triangular tube. Tape the edges of the stem together.

Step 4

Fold down the cut strips so they are perpendicular to the taped stem.

20 Make a landing area by taping four sheets of $8\frac{1}{2}$ in. by 11 in. paper together to form a 17 in. by 22 in. rectangle. **Check students' work.**

Cut out a square target with sides $8\frac{1}{2}$ in. long from a piece of construction paper, and tape it in the center of the rectangle.

17 in.

$8\frac{1}{2}$ in.

22 in.

21. Answers will vary. Check students' work.

21　**a.** Place the landing area on the floor. Launch your autogyro as shown below. Repeat 10 times and record the number of times the stem end of the autogyro lands inside the square target. Redo any trials where the end of the autogyro lands off the paper landing area.

　　b. Repeat part (a), letting your partner make the launches.

22 Use your results from Question 21.
Answers will vary. Check students' work.
　a. What percent of your 10 "jumps" landed on the square target?

　b. What percent of the 20 "jumps" made by you and your partner landed on the square target?

Twirl your autogyro between your hands and release it at shoulder level.

23 **Try This as a Class** Use the jump data from the entire class.

　a. What is the experimental probability that the autogyro lands on the target? that the autogyro does not land on the target?
Answers will vary. Check students' work.
　b. What is the sum of the probabilities in part (a)? 1

FOR ◄ HELP

with *probability*, see
MODULE 1, p. 33

▶ Either the autogyro lands on the target or it does not. The events *the autogyro lands on the target* and *the autogyro does not land on the target* are *complementary events*. Two events are **complementary events** if one or the other must occur, but they cannot both happen at the same time.

24 **Try This as a Class** If two events are complementary, what must be true about their probabilities? *The sum of the probabilities must be 1.*

▶ The theoretical probability of landing on the target can be calculated by finding the ratio of the area of the target to the total landing area. This is a **geometric probability**.

probability of landing on the target = $\dfrac{\text{area of the target}}{\text{total landing area}}$

total landing area

area of the target

25. a. $\frac{17}{88}$, 19.3%

25 **a.** Find the theoretical probability of landing on the target. Write it as a fraction and as a percent rounded to the nearest tenth.

   b. Why do you think this is called a *geometric probability*?
   Sample Response: It is calculated using the geometric concept of area.

26 **Discussion** Use your answers to Questions 22, 23(a), and 25(a).

   a. How does the theoretical probability of landing on the target compare with the experimental probabilities? *Answers will vary.*

   b. Why might there be differences between the theoretical and the experimental probabilities?

27 **a.** Describe two ways you could find the theoretical probability of hitting the landing area but not landing on the target.

   b. What is the theoretical probability of not landing on the target? $\frac{71}{88}$, or about 80.7%

28 ✔ **CHECKPOINT** Use the figure.

   a. Find the probability that a small object dropped on the figure will land on the shaded target. $\frac{3}{8}$, or 37.5%

   b. Find the probability that a small object dropped on the figure will not land on the shaded target. $\frac{5}{8}$, or 62.5%

6 m

10 m

16 m

FOR ◀ HELP
with *theoretical probability*, see **MODULE 1, p. 33**

26. b. Sample Response: Factors other than chance are involved. For example, a draft may affect where the autogyro lands.

27. a. Subtract the theoretical probability of landing on the target from 1; Divide the non-target area by the total landing area.

✔ **QUESTION 28**

...checks that you can find a geometric probability and the probability of a complementary event.

HOMEWORK EXERCISES ▶ See Exs. 19–26 on pp. 391–392.

Key Terms

inequality

Inequalities (pp. 379–381)

The statements $t > 10$ and $13 < x \leq 19$ are examples of inequalities.

$t > 10$ is read
"t is greater than 10."

$13 < x \leq 19$ is read "13 is less than x and x is less than or equal to 19."

> The open circle means 10 is not included.

> The shading means all numbers to the right of 10 are included.

> The filled-in circle means 19 is included.

Polygons (pp. 382–384)

A polygon is a simple, closed flat figure made of segments. A polygon that has four sides is a quadrilateral. A parallelogram is a quadrilateral that has two pairs of parallel sides.

polygon

  convex

  concave

  quadrilateral

  parallelogram

  regular polygon

Area = bh

Area = $\dfrac{bh}{2}$, or Area = $\dfrac{1}{2}bh$

The area of a parallelogram is the product of the length of its **base** and its **height**.

The area of a triangle is half the length of its **base** times its **height**.

You can find the area of some polygons by separating them into triangles and parallelograms.

CLOSURE QUESTION

State the formula for the area of a parallelogram and the formula for the area of a triangle. Then write an inequality describing the possible range of values for geometric probability.

Answer: area of a parallelogram: $A = bh$; area of a triangle: $A = \dfrac{1}{2}bh$; $0 \leq p \leq 1$, where p represents geometric probability.

29 Key Concepts Question

Use the graph of flying speeds in miles per hour.

● ● bald eagle   albatross

● ● red-shouldered hawk

(number line from 15 to 60)

a. Write an inequality for the speed of a red-shouldered hawk.
If h = the speed of a red-shouldered hawk, then $18 \leq h \leq 34$.

b. Which bird has the greatest range of speeds? the albatross

c. Which birds can fly faster than 40 mi/h?
the bald eagle and the albatross

Section ①

Key Terms

Geometric Probability (pp. 385–387)

A probability that is based on lengths, areas, or volumes of figures is a geometric probability.

geometric probability

Example Suppose a point is selected at random on $\overline{RT}$.

The probability that the point is on $\overline{RS}$ is $\dfrac{\text{length of } \overline{RS}}{\text{length of } \overline{RT}} = \dfrac{3}{10}$, or 30%.

Two events are complementary if one event or the other must occur, but they cannot both happen at the same time.

complementary events

In the Example, the events "the distance between the point and point R is less than or equal to 3 cm" and "the distance between the point and point R is greater than 3 cm" are complementary.

The sum of the probabilities of two complementary events is 1.

30 Key Concepts Question An object is dropped onto the landing area shown. What is the probability that the object will land in the shaded region? in the unshaded region?
$\frac{1}{3}$, or $33\frac{1}{3}\%$; $\frac{2}{3}$, or $66\frac{2}{3}\%$

Section ①

Practice & Application Exercises

For Exercises 1–4, write an inequality to represent each statement. Then graph the inequality on a number line.

1. x is less than 8. $x < 8$

2. b is greater than or equal to 3. $b \geq 3$

3. h is greater than 5 and less than or equal to 11. $5 < h \leq 11$

4. 4 is less than p, and p is less than 7. $4 < p < 7$

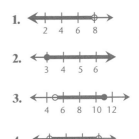

5. **History** The Women's Auxiliary Ferrying Squadron (WAFS) was formed during World War II to train women to fly military aircraft. Initially, candidates were required to have not less than 500 hours of logged flight time. Write an inequality to represent this statement, and then graph the inequality.

If *l* = the hours of logged flight time, then *l* ≥ 500.

```
←——+——+——●——+——→
  300 400 500 600
```

Hummingbirds For Exercises 6–9, use the graphs below.

Lengths of Hummingbirds (in.)

```
←——●——+——+——+——+——+——●——+——→
   2  3  4  5  6  7  8  9
```

Speeds of Hummingbirds (mi/h)

```
←——+——+——+——+——⊕——+——+——→
  40 45 50 55 60 65 70
```

Flight Muscles of Hummingbirds (as percent of total body weight)

```
←—+——●——+——+——+——+——●——+——→
  20 22 24 26 28 30 32 34 36
```

6. The smallest bird in the world is the Cuban bee hummingbird. Estimate its length. about 2.25 in.

7. Estimate the range of lengths of hummingbirds. from about 2.25 in. to about 8.5 in.

8. Write a statement describing the speeds hummingbirds fly. If *s* = the speed of a hummingbird (mi/h), then s < 60.

9. What percent of a hummingbird's body weight is the weight of its flight muscles? Express your answer as an inequality. If *p* = the percent of a hummingbird's body weight that is flight muscle, then 22 ≤ p ≤ 34.

Use the statements and graphs below for Exercises 10–12. An inequality that represents each statement is graphed on the number line below.

"The Wright brothers built the first successful airplane in 1903. The *Wright Flyer I* flew at speeds ranging from 30 mi/h through 35 mi/h."

"A cinnamon teal duck, clocked flying at 32 mi/h, was startled and raced away at 59 mi/h."

▲
The original *Wright Flyer I* is on display in the National Air and Space Museum in Washington, D.C.

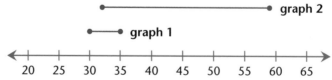

```
graph 2  ●————————————●
graph 1      ●——●

←—+——+——+——+——+——+——+——+——+——+——→
  20  25  30  35  40  45  50  55  60  65
```

10. Which graph represents the speed of the *Wright Flyer I*? graph 1

11. How can you use the graphs to find the numbers that are solutions of both inequalities? Find which parts of the graphs overlap.

12. Write a statement that compares the speeds of the cinnamon teal duck and the Wright brothers' airplane. Sample Response: The greatest speed of the duck was 24 mi/h faster than the greatest speed of the plane.

13. Which of the quadrilaterals below are parallelograms? If a quadrilateral is not a parallelogram, explain why.

square   kite   rhombus   trapezoid   rectangle

14. Open-ended Draw two 5-sided polygons, one that is convex and one that is concave. Sample Response:

15. Challenge Can a parallelogram be concave? Explain.

16. The figures below show three different heights h of $\triangle ABC$.

a. Use each pair of bases and heights to compute the area.
   In each instance, the area is 12 m².

b. If you want to find the area of a triangle, does it matter which side you use as the base? Explain. No; The product of the height and base will be the same, no matter which base is used.

17. a. Which segment represents the height of parallelogram *EFGH* — $\overline{EH}$, $\overline{FH}$, or $\overline{EY}$? Explain your choice.

b. Find the area of parallelogram *EFGH*.
   12 cm²

18. A rough sketch of a glider wing is shown below.

a. Find the area of the wing. 99 ft²

b. The glider has two identical wings. What is its total wing area? 198 ft²

c. The glider's total weight is 920 lb. Use the formula

$$\text{wing loading} = \frac{\text{total weight}}{\text{total wing area}}$$ to find its wing loading.
   about 4.65 lb/ft²

Find the probability that an object dropped on each figure will land on the shaded target.

19.

$\frac{2}{5}$

20.

$\frac{1}{2}$

21.

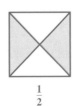

$\frac{1}{2}$

13. square, rhombus, and rectangle; The kite has no pairs of opposite parallel sides and the trapezoid has only 1 such pair. A parallelogram has 2 pairs of opposite parallel sides.

15. No; Sample Response: In any concave polygon, one of the angles measures more than 180°. It is impossible to form a closed polygon by drawing 2 line segments parallel to the 2 line segments forming this angle.

17. a. $\overline{EY}$; Neither of the others are segments perpendicular to $\overline{EF}$ and $\overline{HG}$.

The probability that an object dropped onto the square region below will land inside the shaded circle is $\frac{3}{5}$.

22. What is the probability that the object will land in the unshaded region? $\frac{2}{5}$

23. What is the area of the circle? 60 m²

10 m

10 m

A coin is tossed onto a game board. If the center of the coin lands on the shaded region, player I wins. If not, player II wins.

24. Which game board below is fair to both players, that is, makes their chances of winning equal? Board C

A.
18 in.
7 in.
5 in.
18 in.

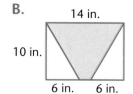

B.
14 in.
10 in.
6 in. 6 in.
5 in.
7 in.

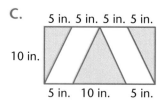

C.
5 in. 5 in. 5 in. 5 in.
10 in.
5 in. 10 in. 5 in.

25. If you want player I to have a greater chance of winning, which game board in Exercise 24 should you choose? Explain.

Board B; The probability of landing in the shaded area is greater for Board B (about 57%), than for Board A (about 42%) or Board C (50%).

Reflecting ◀▶ **on the Section**

26. In Exploration 2, you made a rectangle from ice-cream sticks and slanted them to form a parallelogram with the same area. Now suppose you make a square from four ice-cream sticks as shown. When you slant the sticks, the parallelogram formed has an area *less than* the area of the square. Why does the area change in one case but not the other?

S p i r a l ◀▶ **Review**

Use mental math to write each fraction as a percent. (Module 5, p. 366)

27. $\frac{11}{23}$ about 50% **28.** $\frac{16}{45}$ about $33\frac{1}{3}$% **29.** $\frac{31}{122}$ about 25% **30.** $\frac{49}{251}$ about 20%

Find the prime factorization of each number. (Module 3, p. 156)

31. 12 $2 \cdot 2 \cdot 3$ **32.** 25 $5 \cdot 5$ **33.** 48 $2 \cdot 2 \cdot 2 \cdot 2 \cdot 3$ **34.** 100 $2 \cdot 2 \cdot 5 \cdot 5$

Write each power in standard form. (Module 1, p. 21)

35. 2^2 4 **36.** 5^2 25 **37.** 9^2 81 **38.** 10^2 100

Visual THINKING

Exercise 26 checks your understanding of the areas of parallelograms.

26. In Exploration 2, the area remained the same because, in both instances, it was equivalent to the area of 5 ice cream sticks. In this example, the base of the polygons remains the same, but the height decreases since the lengths of the left and right sides stay the same. Since $A = bh$ and the value of h changes, the areas are different.

Section 1

Extra Skill Practice

For Exercises 1–6, write an inequality to represent each statement.
Then graph the inequality on a number line. 1–4. See below.

1. *a* is greater than 8. $a > 8$

2. *k* is less than or equal to 2. $k \leq 2$

3. *r* is greater than 4 and less than 7.

   $4 < r < 7$

4. *s* is greater than 9 and less than 14. $9 < s < 14$

5. 6 is less than *t*, and *t* is less than or equal to 13.

   $6 < t \leq 13$

6. *b* is greater than 5 and less than or equal to 9.

   $5 < b \leq 9$

Tell whether each figure is a parallelogram. If it is not, explain why.

7.

See below.

8.
Yes.

9.
Yes.

10.
See below.

Classify each polygon as convex or concave.

11.
concave

12.
convex

13.
concave

14.
concave

Find the probability that a small object dropped on each figure will land on the shaded target. $\frac{5}{9}$, or $55\frac{5}{9}\%$

15.

$\frac{1}{3}$, or $33\frac{1}{3}\%$

16.
$\frac{4}{10}$, or 40%

17.

1.
   6 7 8 9

2.
   0 1 2 3

3.
   4 5 6 7

4.
   8 10 12 14

Study Skills ▶ Making Connections

Previewing and reviewing can help you understand and remember the concepts in each section. Before studying a new topic, think about what you already know about it or about related topics. When you have completed the section, think about how the ideas that were new to you fit in with those you already had.

1. Preview the goals and topics of Section 2. Describe any ideas that seem familiar to you. List any terms that are unfamiliar to you.
   Answers will vary. Check students' work.

2. When you have completed Section 2, review its goals and topics. Describe the new ideas that you have learned and, if possible, connect them with topics you already understand. Did you learn anything that caused you to change your thinking about something? If so, how did your ideas change?
   Answers will vary. Check students' work.

7. No; The quadrilateral has only 1 pair of opposite parallel sides and a parallelogram has 2 such pairs.

10. No; The quadrilateral has no pairs of opposite parallel sides and a parallelogram has 2 such pairs.

Section ② Square Roots, Surface Area, and Area of a Circle

GO FLY A KITE!

Setting the Stage

SET UP   *You will need a protractor.*

Over 2000 years before the first gliders were invented, the Chinese had mastered flight in a different way—with kites. In China and other Asian countries, kites were more than toys. They were tools for signaling, for lifting supplies, and even for flying people!

Centuries later, kite flying became a children's hobby in the United States. Francis M. Rogallo's childhood interest in kites inspired him to become an aeronautical engineer and, eventually, to combine a kite with a parachute to create the parawing.

▲ Today, Rogallo's idea is applied to the sport of hang gliding.

Think About It

1 The flying angle of a kite is the angle the kite string forms with the ground. The best flying angle of a kite in moderate winds is from 45° to 60°.

a. Write an inequality for the range of the best flying angles.   If a = the best flying angle of a kite, then $45 \le a \le 60$.

b. Draw a horizontal segment on a sheet of paper to represent the ground. Use a protractor to make a drawing that illustrates the range of the best flying angles of the kite in the air.   See Additional Answers.

2 What shapes might you see if you look at a hang glider in flight? Answers will vary.

Square ROOTS

GOAL

LEARN HOW TO...
- find square roots of perfect squares
- estimate square roots to the nearest tenth

AS YOU...
- investigate the design of a parawing

KEY TERMS
- square root
- principal square root
- perfect square

SET UP *You will need a calculator.*

Francis Rogallo and his wife Gertrude Rogallo experimented with different parawing designs by making paper models and tossing them into the air. When one flew better than the others, they made a larger version out of cloth and went to the beach to test it. They tested model after model, making changes and throwing away the failures.

In kite flying, the ratio of the total weight of the kite to the area of the *sail*— the surface that catches the wind and moves the kite— is very important. This ratio is called *sail loading.*

3 Look back at the definition of *wing loading* on page 384 in Section 1. How is sail loading for kites like wing loading for birds and gliders?
   It is a ratio of weight to area.

4 In flight, a parawing appears to be triangular, but when flattened out, it turns out to be a square. The sail area of a parawing is the area of a square. Find the sail area of each parawing.

a.
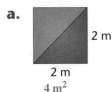
2 m

2 m
4 m²

b.
10 ft

10 ft
100 ft²

c.
4.1 yd

4.1 yd
16.81 yd²

▶ **The area *A* of a square can be found by multiplying the length *s* of a side of the square by itself ($A = s \cdot s$), or by squaring *s* ($A = s^2$).**

$A = s^2$ s

s

To find the length of a side of a square when the area is known, you can look for a number that when multiplied by itself equals the area.

EXAMPLE

Find the length of a side of a square that has an area of 49 cm^2.

SAMPLE RESPONSE

$s^2 = 49$

$s = 7$

Think: $\underline{\ ?\ } \cdot \underline{\ ?\ } = 49$

$7 \cdot 7 = 49$

The length of a side is 7 cm.

▶ The solution, 7, of the equation in the Example is a **square root** of 49.

5 Find the length of a side of a parawing with each area.

a. 16 ft^2 4 ft   **b.** 36 m^2 6 m   **c.** 225 in.^{2} 15 in.

6 Discussion Think about the square roots of 49.

a. Is −7 a square root of 49? Why or why not? Yes; (−7)(−7) = 49

b. Would −7 be a reasonable solution for the length of a side of a parawing? Explain. No; The length of a side must be greater than 0.

▶ The positive solution of the equation $s^2 = 49$ is the **principal square root** of 49 and is written $\sqrt{49}$.

The same symbol with a negative sign, $-\sqrt{49}$, is the negative of the principal square root.

$\sqrt{49} = 7$	$-\sqrt{49} = -7$
The principal square root of 49 is 7.	The negative of the principal square root of 49 is −7.

7 Mental Math Use mental math to find each square root.

a. $\sqrt{64}$ 8   **b.** $-\sqrt{81}$ −9   **c.** $\sqrt{1}$ 1   **d.** $-\sqrt{0}$ 0

▶ A **perfect square** is a number that is the square of a whole number. For example, 25 is a perfect square since $25 = 5 \cdot 5 = 5^2$.

8 Show that each number is a perfect square.

a. 81 $81 = 9 \cdot 9 = 9^2$ **b.** 400   **c.** 121 $121 = 11 \cdot 11 = 11^2$

$400 = 20 \cdot 20 = 20^2$

✔ **QUESTION 9**

...checks that you can find the principal square root of a perfect square.

9 ✔ **CHECKPOINT** Find each square root.

a. $\sqrt{121}$ 11   **b.** $\sqrt{9}$ 3   **c.** $-\sqrt{144}$ −12 **d.** $\sqrt{100}$ 10

10 Try This as a Class Since 52 is not a perfect square, its principal square root is not a whole number.

   a. What two consecutive perfect squares is 52 between? *49 and 64*

   b. Find the principal square root of the perfect squares in part (a).

10. b. $\sqrt{49} = 7$, $\sqrt{64} = 8$

   c. What two whole numbers is $\sqrt{52}$ between? *7 and 8*

   d. Use guess-and-check and a calculator to estimate $\sqrt{52}$ to the nearest tenth. *about 7.2*

   e. 🖩 Calculator Use the [√] key on a calculator to find $\sqrt{52}$. Compare it with your estimate in part (d).
   Sample Response: 7.2111026; Rounded to the nearest tenth it is the same.

11 ✔ **CHECKPOINT** Give two consecutive whole numbers that each principal square root lies between. Then estimate each square root to the nearest tenth.

   a. $\sqrt{12}$ **b.** $\sqrt{73}$ **c.** $\sqrt{150}$
   3 and 4; about 3.5   *8 and 9; about 8.5*   *12 and 13; about 12.2*

✔ QUESTION 11
...checks that you can estimate the square root of a number to the nearest tenth.

▌**HOMEWORK EXERCISES** ▶ See Exs. 1–10 on pp. 405–406.

Exploration 2

Surface AREAS of PRISMS

▌**SET UP** *Work with a partner. You will need: • scissors • tape • centimeter grid paper • two centimeter cubes*

The parawing is not the only kite design based on a square. In 1893, Lawrence Hargrave, an Australian, designed a kite that became the basis for the *biplane*, the type of plane built by the Wright Brothers.

In the Hargrave box kite, squares and rectangles form open rectangular prisms or "boxes."

GOAL
LEARN HOW TO...
◆ identify prisms and their parts
◆ draw a net for a prism
◆ find the surface area of a prism
As YOU...
◆ investigate box kites
KEY TERMS
◆ prism
◆ face
◆ base
◆ vertex
◆ edge
◆ net
◆ surface area

▶ A **prism** is a space figure that has flat surfaces or **faces** shaped like polygons. Two of the faces, the **bases**, are parallel and congruent. The other faces are parallelograms.

rectangular prism

right triangular prism

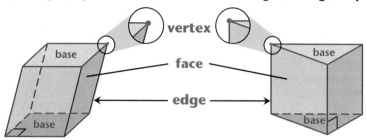

vertex

face

edge

12. Sample Response: The planes that contain the bases do not intersect.

14. c. 5 faces, 6 vertices, and 9 edges; Yes; The prism would still have the same basic structure.

15. a. Sample Response: In the right rectangular prism, the faces connecting the bases are rectangles (not just any parallelograms) and they are all perpendicular to the bases (which is not true in the rectangular prism); In the right triangular prism, as in the right rectangular prism, the faces connecting the bases are rectangles that are perpendicular to the bases.
b. Yes; Any pair of opposite faces could be considered bases.

 QUESTION 16

...checks that you can name prisms and identify their faces, vertices, and edges.

12 Discussion What do you think "the bases are parallel" means?

13 Replace each _?_ with a word or phrase that makes each a true statement.

a. Two faces of a prism meet at a(n) _?_. edge

b. Three edges of a prism meet at a(n) _?_. vertex

c. Prisms are named by the _?_. shapes of the bases

14 Try This as a Class Use the prisms shown above.

a. How many faces, vertices, and edges does the rectangular prism have? 6 faces, 8 vertices, and 12 edges

b. Would the numbers of faces, vertices, and edges of another rectangular prism be the same as in part (a)? Explain.
Yes; The way the prism is constructed would be the same.
c. Repeat parts (a) and (b) for a triangular prism.

15 Discussion Look at the right rectangular prism shown below.

a. How is this prism different from the rectangular prism shown above? How is it like the right triangular prism?

b. Can a rectangular prism have more than one pair of bases? Explain.

c. What is the name for a rectangular prism for which all the faces are congruent?
a square prism or a cube

16 ✔ **CHECKPOINT** Use the prism shown below.

a. What kind of prism is this? a pentagonal prism

b. How many faces, vertices, and edges does this prism have? 7 faces, 10 vertices, 15 edges

398 Module 6 Flights of Fancy

▶ *Surface area* is an important factor to consider in the design of a kite. As you answer Questions 17 and 18, you will find out what surface area is and how to calculate it.

17 The figure shown in the photo below is a **net**, a flat pattern that can be cut out and folded to form a space figure without any gaps or overlap. You can use this net to cover a centimeter cube.
Check students' work.

First

Cut a net like the one above out of centimeter grid paper.

Then

Fold the net along the segments, and use it to cover a centimeter cube.

18 a. Use centimeter grid paper to make as many different nets as possible to cover the cube. Try covering the cube to make sure each net actually works. Then tape each net to a piece of paper to keep a record of it. Check students' work.

b. What is the area of each net you made? 6 cm²

c. The number of square centimeters of paper used to make each net is the cube's **surface area**. What is the surface area of the cube? 6 cm²

19 Use two centimeter cubes to form a prism, as shown. Use centimeter grid paper to determine which of the nets made up of centimeter squares will cover the prism with no overlap. If a net will not cover the prism, explain why not.

19. Net C; Sample Response: Net A would cover only 8 of the 10 faces of the model. Net B would cover 1 face of the model twice and leave 1 face uncovered.

A.   **B.**   **C.**

20 What is the surface area of the prism formed by the two centimeter cubes in Question 19? 10 cm²

▶ **In Questions 17–20, you saw that the surface area of a prism is the sum of the areas of its faces.**

Find the surface area of the right triangular prism.

SAMPLE RESPONSE

A net for the triangular prism is shown below.

Find the area of each face.

face A: 1.2 • 2 = 2.4

face B: 2 • 2 = 4

face C: 1.6 • 2 = 3.2

face D: $\frac{1}{2}$ • 2 • 1 = 1

face E: $\frac{1}{2}$ • 2 • 1 = 1

The surface area is the sum of the areas of the five faces.

Surface Area = 2.4 + 4 + 3.2 + 1 + 1 = 11.6

The surface area is 11.6 m².

21. a. Sample Response:

✔ **QUESTION 21**

... checks that you can find the surface area of a prism.

21 ✔ **CHECKPOINT** Use the drawing below. The drawing shows a variation of Hargrave's box kite that is still flown today.

a. Sketch a net for the faces of a right rectangular prism with length 20 in., width 20 in., and height 36 in. Label the edges of each face with its dimensions. **See above.**

b. Find the surface area of the prism. 3680 in.²

c. Find the area of the material covering the boxes. 1760 in.²

d. What fraction of the 20 in. × 20 in. × 36 in. prism is covered? about $\frac{1}{2}$

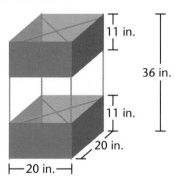

HOMEWORK EXERCISES ▶ **See Exs. 11–15 on pp. 406–407.**

AREA OF A CIRCLE

SET UP *You will need:* • *Labsheet 2A* • *scissors* • *tape* • *ruler*

Probably nowhere in the world does enthusiasm for kites run as high as it does in Japan. In the early years of this century, tens of thousands of people flocked to kite-flying festivals held in open fields far from the cities' kite-destroying power lines.

In Japan there was also a strong drive to build ever bigger and better kites, such as the centipede kite shown at the right. The frame of a centipede kite is constructed with bamboo, and silk is used to cover the circles.

Centipede kites can be hundreds of feet long. Due to their length, centipede kites require great skill to fly. By adding circular sections after the kite was in the air, a kite enthusiast constructed a centipede kite that was over a quarter of a mile long!

▲ This modern centipede kite is 110 ft long.

▲ It took 30 people to fly this huge centipede kite during the annual kite flying festival held along the Edo river in Japan in 1964.

22. Sample Response:

FOR ◀ HELP

with *the parts of a circle* and *circumference*, see **MODULE 4, p. 241**

22 Sketch a circle. Draw and label each segment and indicate each measure.

  a. a diameter   **b.** a radius

  c. the circumference   **d.** the area

23 Discussion A centipede kite is made from circular pieces of silk. How can you estimate the amount of silk in a centipede kite?

▶ **In Section 1 you used rectangles to develop a formula for the area of a parallelogram. You can use the same idea to find the area of one of the circles in a centipede kite.**

23. Sample Response: Find the area of the smallest square of paper that the circle will fit onto. Multiply that area by the number of circles in the kite.

24 **Use Labsheet 2A.** Follow the directions below. Check students' work.

Cut out the *Circle.* Then cut apart the eight sectors and arrange them to form the figure shown. Tape the figure to a sheet of paper.

Use a ruler to draw segments across the top and bottom of your figure. Extend the sides of the figure to meet the bottom segment.

25 What kind of polygon is the new figure you drew in Question 24?
   a parallelogram

26 **Try This as a Class** Use the figure you made in Question 24.

26. a. Sample Response: Measure the height and the base of the parallelogram. Then, use the formula $A = bh$ to find its area; about 50 cm²; Yes; The parts of the circle that don't fit within the parallelogram and the parts of the parallelogram that don't fit within the circle are very small compared with the total area.

   a. Estimation Explain how you could use the new figure you drew to estimate the area of the circle. Then estimate the area. Do you think this is a good estimate? Why or why not?

   b. How is the length of the base of the figure related to the circumference of the circle? It is about one-half the circumference.

   c. How is the height of the figure related to the radius of the circle? It is about the same.

27 **Discussion** Examine the drawings shown.

27. b. The base of the parallelogram *b* is one-half the circumference of the circle *C*.

   a. As a circle is cut into more and more sectors and put back together as shown, what begins to happen to its shape?
   It more nearly approximates a parallelogram.

   b. The area *A* of a parallelogram is found by multiplying the length of its base *b* by the height *h*, or $A = bh$. Use your figure to explain why this formula can be written as $A = \frac{1}{2}Cr$ to find the area of a circle, where *C* is the circumference and *r* is the length of the radius of the circle.

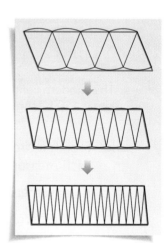

28 The circumference *C* of a circle is equal to $2\pi r$, where *r* is the length of the radius. Rewrite the formula $A = \frac{1}{2}Cr$ by substituting $2\pi r$ for *C*.

$$A = \frac{1}{2} \cdot 2\pi r \cdot r$$

29 The area of a circle with radius *r* is $A = \pi r^2$. Compare πr^2 with the expression you wrote for Question 28. Do they have the same value? Explain.

29. $A = \frac{1}{2} \cdot 2\pi r \cdot r = \left(\frac{1}{2} \cdot 2\right) \cdot \pi \cdot (r \cdot r) = 1 \cdot \pi \cdot r^2 = \pi r^2$; Yes, They are equivalent.

▶ **You can use the equation $A = \pi r^2$ to find the area of a circle when you know the length of its radius.**

EXAMPLE

Find the area of a circle with radius 3.2 cm. Use 3.14 for π to find the approximate area.

3.2 cm

SAMPLE RESPONSE

Exact Area

$A = \pi r^2$

$\quad = \pi (3.2)^2$

$\quad = \pi (10.24)$

$\quad = 10.24\pi$

The exact area is 10.24π cm².

Approximate Area

$A = \pi r^2$

$\quad = \pi (3.2)^2$

$\quad \approx 3.14(10.24)$

$\quad \approx 32.15$

> This is an approximation because 3.14 is an approximation for π.

The approximate area is 32.2 cm².

For Questions 30–31, use 3.14 or the 🔲π key on a calculator.

30 **Try This as a Class** Use your figure from Question 24.

   a. Use $A = \pi r^2$ to write an expression that represents the exact area of the *Circle*. $A = 16\pi$ cm²

   b. Find the approximate area of the *Circle*. Possible answers: 50.24 cm² or 50.27 cm²

   c. If you were planning to make a circle kite with a 4 cm radius, would you use your answer from part (a) or from part (b) to order the material? Why? b; It is not possible to measure 16π cm.

   d. How does the area of the circle from part (b) compare with the estimated area of the figure in Question 26(a)?
      Sample Response: They are very close.

31 ✔ **CHECKPOINT** A centipede kite has 10 in. diameter circles.

   a. Find the exact area of one circle. 25π in.²

   b. Find the approximate area of one circle. 78.5 in.² or 78.54 in.²

   c. About how many square inches of silk were used to make all 11 circles of the kite? Possible answers: 863.50 in.² or 863.94 in.²

✔ **QUESTION 31**

...checks that you can find the area of a circle.

▌**HOMEWORK EXERCISES** ▶ See Exs. 16–23 on p. 407.

Key Terms

square root

principal
square root

perfect
square

prism

  base
  face
  vertex
  edge

net

surface area

Square Roots (pp. 395–397)

If $A = s^2$, then s is a square root of A.

Example Find the square roots of 900.

Since $(30)^2 = 900$ and $(-30)^2 = 900$, the square roots of 900 are 30 and –30.

Every positive number has two square roots. The principal square root of a positive number, indicated by $\sqrt{\ }$, is the positive square root. A number is a perfect square if its principal square root is a whole number.

Examples $\sqrt{256} = 16$, so 256 is a perfect square.
$\sqrt{14} \approx 3.74$, so 14 is not a perfect square.

Prisms and Surface Area (pp. 397–400)

A prism is a space figure that has flat surfaces shaped like polygons. Pairs of faces meet in segments called edges, and the edges meet in points called vertices.

The **bases** are congruent and parallel. The other **faces** are shaped like parallelograms. The prisms you see from this point on in the book will be right prisms.

The surface area of a prism is the sum of the areas of all its faces. You can use a net to help find the surface area of a prism.

32 Key Concepts Question Use the rectangular prism below.

a. Draw a net showing the faces of the prism. Label the edges of each face with its dimensions. **See Additional Answers.**

4.5 cm

3 cm

b. What is the surface area of the prism? 162 cm²   9 cm

Area of a Circle (pp. 401–403)

The area of a circle A is equal to πr^2, where r is the **radius** of the circle.

Example Find the area of a circle with **radius 5.5 in.**

$$A = \pi r^2 = \pi(5.5)^2 = \pi(30.25)$$

The exact area of the circle is 30.25π in.^{2}.

$$A \approx 3.14 \cdot 30.25 = 94.985$$

The approximate area of the circle is 94.99 in.^{2}.

> You can approximate the area by using 3.14 or the **π** key on a calculator.

---

33 Key Concepts Question Use the figure.

a. The square has an area of 169 in.^{2}. Find the length of a side. **13 in.**

b. What is the exact area of a circle with a diameter equal to the length in part (a)?
42.25π in.^{2}

CLOSURE QUESTION

State the formulas for the area of a square and the area of a circle. Explain a concept that these formulas have in common.

Sample Response: The formula for the area of a square with side s is $A = s^2$. The formula for the area of a circle with radius r is $A = \pi r^2$. Both formulas involve finding squares of numbers; in one case, the side of the square and, in the other, the radius of the circle.

Section ②
Practice & Application Exercises

1. History In 1821, Captain Dansey of the British Royal Artillery designed a square kite for rescuing shipwreck victims. The kite had an area of 81 ft^2. Find the dimensions of the kite. **9 ft × 9 ft**

Find each square root. If the square root is not a whole number, find the two consecutive integers it is between.

2. $\sqrt{196}$ 14   **3.** $-\sqrt{225}$ –15   **4.** $-\sqrt{169}$ –13   **5.** $\sqrt{2.56}$ 1 and 2

Estimate each square root to the nearest tenth.

6. $\sqrt{93}$
about 9.6

7. $\sqrt{205}$
about 14.3

8. $\sqrt{17}$
about 4.1

9. $\sqrt{546}$
about 23.4

10. **Kites** You can use the formula $m = 7\sqrt{\dfrac{w}{A}}$, where m is the minimum wind speed, w is the weight in ounces, and A is the area in square feet of the surface used to lift the kite, to calculate the minimum wind speed in miles per hour required to fly a box kite. Find the minimum wind speed required to lift a box kite with a weight of 5.6 oz and an area of 8.71 ft^2.   about 5.61 mi/h

11. b. 42 cm^2; Each time a cube is added, one face is lost and 5 are added for a total increase in area of 4 cm^2. Surface area = 6 + 4n, where n is the number of added cubes.

11. **Visual Thinking** Four prisms were made from centimeter cubes.

   a. Find the surface area of each prism.   6 cm^2, 10 cm^2, 14 cm^2, 18 cm^2

   b. Look for a pattern in your answers for part (a). What would be the surface area of a prism made with 10 centimeter cubes arranged in the same way? How did you find your answer?

12. **Visual Thinking** A net for a cereal box is shown below. It was formed by cutting the box open and flattening it.

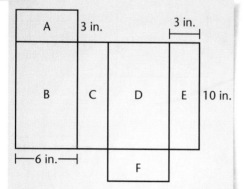

   a. If the box were put back together, which faces do you think would be the top and the bottom?   A and F

   b. The lengths of some edges of the box are labeled. Make a sketch of the net and label the dimensions of each face.   See below.

   c. Find the surface area of the cereal box.   216 in.^{2}

   d. Suppose the cost of the cardboard to make a box is 0.3¢ per square inch. How much does the cardboard for one box cost?   64.8¢

   e. If you had to make 1000 boxes, what would your cost be? $648

   f. Why is surface area important in the design of a cereal box?

12. b. Sample Response:

f. Sample Response: The greater the surface area, the greater the cost of manufacturing the box.

13. Use the rectangular prism shown.

   a. Sketch a net for the prism.
      See Additional Answers.

   b. Find the area of each face.
      150 cm^2, 150 cm^2, 40 cm^2, 40 cm^2, 60 cm^2, 60 cm^2

   c. Find the surface area of the prism.
      500 cm^2

14. Find the surface area of the right triangular prism shown. (*Hint:* Look carefully at the labels.)
      156 in.^{2}

15. Challenge Suppose the boxes for a Hargrave kite like the one shown on page 400 are made with faces that are all congruent squares. Suppose 2500 in.² of fabric is used to cover eight of the faces. How long is each edge of a box in the kite? *about 17.7 in.*

Use π to write an expression for the exact area of each circle. Then use 3.14 or the key on a calculator to find the approximate area.

16.
6.3 cm

17.
121 m

18.
π in.

Find the radius of a circle with each area.

19. $A = 225$ ft²
about 8.46 ft

20. $A = 0.49$ m²
about 0.4 m

21. $A = 16.81$ yd²
about 2.31 yd

22. Japanese Archery In *kyudo,* a form of Japanese archery, archers aim at circular targets or *mato.* *See below.*

a. Find the areas of targets that have diameters of 36 cm, 18 cm, and 9 cm.

b. Look at your answers from part (a). If the diameter of a circle is one half the diameter of another circle, will its area also be one half the area of the other circle? Explain.

Reflecting ◀▶**on the Section**

Be prepared to report on the following topic in class.

23. Describe a situation in which it would be helpful to know the surface area of a prism. *Sample Response: You need to know the surface area of the walls of a room in order to know how much paint or wallpaper to buy.*

Spiral ◀▶**Review**

Write an inequality to represent each statement. (Module 6, p. 388)

24. *t* is greater than 11. $t > 11$

25. *p* is less than or equal to 6. $p \leq 6$

Use division to write each fraction as a decimal. (Module 4, p. 256)
Decimals are rounded to the nearest thousandth.

26. $\frac{1}{8}$ 0.125

27. $\frac{2}{5}$ 0.400

28. $\frac{14}{23}$ 0.609

29. $\frac{21}{31}$ 0.677

Write each fraction in lowest terms. (Module 3, p. 170)

30. $\frac{2}{4}$ $\frac{1}{2}$

31. $\frac{3}{12}$ $\frac{1}{4}$

32. $\frac{15}{25}$ $\frac{3}{5}$

33. $\frac{18}{48}$ $\frac{3}{8}$

---

*Sidebar answers:*

16. 39.69π cm²; Possible answers: 124.63 cm² or 124.69 cm²

17. 3660.25π m²; Possible answers: 11,493.19 m² or 11,499.02 m²

18. $\frac{\pi^3}{4}$ in.² ; Possible answers: 7.74 in.² or 7.75 in.²

The most common *kyudo* target is the 36 cm *mato* used for *kinteki* (regular close-range shooting).

Oral Report

Exercise 23 checks that you understand the surface area of a prism.

22. a. 324π cm², 81π cm², 20.25π cm²
b. No; If the radius of the larger circle is *r*, then the radius of the smaller circle is $\frac{r}{2}$. So, for the smaller circle, $A = \pi \cdot \left(\frac{r}{2}\right)^2 = \pi \cdot \frac{r^2}{4}$, or $\frac{1}{4}$ the area of the larger circle, $\pi \cdot r^2$.

Wild Wings

You will need: • *Project Labsheet A* • *ruler* • *tape*
• *balance scale (optional)*

Ideas for making a faster plane, or for making a glider that flies higher or farther, can come from many sources. In 1967, a magazine organized a paper airplane competition in the hope that the designs might lead to future jet designs. In this project, you will make gliders, analyze their designs, and suggest ways to improve their flying ability.

Surface Area of a Prism Follow the directions to make a Wild Wing, fly it, and find its sail loading, or weight divided by surface area.

1–2. Check students' work.

 1 **Use Project Labsheet A.**
Follow the steps to *Create a Wild Wing.*

2 Fly your Wild Wing by throwing it overhand as shown below.

The folded edge should face forward.

 3 a. Find the outside surface area of your Wild Wing in square feet. **about 0.15 ft²**

b. Use a scale or the table to find your Wild Wing's weight. **Sample Responses: 0.17 oz, 0.11 oz, 0.18 oz**

c. What is the sail loading of your Wild Wing in ounces per square foot?

Type of paper	Weight of $8\frac{1}{2}$ in. × 11 in. sheet (oz)
copier	0.17
notebook	0.11
construction	0.18

Sample Responses: copier paper: 1.1 oz/ft² , notebook paper: 0.73 oz/ft² , construction paper: 1.2 oz/ft²

Find each square root.

1. $\sqrt{64}$ 8   2. $\sqrt{256}$ 16   3. $\sqrt{49}$ 7   4. $\sqrt{289}$ 17

Estimate each square root.

5. $\sqrt{79}$ about 8.9   6. $\sqrt{90}$ about 9.5   7. $\sqrt{30}$ about 5.5   8. $\sqrt{249}$ about 15.8

For Exercises 9 and 10, use the prism shown.

9. What kind of prism is this? a hexagonal prism

10. How many faces, vertices, and edges does this prism have?
    8 faces, 12 vertices, 18 edges

2 cm

6 cm

8 cm

11. Use the rectangular prism shown at the left.

    a. Sketch a net for the prism.
      See Additional Answers.
    b. Find the surface area of the prism.
      152 cm^2

Use π to write an expression for the exact area of each circle. Then use 3.14 or the ▪π▪ key on a calculator to find the approximate area.

12.

52 in.

13.

2.4 cm

14.

630 mm

676π in.^{2} ; Possible answers: 2122.64 in.^{2} or 2123.72 in.^{2}

5.76π cm^2 ; Possible answers: 18.09 cm^2 or 18.10 cm^2

99,225π mm^2 ;
Possible answers: 311,566.5 mm^2 or 311,724.53 mm^2

Standardized Testing ◀▶ Multiple Choice

1. Find the exact area of a circle whose radius is 3 cm long. B

   Ⓐ 3π cm^2 Ⓑ 9π cm^2 Ⓒ 6π cm^2 Ⓓ 9 cm^2

2. Choose the greatest measure. Use 3.14 for π. C

   Ⓐ $\sqrt{420}$ cm^2 Ⓑ Area of a circle with a diameter of 5 cm

   Ⓒ Surface area of a cube with an edge of 2 cm

Section ③ Triangles and Similarity

IN THIS SECTION

EXPLORATION 1
◆ Scale Drawings and Similarity

EXPLORATION 2
◆ Unknown Measures in Similar Figures

BARNSTORMING

WARM-UP EXERCISES

Write each ratio in two other ways.

1. 3 : 4 $\frac{3}{4}$; 3 to 4

2. $\frac{2}{7}$ 2 : 7; 2 to 7

3. 6 to 1 $\frac{6}{1}$; 6 : 1

Solve each proportion.

4. $\frac{8}{12} = \frac{20}{y}$ 30

5. $\frac{x}{4} = \frac{5}{6}$ $\frac{10}{3}$

6. $\frac{9}{5} = \frac{m}{12}$ 21.6

▼ Transferring from a speeding car to a plane was one of the barnstormers' favorite stunts.

◄··· Setting the Stage

Bessie Coleman was the first African-American woman to earn a pilot's license. Born in Texas in 1893, she did well in school, but could not afford to finish college. Eventually she moved to Chicago, where she opened a chili parlor and saved her money to become a pilot. When she was refused admittance to flight school in the United States due to discrimination, she used her savings to travel to France for pilot training.

In 1921 Bessie Coleman returned to the United States as a trained pilot. She traveled around the country as a *barnstormer*, giving flying exhibitions. She thrilled thousands with her daring aerial feats. The money she earned was saved toward her dream of opening a flying school to train other African-American pilots.

Think About It

1 How long ago was Bessie Coleman born?
Check students' work.

2 How old was Bessie Coleman when she returned to the United States? 27 or 28 years old

3 What do you think a "barnstormer" is?
Sample Response: a person who travels from place to place putting on performances, usually in rural areas

SCALE DRAWINGS and SIMILARITY

GOAL

LEARN HOW TO...
- identify similar and congruent polygons
- find the scale of a drawing or model

AS YOU...
- learn about the Curtiss Jenny airplane used by barnstormers

KEY TERMS
- corresponding parts
- scale of a drawing

SET UP | *Work with a partner. You will need:* • *Labsheet 3A*
• *ruler* • *protractor*

In the book *Epic of Flight: Barnstormers & Speed Kings* by Paul O'Neil and the Editors of Time-Life Books, barnstormers are described this way:

> The barnstormers, as they called themselves, [wandered] from coast to coast to perform in rough pastures, at big-city air shows and, when fortune beckoned, in motion-picture melodramas.
>
> At first, these . . . fliers could keep their stomachs and fuel tanks full by merely offering rides—for five dollars and up—in their Curtiss Jennys. Then, as novelty wore thin, the barnstormers teamed up to develop repertoires of spectacular tricks.

The Curtiss JN-4, referred to as a *Jenny*, was a favorite airplane of barnstorming pilots such as Bessie Coleman.

Use Labsheet 3A for Questions 4–7.

4 **a.** Two *Curtiss Jennys* are shown on the labsheet. Follow the instructions to make cutouts of the planes. **Check students' work.**

b. Place the large plane 60 cm from and parallel to the edge of a table and tape it in place. Then, while viewing with one eye from the edge of the table, position the small plane so it *exactly* blocks out your view of the large plane.
Check students' work.

c. How far is the small plane from the edge of the table? **about 30 cm**

d. Write the ratio of the distance in part (c) to 60 cm (the distance from the large plane to the edge of the table). **about $\frac{30}{60}$**

e. Which ratio is closest to your answer to part (d): *1 : 1, 1 : 2, 1 : 3,* or *1 : 4*? How did you determine this?
1:2; I divided the numerator and denominator by 30.

5 a. Measure the length of each plane to the nearest tenth of a centimeter. about 7.0 cm, about 13.9 cm

b. What is the ratio of the length of the small plane to the length of the large plane? about 1 : 2

c. How does this ratio compare with the one you found in Question 4(e)? It is the same.

6 a. What do you think the ratio of the height of the small plane to the height of the large plane will be? Why? about 1 : 2; Sample Response: I think it will be the same as the ratio of the lengths.

b. Measure the height of each plane. What is the ratio of the height of the small plane to the height of the large plane? about 1 : 2

7 a. Measure ∠A, the angle between the tail and the body, on the drawing of each plane. (You may need to extend the sides to measure the angle.) What do you notice about the measures of the angles? They are both about 135°.

b. How do you think the measure of ∠B on the small plane is related to the measure of ∠B on the large plane?
Sample Response: I think they will be the same.

c. Measure ∠B on each drawing. Was your prediction in part (b) correct? Explain. Yes; The measure of ∠B on each drawing is about 50°.

FOR◀HELP

with *similar* figures, see
MODULE 4, p. 299

▶ The small drawing of the Jenny is similar to the large drawing of the Jenny. When two figures are similar, for each part of one figure there is a **corresponding part** on the other figure. For example, the diameter of the wheel on the large plane corresponds to the diameter of the wheel on the small plane.

8 Try This as a Class Think about your results in Questions 5–7.

a. When two figures are similar, what do you think is true about their corresponding angles? They are congruent.

b. What do you think is true about the ratios of the lengths of their corresponding parts? They are the same.

9 Try This as a Class △ABC below is similar to △GDF. This is written △ABC ~ △GDF. How does the statement △ABC ~ △GDF show which parts of the triangles are corresponding parts?

The order that the vertices of each triangle are written in tells what angles correspond and what sides correspond. For example, side $\overline{AC}$ corresponds to side $\overline{GF}$.

10 ✔ **CHECKPOINT** Use the measures of corresponding angles and the lengths of corresponding sides to show that △ABC ~ △GDF.

11 Discussion Recall from Module 4 that polygons are congruent if they have the same shape *and* the same size. For example, △PQR below is congruent to △WXV. This is written △PQR ≅ △WXV.

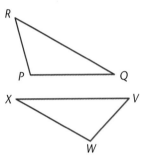

a. Identify the corresponding angles and the corresponding sides of the triangles.

b. Are congruent polygons always similar? Explain.

c. Are similar polygons always congruent? Explain.

No; The polygons will have the same shape but not necessarily the same size.

▶ **You have been working with *scale drawings* of a Curtiss Jenny. The drawings are similar to a "full size" drawing of the plane. The scale of a drawing is the ratio of a length measurement on the drawing to the measurement of the corresponding part on the object represented.**

12 ✔ **CHECKPOINT** A Curtiss Jenny has a length of about 8 m.

a. What is the length of a Curtiss Jenny in centimeters? 800 cm

b. Choose one of the drawings. What is the length in centimeters of the Jenny in the drawing? What is the scale of the drawing?

c. Use the drawing and the scale to estimate the height of an actual Jenny in meters. about 3 m

HOMEWORK EXERCISES ▶ See Exs. 1–10 on p. 418.

✔ **QUESTION 10**

…checks that you can use the measures of the sides and angles to show that two polygons are similar.

11. a. $\angle P \cong \angle W$, $\angle Q \cong \angle X$, $\angle R \cong \angle V$, $\overline{PQ} \cong \overline{WX}$, $\overline{RP} \cong \overline{VW}$, $\overline{RQ} \cong \overline{VX}$

b. Yes; If they have the same shape, corresponding angles are congruent. If they have the same size, the ratios of the lengths of their corresponding sides will be $\dfrac{1}{1}$.

✔ **QUESTION 12**

…checks that you can find the scale of a drawing and use it to find an unknown measurement.

12. b. small plane: about 7.0 cm, about $\dfrac{1}{114}$; large plane: about 13.9 cm, about $\dfrac{1}{58}$

GOAL

LEARN HOW TO...
♦ classify triangles by the measures of their angles
♦ find unknown measures of similar figures

AS YOU...
♦ use scale drawings of a Curtiss Jenny

KEY TERMS
♦ acute triangle
♦ obtuse triangle
♦ right triangle

UNKNOWN MEASURES in SIMILAR FIGURES

SET UP *Work with a partner. You will need:* • *Jenny cutouts from Exploration 1* • *ruler* • *protractor*

▶ In Question 4 on page 411, you experimented with where to place the cutout of the small plane in order to exactly block your view of the large plane.

13 a. Suppose the large plane is 40 cm from the edge of the table. How far from the edge do you think the small plane must be placed in order to block the view of the large plane? **20 cm**

b. Tape the large plane 40 cm from the edge of the table. Then tape the small plane in the place you predicted in part (a).
Check students' work.

c. Does the small plane block your view of the large plane? Explain.
Yes; The drawings are similar with a ratio of 1:2. When the large drawing is twice as far from your eye as the small one, the two appear to be the same size.

▶ You can use similar triangles to find where to place the small plane. But first you need to explore some properties of similar triangles.

14 a. Draw two different triangles that each contain a 30° and a 70° angle. Label one as Triangle A and the other as Triangle B.
Check students' work.

b. What is the measure of the third angle of each triangle? **80°**

c. Measure the length of each side of the triangles to the nearest millimeter and write each ratio below in decimal form. Round each answer to the nearest hundredth. The three ratios are equal.

♦ shortest side of Triangle A : shortest side of Triangle B

♦ longest side of Triangle A : longest side of Triangle B

♦ remaining side of Triangle A : remaining side of Triangle B

15 Repeat Question 14 using two triangles that each contain a 20° and a 50° angle.

16 **Discussion** Use the triangles you drew in Questions 14 and 15.

    a. Are the triangles you drew in Question 14 similar? Are the ones you drew in Question 15 similar? Explain.

    b. If the measures of two angles of one triangle are equal to the measures of two angles of another triangle, what seems to be true about the triangles? The triangles are similar.

17 **Try This as a Class** Use the triangles you drew in Questions 14 and 15. Sample responses are given.

    a. The triangles you drew in Question 14 are **acute triangles**. How would you define an acute triangle?
    a triangle in that has only acute angles

    b. The triangles you drew in Question 15 are **obtuse triangles**. How would you define an obtuse triangle?
    a triangle that has an obtuse angle

    c. How would you define a **right triangle**? Draw an example of a right triangle.

▶ In similar polygons, the ratios of the lengths of the corresponding sides are equal, and the corresponding angles have equal measures. So, you can often use known measures of one polygon to find unknown measures of a similar polygon.

EXAMPLE

△**ABC** ~ △**XYZ**. Find XZ.

XZ is read as, "the length of $\overline{XZ}$."

SAMPLE RESPONSE

$\overline{AB}$ and $\overline{XY}$ are corresponding sides.

$\overline{AC}$ and $\overline{XZ}$ are corresponding sides.

So, $\dfrac{AB}{XY} = \dfrac{AC}{XZ}$

$\dfrac{12}{9} = \dfrac{8}{XZ}$

$XZ = 6$

XZ is 6 cm.

18 **Discussion** Describe two ways to solve the proportion in the Example. Use cross products; Divide both sides by 8 to solve for $\frac{1}{XZ}$, then find the reciprocal of the answer.

---

15. **a.** Check students' work.
b. 110°
c. The three ratios are equal.

16. **a.** Yes; Yes; Measures of the corresponding angles are equal and the ratios of the lengths of corresponding sides are equal.

17. **c.** a triangle that has one right angle; Sample Response:

QUESTION 19

...checks that you can find unknown measures of similar figures.

19 ✔ **CHECKPOINT** △PQR ~ △STV.

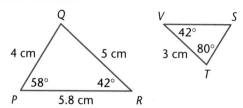

a. What is the measure of ∠VST? of ∠PQR? 58°, 80°

b. Find VS and ST. 3.48 cm, 2.4 cm

▶ If the small plane exactly blocks the view of the large one, then when the cutouts are viewed from the side, you can imagine two right triangles—a small one, △ABE, and a large one, △ACD.

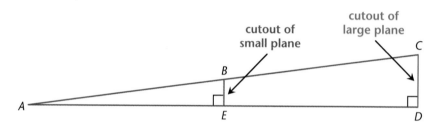

cutout of large plane

cutout of small plane

20. Since ∠A is in both triangles and since ∠AEB and ∠D each measure 90°, the measures of two angles of △ABE are equal to the measures of two angles of △ACD.

20 **Discussion** How do you know △ABE ~ △ACD?

21 **Try This as a Class** Use the Jenny cutouts and the diagram above.

a. Side $\overline{BE}$ in △ABE corresponds to side $\overline{CD}$ in △ACD. What is the ratio of BE to CD? 1 : 2

b. Which side of △ABE corresponds to $\overline{AD}$ in △ACD? $\overline{AE}$

c. What is the ratio of AE to AD? How do you know?

21. c. 1 : 2; △ABE ~ △ACD and the ratio of the lengths of corresponding sides is 1 : 2.

d. If $\overline{AD}$ is 40 cm long, what is the length of $\overline{AE}$? Explain. 20 cm; $\frac{AE}{AD} = \frac{1}{2}$

22 a. Where is the eye of the viewer located in the diagram? at point A

b. Is $\overline{AD}$ 40 cm long? Explain. Sample Response: Not necessarily, but $\overline{AD}$ has to be twice as long as $\overline{AE}$. So if $\overline{AE}$ is 20 cm, then $\overline{AD}$ is 40 cm.

23 a. Use your results from Questions 20–22 to improve your prediction of where to place the small plane when the large plane is 40 cm from the edge of the table. 20 cm from the edge

b. Check your prediction. Answers will vary.

HOMEWORK EXERCISES ▶ See Exs. 11–21 on p. 419.

Section 3
Key Concepts

Similar and Congruent Figures (pp. 411–416)

Similar figures have the same shape but not necessarily the same size. In similar polygons, the measures of the corresponding angles are equal and the ratios of the lengths of the corresponding sides are equal.

Example Trapezoid *ABCD* is similar to trapezoid *MNQP*.

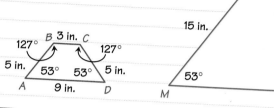

$\overline{NQ}$ and $\overline{BC}$ are corresponding sides. Since $\frac{NQ}{BC} = \frac{9}{3} = 3$, each side of trapezoid *MNQP* is three times as long as the corresponding side of trapezoid *ABCD*.

Similar figures that have the same shape and the same size are congruent. The lengths of corresponding sides and the measures of corresponding angles of congruent polygons are equal.

The scale of a model or drawing is the ratio of a length on the model or drawing to the length of the corresponding part on the actual object.

Classifying Triangles (p. 415)

Triangles can be classified by the measures of their angles.

An acute triangle has only acute angles.

An obtuse triangle has one obtuse angle.

A right triangle has one right angle.

Key Terms

corresponding parts

CLOSURE QUESTION

What is needed to show that two triangles are similar? How is this different from showing that two triangles are congruent?

Sample Response: For similarity, show that the measures of corresponding angles are equal and that the ratios of the lengths of corresponding sides are equal. For congruence, the measures of the corresponding angles must be equal and the lengths of the corresponding sides must also be equal.

scale of a drawing

acute triangle

obtuse triangle

right triangle

Key Concepts Questions

24 The height of trapezoid *ABCD* in the Example above is 4 in. What is the height of trapezoid *MNQP*? **12 in.**

25 On a map, two cities are 1.5 in. apart. The scale of the map is 1 in. : 50 mi. What is the actual distance between the two cities? **75 mi**

Section 3 Practice & Application Exercises

Tell whether the polygons in each pair are *similar*, *congruent*, or *neither*. If the polygons are similar or congruent, write a statement that can be used to identify the corresponding parts.

1.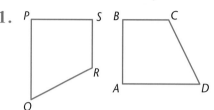

congruent and similar; *ABCD* ≅ *PSRQ*

2.

neither

3.

similar; *FGHKL* ~ *EABCD* or *FGHKL* ~ *AEDCB*

4.

similar; *SVW* ~ *ZYX*

Aviation A scale drawing of a passenger plane is shown below. Each centimeter on the drawing corresponds to 1200 cm on the plane. Estimate each measurement on the plane in meters.

5. length about 70.8 m   6. height about 20.4 m   7. wingspan about 64.8 m

Microscopes A microscope magnifies an object to make it appear larger. The amount of magnification can be described by using a scale. For each scale, how long does a 9 mm long housefly appear to be when seen through a microscope?

8. 10:1 90 mm   9. 20:1 180 mm   10. 200:1 1800 mm, or 1.8 m

Classify each triangle as *acute*, *obtuse*, or *right*.

11.
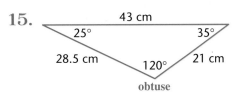
7 in. /80°\ 7 in.
50°   50°
9 in.
acute

12.
3 ft |53° 5 ft
37°
4 ft
right

13.
2.5 cm
60°
2.5 cm   60°
60°
2.5 cm
acute

14.
7 m /◇\ 7 m
45°   45°
9.9 m
right

15.
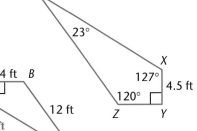
43 cm
25°   35°
28.5 cm   21 cm
120°
obtuse

Use the similar polygons shown below for Exercises 16–19.

16. $\overline{XY}$ corresponds to $\overline{DA}$. What angle corresponds to ∠*XYZ* and what is its measure? ∠*DAB*, 90°

17. Find the measures of ∠*ABC*, ∠*BCD*, and ∠*CDA*. 120°, 23°, 127°

18. Which segment corresponds to $\overline{DC}$? What is its length? $\overline{XW}$, 19.5 ft

19. Find the lengths of $\overline{WZ}$ and $\overline{YZ}$. 18 ft, 6 ft

W
23°
X
127°
4.5 ft
120°
Z   Y

A 4 ft B
3 ft
D   12 ft
13 ft
C

20. **Open-ended** Draw two similar triangles in which the ratio of the corresponding sides is 2.5 to 1. Explain how you know the two triangles are similar. Check students' drawings. Sample Response: Corresponding angles are congruent.

Reflecting ◀▶ on the Section

21. The polygons in each pair shown below are similar.

A.

B.

C.

a. For each pair of polygons shown, write a ratio that compares the lengths of the sides. 3 : 1; 2 : 1; 5 : 2

b. For each pair of polygons shown, write the ratio of the area of the smaller polygon to the area of the larger polygon.
1 : 9; 1 : 4; 4 : 25

c. How are the ratios of the areas in part (b) related to the scale you found for each pair of polygons in part (a)?
The ratios of the areas are the squares of the scales.

Find the surface area of each prism. (Module 6, p. 404)

22.
920 in.²

18 in.

10 in. 10 in.

23.
17.18 cm²

3.6 cm

2 cm

1.3 cm   3 cm

Find each difference. (Module 3, p. 183)

24. $3\frac{1}{8} - 2\frac{1}{4}$ $\frac{7}{8}$

25. $4\frac{1}{2} - 3\frac{1}{2}$ 1

26. $5\frac{1}{2} - 2\frac{1}{2}$ 3

For each angle, find the measure of a supplementary angle.
(Module 2, p. 83)

27. 72° 108°

28. 90° 90°

29. 112° 68°

30. 155° 25°

Career ◼ Connection

Artist: Jesse Treviño

Jesse Treviño paints the people and landmarks of San Antonio, Texas, in a realistic style. At first glance, you might mistake his paintings for photographs.

31. Jesse Treviño used one of his paintings, *The Spirit of Healing*, as the model for a hospital mural. The original painting is 4 ft across and about 8 ft 10 in. high.

a. The hospital mural is about 39 ft 7 in. across. About how high is it? about 87 ft 5 in.

b. The painting shown is titled *La Raspa*. Suppose Jesse Treviño used this painting as the model for a mural. Using the same scale that was used for the *The Spirit of Healing* mural, what would be the dimensions of the *La Raspa* mural?

about 39 ft 7 in. high and 54 ft 5 in. across

4 ft

5 ft 6 in.

▲

During combat in Vietnam, Jesse Treviño lost his right hand, the hand he used for painting. When he came home, he taught himself to paint with his left hand.

La Raspa is a Spanish phrase that translates as "Snow Cone."

Section 3
Extra Skill Practice

$\triangle XYZ$ is similar to $\triangle TUV$.

Y 2.25 in. X
V 66° 2.5 in. 1 in.
Z
24°
T 4.5 in. U

1. $\overline{XY}$ corresponds to $\overline{TU}$. What segments correspond to $\overline{ZX}$ and $\overline{YZ}$? $\overline{VT}, \overline{UV}$

2. Find the measures of $\angle XYZ$, $\angle YZX$, and $\angle ZXY$. 24°, 66°, 90°

3. Find the lengths of $\overline{UV}$ and $\overline{VT}$. 5 in., 2 in.

Classify each triangle as acute, obtuse, or right.

4. right

5. acute
85°
50° 45°

6. obtuse
128° 17°
35°

7.
30°
35°
115°
obtuse

8. acute
47°
60°
73°

9. right
90°
64° 26°

Trapezoid EFGH is similar to trapezoid LMNK.

4 cm
F 115° 125° G
2.1 cm 1.9 cm 2.3 cm
E 65° 55° H
6.2 cm

2.6 cm
M 115° N
L K

10. The height of trapezoid EFGH is 1.9 cm. What is the height of trapezoid LMNK? about 1.2 cm

11. Find the measures of $\angle MNK$, $\angle NKL$, and $\angle KLM$. 125°, 55°, 65°

12. Find the lengths of $\overline{LM}$, $\overline{NK}$, and $\overline{KL}$. about 1.4 cm, about 1.5 cm, about 4.0 cm

Standardized Testing ◆ Free Response

1. Must two pentagons that have congruent angles be similar? Why or why not? No; The ratios of lengths of corresponding sides may not be equal. For example, two house-shaped pentagons could have corresponding angles congruent, but one could have all side lengths equal and one could have vertical sides twice as long as the other sides.

2. Must two pentagons that have congruent sides be similar? Why or why not? No; The measures of corresponding angles may not be equal. For example, a house-shaped pentagon and a regular pentagon could have congruent sides but would have different angle measures.

WARM-UP EXERCISES

Use a protractor to find the measure the angles in each figure.

1.

2.

a. *m*∠1   75°; 61°
b. *m*∠2   105°; 109°
c. *m*∠3   75°; 110°
d. *m*∠4   105°; 80°

W!NG!NG IT!

◄◄◄ *Setting the Stage*

The first successful powered airplane flight occurred at Kill Devil Hills, near Kittyhawk, North Carolina, on December 17, 1903. With Orville Wright at the controls, the *Wright Flyer I* lurched to an altitude of almost 10 ft and flew about 120 ft before returning to the ground. The whole flight, from liftoff to landing, lasted only about 12 seconds.

On early planes such as the *Wright Flyer III,* shown in the diagram below, vertical struts and diagonal wires helped support the airplane's wings. Why were these supports important? Were both types necessary? In this section, you will explore these questions by making and examining wings.

► The *Wright Flyer I* was grounded by a gust of wind on its fourth flight. However, the Wright Brothers continued to improve on its design. Their *Wright Flyer III,* built in 1905, was the first practical plane.

Think About It

1 a. What was the speed in feet per second of the *Wright Flyer I* during its first flight? **10 ft/s**

b. Can you run this fast? Explain. Sample Response: Yes; 10 ft/s is about 6.8 mi/h.

▶ ▶▶▶▶▶▶▶▶▶▶▶▶▶▶▶▶▶▶▶▶▶▶▶▶▶▶▶▶

ANGLES FORMED BY A
TRANSVERSAL

SET UP | *Work with a partner. You will need:*
- *Labsheets 4A and 4B • scissors • ruler • tape*
- *2 index cards (3 in. by 5 in.) • protractor*

2 **Use Labsheet 4A.** You can investigate the purpose of the vertical struts by creating Wing 1 from index cards. Follow the steps on the labsheet to *Build a Wing.* Check students' work.

3 **a.** What is the purpose of the vertical struts? They keep the bases of the wing parallel.

   b. Is your wing rigid? How could you make it stronger?
   No; Use stronger materials and add more vertical supports

   c. How are the bases of the wing related? They are congruent and parallel.

▶ **You can use segments to draw a simplified model of the wing design. In the drawing, two parallel lines are intersected by other lines called transversals.**

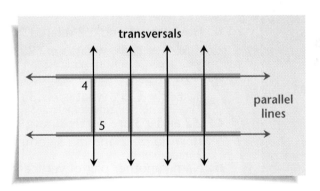

4 **a.** In the drawing above, what is true about *m*∠4 and *m*∠5?
   They are equal.

   b. Locate ∠4 and ∠5 from part (a) on your paper model of Wing 1. As you move the top base to the right, what happens to *m*∠4 and *m*∠5? They decrease.

   c. How do you think *m*∠4 and *m*∠5 compare?
   They are equal.

▶ When a transversal intersects two parallel lines, eight angles are formed. These angles are related to each other.

5 **a.** ∠1, ∠2, ∠7, and ∠8 are all **exterior angles**. Why do you think they are called exterior angles? They are on the exterior of, or outside, the parallel lines.

Exterior Angles

b. ∠3, ∠4, ∠5, and ∠6 are all **interior angles**. How does this name describe their location? The angles are in the interior of, or inside, the parallel lines.

Interior Angles

6 **Corresponding angles** come in pairs. ∠1 and ∠5 are corresponding angles, and so are ∠4 and ∠8.

Corresponding Angles

a. Name two other pairs of corresponding angles. ∠3 and ∠7, ∠2 and ∠6

b. How do you think the measures of corresponding angles compare? They are equal.

FOR ◀ HELP
with *supplementary angles*, see
MODULE 2, p. 83

7 **a.** How are ∠1 and ∠2 related? If *m*∠1 = 125°, what is *m*∠2? They are supplementary angles; 55°

Vertical Angles

b. How are ∠1 and ∠3 related? If *m*∠1 = 125°, what is *m*∠3? They are supplementary angles; 55°

c. ∠2 and ∠3 are **vertical angles**. How do *m*∠2 and *m*∠3 compare? They are equal.

d. Name another pair of vertical angles. Possible answers: ∠1 and ∠4, ∠5 and ∠8, ∠6 and ∠7

8 ∠3 and ∠6 are **alternate interior angles**.

8. a. The angles are in the interior of, or inside, the parallel lines and they are on alternate, or opposite, sides of the transversal.

a. How does the term describe the location of these angles?

Alternate Interior Angles

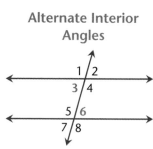

b. Name another pair of alternate interior angles. ∠4 and ∠5

c. How do you think the measures of alternate interior angles compare? They are equal.

▶ **In Question 9, you can check the observations you made in Questions 6–8 and find other relationships among the angles.**

Use Labsheet 4B for Questions 9 and 10.

9 Use a ruler to *Draw a Transversal* through the parallel lines. Then use a protractor to find the measures of the eight angles formed.
Answers will vary. Check students' work.

10 Try This as a Class Use your answers to Question 9.

   a. How do the measures of the corresponding angles compare?
They are equal.

   b. How do the measures of the alternate interior angles compare?
They are equal.

   c. How do the measures of the **alternate exterior angles** compare? *They are equal.*

   d. How do the measures of the vertical angles compare?
They are equal.

   e. How do your answers in parts (a), (b), and (d) compare with your answers in Questions 6(b), 7(c), and 8(c)? *They are the same.*

   f. Compare your answers in parts (a)–(d) with your classmates'. Are the relationships in parts (a)–(d) true for any transversal drawn through parallel lines? *Yes.*

11 ✔ **CHECKPOINT** The figure below shows parallel lines $\overleftrightarrow{PS}$ and $\overleftrightarrow{LT}$ cut by transversal $\overleftrightarrow{MR}$. Without using a protractor, find the measure of each named angle.

   a. ∠PQM 34°   **b.** ∠TNR 34°   **c.** ∠MNT 146°

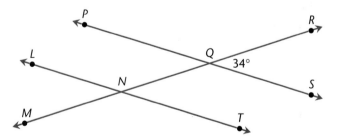

✔ **QUESTION 11**

...checks that you can use the relationships among angles formed by a transversal and parallel lines.

12 Discussion How do you think the Wright brothers could have checked that the bases of their plane's wings were parallel?
If the measures of the alternate interior angles formed by the struts and the wings were equal, the wings were parallel.

HOMEWORK EXERCISES ▶ See Exs. 1–15 on pp. 430–431.

GOAL

LEARN HOW TO...
* find the sum of the measures of the angles of triangles and quadrilaterals

AS YOU...
* experiment with ways to make your wing rigid

KEY TERM
* diagonal

Exploration 2

ANGLES of TRIANGLES and QUADRILATERALS

SET UP *Work with a partner. You will need:*
* *scissors* • *ruler* • *tape* • *4 index cards (3 in. by 5 in.)*
* *wing from Exploration 1*

▶ The nonvertical supports on the *Wright Flyer III* shown on page 422 provide a different type of support for the wings. In this exploration you will explore the effect of supports like these on wing design.

13. Check students' work.

13 **Use Labsheet 4A.** Create Wing 2 using nonvertical supports. Follow the directions on Labsheet 4A to make Base 1 and the four supports. Then tape one end of each support to Base 1.

Fold the tabs away from each other so they do not overlap.

Base 2

Base 1

a. For Base 2, draw two support lines. Draw each support line $1\frac{1}{2}$ in. from an end.

b. Tape the free end of each support to a support line of Base 2. Two supports will be taped to each support line.

14 Is the wing you made in Exploration 1 stronger than the one in Question 13? Which wing is rigid? No; the one made in Question 13

▶ You can use the angle relationships you discovered in Exploration 1 to help you find the sum of the measures of the angles of a triangle.

15 **Try This as a Class** Use the diagram of Wing 2 below.

a. Find the sum: $m\angle 1 + m\angle 2 + m\angle 3 = \underline{\quad?\quad}$. 180°

b. Which angle, $\angle 2$ or $\angle 4$, is congruent to $\angle 1$? Why?
∠4; The bases are parallel and the angles are alternate interior angles.

c. Which angle, $\angle 2$ or $\angle 5$, is congruent to $\angle 3$? Why?
∠5; The bases are parallel and the angles are alternate interior angles.

d. Rewrite the equation in part (a) by replacing $\angle 1$ and $\angle 3$ with the angles that are congruent to them.
$m\angle 4 + m\angle 2 + m\angle 5 = 180°$

e. What is the sum of the measures of the angles of a triangle? 180°

▶ **You can use a different method to confirm your results in Question 15.**

16 a. Follow the directions below to find the sum of the measures of the angles of a triangle. *Check students' work.*

First	Next	Then
Use a ruler to draw a triangle. Then cut out the triangle.	Tear off the angles at each corner.	Arrange the angles so the vertices all meet at one point.

b. What do you notice about the arrangement of the three angles? What is the sum of their measures? Why?

The angles form a straight angle; 180°; A straight angle has a measure of 180°.

▶ **One way to make Wing 1 rigid is to add a nonvertical support.**

17 a. Follow the directions below to add a nonvertical support.
Check students' work.

First

Then

Cut out a $1\frac{1}{2}$ in. by $2\frac{1}{4}$ in. nonvertical support from an index card. Fold $\frac{1}{4}$ in. tabs on each end of the support.

Slide the nonvertical support between two vertical supports in Wing 1 and tape it in place.

b. Discussion What do Wing 2 and the new Wing 1 have in common? What makes a structure rigid?

nonvertical supports; A structure is rigid if its parts cannot be shifted in relation to one another without disconnecting them. Triangles are rigid, but quadrilaterals are not. Adding nonvertical supports in the appropriate places can turn a nonrigid structure into a rigid structure.

▶ **You can use what you know about triangles to find the sum of the measures of the angles of a rectangle.**

18. a. ; 2 triangles

18 a. Sketch the rectangle in Wing 1 that contains the nonvertical support. How many triangles is the rectangle divided into by the nonvertical support?

b. What is the sum of the measures of the angles in each of the triangles that make up the rectangle? 180°

c. Use your answers in parts (a) and (b) to find the sum of the measures of the angles of a rectangle. 360°

▶ **A rectangle is one type of quadrilateral. Now you'll find the sum of the measures of the angles of any quadrilateral.**

19 Try This as a Class Use the quadrilaterals below.

trapezoid   rhombus   concave quadrilateral

a. What do you think is the sum of the measures of the angles of each figure? *Sample Response:* 360°

b. A **diagonal** is a segment that connects two nonconsecutive vertices of a polygon. How can you use diagonals to find the sum of the measures of the angles of each figure?

20 Use the method shown in Question 16 to find the sum of the measures of the angles of a quadrilateral. 360°

21 ✔ CHECKPOINT Find the sum of the measures of the angles of each polygon highlighted in each wing design.

a.
360°

b.
180°

c.
540°

22 Discussion Which wing design in Question 21 is rigid? Which do you think would be strongest? Explain your choices.

HOMEWORK EXERCISES ▶ See Exs. 16–23 on p. 431.

CLOSURE QUESTION

Name four types of angle relationships formed when two parallel lines are cut by a transversal. Then state the sum of the measures of the angles of a triangle and the sum of the measures of the angles of a quadrilateral.

Possible answers: interior angles, exterior angles, alternate interior angles, alternate exterior angles, corresponding angles, and vertical angles; The sum of the measures of the angles of a triangle is 180°, and the sum of the measures of a quadrilateral is 360°.

19. b. Use diagonals to divide the quadrilateral into two triangles and find the sum of the measures of the angles of the triangles.

22. The wing design in (a) is rigid, but the others are not. In (b), the lower base of the wing can tilt upward

✔ QUESTION 21

...checks that you can find the sums of the measures of the angles of a triangle and a quadrilateral.

or downward. In (c), the lower base can shift position since the rectangles formed by the supports aren't rigid; Sample Responses: Wing design (a) may be strongest because it is rigid or wing design (c) may be strongest because it has more supports.

Key Concepts

Key Terms

Parallel Lines and Transversals (pp. 423–425)

A line that intersects two lines is a transversal. When a transversal intersects parallel lines, the measures of the eight angles formed are related.

transversal

Example In the figure below, line *r* intersects parallel lines *p* and *q*.

interior angles

∠1 ≅ ∠8, since alternate exterior angles are congruent.

∠3 ≅ ∠6, since alternate interior angles are congruent.

alternate interior angles

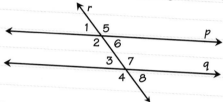

exterior angles

∠2 ≅ ∠4, since corresponding angles are congruent.

∠3 ≅ ∠8, since vertical angles are congruent.

alternate exterior angles

corresponding angles

Sums of the Measures of the Angles of a Triangle and of a Quadrilateral (pp. 426–428)

The sum of the measures of the angles of a triangle is 180°.
The sum of the measures of the angles of a quadrilateral is 360°.

vertical angles

Example

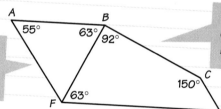

The sum of the measures of the angles of △*ABF* is 180°.

The sum of the measures of the angles of quadrilateral *BCDF* is 360°.

A diagonal is a segment whose endpoints are two nonconsecutive vertices of a polygon. In the Example, $\overline{FB}$ is a diagonal of *ABCDF*.

diagonal

Key Concepts Questions

23 Suppose that *m*∠5 is 130° in the first Example above. Find the measures of all the other angles shown. $m\angle 2 = m\angle 4 = m\angle 7 = 130°,$ $m\angle 1 = m\angle 6 = m\angle 3 = m\angle 8 = 50°$

24 Find each unknown angle measure in pentagon *ABCDF* in the second Example above. $m\angle AFB = 62°, m\angle CDF = 55°$

Closure Question
See page 428.

Practice & Application Exercises

In the photo of a staircase, two parallel lines *a* and *b* are cut by transversal *c*. Use the diagram for Exercises 1–7.

1–7. Possible answers are given.

For Exercises 1–6, name an angle or a pair of angles that fits each description.

1. interior angle ∠2, ∠3, ∠6, ∠7

2. exterior angle ∠1, ∠4, ∠5, ∠8

3. pair of alternate interior angles
∠2 and ∠7, ∠3 and ∠6

4. pair of alternate exterior angles
∠1 and ∠8, ∠4 and ∠5

5. pair of corresponding angles
∠1 and ∠3, ∠2 and ∠4, ∠5 and ∠7, ∠6 and ∠8

6. pair of vertical angles ∠1 and ∠6, ∠2 and ∠5, ∠3 and ∠8, ∠4 and ∠7

8. a. Sample Response: ∠1 and ∠6 are corresponding angles formed by 2 parallel lines and a transversal, so ∠6 and ∠4 are alternate interior angles formed by 2 parallel lines and a transversal, so $m\angle 1 = m\angle 6$. and $m\angle 6 = m\angle 4$. Then $m\angle 1 = m\angle 6 = m\angle 4$ and $m\angle 1 = m\angle 4$.

c. Yes; The sides of any parallelogram can be extended to form two pairs of parallel lines, so the reasoning used in Question 8a would apply.

9. a. Sample Response: Since they form a straight angle, $m\angle 4 + m\angle 5 = 180°$. Since ∠3 and ∠5 are corresponding angles formed by 2 parallel lines and a transversal, $m\angle 3 = m\angle 5$. Substituting $m\angle 3$ for $m\angle 5$ in the first equation, $m\angle 4 + m\angle 3 = 180°$. So, ∠3 and ∠4 are supplementary.

7. The measure of ∠1 is 55°. What is the measure of each angle you named in Exercises 1–6? $m\angle 6 = m\angle 3 = m\angle 8 = 55°$, $m\angle 2 = m\angle 5 = m\angle 4 = m\angle 7 = 125°$

8. Challenge The two pairs of parallel lines below form a parallelogram.

a. Explain why ∠1 and ∠4 are congruent.

b. How do the measures of ∠2 and ∠3 compare?
They are equal.

c. Do you think angles in other parallelograms are related in the same way? Explain.

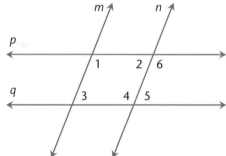

9. Use the parallelogram in Exercise 8.

a. Explain how to use ∠5 to show that ∠3 and ∠4 are supplementary.

b. What other pairs of angles of the parallelogram are supplementary? ∠1 and ∠2, ∠1 and ∠3, ∠1 and ∠5, ∠2 and ∠4, ∠2 and ∠6, ∠3 and ∠6, ∠4 and ∠5, ∠5 and ∠6

c. Use pairs of supplementary angles to find the sum of the measures of the angles of the parallelogram without using a protractor. 360°

Line *u* is parallel to line *t* in the figure below. Tell whether each statement is *True* or *False*. Explain your reasoning.

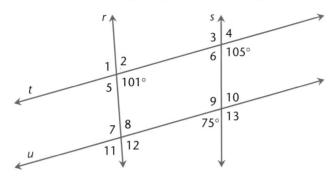

10. $m\angle 1 = 101°$

11. $m\angle 8 = 79°$

12. $m\angle 12 = 75°$

13. $m\angle 4 = 105°$

14. $m\angle 9 + m\angle 6 = 180°$

15. $m\angle 10 = m\angle 11$

Find the unknown angle measure in each triangle or quadrilateral.

16.

17.

18.

The measures of two of the angles of a triangle are given. Find the measure of the third angle of each triangle. Then tell whether the triangle is *acute, obtuse,* or *right*.

19. 10° and 75° 95°, obtuse

20. 33° and 57° 90°, right

21. 61° and 64° 55°, acute

22. 123° and 31° 26°, obtuse

R e f l e c t i n g ◀▶on the Section

23. Suppose you draw both diagonals of a quadrilateral, as shown.

    a. How many nonoverlapping triangles are formed? 4 triangles

    b. What is the sum of the measures of the angles of the triangles?
    720°

    c. What is the sum of the measures of the angles formed at the intersection of the diagonals? 360°

    d. Explain how you can use your answers to parts (b) and (c) to show that the sum of the measures of the angles of a quadrilateral is 360°.

10. True; ∠1 and the 101° angle are vertical angles.

11. True ∠7 and the 101° angle have the same measure since they are alternate interior angles, and ∠7 and ∠8 are supplementary angles, so $m\angle 8 = 180° - 101° = 79°$.

12. False; ∠12 and the 101° angle are corresponding angles, so $m\angle 12 = 101°$.

13. False; ∠4 and the 105° angle are supplementary angles, so $m\angle 4 = 75°$.

14. True; ∠6 is supplementary to a 105° angle, so $m\angle 6 = 75°$ and ∠9 is supplementary to a 75° angle, so $m\angle 9 = 105°$. Therefore, $m\angle 9 + m\angle 6 = 105° + 75° = 180°$.

15. False; ∠10 and the 75° angle are vertical angles, so $m\angle 10 = 75°$. ∠11 and ∠12 are supplementary and $m\angle 12 = 101°$ since it is a corresponding angle to a 101° angle. Therefore, $m\angle 11 = 180° - 101° = 79°$ and $m\angle 10 \neq m\angle 11$.

23. d. The sum of the measures of the angles of the quadrilateral is equal to 720° − 360° = 360° (that is the sum of the measures of the angles of the four triangles minus the sum of the measures of the angles at the intersection of the diagonals).

Classify each triangle as *acute, obtuse,* or *right*. (Module 6, p. 417)

24.
28° 62°
right

25.
27° 23°
130° obtuse

26.
86° 37°
57°
acute

Solve each equation. Check each solution. (Module 4, p. 300)

27. $3 + 2x = 6$ $\frac{3}{2}$

28. $2n - 7 = 39$ 23

29. $\frac{y}{2} - 10 = 5$ 30

Find the volume of a cube with each side length. (Module 1, p. 21)

30. 3 cm   27 cm³

31. 4 in.   64 in.³

32. 1 ft   1 ft³

33. 10 cm   1000 cm³

36. a. The number of triangles is 2 less than the number of sides.

b. Multiply 180° by 2 less than the number of sides.

Extension ▶ ▶

The Sum of the Measures of the Angles of Any Polygon

The sum of the measures of the angles of any polygon can be determined using triangles.

34. **a.** How many diagonals can be drawn from a vertex of a hexagon?
    3 diagonals
    b. How many triangles are formed by the diagonals?
    4 triangles
    c. What is the sum of the measures of the angles of the hexagon? 720°

35. Copy and complete the table to find the sum of the angles of polygons with 3, 4, 5, 6, 7, and 8 sides. See Additional Answers.

Polygon	Name of polygon	Number of sides	Number of triangles formed by the diagonals from one vertex	Sum of the measures of the angles
△	triangle	3	1	180°
▱	quadrilateral	4	2	360°

36. **a.** For each polygon, how is the number of triangles related to the number of sides? See above.

b. How can you find the sum of the measures of the angles of any polygon? See above.

c. What is the sum of the measures of the angles of a nonagon (a 9-sided polygon)? 1260°

d. The sum of the measures of the angles of a polygon is 1980°. How many sides does the polygon have? 13 sides

Wild Wings

Using Similar Figures Do you think a larger Wild Wing will fly as well as the one you made for Project Question 1 on page 408? To find out, you'll construct a Wild Wing on which every face is twice as long and twice as wide.

SET UP

You will need:
- *Project Labsheet A*
- *ruler*
- *tape*

4 **Use Project Labsheet A.** Tape four sheets of paper together to make a 17 in. by 22 in. sheet. Repeat the steps to *Create a Wild Wing,* but make the tail end 4 in. wide. Check students' work.

5. Answers will vary. Check students' work.

5 a. Try flying your new Wild Wing. Do you think it flies better than the first one you made? Explain why or why not.

b. Work with a partner to design a test to decide whether the larger Wild Wing flies better than the smaller one.

c. Conduct your test. Then write a report on your conclusions.

The figure below shows two parallel lines, *x* and *y*, cut by transversal *z*. Use this diagram for Exercises 1–12.
Name the angles or pairs of angles that fit each description.

1. four interior angles ∠3, ∠4, ∠5, ∠6

2. four exterior angles ∠1, ∠2, ∠7, ∠8

3. two pairs of alternate interior angles
∠3 and ∠6, ∠4 and ∠5

4. two pairs of alternate exterior angles
∠1 and ∠8, ∠2 and ∠7

5. two pairs of vertical angles
Possible answers: ∠1 and ∠4, ∠2 and ∠3, ∠5 and ∠8, ∠6 and ∠7

6. two pairs of corresponding angles
Possible answers: ∠1 and ∠5, ∠3 and ∠7, ∠2 and ∠6, ∠4 and ∠8

Find the measure of each angle if the measure of ∠1 is 67°.

7. ∠3 113° | **8.** ∠4 67° | **9.** ∠5 67°

10. ∠6 113° | **11.** ∠7 113° | **12.** ∠8 67°

Find the unknown angle measure in each triangle or quadrilateral.
Label each triangle as *acute*, *obtuse*, or *right*.

13.
65°
52°; acute
63°

14.
120°
111°
63°   66°

15.
45°; right
45°

$\overline{AB}$ and $\overline{DF}$ are parallel. Identify all pairs of congruent angles and explain how you know they are congruent.

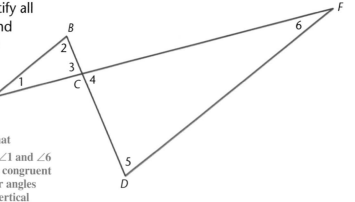

Since $\overline{AF}$ and $\overline{BD}$ are transversals that intersect parallel lines $\overleftrightarrow{AB}$ and $\overleftrightarrow{DF}$, ∠1 and ∠6 are alternate interior angles and are congruent and ∠2 and ∠5 are alternate interior angles and are congruent. ∠3 and ∠4 are vertical angles and are also congruent.

FOR ASSESSMENT AND PORTFOLIOS

LOCATING THE HUB

SET UP *You will need: • Extended Exploration Labsheet • ruler*

The Situation See the Resource Book for a detailed discussion of this Extended Exploration.

Many airlines plan their routes using a hub-and-spoke system. In this system, most flights land at or leave from a centrally located city, called a *hub.* Suppose a small airline flies to three major cities: Dallas, Texas; Omaha, Nebraska; and Cincinnati, Ohio.

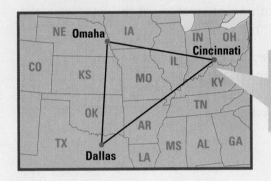

Draw a triangle like this on the *Map of the Central Region of the United States.*

The Problem

The airline wants to use a fourth city as a hub, and to keep the total air miles between the hub and each of the three major cities it serves as small as practical. Which city should the airline choose as its hub?

Something to Think About Sample Response: distances between cities; location of and routes into existing airports; inside; Yes.

◆ What information would help you choose a city to be the hub?

◆ Is the best hub *inside, outside,* or *on* the triangle that has the three major cities as its vertices?

◆ Would a city's population, weather, or geography affect the decision?

Present Your Results

Present your choice for a hub city in a written report. Include an explanation of how you reached your decision. Answers will vary. Check students' work.

Section 5

Volume of a Prism and Metric Relationships

IN THIS SECTION

EXPLORATION 1
◆ Volume of a Prism

EXPLORATION 2
◆ Relationships among Metric Units

EXPLORATION 3
◆ Weighted Networks

A WHALE OF A PROBLEM

···Setting the Stage

On January 7, 1996, Phyllis Bell, president of the Oregon Coast Aquarium, signed for a package that had flown over 2000 miles in less than 24 hours. There was nothing unusual about this. However, the package itself turned out to be quite unusual.

It was delivered atop a flatbed trailer towed by a truck. Inside the package was a 21 ft long whale named Keiko, the star of the movie *Free Willy*. He had just arrived at his new home!

▲ Keiko is lowered into his new pool by a sling attached to a giant crane.

Think About It

1 The shipping company that transported Keiko delivers about 12 million items each day. About 1.3 million of these items are shipped by airplane. What percent of the daily deliveries is this? about 11%

2 a. Keiko is an orca, a type of whale that is also called a killer whale. Orcas feed on large fish, squid, and smaller marine mammals. About how much do you think an orca weighs?
Answers will vary. Sample Response: about 3000 kg

b. What factors, other than Keiko's weight, do you think were important to think about when planning how to ship him?
Answers will vary. Sample Response: his size, his natural environment, his physical needs

3 What was the advantage of shipping the whale by plane instead of by truck or by ship? The trip would take less time.

▶ In this section you'll learn about Keiko's journey from Mexico City to his new home in Oregon.

WARM-UP EXERCISES

Find the volume of each figure.

1. a cube with side lengths of 6.2 cm
238.328 cm^3

2. a rectangular block with a length of 3 m, a width of 2.5 m, and a height of 8 m
60 m^3

Convert each measure.

3. 1 m = _?_ cm
100

4. 1000 g = _?_ kg
1

5. 1000 mL = _?_ L
1

VOLUME of a PRISM

SET UP *Work with a partner. You will need 48 centimeter cubes.*

Keiko had grown too large for his 27.4 m × 13.1 m × 6.1 m pool at *Reino Aventura* (Adventure Kingdom) in Mexico City. The solution was to build a new 45.7 m × 22.9 m × 7.6 m pool for him at the Oregon Coast Aquarium.

▸ **To compare the sizes of two pools, you need to know their volumes.**

4 What is the volume of a centimeter cube? 1 cm³

For Questions 5–7, use the rectangular prism shown below.

5 **a.** Use centimeter cubes to build the rectangular prism shown. The prism has one layer of cubes.
  Check students' work.
  b. What are the area of a base and the height of this prism? 12 cm², 1 cm

FOR ◂ HELP
with *the volume of a cube*, see
MODULE 1, p. 21

  c. What is the volume of the prism in cubic centimeters? How is the volume related to the area of a base?
  12 cm³; The volume is the area of the base times 1 cm.

6 **a.** Add a second layer to your prism. What are the area of a base and the height of the new prism? 12 cm², 2 cm

  b. Find the volume of the new prism in cubic centimeters. How is the volume related to the area of a base and the height?
  24 cm³; The volume is the area of the base times 2 cm.
  c. Before adding more layers to your prism, predict what its volume would be if its height were 4 cm. Check your answer by adding extra layers and counting the centimeter cubes.
  48 cm³; Check students' work.

7 **Discussion** What would be the volume of a prism with the same base as the rectangular prism shown but with 20 layers? How did you find your answer? 240 cm³; Sample Response: I multiplied the area of the base by the height, 20 cm.

8 a. Use 36 cubes to build a rectangular prism. Record the dimensions (length, width, and height), the area of a base, the volume, and the surface area of the prism in a table. See Additional Answers.

b. Make four more rectangular prisms with different dimensions. Use 36 cubes for each prism. Record the dimensions, the area of a base, the volume, and the surface area of each prism in your table. See Additional Answers.

c. What do you notice about the volumes of the prisms? the surface areas?
The volumes are the same; The surface areas are different.

d. Does your method from Question 7 work for finding the volumes of these rectangular prisms? Explain. Sample Response: Yes; The volume is the area of the base multiplied by the height.

9 Try This as a Class Think about the prisms in Question 8.

a. What is the least surface area that a prism made with 36 cubes can have? What is the greatest surface area?
66 cm²; 146 cm²

b. Do you think there is a least surface area for rectangular prisms with a volume of 36 cm³? a greatest surface area? Explain.
See below.

10 ✔ CHECKPOINT The area of the bottom of a shoe box is 50 in.² and it is 4 in. deep. What is the volume of the shoe box? 200 in.³

▶ **Not all prisms are rectangular. In Question 11 you'll compare the volumes of two different kinds of prisms.**

11 a. Use centimeter cubes to build the rectangular prism shown. What is the volume of the prism?

6 cm³

b. Suppose the prism were cut in half as shown. What kind of prisms are formed? What are the height and the area of a base of one of the prisms? How did you find the area of a base?
See above.

c. Find the volume of one of the prisms formed in part (b). Describe your method. See above.

d. Record the height, the area of a base, and the volume of one of the prisms in a table. See Additional Answers.

e. Add 4 more layers to the rectangular prism you built in part (a). Each time you add a layer, record in your table the height, the area of a base, and the volume of one of the prisms formed by cutting the prism in half as in part (b).
See Additional Answers.

---

11. b. triangular prisms; 1 cm, 3 cm²; Sample Response: I found one-half the area of the base of the rectangular prism.

c. 3 cm³; Sample Response: I found one-half the volume of the rectangular prism.

✔ QUESTION 10

...checks that you can find the volume of a rectangular prism.

---

9. b. Sample Response: I think a cube with a volume of 36 cm³ would have the least surface area but I don't think there is a greatest surface area. Think of a prism with a square base. If the length of a side of the base is 1 cm, the surface area is 146 cm². If the length of a side is $\frac{1}{2}$ cm, the surface area is 288.5 cm². If it is $\frac{1}{10}$ cm, the surface area is 1440.02 cm². The smaller you choose the length of the side, the larger the surface area gets.

---

12 **Try This as a Class** Look at the table you made in Question 11.

    a. What patterns do you see in the data? Sample Response: The volume is equal to the product of the area of the base and the height.

    b. Find the volume of a triangular prism with 20 layers and the same base as the prisms in Question 11. Explain your method. 60 cm³; Sample Response: I multiplied the area of the base, 3 cm², by the height, 20 cm.

    c. How is finding the volume of a triangular prism related to finding the volume of a rectangular prism? For either volume, multiply the area of the base by the height.

    d. Explain how you can find the volume of any prism without using cubes. Sample Response: Multiply the area of the base by the height.

    e. Use your method to find the volume of the prism shown. Build the prism with centimeter cubes to check your result. 16 cm³

13 Suppose Keiko's old and new pools were rectangular prisms. Keiko's new pool is 45.7 m × 22.9 m × 7.6 m. His old pool is 27.4 m × 13.1 m × 6.1 m. About how many times larger would the volume of his new pool be compared with his old one? about 3.6 times

> **HOMEWORK EXERCISES** ▶ See Exs. 1–6 on pp. 446–447.

14. Sample Response: the mass of the water in the shipping container; The plane could carry up to 22,600 kg. If there was a concern about the combined mass, and Keiko's mass was only 3200 kg, the container and water together must have had much greater mass than Keiko. I think the container and the water in it *each* probably had a mass greater than Keiko's mass.

Exploration 2

RELATIONSHIPS AMONG METRIC UNITS

Building a new pool for Keiko solved one problem, but it created another—how to transport Keiko 2200 mi quickly and safely. A shipping company driver whose route included the Oregon Coast Aquarium came up with the solution.

The shipping company would use a cargo plane that could carry up to 22,600 kg of cargo, so carrying a 3200 kg whale would be no problem. But would the plane be able to carry the whale, the shipping container, and the water in the container?

14 Which do you think was greater, Keiko's mass or the mass of the water in his 8.23 m × 1.98 m × 2.13 m shipping container? Why? See above.

▶ The size of Keiko's shipping container can be measured using units of volume or *capacity*. A container's **capacity** is the amount of fluid it can hold. In the metric system, mass, capacity, and volume are related.

A volume of one cubic centimeter (cm³) has …   … a capacity of one **milliliter (mL)** and …   … a **mass** of one **gram (g)** when filled with water.

15 Try This as a Class A container is shaped like a rectangular prism and measures 10 cm × 8 cm × 6 cm.

a. What is the volume of the container in cubic centimeters? 480 cm³

b. What is its capacity in milliliters? 480 mL

c. Suppose the container is filled with water. What is the mass of the water? 480 gm

...checks that you can use the relationships among the volume, mass, and capacity of water in metric units.

16 ✔ **CHECKPOINT** A bottle holds 473 mL of water.

a. What is the volume of the water in cubic centimeters? 473 cm³

b. What is its mass in grams? 473 g

▶ The relationship among volume, capacity, and mass was shown using cubic centimeters, milliliters, and grams. For larger amounts of fluid, such as the water in Keiko's shipping container, **liters (L)** are used to measure capacity and **kilograms (kg)** are used to measure mass.

17 Discussion A liter of liquid will fill a cube measuring 10 cm on each edge.

a. What is the volume in cubic centimeters of a cube measuring 10 cm on each edge? 1000 cm³

b. Use your answer from part (a) to find the number of milliliters in a liter. 1000 mL

c. What is the mass of a liter of water in grams? 1000 g

d. A kilogram is 1000 grams. What is the mass of a liter of water in kilograms? 1 kg

18 a. The prefix *milli* means one thousandth. Why is *milli* used in the word *milliliter?* A milliliter is one thousandth of a liter.

b. The prefix *kilo* means one thousand. Why is *kilo* used in the word *kilogram?* A kilogram is 1000 grams.

19 Discussion Explain how to make the following conversions.

a. 3560 mL = __?__ L
Divide by 1000.

b. 6.5 L = __?__ mL
Multiply by 1000.

c. 250 g = __?__ kg
Divide by 1000.

d. 12 kg = __?__ g
Multiply by 1000.

20 ✔ **CHECKPOINT** Since whales breathe air just as humans do, it was not necessary to completely cover Keiko with water during his trip. Keiko's 8.23 m long by 1.98 m wide shipping container was filled to a depth of only about 90 cm.

a. Find the approximate volume of the water in Keiko's shipping container in cubic centimeters. 14,665,860 cm³

b. About how many milliliters of water were in the container? How many liters is this? 14,665,860 mL; 14,665.86 L

c. What was the mass of the water in the container in grams? How many kilograms is this? 14,665,860 g; 14,665.86 kg

90 cm
8.23 m
1.98 m

✔ **QUESTION 20**

... checks that you can compute volume, mass, and capacity.

21 a. Which had a greater mass, Keiko or the water in his shipping container? the water

b. The shipping container had a mass of about 4500 kg. Find the approximate total mass of Keiko, the container, and the water. about 22,366 kg

22 According to one report, the water in Keiko's shipping container appeared to be about 150 cm deep.

a. What would the mass of the water in the shipping container have been if it were actually 150 cm deep? about 24,443 kg

b. Would the cargo plane have been able to carry Keiko, the water from part (a), and the shipping container? Explain.

c. How would you explain the statement that the water was 150 cm deep during shipping? The height of the water rose when Keiko was placed in the container.

22. b. No; The combined weights of Keiko, the container, and the water would be about 32,143 kg and that would exceed the limit of 22,600 kg.

HOMEWORK EXERCISES ▶ See Exs. 7–19 on p. 447.

GOAL

LEARN HOW TO...
◆ use networks

AS YOU...
◆ analyze delivery routes

KEY TERMS
◆ network
◆ vertex of a network
◆ arc of a network
◆ weighted network

Exploration 3

WEIGHTED Networks

SET UP *You will need Labsheet 5A.*

Transporting a whale from Mexico City to Oregon in less than a day is amazing. But few people consider overnight delivery of smaller packages amazing. Fleets of airplanes and efficient routing help make overnight delivery possible.

In 1988 the world's largest express package delivery company acquired nearly 40 planes by buying another company. But more importantly, the company also took over the overseas delivery routes of the company it bought. These routes are represented in the diagram below the map.

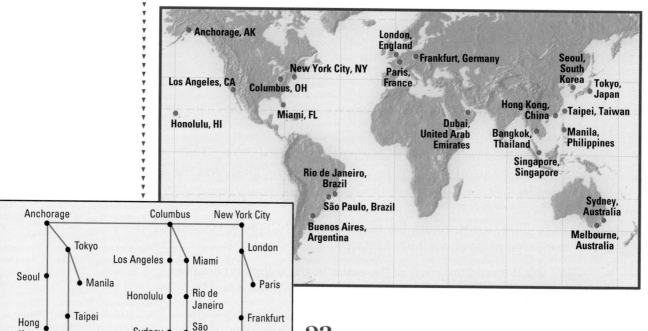

23 Using the routes shown at the left, which cities might a package travel through when shipped from Columbus, Ohio, to Manila? New York City, London, Frankfurt, Dubai, Singapore, Taipei, Tokyo, Anchorage

▶ The figure above is a *network*. A **network** consists of points or **vertices**, and **arcs** that connect the vertices. Arcs can be curves or segments.

24 **Discussion** Use the network on page 442.

    a. How does the network show that there was a direct delivery route from Singapore to Dubai but not from Singapore to Melbourne? *There is a single arc connecting Singapore and Dubai but no arc connecting Singapore and Melbourne.*

    b. Melbourne is 3759 mi from Singapore. Dubai is 3615 mi from Singapore. Does the network show that Singapore is closer to Dubai than to Melbourne? Explain.

    c. Suppose the arc connecting Singapore to Dubai had been drawn as a segment. Why would this have been confusing? *Yes; The segment would have to intersect other arcs, implying connections that may not exist.*

24. b. No; The vertices for Singapore and Melbourne are closer than those for Singapore and Dubai. So, the placement of cities on the network must not relate to distance.

▶ **The network below shows the international routes before the purchase of the smaller company.**

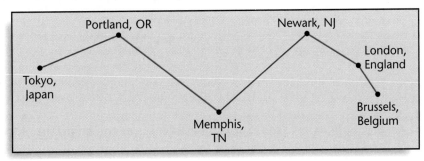

25 ✔ **CHECKPOINT** Use Labsheet 5A. The vertices of a network for the *Combined International Routes* are shown on the labsheet.

    a. Connect the vertices with arcs to show the combined routes of the two companies. Use the network above and the one on page 442 to help you. *See Additional Answers.*

    b. There are no arcs that directly connect Columbus, Ohio, and Sydney, Australia. What does this tell you?

    c. How many arcs connect London directly to other vertices? *5 arcs*

    d. How many vertices are directly connected to Tokyo by arcs? *4 vertices*

✔ **QUESTION 25**

... checks that you can identify arcs and vertices and interpret a network.

25. b. There is no direct delivery route between Columbus and Sydney.

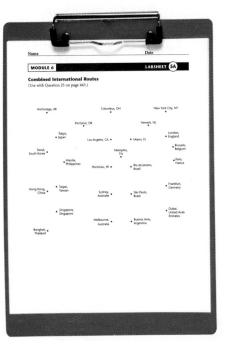

A driver for a shipping company may deliver as many as 500 packages in a day, so drivers' routes must be efficiently planned. To route their trucks, a shipping company can use **weighted networks** like the one below, where the arcs are labeled with travel times in minutes between delivery points.

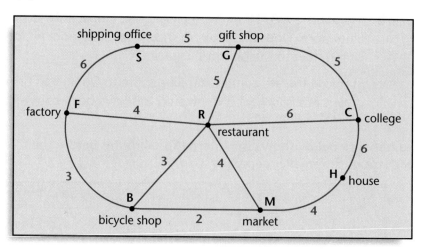

26. Sample Response: The length of the arc between the bicycle shop and the market is about the same as that between the market and the house. However, the time needed to travel from the market to the house is twice that needed to travel from the bicycle shop to the market.

26 How can you tell that the network above is not drawn to scale?

27 **Try This as a Class** Suppose a driver is at the shipping office and must deliver a package to the house. One route the driver could use is to go from S to G to C to H. This route can be written as S–G–C–H.

  a. What is the travel time for this route? 16 min

  b. What is another route the driver can use? What is the travel time for this route? Some possible answers: S–F–B–M–H, 15 min; S–F–R–M–H, 18 min; S–F–R–C–H, 22 min; S–G–R–C–H, 22 min; S–G–R–M–H, 18 min

✔ QUESTION 28

... checks that you can interpret a weighted network.

28. b. Possible answers:
S–F–B–R–M–H–C–G–S, 36 min;
S–F–R–B–M–H–C–G–S, 35 min;
S–G–R–C–H–M–B–F–S, 37 min;
S–G–C–H–M–B–R–F–S, 35 min;
S–F–B–M–H–C–R–G–S, 37 min

28 **✔ CHECKPOINT** Suppose a driver must start at the shipping office, deliver packages to each delivery point, and return to the shipping office.

  a. One route the driver can use is S–G–C–H–M–R–B–F–S. Find the travel time for this route. 36 min

  b. What is another route the driver can use? What is the travel time for this route?

29 For the situation in Question 28, find the fastest route that starts at the shipping office, goes through each delivery point, and returns to the shipping office. What is its total travel time? S–F–R–B–M–H–C–G–S or S–G–C–H–M–B–R–F–S; 35 min

HOMEWORK EXERCISES ▶ See Exs. 20–25 on p. 448.

Key Concepts

Volume of a Prism (pp. 437–439)

The volume V of a prism is the product of the area of the base B and the height h.

Example Find the volume of the rectangular prism below.

$$\text{Area of base} = 2 \cdot 3$$
$$= 6$$

$$\text{Volume} = \text{Area of base} \times \text{height}$$
$$V = Bh$$
$$= 6 \cdot 5$$
$$= 30$$

5 cm

3 cm   2 cm

The volume is 30 cm³.

Mass, Capacity, and Volume (pp. 439–441)

In the metric system, mass, capacity, and volume are related:

A volume of one cubic centimeter (1 cm³) …

… has a capacity of one milliliter (1 mL) and …

… a mass of one gram (1 g) when filled with water.

1 L of liquid fills a cube with 10 cm edges. There are 1000 mL in a liter.

The mass of a liter of water is one kilogram. A kilogram is 1000 grams.

mass
  gram (g)
  kilogram (kg)

capacity
  milliliter (mL)
  liter (L)

CLOSURE QUESTION

Name two other metric measures that are equivalent to one cubic centimeter (1 cm³) of water. Then explain what is meant by a network.

Answer: a capacity of one milliliter (1 mL) and a mass of one gram (1 g); Sample Response: A network is a set of points, called vertices, that are connected by curves or segments, called arcs.

Key Concepts Questions

30 **a.** What is the difference between volume and surface area?

b. What kind of units are used to measure each? cubic units, square units

31 Give a possible length, width, and height for a container filled with 2.4 kg of water.
Sample Response: 100 cm, 3 cm, 8 cm

Continued on the next page

30. a. Sample Response: Volume is the amount of space inside a three-dimensional object. Surface area is the number of square units needed to cover the outside of a space figure.

Key Terms

network

vertex

arc

weighted
network

Networks (pp. 442–444)

A network is a figure made up of points called vertices that are connected by segments or curves called arcs. A network in which the arcs are labeled with numbers representing such things as distances or times is a weighted network.

Example One path from vertex E to vertex B is E–C–B. The length of this path is 5 + 3 = 8.

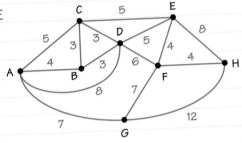

32. a. Possible answers:
A–B, 4; A–C, 5; A–G, 7;
B–C, 3; B–D, 3; C–D, 3;
C–E, 5; D–E, 5; D–F, 6;
E–F, 4; E–H, 8; F–G,7;
F–H, 4; G–H, 12
b. Possible answers: A
and D, E, F, or H; B and
E, F, H, or G; C and F, H,
or G; D and G, or H; E
and G

32 Key Concepts Question Use the network in the Example above.

  a. Name two vertices in the network that are connected directly by an arc. What is the weight of the arc between them?

  b. Name two vertices that are not connected directly by an arc.

  c. The shortest path from A to H in the network is A–B–D–F–H. Find the length of this path. **17**

Section 5

YOU WILL NEED

For Ex. 36
♦ Labsheet 5B

Practice & Application Exercises

Find the volume of each prism.

1. 4.5 cm 3 cm 9 cm
121.5 cm³

2. 10 cm² 2 cm
20 cm³

3. 4 cm 6 cm 5 cm 12 cm 7.5 cm
180 cm³

4. a. Suppose wedges like the one at the left are being manufactured for door stops. What is the volume of one wedge? **300 cm³**

  b. How many wedges can be cut out of a block of wood that is a rectangular prism 10 cm × 30 cm × 12 cm? **12 wedges**

5. If the area of the base of a rectangular prism is 15 cm² and its volume is 75 cm³, what is the height of the prism? *5 cm*

6. A cement block that has the shape and dimensions shown will be used as a parking curb. Find the volume of the block. *5600 in.³*

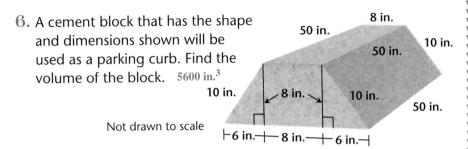

50 in.
8 in.
10 in.
50 in.
10 in.
10 in.
10 in.
50 in.
8 in.
Not drawn to scale
⊢6 in.—⊢ 8 in.—⊢6 in.⊣

Marine Biology **Replace each ? with the number that makes the statement about orcas true.**

7. In one day, an orca can eat 91 kg or __?__ g of fish. *91,000*

8. In one day, an orca can swim 121,000 m or __?__ km. *121*

9. The average length of an adult male orca is 0.0075 km or __?__ m. *7.5*

10. In one year, Keiko eats an average of about 27,000,000 g or __?__ kg of food. *27,000*

Replace each ? with the number that makes the statement true.

11. 2700 L = __?__ kL *2.7*   12. 1.5 kL = __?__ L *1500*

13. 172 mL = __?__ L *0.172*   14. 3.75 L = __?__ mL *3750*

15. 215 cm³ = __?__ mL *215*   16. 0.7 L = __?__ cm³ *700*

Keiko's new tank has underwater viewing windows. ▼

17. Keiko's new home at the Oregon Coast Aquarium is a tank that measures about 45.7 m × 22.9 m × 7.6 m.

   a. What is the volume of the tank in cubic centimeters? *7,953,628,000 cm³*

   b. What is the capacity of the tank in liters? *7,953,628 L*

   c. If the tank were completely filled with water, what would be the mass of the water in kilograms? *7,953,628 kg*

18. The capacity of a soft drink can is 355 mL. The empty can has a mass of 15 g. If the can is filled with water, what is the combined mass of the water and the can in grams? *370 g*

19. **Weather** The record for rainfall during a single day in the northern hemisphere occurred in Taiwan in 1963. In one 24-hour period, 125 cm of rain fell.

   a. Find the number of liters of rain that fell on 1 m² of land. *1250 L*

   b. Find the mass in kilograms of the rain that fell on 1 m² of land. *1250 kg*

Aviation History Use the network below for Exercises 20–22. The network shows parts of existing or proposed transatlantic air routes in 1937. The lengths in miles of several of the routes are given.

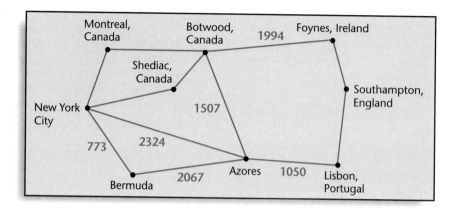

The first nonstop transatlantic airmail service began in 1938. The flight from New York to Lisbon, Portugal, to Marseilles, France, took 29 h.

20. Find the length of the path New York City–Azores–Lisbon. 3374 mi

21. Find the length of the path New York City–Bermuda–Azores–Lisbon. 3890 mi

22. Challenge There are other paths from New York to Lisbon. List as many of them as you can.

22. Possible answers:
New York–Montreal–Botwood–Foynes–Southampton–Lisbon, New York–Montreal–Botwood–Azores–Lisbon, New York–Shediac–Botwood–Foynes–Southampton–Lisbon, New York–Shediac–Botwood–Azores–Lisbon, New York–Azores–Botwood–Foynes–Southampton–Lisbon, New York–Bermuda–Azores–Botwood–Foynes–Southampton–Lisbon

Use the network below for Exercises 23 and 24. This network shows road mileage between selected United States cities.

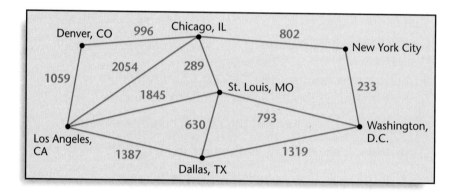

23. Find the shortest path from Los Angeles to New York.
Los Angeles–Chicago–New York

24. Los Angeles–Denver–Chicago–New York–Washington–St. Louis–Dallas–Los Angeles or Los Angeles–Dallas–St. Louis–Washington–New York–Chicago–Denver–Los Angeles

24. Find the shortest path that starts in Los Angeles, visits all the other cities at least once, and returns to Los Angeles.

Reflecting **on the Section**

25. Make a network where the vertices are important locations in your classroom or school. Connect the vertices with arcs representing possible paths between the locations. Then describe a path that you regularly follow during the school day. Answers will vary.
Check students' work.

S p i r a l ◀▶ Review

Find each unknown angle measure. (Module 6, p. 429)

26.

113°

27.

19°

28.
135° 30°
105°

Use the box-and-whisker plots shown. (Module 5, p. 337)

Masses of Largest Types of Whales (1000 kg)

0   20   40   60   80   100   120

●── 10 largest types of toothed whales

10 largest types of baleen whales

29. How is the largest type of toothed whale shown on the graph?
by the endpoint of the right-hand whisker in the upper box plot

30. Estimate the range of each of the data sets.
toothed whales: about 40,000 kg; baleen whales: about 125,000 kg

Use 3.14 to find the area of a circle with each radius. (Module 6, p. 405)

31. 2.5 cm
19.625 cm²

32. 4 in.
50.24 in.²

33. 10 m
314 m²

34. 1.38 cm
about 5.98 cm²

Extension ▶ ▶

Traversable Networks

A network is *traversable* **if it can be drawn without lifting your pencil off the paper or drawing any arc more than once.**

35. Sketch each network at the right and convince yourself that the upper one is traversable and the lower one is not.
Check students' work.

This network is traversable.

36. Use Labsheet 5B. Follow the instructions for *Testing for Traversability* to discover when a network is traversable.
See Additional Answers.

This network is not traversable.

Each network in Exercises 37–39 is not traversable. Copy each network and add arcs to make it traversable. Sample responses are given.

37.

38.

39.

Extra Skill Practice

Find the volume of each prism.

1. 2.6 in.² 5.2 in.³ 2 in. 1 in.

2. 27 in.³ 3 in. 3 in. 3 in.

3. 7.5 m 3 m 118.125 m³ 10.5 m 8.08 m

4. 4 ft 4 ft 10 ft 160 ft³

5. 5 m 30 m³ 8 m 1.5 m

6. 4.5 cm 7.5 cm 1.5 cm 50.625 cm³

Replace each ? with the number that makes the statement true.

7. 12 kg = ? g 12,000

8. 3.5 kL = ? mL
   3,500,000

9. 47 mL = ? cm³ 47

10. 14 L = ? mL 14,000

11. 77 g = ? kg 0.077

12. 94 L = ? kL 0.094

This network shows approximate road distances in kilometers between some cities in India.

13. Find the length of the route from Jodhpur to Calcutta that goes through Jaipur, Kanpur, and Patna. 1995 km

14. Find the length of the route Ahmadabad–Jodhpur–Jaipur–New Delhi. 1062 km

New Delhi   415   Kanpur
271   524
Jaipur
336
1203   550
Jodhpur   Patna
1570   585
455   961   Calcutta
1074
Ahmadabad   976   Nagpur

Standardized Testing ◀▶ **Open-ended**

Draw a prism and label the dimensions in metric units. If you filled your prism with water, what would be the mass of the water? Answers will vary. Check students' work.

Wild Wings

7. b. Rectangular Wild Wings: about 11.6 in.^{3}, about 92.6 in.^{3}; Triangular Wild Wings: about 8.9 in.^{3}, about 71.3 in.^{3}; The volume is 8 times as great.

You have constructed two gliders and developed a test to decide which flies better. Now you'll compare some of the physical traits of the gliders and make recommendations to build a better glider.

 6 Make a table that displays the information on the notebook for each Wild Wing. **See Additional Answers.**

1. the exterior surface area
2. the weight
3. the sail loading

 7 Suppose both Wild Wings had a top and a bottom base.

a. Place the small Wild Wing inside the large one. How many small Wild Wings can fit in the large one? **8**

b. What is the volume of each Wild Wing? How many times larger is the large Wild Wing than the small one? **See above.**

 8 **Try This as a Class** In what ways is the larger Wild Wing like the small one? In what ways is it different?

Sample Response: Both have the same shape and sail loading; The volumes, weights, and surface areas are different.

9 Form a discussion group with three other students. Meet with them to discuss your findings and answer the following questions. **Check students' work.**

a. Which Wild Wing flew better? How did your test prove this?

b. If you wanted to create a better Wild Wing, how would you change the surface area or weight?

c. What other design changes would you make?

You will need: • *metric ruler* (Ex. 13)

Write and graph inequalities to represent each situation.
(Sec. 1, Explor. 1)

1. In a recent year, about 50% of airplane captains earned from $7514 to $11,267 each month. If *s* = salary in dollars, then $7514 \leq s \leq 11,627.$

7514   11,627

2. In a recent year, about 44% of flight attendants worked at least 80 hours but less than 85 hours each month. If *t* = the number of hours worked each month, then $80 \leq t < 85.$

70   75   80   85

The dimensions of the parallelograms and triangles in the kite are in feet.

3. Find the area of the kite. (Sec. 1, Explor. 2)

4. Find the probability that a raindrop that falls on the kite hits one of the gold parallelogram regions. (Sec. 1, Explor. 3) $\frac{12}{22},$ or $\frac{6}{11}$

22 ft²
4   4
1.5   5   1.5
2   2

Find each square root. If the square root is not an integer, estimate it to the nearest tenth.
(Sec. 2, Explor. 1)

5. $\sqrt{121}$ 11

6. $\sqrt{20}$ 4.5

7. $\sqrt{175}$ 13.2

Use the triangular prism shown for Exercises 8 and 9.
(Sec. 2, Explor. 2)

8. Sketch a net for the prism. Label the dimensions of each face. See Additional Answers.

9. Find the surface area of the triangular prism. 79 cm²

2 cm
2.5 cm
4 cm
5 cm
6 cm

Find the exact area of each circle. Then use 3.14 for π to find the approximate area. (Sec. 2, Explor. 3)

10.

5 cm

25π cm²; 78.5 cm²

11.
20 mm

100π mm²; 314 mm²

12.
3.5 ft

3.0625π ft²; about 9.6 ft²

13. The figure at the right is a scale drawing of a prototype space shuttle. The actual height of the proposed shuttle is 67 ft. (Sec. 3, Explor. 1)

67 ft

a. Measure the height of the drawing in millimeters. What is the scale of the drawing? 1 mm : 2 ft

b. Estimate the wingspan of the proposed shuttle.
about 64 ft

14. Quadrilateral *ABCD* is similar to quadrilateral *FEHG*. Find the measures of all the unlabeled segments and angles.

(Sec. 3, Explor. 2) *CD* = 3.5 cm, *EF* = 2.4 cm, *FG* = 5.2 cm; *m∠ABC* = 120°, *m∠FEH* = 120°, *m∠EHG* = 105°, *m∠GFE* = 67°

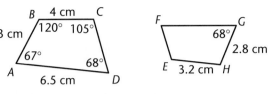

15. Lines *m* and *n* are parallel. Find the measures of angles 1, 2, 3, 4, 5, 6, and 7. (Sec. 4, Explor. 1) *m∠1* = *m∠3* = *m∠7* = 127°, *m∠2* = *m∠5* = *m∠6* = *m∠4* = 53°

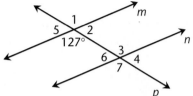

The measures of two of the angles of a triangle are given. Find the measure of the third angle of each triangle and tell whether the triangle is *acute, obtuse,* or *right*. (Sec. 4, Explor. 2)

16. 18° and 72° 90°, right   **17.** 22° and 63° 95°, obtuse   **18.** 37° and 58° 85°, acute

Use the prism for Exercises 19 and 20. (Sec. 5, Explor. 1)

19. What is the volume of the prism in cubic centimeters? 3000 cm³

20. What is the capacity of the prism in milliliters? in liters? 3000 mL; 3 L

8 cm
25 cm
15 cm

Replace each ? with the number that makes the statement true.
(Sec. 5, Explor. 2)

21. 2345 mL = __?__ L 2.345 **22.** 0.75 L = __?__ mL 750 **23.** 4 g = __?__ kg 0.004

For Exercises 24–26, use the network below, which shows driving distances in miles between five cities. (Sec. 5, Explor. 3)

24. Which cities shown are connected directly to Portland? Seattle, Walla Walla, Boise

25. How long is the Portland–Seattle–Spokane route? 448 mi

26. Find a route from Portland to Spokane that is shorter than the route in Exercise 25.
Portland–Walla Walla–Spokane

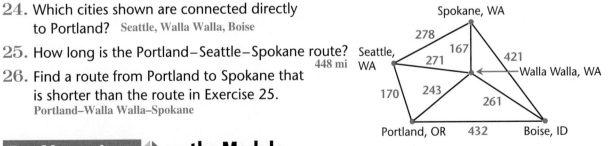

Reflecting ▶on the Module

27. Writing Write a description of how you would find the surface area and volume of a piece of furniture in your classroom. Include a sketch of the piece of furniture. Answers will vary. Check students' work.

HEALTH
and FITNESS

MODULE 7 · SECTION OVERVIEW

1 Cylinders and Graphs

As you investigate Calorie use:

- ◆ Find the volumes of cylinders
- ◆ Find slopes and graph formulas
- ◆ Recognize misleading graphs

2 Percent Equations

As you study heart rate data:

- ◆ Use percents greater than 100%
- ◆ Find percent of change

3 Customary Capacity and Inequalities

As you interpret nutrition labels on food products:

- ◆ Convert customary units of capacity
- ◆ Write and solve inequalities
- ◆ Make box-and-whisker plots

4 Circle Graphs, and Choosing a Graph

As you examine sleeping habits and the importance of rest:

- ◆ Make circle graphs
- ◆ Choose an appropriate graph to display data

5 Quadrilaterals

As you analyze the USDA Food Guide Pyramid:

- ◆ Classify quadrilaterals
- ◆ Find the areas of trapezoids

The Module Project

The Picture of Health

How can you inform people about a health issue that affects their lives? You'll research the statistics on a health or fitness issue and make colorful, eye-catching visual displays that get across your message.

More on the Module Project
See pp. 469, 510, and 523.

INTERNET
To learn more about the theme:
http://www.mlmath.com

IN THIS SECTION

EXPLORATION 1
◆ Volume of a Cylinder

EXPLORATION 2
◆ Formulas and Graphs

EXPLORATION 3
◆ Misleading Graphs

WARM-UP EXERCISES

Find the area of each figure.

1.

11.5 m
6.2 m

71.3 m²

2.
(7.8 cm)

about 47.8 cm²

Evaluate each expression when $a = 3$ and $b = 6$.

3. $a + 2b$ 15

4. $a^2 - b$ 3

5. $5a + ab + 4b$ 57

BURNING CALORIES

◄··Setting the Stage

In this module, you'll learn about nutrition and other health- and fitness-related topics. The mathematics you learn will help you make the best choices for your own well-being.

Exercise is a great way to burn excess energy and to relieve stress. You may be surprised to learn that a 100 lb person burns 11.4 Calories while sitting and talking for 10 min. That same person would burn 45.5 Calories in 10 min of playing basketball.

Think About It

1 About how many times as many Calories does a person burn playing basketball instead of sitting and talking about it?
Sample Response: about 4 times

2 Which of the exercises shown do you think burns the most Calories?
Sample Response: swimming

PLAYING BASKETBALL

WALKING UP STAIRS

WALKING DOWN STAIRS

SWIMMING

▶ In this section you'll explore what a Calorie is and determine which of the exercises above burn the most Calories.

GOAL

LEARN HOW TO...
◆ find the volume
  of a cylinder

AS YOU...
◆ explore the
  meaning of
  Calorie

KEY TERM
◆ cylinder

VOLUME of a CYLINDER

You have probably heard the word *Calorie* many times, but what is
a Calorie? Technicians determine the number of Calories in a food by
burning the food and measuring how much heat it generates. The
experiment below may help you understand.

First water is placed
in a pot and its tem-
perature is recorded.

Then the water tem-
perature is recorded
again after the peanut
has been burned.

Next a peanut is lit
and allowed to burn
below the pot.

3 Discussion One Calorie (1 Cal) is the amount of heat required to
raise the temperature of 1 L of water one degree Celsius (1°C).

a. How many Calories does it take to raise the temperature of
1 L of water 3°C? of 3 L of water 1°C? 3 Cal; 3 Cal

b. Suppose your class burned a peanut as shown above, and the
temperature of the water was recorded before and after the
peanut was burned. What do you need to know to determine
the number of Calories in the peanut? the volume of the water

▶ The container used in the experiment is a circular *cylinder*. A circular
cylinder is a space figure with two congruent parallel circular bases.
In this book, all the cylinders are circular cylinders.

To find the volume of a cylinder, you can use the same formula you
use to find the volume of a prism.

$$V = B \cdot h$$

volume   area of   height
          a base

rectangular
prism

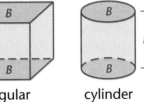

cylinder

▶ **To find the volume of a cylinder, you first need to find the area of its base.**

4

a. Write an equation you can use to find the **area of a base** of a cylinder. $A = \pi r^2$

b. Rewrite the equation for the volume of a cylinder, $V = Bh$, using your answer in part (a). $V = \pi r^2 h$

c. What measurements do you need to know before you can find the volume of a cylinder?
the radius of the base and the height of the cylinder

FOR◀HELP

with *metric units of volume and capacity*, see
MODULE 6, p. 445

5 Suppose a class used the cylinder shown to perform the Calorie experiment.

a. Find the volume of the water in the container to the nearest cubic centimeter (cm^3). Use 3.14 for π.
about 1000 cm^3

b. One cubic centimeter holds one milliliter of water. How many milliliters of water are in the container? How many liters?
about 1000 mL; 1 L

c. Suppose that before the experiment was performed, the temperature of the water was 25°C. After the peanut was burned, the temperature of the water was 29.5°C. According to the definition of Calorie, how many Calories did the peanut contain? 4.5 Cal

14 cm

6.5 cm

✔ **QUESTION 6**

…checks that you can find the volume of a cylinder.

6 ✔ **CHECKPOINT** Suppose a class planned to conduct the Calorie experiment. Choose the letter of each cylinder below that they could use to hold 1 L of water. Explain your choice. B; Cylinders A and C hold less than 1000 cm^3.

A. 7.6 cm
19.0 cm

B. 15.8 cm
8.9 cm

C. 10.2 cm
11.5 cm

7. Sample Response: The milkshake, celery stalk, and bowl of soup are dehydrated and burned inside a bomb calorimeter. The bomb is surrounded by a bucket of water. The Calorie content of the food is found by measuring the rise in temperature of the water as the food is burned. One Calorie is the amount of heat required to raise the temperature of 1 L of water one degree Celsius (1°C).

7 **Discussion** How do you think technicians determine the Calorie content of a milk shake? a celery stalk? a bowl of soup?

HOMEWORK EXERCISES ▶ See Exs. 1–8 on pp. 465–466.

Formulas AND Graphs

SET UP *You will need graph paper.*

▶ In Exploration 1 you investigated the Calorie content of food. In this exploration you'll examine the number of Calories burned during exercise.

For any exercise, the actual number of Calories burned depends on body weight. The formula below gives a good estimate of the number of Calories most people burn playing 10 min of basketball.

Calories burned playing basketball for 10 min

body weight in pounds

$$C = 0.455b$$

8 Copy and complete the table. For each body weight b in pounds, find the number of Calories C burned in 10 min of basketball playing.

b	C
100	?
150	?
175	?
200	?

8.

b	C
100	45.5
150	68.25
175	79.625
200	91

▶ The relationship between body weight and Calories burned can be shown with a graph.

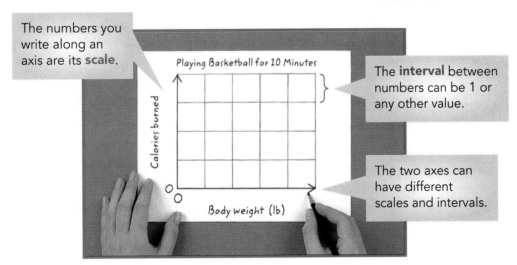

The numbers you write along an axis are its **scale**.

The **interval** between numbers can be 1 or any other value.

The two axes can have different scales and intervals.

Playing Basketball for 10 Minutes

Calories burned

Body weight (lb)

9 **Try This as a Class** Use the table of values you made in Question 8.

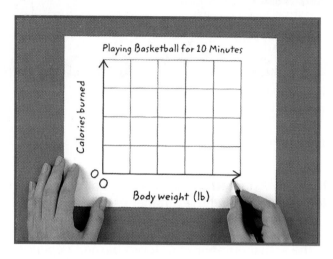

9. e.

Calories Burned While Playing Basketball

10. a.

b	C
100	60.6
150	90.9
175	106.05
200	121.2

b. **Calories Burned While Swimming or Playing Basketball**

a. Look at the graph. What data will the horizontal axis show? body weight in pounds

b. What are some reasonable values to include on the horizontal axis of your graph? Sample Response: weights from 100–200 lb

c. Look at the body weights in your data table. Use the maximum and minimum values and your answer to part (b) to decide what values should be on the horizontal axis. 100–200 lb

d. What interval should you use on the horizontal axis? Sample Response: 25 lb

e. Graph the data from your table on graph paper. See above.

f. Connect the points on your graph. What do you notice? The points lie along a line.

▶ You can use the coordinate plane from Question 9 to graph the formula for the Calories burned in 10 min of swimming.

10 The formula $C = 0.606b$ gives the number C of Calories burned during 10 min of swimming for a body weight b in pounds.

a. Make a table of values for this equation.

b. Plot your points on the graph and connect them. Write a title above your graph that describes both sets of data.

11 **a.** How many Calories does an 80 lb person burn playing basketball for 10 min? swimming for 10 min? 36.4 Cal, 48.48 Cal

b. How many Calories does a 220 lb person burn playing basketball for 10 min? swimming for 10 min? 100.1 Cal, 133.32 Cal

12 The graph at the right shows the number of Calories burned by swimming for 10 min.

Swimming for 10 Minutes

B (150, 90.9)

A (100, 60.6)

Calories burned

Body weight (lb)

a. What is the number of Calories burned at point *A*? point *B*?
60.6 Cal, 90.9 Cal

b. What is the change in the Calories burned between points *A* and *B*? This is the **rise**. Why do you think it is called the rise?

c. What is the weight at point *A*? at point *B*? 100 lb, 150 lb

d. What is the change in weight between points *A* and *B*? This is the **run**. an increase of 50 lb

e. The **slope** of the line is the ratio of the rise to the run. What is the slope of the line for swimming? $\frac{30.3}{50}$, or 0.606

f. Why do you think points *A* and *B* were chosen rather than other points on the line? The coordinates of the points are fairly easy to estimate because each is near the intersection of two lines on the grid.

13 ✔ **CHECKPOINT** Use the graph you made in Question 9 showing the number of Calories burned playing basketball. Find the slope of the line. Sample Response: about $\frac{45}{100}$, or $\frac{9}{20}$

14 Discussion Use your answers to Questions 12 and 13.

a. How can the slopes of the swimming and basketball lines help you decide which exercise burns more Calories?
The greater the slope, the greater the number of Calories burned per pound.

b. The slope of the line for watching TV for 10 min is 0.076. Is this slope *greater than* or *less than* the slope for swimming? for playing basketball? less than; less than

c. What do you think the line for watching TV would look like on your graph? Sample Response: The slope of the line would be much less steep than the slopes of the lines for basketball and for swimming.

HOMEWORK EXERCISES ▶ See Exs. 9–20 on pp. 466–467.

12. b. an increase of 30.3 Calories; It gives the number of units the graph rises between points *A* and *B*.

✔ **QUESTION 13**

...checks that you can find the slope of a line.

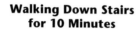

GOAL

LEARN HOW TO...

♦ determine how the scale affects the appearance of a graph

AS YOU...

♦ identify misleading graphs

MISLEADING Graphs

SET UP You will need: • Labsheet 1A • graph paper

▶ If you do not study them carefully, graphs can be misleading. For example, if you want to burn the most Calories, should you walk up stairs or down them? The graphs below seem to show that it does not make very much difference.

Walking Down Stairs for 10 Minutes

Walking Up Stairs for 10 Minutes

15 a. How many Calories does a 170 lb person burn walking up stairs for 10 min? down stairs for 10 min? about 100 Cal; about 35 Cal

b. Does a 170 lb person burn more Calories walking up stairs or down stairs? walking up stairs

16 Discussion Look at the scale on the vertical axis of each graph.

a. How are the scales different? The scales on the vertical axes have different ranges and intervals.

b. How does the interval chosen affect the steepness of the line on a graph? The same line will appear steeper on a graph with smaller intervals.

c. Estimate the slope of each line. Does the slope tell you which type of exercise burns more Calories? Explain.

Sample Response: about 0.15, about 0.6; Yes; Since the slope of the second graph is greater, walking up stairs burns more Calories.

▶ **Changes in the horizontal scale can also affect the look of a graph.**

17. See Additional Answers.

17 The graph at the right shows the relationship between body weight and Calories burned while reading.

Reading for 10 Minutes

Calories burned vs. Body weight (lb)

a. Suppose each interval on the horizontal scale were changed to represent 20 lb instead of 10 lb. About how much shorter would the horizontal axis be?

Predict how a scale change from 10 lb to 20 lb intervals would affect the line on the graph.

b. Suppose each interval on the horizontal scale were changed to represent 5 lb instead of 10 lb. Predict how that scale change would affect the line on the graph.

c. **Use Labsheet 1A.** Make two graphs of the data, *Changing the Horizontal Scale* to 20 lb and to 5 lb intervals. How accurate were the predictions you made in parts (a) and (b)?

▶ **You just saw how changing the scale on a graph can make the data look different, but there are other ways that graphs can be misleading. The graph below compares the numbers of Calories in different juices.**

18. a. The lengths of the diameters of the cans are in the same proportions as the number of Calories of the juices.
b. grapefruit: 4220 mm³, apple juice: 6594 mm³, prune juice: 16,881 mm³ (Volumes were calculated using 3.14 for π and rounding to the nearest cubic millimeter.)

18 Prune juice has about twice as many Calories as the same amount of grapefruit juice. Grapefruit juice has about 80% of the Calories as the same amount of apple juice.

a. How are the relationships among the Calorie contents of prune, grapefruit, and apple juice shown on the graph?

See above.

b. In the graph, each can is drawn 21 mm high. The widths of the drawings for prune, apple, and grapefruit are 32 mm, 20 mm, and 16 mm, respectively. Find the volume of each can in the graph.

See above.

c. **Discussion** Do you think this graph accurately shows how the Calorie contents of the juices compare? Explain.

No; The relationships between the volumes of the cans don't reflect the relationships between the number of Calories in the juices.

HOMEWORK EXERCISES ▶ See Exs. 21–22 on p. 467.

Key Concepts

Key Terms

cylinder

Volume of a Cylinder (pp. 457–458)

To find the volume of a cylinder, multiply the area of the base by the height.

area of the base of a cylinder

$$V = Bh = \pi r^2 h$$

scale

Choosing a Scale for a Graph (pp. 459–460)

The numbers written along an axis of a graph are its scale. Usually, the maximum and minimum data values determine the range of the scale. The size of the interval depends on how spread out the data are.

slope

Finding the Slope of a Line (p. 461)

The slope of a line is the ratio of the rise to the run.

rise

run

Example

Find the slope of the line on the graph.

Sleeping for 10 Minutes

Calories burned / Body weight (lb)

(100, 6.8)   (150, 10.2)

A 100 lb person burns 6.8 Cal while sleeping 10 min.
A 150 lb person burns 10.2 Cal while sleeping 10 min.

$$\text{slope} = \frac{\text{rise}}{\text{run}} = \frac{\text{change in the number of Calories}}{\text{change in body weight}} = \frac{10.2 - 6.8}{150 - 100} = \frac{3.4}{50} = 0.068$$

Key Concepts Questions

19 A cylinder has a radius of 4 cm and a volume of 402 cm³. What is the height of the cylinder? Round your answer to the nearest centimeter. 8 cm

20 Find the slope of a line with each rise and run.

a. rise 4   **b.** rise 6   **c.** rise 3   **d.** rise 1 $\frac{1}{3}$
    run 4 1   run 2 3   run 1 3   run 3

Section ① Key Concepts

Misleading Graphs (pp. 462–463)

The scales chosen for a graph will affect the way the data appear.

Example The graphs show the numbers of Calories from two nutrients.

Calories from Carbohydrates

Calories from Protein

CLOSURE QUESTION

State the formula for the volume of a cylinder in two ways and tell what each variable represents. Then explain what is meant by the slope of a line.

Sample Response:

$V = Bh = \pi r^2 h$ where V is the volume, B is the area of the base, h is the height, and r is the radius of the base; the slope of a line is $\frac{rise}{run}$ or the vertical change divided by the horizontal change.

Key Concepts Question

21 **a.** Compare the graphs in the Example above. Why are the graphs misleading? *The scales on the vertical axes are not the same.*

b. How should you change the scales on the graphs to better represent the data? *Use the same scale for both graphs.*

Section ① Practice & Application Exercises

YOU WILL NEED

For Exs. 9–11, 20, 21:
♦ graph paper

For Exercises 1–8, use 3.14 or the π key on a calculator. Round each answer to the nearest hundredth. *Answers to Exercises 1–8 are given using the π key. Final zeros in decimal places have been dropped.*

Find the volume of each cylinder.

1. 3 ft 127.23 ft³
    4.5 ft

2. 4312 m³
    28 m
    Area of base = 154 m²

3. 1 cm 69.12 cm³
    22 cm

4. Suppose a 5 in. long section of pipe has an inside diameter of 1 in.

   a. What is the volume of the pipe section? 3.93 in.³

   b. **Challenge** Will a 2 in. diameter pipe section with the same length hold twice as much liquid? Explain.

      No; If the radius is doubled, the volume is 4 times as great.

Find the unknown measure for each cylinder.

5. $r = 2$ in., $h = 3$ in., $V \approx \underline{\ ?\ }$ in.³ 37.7

6. $B = 5$ in.², $h = \underline{\ ?\ }$ in., $V = 40$ in.³ 8

7. $B = \underline{\ ?\ }$ ft², $h = 3$ ft, $V = 48$ ft³ 16

8. $r \approx \underline{\ ?\ }$ cm, $h = 4$ cm, $V \approx 12.56$ cm³ 1

9. The number of Calories burned in 10 min of studying can be described by the formula $C = 0.136b$, where C is Calories and b is body weight in pounds. See Additional Answers.

   a. Make a table of values for the numbers of Calories burned by 75 lb, 100 lb, 150 lb, and 200 lb people in 10 min of studying.

   b. Plot the data points and connect them.

   c. Find the slope of the line in part (b).

   d. Estimate how many Calories you burn in 10 min of studying.

10. **Insects** A mosquito completes about 600 up-and-down wing beats in 1 s of flight. See Additional Answers.

    a. Suppose you make a graph with numbers of wing beats on the vertical axis and numbers of seconds on the horizontal axis. What scale would you use for each axis? Explain.

    b. Draw and label a graph of the data.

11. **Exercise** Use the table below. See Additional Answers.

Numbers of Calories Burned in 10 min Periods of Activity				
Activity	Body Weight			
	75 lb	100 lb	150 lb	200 lb
	5.1 Cal	6.8 Cal	10.2 Cal	13.6 Cal
	14.2 Cal	18.9 Cal	28.4 Cal	37.8 Cal

    a. What scales would you use to make graphs relating body weights and Calories burned for each activity?

    b. Make a graph for each activity on a separate coordinate plane.

Find the slope of each line.

12.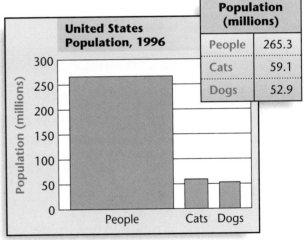

$\frac{2}{3}$, or 0.$\overline{6}$

y-axis values: 4, 3, 2, 1, 0
Points: (3, 3), (0, 1)
x-axis: 0 1 2 3 4 x

13.

$\frac{3}{2}$, or 1.5

y-axis values: 4, 3, 2, 1, 0
Points: (3, 3), (1, 0)
x-axis: 0 1 2 3 4 x

14.

$\frac{1}{4}$, or 0.25

y-axis values: 4, 3, 2, 1, 0
Points: (4, 3), (0, 2)
x-axis: 0 1 2 3 4 x

15.

2

y-axis values: 4, 3, 2, 1, 0
Points: (2, 4), (1, 2)
x-axis: 0 1 2 3 4 x

Find the slope of a line with each rise and run.

16. rise 9   3
run 3

17. rise 10   2
run 5

18. rise 5 $\frac{1}{2}$, or 0.5
run 10

19. rise 5   1
run 5

20. Writing On graph paper, sketch a line with each slope in Exercises 16–19. How does a line with a slope greater than 1 compare with a line with a slope less than 1? See above.

21. The data in the table show the populations of people, cats, and dogs in the United States in 1996. The data were used to make the graph shown.

Population (millions)	
People	265.3
Cats	59.1
Dogs	52.9

a. Does the graph use height or area to represent the populations? height

b. Explain why the graph is misleading. See above.

c. Make a different graph that is not misleading. See above.

United States Population, 1996

Population (millions): 300, 250, 200, 150, 100, 50, 0
People   Cats Dogs

Reflecting ◀▶ on the Section

22. Find a graph in a newspaper or magazine. Is the graph effective? Is it accurate? Could it be considered misleading? Explain your answers. Answers will vary. Check students' work.

20. Sample Response:

y-axis: 20, 19, 18, 17, 16, 15, 14, 13, 12, 11, 10, 9, 8, 7, 6, 5, 4, 3, 2, 1, 0
x-axis: 0 1 2 3 4 5 6

It is steeper.

21. b. The heights of the graphs are in the same proportion as the populations, but the areas are not.
c. Sample Response:

The Population of People, Cats, and Dogs in the United States (millions)

250, 200, 150, 100, 50, 0
People Cats Dogs

RESEARCH

Exercise 22 checks that you can evaluate the effectiveness of graphs.

Spiral ◀▶Review

Find the volume of each prism. (Module 6, p. 445)

23.
48 cm³
3 cm
4 cm
4 cm

24.
216 in.³
8 in.
9 in.
6 in.

25.
2187 cm³
18 cm
13.5 cm
18 cm

For each spinner, find the theoretical probability that the pointer will land on the number shown. (Module 1, p. 33)

26.
2 4
2 2
4 4
2 6
$\frac{4}{8}$, or $\frac{1}{2}$

27.
2 3
1 4
6 5
4 2 6
$\frac{2}{9}$

28. Suppose each spinner above is spun 100 times. For each spinner, about how many times do you expect the outcome to be "2"?

about 50 times, about 22 times

Write each ratio in percent form. (Module 5, p. 366)

29. 4 : 100 4%   30. 8 : 50 16%   31. 13 : 20 65%   32. 48 : 200 24%

Extension ▶▶

Negative, Zero, and Undefined Slopes

In this section, the slopes of the lines were always greater than 0. There are also lines with slopes that are less than 0, equal to 0, or undefined.

33. a. For each graph below, find the slope of the line. 0, –2, undefined

Graph A

(1, 2) (3, 2)

Graph B

(2, 3)
(3, 1)

Graph C

(1, 4)
(1, 1)

b. Explain why the slope of the line on Graph C is *undefined*. Since the slope $= \frac{\text{rise}}{\text{run}} = \frac{3}{0}$ and division by 0 is undefined, the slope is undefined.

c. Explain how a line with a negative slope looks different from a line with a positive slope. A line with a negative slope slants downward from left to right, while a line with a positive slope slants upward from left to right.

Beginning
the
Module
Project

The Picture of Health

SET UP *You will need Project Labsheet A.*

Visual displays help people understand and
remember facts or data. In this module you'll
learn new ways to graph data, when it is
appropriate to use a graph, and how a graph
can be misleading. At the end of the module,
you'll make a graph to help people understand
a health or fitness issue.

Choosing a Data Display Two important features
of any data display are its visual appeal and how
well it represents the data.

Use Project Labsheet A for Project Questions 1 and 2.

1 Look at the *Three Bicycle Riding Graphs*. Which graph
gets your attention? Why? Answers will vary. Check students' work.

2. See Additional Answers.

2 a. Which graph do you think best shows
how the number of people who
ride bicycles varies among different
age groups?

b. Is the number of 12–17 year olds and
25–34 year olds who ride bicycles
about the same? Which graph would
you use to support your answer? Why?

3 At the end of this module, you'll make
your own graph about a health or fitness
issue. Think of a health or fitness issue
that would be interesting to middle
school students. Then begin looking for
data for your graph.

Extra Skill Practice

Find the unknown measure for each cylinder. Use 3.14 or the π key on a calculator. Answers are given using the π key.

1. $r = 3$ yd, $h = 2$ yd, $V \approx$ ___?___ yd^3 56.5

2. $r \approx$ ___?___ cm, $h = 5$ cm, $V \approx 62.8$ cm^3 2

Find the slope of a line with each rise and run.

3. rise 2 1
   run 2

4. rise 5 $\frac{1}{2}$, or 0.5
   run 10

5. rise 3 $\frac{3}{4}$, or 0.75
   run 4

6. rise 3 3
   run 1

7. rise 12 2
   run 6

Use the graphs for Exercises 8 and 9.

8. About how many Calories does a 100 lb person burn in 10 min while reading? while dancing?
   Sample Response: about 8 Cal, about 25 Cal

9. Are these graphs misleading? If they are, explain why and redraw them so that they are not misleading. See Additional Answers.

Study Skills ▸ **Using Graphic Organizers**

A *graphic organizer* is a visual display that can help you relate ideas and organize information. A flow chart illustrates a sequence of steps.

1. a. Describe the steps of the process shown in the flow chart below.
      If the starting number is not divisible by 2, you add 1 to make it an even number.
   b. Describe what happens when $x = 9$.
      Since 9 is not divisible by 2, you add 1 to generate 10.

Even Numbers

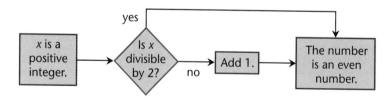

2. Think of a process that involves following steps in order. Draw a flow chart to illustrate this process. Answers will vary. Check students' work.

IN THIS SECTION

EXPLORATION 1
◆ Percents Greater than 100%

EXPLORATION 2
◆ Percent of Change

HEART RATES

WARM-UP EXERCISES

1. 62 is what percent of 93? $66\frac{2}{3}\%$

2. What is 12% of 54? 6.48

3. 18 is 10% of what number?   180

Evaluate each expression.

4. $314 - 297 \div 9 + 3$
   284

5. $6 \cdot 4 - \frac{8}{2} - 12 \cdot 2$
   -4

6. $0.45 - 0.07 \cdot 0.09 + 2.5$ 2.9437

Setting the Stage ▶▶▶▶▶▶▶▶▶▶▶▶▶▶▶▶▶▶▶▶▶

The reading below from James Ramsey Ullman's *Banner in the Sky* describes part of 16-year-old Rudi Matt's first climb as a member of a mountain climbing team in the Alps.

BANNER IN THE SKY *by James Ramsey Ullman*

He moved from the broad ledge to the narrow one. . . . He took a careful step—a second step—a third. One more would bring him to the jutting platform. But before he could take it there was a soft tremor beneath his feet. One moment, his footing was a seemingly solid band of mountain granite; in the next, it was a crumbling mass of loose fragments. With a violent leap he thrust himself clear, lunged forward and landed on the platform, and in the same instant, behind him, the whole ledge on which he had been standing disintegrated and plunged in spinning fragments into space below.

For perhaps a minute he stood motionless. Leaning in against the rock, he struggled to control the rasp of his breathing and the pounding of his heart. Then, when he had half succeeded, he turned and took stock of his position.

Think About It

1 What does it mean to have a pounding heart? Why do you think Rudi's heart was pounding? Sample Response: to have a heart that is beating harder and faster than usual; He was frightened.

2 Describe the changes in Rudi's heart rate during the time covered in the reading. Sample Response: Rudi's heart rate increased because of physical activity and fear. Then, the rate decreased when Rudi stood still and calmed down.

GOAL

LEARN HOW TO...
◆ find percents
  greater than 100%

AS YOU...
◆ compare your
  resting and active
  heart rates

Exploration 1

PERCENTS GREATER THAN 100%

SET UP *You will need:* • *Labsheet 2A*
• *watch or clock with a second hand*

Have you ever wondered how much your heart rate
increases when you climb stairs, run for the bus,
or watch an exciting movie? Before you can calculate
the change in your heart rate, you need to measure
your resting heart rate while sitting still.

You can feel the action of your beating heart at pulse points
where the arteries come close to the skin. This is why we use the
pulse to measure heart rate.

3 Place the index and middle finger of one hand so that you can feel
your pulse in your wrist. Count how many times your heart beats
for each number of seconds. Record each count. Sample responses are given.

   a. 6 s 8   **b.** 10 s 10   **c.** 20 s 22

4. Sample Response:
80 beats/min, 60 beats/min,
66 beats/min

4 Rewrite each count in Question 3 as a rate in beats per minute.

5 Do you think one time span is more accurate than the others for
counting your pulse? Why? Sample Response: Yes; The longer the time
interval, the less affect minor variations will have on the result.

▶ **In this section, your resting heart rate is your rate per minute based
on your count for 20 s. Now you'll find your active heart rate.**

6 a. Following the directions of your teacher, do some physical activity for two minutes. Then immediately count your pulse for 20 s and record the number of beats. Sample Response: 46 beats

   b. Rewrite your count from part (a) as a rate in beats per minute. Use this rate as your active heart rate throughout this section.

   138 beats/min

7 Use Labsheet 2A. Gather the heart rate data from all class members. Record the data in the first two columns of the *Heart Rate Data* table. Answers will vary. Check students' work.

▶ **Percents Greater than 100%** Suppose Jane's resting heart rate is 60 beats per minute and her active heart rate is 96 beats per minute. One way to compare these two rates is to ask: "Jane's active heart rate is what percent of her resting heart rate?"

One way to visualize the comparison between Jane's active heart rate and her resting rate is with a percent bar model like the one in the Example below.

FOR ◄ HELP

with *percent bar models*, see

MODULE 5, p. 352

EXAMPLE

Use the resting heart rate as the whole, or 100%.

The active heart rate is greater than the resting heart rate, so the percent is greater than 100%.

8 How many heart beats is 50% of 60? 100% of 60?   30 beats; 60 beats

9 Since 150% = 100% + 50%, how many heartbeats is 150% of 60? How many heartbeats is 200% of 60? 90 beats; 120 beats

10 Use the percent bar model above and your answers to Question 9 to estimate what percent Jane's active heart rate is of her resting heart rate. about 160%

11 ✔ **CHECKPOINT** Maura's resting heart rate is 80 beats per minute and her active heart rate is 140 beats per minute. Estimate what percent Maura's active heart rate is of her resting heart rate.   about 175%

✔ **QUESTION 11**

...checks that you can estimate percents greater than 100%.

▶ **Using an Equation to Find a Percent** You can use an equation to find what percent Jane's active heart rate is of her resting heart rate.

EXAMPLE

96 is what percent of 60?

SAMPLE RESPONSE

Using an equation

p is the unknown part of 100 percent.

96 is what percent of 60?

$$96 = \frac{p}{100} \cdot 60$$

$$96 = \frac{60p}{100}$$

$$100 \cdot 96 = 60p$$

$$\frac{9600}{60} = p$$

$$160 = p$$

Using a proportion

$$\frac{96}{60} = \frac{p}{100}$$

$$60p = 100 \cdot 96$$

Use cross products.

$$p = \frac{9600}{60}$$

$$p = 160$$

96 is 160% of 60.

12 Maura's active heart rate (140 beats/min) is what percent of her resting heart rate (80 beats/min)? **175%**

✔ QUESTION 13

...checks that you can find a percent greater than 100%.

13 ✔ CHECKPOINT Find each percent.

a. 40 is what percent of 32? **b.** 52 is what percent of 40?
　　　　　　　　　　125%　　　　　　　　　　　　　　　130%

Use Labsheet 2A for Questions 14 and 15.

14 Look back at your resting and active heart rates recorded in the *Heart Rate Data* table. Your active heart rate is what percent of your resting heart rate? Round to the nearest whole percent.
Answers will vary. Check students' work.

▶ Increasing your heart rate to reach a target rate between 60% and 85% of your maximum heart rate is important when you exercise. To find your maximum heart rate, subtract your age from 220.

15. Answers will vary. Check students' work.
15 a. What is your maximum heart rate?

b. What is your minimum target heart rate? What is your maximum target heart rate?

c. Was your active heart rate in the target heart rate interval?

HOMEWORK EXERCISES ▶ See Exs. 1–9 on p. 480.

PERCENT of Change

SET UP *You will need Labsheet 2A.*

GOAL

LEARN HOW TO...
◆ find a percent of increase or decrease

AS YOU...
◆ examine resting and active heart rates

KEY TERM
◆ percent of change

▸ **Another way to compare resting and active heart rates is to look at the difference between these rates. You can then use percent to compare the difference with the original amount.**

16. Answers will vary. Check students' work.
16 Use Labsheet 2A. Use your heart rate data from the *Heart Rate Data* table.

    a. Find the difference between your active heart rate and your resting heart rate.

    b. Is the difference in part (a) *greater than* or *less than* your resting heart rate?

▸ **Percent of change is the percent by which an amount increases or decreases from its original amount.**

Camila's resting heart rate is 70 beats per minute when she is awake.

When she is sleeping, her heart rate slows to 63 beats per minute.

17 a. What is the difference between Camila's two heart rates?
                                      7 beats/min

    b. The difference you found in part (a) is what percent of Camila's resting heart rate when she is awake? 10%

    c. Is the percent of change you found in part (b) a *percent of increase* or a *percent of decrease*? Explain.
    percent of decrease; Her heart rate decreased when Camila was sleeping.

Use the heart rate data in the table below for Questions 18–20.

Heart Rate Data				
Student	Resting heart rate	Active heart rate	Difference (active – resting)	Percent of increase
Nancy	57	102	45	?
Bruce	63	126	63	?
Mei	66	99	33	50%
Terry	72	180	108	?
Ella	78	117	39	?
Kamau	72	144	72	100%
Jerome	81	168	87	?

18 a. Mei's heart rate increased 50%. The difference between her active and resting heart rates is what fraction of her resting heart rate? $\frac{33}{66}$, or $\frac{1}{2}$

 b. Find another student whose heart rate increased 50%. Ella

19 a. Kamau's heart rate increased 100%. How does the difference between his active and resting heart rates compare with his resting heart rate? It is the same.

 b. Find another student whose heart rate increased 100%. Bruce

20 To find his active heart rate, Terry jogged in place.

 a. The difference between Terry's active and resting heart rates is 108 beats per minute. This difference is how many times his resting heart rate? 1.5 times

 b. If Terry's heart rate had increased 100%, what would the difference in the two rates be? 72

 c. If Terry's heart rate had increased 50%, what would the difference in the two rates be? 36

 d. Terry's heart rate increased 108 beats per minute. What is the percent of increase? 150%

21 Nancy's heart rate increased from 57 to 102 beats per minute. This is a difference of 45 beats per minute. Will the percent of increase in Nancy's heart rate be *greater than 100%, less than 50%,* or *between 50% and 100%?* between 50% and 100%

▶ **Using an Equation** You can write an equation to find a percent of change. First you need to know the amount of change.

After exercising, Nancy's heart rate increased from 57 to 102 beats per minute. Find the percent of change in her heart rate.

SAMPLE RESPONSE

First find the difference in her heart rates: $102 - 57 = 45$
Then ask:

The **difference** is what percent of the **original amount**?

45 is what percent of **57**?

$$45 = \frac{x}{100} \cdot 57$$

x is the unknown part of 100 percent.

$$45 = \frac{57x}{100}$$

$$4500 = 57x$$

Round to the nearest whole number.

$$79 \approx x$$

The symbol $\approx$ means "is approximately equal to."

45 is about 79% of 57, so Nancy's heart rate increased about 79%.

22 ✔ **CHECKPOINT** Jerome's heart rate increased from 81 beats per minute to 168 beats per minute. Find the percent of increase in Jerome's heart rate. *about 107%*

23 **Use Labsheet 2A.** 23a–b. Answers will vary. Check students' work.

   a. Find the percent of change in your heart rate from resting to active.

   b. Complete the *Difference* and *Percent of increase* columns of the table.

   c. Find an example where one student has a higher active heart rate but a lower percent of increase than another student. Explain how this happens.

   d. Find two students whose heart rates increased by the same number of beats. Are their percents of increase the same? If not, explain how this happens.

✔ **QUESTION 22**

...checks that you can find a percent of change.

23. **c.** Sample Response: The percent of increase also depends on the resting heart rate. If the resting heart rate is high and the difference between the two heart rates is low, the percent of increase will be low.
d. Not necessarily; Their resting heart rates may be different so their percents of increase may be different.

HOMEWORK EXERCISES ▶ See Exs. 10–24 on pp. 480–482.

You can use spreadsheet software to answer Question 23 on page 477. You can set up the spreadsheet to find the differences between resting heart rates and active heart rates, as well as the percents of increase.

Step 1 Set up your spreadsheet with the same headings as the table on Labsheet 2A. Enter the class data about heart rates.

File Edit Format Calculate Options View
RESTING AND ACTIVE HEART RATES

B4 × √ 120

	A	B	C	D
1	Resting Heart Rate	Active Heart Rate	Difference (Active – Resting)	Percent of Increase
2	50	90		
3	70	140		
4	80	120		

Step 2 In cell C2 (the box in column C and row 2) enter a formula that will calculate the difference between resting and active heart rates. Every formula must begin with an equals sign.

The formula takes the number in cell B2 and subtracts the number in cell A2.

File Edit Format Calculate Options View
RESTING AND ACTIVE HEART RATES

C2 × √ = B2 – A2

	A	B	C	D
1	Resting Heart Rate	Active Heart Rate	Difference (Active – Resting)	Percent of Increase
2	50	90	40	
3	70	140		
4	80	120		

The result appears in cell C2.

Step 3 In cell D2, enter the formula "= C2/A2*100" to find the percent of increase.

Step 4 Use the *fill down* command in columns C and D to apply the formulas to the data in the remaining rows.

Calculate
Move...
Fill Right
Fill Down
Sort...
Insert Cells...
Delete Cells...
Calculate Now
Auto Calc

File Edit Format Calculate Options View
RESTING AND ACTIVE HEART RATES

D2 × √ = C2 / A2 * 100

	A	B	C	D
1	Resting Heart Rate	Active Heart Rate	Difference (Active – Resting)	Percent of Increase
2	50	90	40	80
3	70	140	70	100
4	80	120	40	50

Key Term

Percents Greater than 100% (pp. 472–474)

You can write equations to solve percent problems. Some percent problems involve percents greater than 100%.

Example

45 is what percent of 40?

$$45 = \frac{x}{100} \cdot 40$$

$$45 = \frac{40x}{100}$$

x is the unknown part of 100 percent.

$$4500 = 40x$$

$$112.5 = x$$

45 is 112.5% of 40.

Think: 45 is greater than 40, so 45 is more than 100% of 40.

Percent of Change (pp. 475–477)

You can find the percent of change between two numbers by comparing the difference of the numbers with the original amount.

percent of change

Example

Kenyatta's heart rate changed from 70 to 91 beats per minute. What is the percent of change?

Find the difference.
    $91 - 70 = 21$

Find the percent.
    21 is what percent of 70?

CLOSURE QUESTION

When will you have a percent greater than 100? Describe how to find the percent of change.

Sample Response: When the resulting value is larger than the original number that you are finding the percent of; The percent of change is found by comparing the difference of the numbers with the original amount.

24 **Key Concepts Question** Find the percent of change in Kenyatta's heart rate in the Example above. Is the change an *increase* or a *decrease*? How can you tell?

30%; increase; The second number is greater than the original.

Section 2
Practice & Application Exercises

1. Muriel's resting heart rate is 65 beats per minute. After 2 min of exercise, her heart rate is 117 beats per minute. Muriel's active heart rate is what percent of her resting heart rate? *180%*

Find each percent.

2. 15 is what percent of 75? *20%*

3. 12 is what percent of 96? *12.5%*

4. 80 is what percent of 50? *160%*

5. 108 is what percent of 80? *135%*

6. 255 is what percent of 255? *100%*

7. 152 is what percent of 76? *200%*

8. Phil's active heart rate is 200% of his resting heart rate. If his resting heart rate is 64 beats per minute, what is his active heart rate?
128 beats per min

9. Jerry's resting heart rate is 72 beats per minute. He wants to increase his heart rate 125%. What should his active heart rate be?
162 beats per min

10. **Computers** In 1984, there were 12,284,000 students aged 3 to 17 years old using a computer at school in the United States. In 1993, the number had risen to 28,848,000. What is the percent of increase in computer use at school from 1984 to 1993? Round your answer to the nearest percent. *135%*

11. **Biology** Some mammals that spend time under water have lower heart rates (in beats per minute) when they dive. Copy and complete the table. *See table.*

Animal	◄ American beaver	▼ Manatee	▲ Bottle-nosed dolphin	▼ Harbor seal
Surface heart rate	140	55	110	100
Diving heart rate	10	30	50	10
Difference (surface – diving)	? 130	? 25	? 60	? 90
Percent of decrease	? 93%	? 45%	? 55%	? 90%

Find each percent of change.

12. original value: 60
final value: 85 $41\frac{2}{3}\%$ increase

13. original value: 12
final value: 8 $33\frac{1}{3}\%$ decrease

14. original value: 150
final value: 250 $66\frac{2}{3}\%$ increase

15. original value: 48
final value: 180 275% increase

16. original value: 10
final value: 125 1150% increase

17. original value: 35
final value: 14 60% decrease

Use the table for Exercises 18–20.

18. a. Find the percent of change in the number of people visiting Mexico from 1988 to 1989. Is this a percent of *increase* or *decrease*? 5%; increase

b. Find the percent of change in the number of people visiting Mexico from 1992 to 1993. Is this a percent of *increase* or *decrease*? about 5%; decrease

\multicolumn{2}{c}{**Visits to Mexico by People Living in the United States**}	
Year	Number of visitors
1987	13,074,000
1988	13,463,000
1989	14,163,000
1990	16,381,000
1991	15,042,000
1992	16,114,000
1993	15,285,000

19. Calculator Scientific calculators follow the order of operations. Choose the letter of the expression that you would enter to find the percent of increase in visitors from 1991 to 1992. Explain your choice.

A. 16114000 − 15042000 ÷ 15042000 • 100

B. (16114000 − 15042000) ÷ 15042000 • 100

C. 15042000 ÷ 16114000 • 100 See below.

20. Between which two years does the greatest percent of increase occur? How much is it? between 1989 and 1990; about 16%

21. Sale Prices Martina saw this sign in a store window: "Buy one sweater at the regular price and get a second sweater of equal or lesser value at half price." Suppose Martina bought two sweaters. The regular prices of the sweaters were $26.99 and $28.99.

a. How much did Martina pay for the two sweaters? $42.49

b. What percent of the total regular price for both sweaters was her discount (the amount of money she saved due to the sale)? Round your answer to the nearest whole percent. 24%

19. B; Since there are no parentheses in A, the original amount, rather than the change in the original amount, is divided by the original amount; The expression in C has nothing to do with percent of change.

Journal

Exercise 24 checks that you understand percent of change and percents greater than 100%.

22. **Writing** When an amount doubles, how much is the percent of change? Explain.

23. **Challenge** A store had an end-of-the-season sale. The first week of the sale, all seasonal items were marked 40% off the original price.

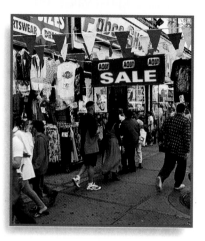

The store continued the sale a second week and marked down all seasonal items an additional 60% off the discounted price. Is the store offering 100% savings in the second week of the end-of-the-season sale? Explain.

Reflecting▷ on the Section

Write your response to Exercise 24 in your journal.

24. A student's heart rate increases from 60 beats per minute to 135 beats per minute. Without finding the percent of increase, explain how you know that the percent of change will be greater than 100%.   The difference is greater than 60.

Spiral◁▷Review

Find the slope of a line with each rise and run. (Module 7, p. 464)

25. rise 3
run 3 1

26. rise 4.5
run 9
$\frac{1}{2}$, or 0.5

27. rise 6
run 4
$\frac{3}{2}$, or 1.5

28. rise 2
run 8
$\frac{1}{4}$, or 0.25

Find the product. Write each product in lowest terms. (Module 4, p. 241)

29. $\frac{5}{6} \cdot \frac{3}{4}$ $\frac{5}{8}$

30. $2\frac{1}{3} \cdot \frac{4}{5}$ $1\frac{13}{15}$

31. $1\frac{5}{6} \cdot 3\frac{1}{4}$ $5\frac{23}{24}$

32. Choose two animal heart-rate intervals from the table below. Write an inequality for each, then graph each inequality on a number line. (Module 6, p. 388)   See Additional Answers.

Resting Heart Rates (beats per minute)			
canary	500 to 800	dog	70 to 120
mouse	300 to 500	person	60 to 80
chicken	300 to 350	lion	40 to 50
cat	120 to 140	elephant	25 to 50

Section ② Extra Skill Practice

Find each percent.

1. 65 is what percent of 13? 500%

2. 160 is what percent of 128? 125%

3. 75 is what percent of 25? 300%

4. 60 is what percent of 40? 150%

5. 75 is what percent of 40? 187.5%

6. 92 is what percent of 60? 153.$\overline{3}$%

7. 195 is what percent of 195? 100%

8. 172 is what percent of 86? 200%

Find each percent of change.

9. original value: 18
   final value: 32 77.$\overline{7}$% increase

10. original value: 8
    final value: 2 75% decrease

11. original value: 50
    final value: 150 200% increase

12. original value: 10
    final value: 20 100% increase

13. Lizette's active heart rate is 150% of her resting heart rate. If her resting heart rate is 68 beats per minute, what is her active heart rate? 102 beats/min

14. Bryan's heart rate increased from 72 to 94 beats per minute. What is the percent of change in his heart rate? about a 31% increase

15. Jena's heart rate decreased from 89 to 75 beats per minute. What is the percent of change in her heart rate? about a 16% decrease

16. Last year the school newspaper printed 650 copies of each issue. This year, 800 copies of each issue were printed. What is the percent of increase in the number of copies printed from last year to this year? about 23%

17. Elizabeth Martin owns a company. Last year, the company's profit was $250,000. This year, the company expects a profit of $300,000. What would be the percent of change in the company's profit? Is this a percent of *increase* or *decrease*? 20%; increase

Standardized Testing ◀▶ Open-ended

Sketch a cylinder and label its height and the radius of a base. Sketch and label the dimensions of a second cylinder that has the same height as your first cylinder but a larger base. Find the percent of change in the volume that occurs when you enlarge the base of the first cylinder to match the base of the second cylinder.

Answers will vary. Sample Response: If the base radii of the first and second cylinders are 5 cm and 10 cm respectively, and the height of both cylinders is 10 cm, then the percent increase in the volume is $\frac{\text{vol. of cyl. 2} - \text{vol. of cyl. 1}}{\text{vol. of cyl. 1}} \cdot 100 = \frac{1000\pi - 250\pi}{250\pi} \cdot 100 = 300\%$. In general, if the original radius is r and the increase in the radius is n, the percent of increase is $\frac{2rn + n^2}{r^2} \cdot 100$.

FOR ASSESSMENT AND PORTFOLIOS

The **$1 Million** GIVEAWAY

The Situation

See the Resource Book for a detailed discussion of this Extended Exploration.

A health food company is planning a sales promotion to encourage people to try a new citrus drink. Under the bottle cap of each citrus drink, there is a number printed. A prize of $1000 will be given to anyone who collects bottle caps with numbers that total exactly 100. The company has already manufactured bottle caps that contain the following numbers: 3, 15, 18, 33, 45, 66, 75, 84, and 90.

The Problem

The company is going to manufacture bottle caps that contain one additional number. In order to advertise the promotion as a "$1 Million Giveaway," the company wants 1000 people to win, but also wants to be certain that there will not be more than 1000 winners. What additional number would you recommend the company use? How many bottle caps should the company manufacture that contain that number?

Something to Think About

♦ What do the numbers 3, 15, 18, 33, 45, 66, 75, 84, and 90 have in common? The numbers are all multiples of 3.

♦ If these are the only numbers the company prints on the bottle caps, will there be any winners? How do you know? No; The sum of a set of numbers that are multiples of 3 is a multiple of 3. Since 100 is not a multiple of 3, it cannot be the sum.

Present Your Results

Write your recommendation to the company. Describe the strategies you used to make your decision. See Additional Answers.

IN THIS SECTION

EXPLORATION 1
◆ Customary Units of Capacity

EXPLORATION 2
◆ Solving Inequalities

EXPLORATION 3
◆ Making Box-and-Whisker Plots

HEALTHY CHOICES

Warm Up Exercises
See page 486.

1. Sample Response: It depends; Is the spaghetti being served as a main dish or a side dish? To a child or to an adult?

Setting the Stage ▸▸▸▸▸▸▸▸▸▸▸▸▸▸▸▸▸▸▸▸▸▸▸▸▸▸▸▸▸▸▸▸

What should you have for lunch? The choice is yours, and it can be a healthy one if you take a moment to understand the nutrition facts for various foods. Does this sound like too much trouble? It's not—just look at the food label.

In this section, you'll find out how much fat is too much.

Spaghetti
IN TOMATO SAUCE WITH CHEESE

Nutrition Facts
Serving Size: 1 cup (252g)
Servings Per Container: about 2

Amount Per Serving

Calories 210	Calories from Fat 20

	% Daily Value*
Total Fat 2g	**3%**
Saturated Fat 1g	**5%**
Cholesterol 5mg	**2%**
Sodium 1,020 mg	**43%**
Total Carbohydrate 41g	**14%**
Dietary Fiber 3g	**12%**
Sugars 14g	
Protein 7g	

Vitamin A 10%	Vitamin C 0%
Calcium 4%	Iron 10%

* Percent Daily Values are based on a 2,000 calorie diet. Your daily values may be higher or lower depending on your calorie needs.

Think About It

Look at the nutrition label at the right from a can of prepared spaghetti.

1 Do you think 1 cup is a realistic serving size? Explain.
See above.

2 What happens to the amounts of fat and other nutrients if you double the serving size? **The amounts double.**

"Daily value" is often the most you need each day.

3 One serving of canned spaghetti contains 2 g of fat. For most foods, each gram of fat contains 9 Calories. How many of the Calories in one serving of canned spaghetti are from fat? How does this compare with the Calorie information at the top of the label?
18 Cal; It is similar.

4 How much Vitamin C does a serving of canned spaghetti have? **none**

Replace each __?__ with
the number that makes
each statement true.
1. 2 ft = __?__ in.   24
2. 3 yd = __?__ ft   9
3. 35 cm = __?__ m
   0.35
Solve using mental math.
4. 3 + x = 8   5
5. 4 · x = 36   9
6. 83 − x = 44   39

When the amount of a vitamin or mineral in a food is less than 2% of the daily value, "0%" may be written on the nutrition label.

5 Nutritionists say people need at least 60 mg of Vitamin C each day.

a. Suppose one serving of canned spaghetti has 0.2 mg of Vitamin C. What percent of the daily value would you get in one serving? Round to the nearest tenth of a percent. Is this the same as 0%?   0.3%; No, but according to the standards for labels, it would be considered 0%.

b. How much Vitamin C should a food contain to have at least 1% of the daily value? 2% of the daily value?   at least 0.6 mg; at least 1.2 mg

GOAL

LEARN HOW TO...
◆ convert customary units of capacity

AS YOU...
◆ interpret nutrition labels on food products

KEY TERMS
◆ tablespoon (tbsp)
◆ cup (c)
◆ fluid ounce (fl oz)
◆ pint (pt)
◆ quart (qt)
◆ gallon (gal)

Exploration 1

CUSTOMARY UNITS of CAPACITY

▶ Besides nutritional information, food labels list the size of a serving and the number of servings in a container. For liquid foods, the serving size is listed in **tablespoons (tbsp)**, **cups (c)**, or **fluid ounces (fl oz)**. If you read them carefully, the labels can tell you how these customary units of capacity are related.

6 The label at the right is from a jar of gravy. The container holds 12 fl oz. How many fluid ounces are in $\frac{1}{4}$ c? $\frac{1}{2}$ c? 1 c?
2 fl oz, 4 fl oz, 8 fl oz

Nutrition Facts
Serving Size: 1/4 cup (60 g)
Servings Per Container: 6

Amount Per Serving

Calories 25   Calories from Fat 10

7 A recipe calls for $2\frac{1}{2}$ c of tomato sauce. How many 15 fl oz cans of tomato sauce will be enough to make the recipe? How much tomato sauce will be left?   2 cans; 10 fl oz

8 a. What is the capacity, in fluid ounces, of the bottle of pancake syrup with the label shown? **24 fl oz**

b. The amount of syrup listed on the front of the bottle is 1 pt 8 fl oz. How many fluid ounces are in a **pint (pt)**? **16 fl oz**

c. How many cups are in a pint? **2 c**

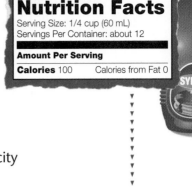

9 The label on a jar of mayonnaise lists the capacity of the jar as 32 fl oz or 1 qt.

a. How many tablespoons are in a fluid ounce? **2 tbsp**

b. How many cups are in a **quart (qt)**? How many pints are in a quart? **4 c; 2 pt**

10 The nutrition label for low fat milk is shown at the right.

a. The container of low fat milk holds how many pints? **4 pt**

b. The capacity is listed on the container as $\frac{1}{2}$ gal. How many pints are in a **gallon (gal)**? **8 pt**

11 Copy the table below. Then look back at your work in Questions 6–10 to complete the table.

Unit of measure	Symbol	Relationship	
tablespoon	tbsp	1 tbsp = __?__ fl oz	0.5
cup	c	1 c = __?__ fl oz	8
pint	pt	1 pt = __?__ c	2
quart	qt	1 qt = __?__ pt = __?__ c	2; 4
gallon	gal	1 gal = __?__ qt = __?__ pt = __?__ c	4; 8; 16

12 ✔ **CHECKPOINT** A small teacup holds 4 fl oz of mint tea. How much mint tea does it contain in each indicated unit?

a. tablespoons **8 tbsp** **b.** cups $\frac{1}{2}$ c **c.** quarts $\frac{1}{8}$ qt **d.** pints $\frac{1}{4}$ pt

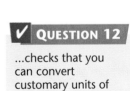

✔ **QUESTION 12**

...checks that you can convert customary units of capacity.

HOMEWORK EXERCISES ▶ See Exs. 1–8 on pp. 494–495.

Exploration 2

SOLVING INEQUALITIES

Nutritionists use your daily Calorie needs to decide how much protein, carbohydrate, and fat you need. Tony is a 13-year-old boy who needs about 2800 Cal per day. The table below shows how much protein, carbohydrate, and fat were in Tony's breakfast, lunch, and dinner one day.

Meal	Protein (g)	Carbohydrate (g)	Fat (g)	Calories
Breakfast	10.7	33.1	5.2	208
Lunch	21.9	117.6	29.8	797
Dinner	58.3	204.9	53.8	1525

13 Discussion Do you think Tony is close to achieving his goal of 2800 Cal per day? Yes.

▶ **Of all nutrients, only proteins, carbohydrates, and fats produce energy. This energy is measured in Calories. For most foods, each gram of protein or carbohydrate provides about 4 Cal. Each gram of fat provides about 9 Cal.**

14 Some nutritionists believe that to have a healthy diet, 12% of your daily Calorie intake should come from protein. Depending on your sex, age, and activity level, your daily Calorie needs may be as low as 1600 Cal or as high as 2800 Cal.

   a. According to the guideline stated above, how many of the Calories in a 1600 Cal daily total should come from protein? 192 Cal

   b. How many Calories should come from protein in a 2800 Cal daily total? 336 Cal

15 a. Use your answers to Question 14 to write an inequality that represents the number of Calories from protein *p* that a person should consume in one day based on the total numbers of Calories indicated. $192 \le p \le 336$

b. Rewrite the inequality in part (a) to show the number of grams of protein a person should consume in one day.
$48 \le g \le 84$

c. Did Tony get enough protein? Yes.

▶ **Carbohydrates should account for 55% or more of your diet. For a daily intake of 2000 Cal, over 1100 Calories should come from carbohydrates. Because the amount is 55% *or more*, carbohydrate need is modeled with an inequality.**

16 Discussion The inequality below describes the minimum number *c* of grams of carbohydrates needed based on a daily Calorie need of *d*.

$$4c \ge 0.55d$$

a. What does 0.55*d* represent?
the desirable number of Calories
from carbohydrates

b. Why is *c* multiplied by 4?
Each gram of carbohydrates
provides 4 Cal.

▶ **If you know a person's Calorie needs, you can use the inequality $4c \ge 0.55d$ to find the minimum number of grams of carbohydrates needed.**

EXAMPLE

Suppose Rowena Thompson needs 1600 Cal each day. How many grams of carbohydrates does she need daily?

SAMPLE RESPONSE

$$4c \ge 0.55d$$

$$4c \ge 0.55 \cdot 1600$$ — Substitute **1600** for **d**.

$$4c \ge 880$$

$$\frac{4c}{4} \ge \frac{880}{4}$$ — Divide both sides by **4**.

$$c \ge 220$$

Rowena Thompson should have at least 220 g of carbohydrates each day.

17 Tony needs 2800 Cal per day. Write an inequality to represent the number of grams of carbohydrates he should get each day.
$4c \ge 1540$, or $c \ge 385$

18 Try This as a Class The inequality $4c + 4 \cdot 355.6 \geq 0.55 \cdot 2800$ can be used to find the *additional* grams of carbohydrates that Tony still needs after eating breakfast, lunch, and dinner.

a. Simplify the inequality by finding the products $4 \cdot 355.6$ and $0.55 \cdot 2800$. Then rewrite the inequality. $4c + 1422.4 \geq 1540$

b. What should you do to solve for the variable *c*?
Subtract 1422.4 from both sides of the inequality and then divide both sides by 4.

c. Finish solving the inequality. How many more grams of carbohydrates does Tony need to get to the 55% minimum? 29.4 g

✔ **QUESTION 19**

...checks that you can solve inequalities.

19 ✔ **CHECKPOINT** Solve each inequality.

a. $8x \leq 28$ $x \leq 3.5$ **b.** $37 \leq 5x$ $x \geq 7.4$ **c.** $59.5 < x + 33.5$ $x > 26$

d. $x - \dfrac{1}{4} \geq -\dfrac{3}{4}$ $x \geq -\dfrac{1}{2}$ **e.** $7x + 4 \leq 50$ $x \leq 6\dfrac{4}{7}$ **f.** $3x - 2 < 14$ $x < 5\dfrac{1}{3}$

20 Many nutritionists believe that no more than 30% of your daily Calorie intake should come from fat.

a. Write an inequality to describe the maximum number of grams of fat a person should have each day. Use the variables *d* for daily Calorie need, and *f* for grams of fat. $9f \leq 0.3d$

b. Use your inequality to find Tony's *maximum fat gram goal,* or the maximum number of grams of fat he should have each day. $93\dfrac{1}{3}$ g

c. Was Tony within his maximum fat gram goal? Yes.

21. apple, apple juice, banana, 1 oatmeal cookie, orange, pear, popcorn, or combinations such as apple, apple juice, and popcorn

21 Discussion Which food(s) in the table could Tony snack on after dinner and still meet his Calorie, fat, protein, and carbohydrate goals for the day?

Snack	Protein (g)	Carbohydrate (g)	Fat (g)	Calories
apple	0.3	21.1	0.5	81
apple juice	0.3	27.6	0.3	111
banana	1.2	26.7	0.6	105
chocolate brownie	1.0	20.0	5.0	130
oatmeal cookies (2)	2.2	24.4	6.4	160
orange	1.4	16.3	0.1	65
pear	0.7	25.1	0.7	98
popcorn	1.8	10.7	0.7	54
vanilla ice cream	4.8	31.7	14.3	269

HOMEWORK EXERCISES See Exs. 9–19 on pp. 495–496.

MAKING BOX-and-WHISKER PLOTS

GOAL

LEARN HOW TO...
- ◆ make a box-and-whisker plot

AS YOU...
- ◆ examine the amounts of sugar in foods

KEY TERMS
- ◆ lower extreme
- ◆ upper extreme
- ◆ lower quartile
- ◆ upper quartile

SET UP *You will need Labsheets 3A and 3B.*

Have you ever heard the warning, "Don't eat too many sweets!"? Are some foods especially high in sugars compared with others?

▸ **In this exploration, you'll look at the amounts of sugar in candy bars and desserts, and then answer the question, "Is there more sugar in a piece of pie or in a candy bar?" One way to find out is to make a box-and-whisker plot.**

A box-and-whisker plot shows how spread out the data values are.

22 Use the box-and-whisker plot to identify the minimum and maximum data values, and the median. **19, 47, 26**

Amounts of Sugar in 20 Candy Bars (g)

▸ **To find out how the amounts of sugar in these candy bars compare with the amounts in the desserts listed on Labsheet 3A, you'll make a box-and-whisker plot of the amounts of sugar in the desserts.**

Use Labsheet 3A for Questions 23–26.

23 **Step 1** Order the data.

Order the *Sugar Contents of 20 Desserts* from least to greatest.

4 9 11 13 14 16 17 17 18 19 19 20 20 20 22 23 28 28 45 47

24 [Step 2] Find the *extremes* of the data.

The **lower extreme** is the least value in the set of data. The **upper extreme** is the greatest data value.

a. Record the lower extreme of the grams of sugar in the *Table of Box-and-Whisker Plot Points.* 4

b. Record the upper extreme of the grams of sugar in the *Table of Box-and-Whisker Plot Points.* 47

25 [Step 3] Find the median of the data.

a. Find and record the median of the sugar data. 19

b. About what percent of the data values lie above the median? below the median? about 50%; about 50%

26 [Step 4] Find the *quartiles*.

Draw a vertical segment through the middle data item or between the two middle items. Circle the data values in your ordered list that are to the left of the segment. The median of these values is the **lower quartile** of the data.

Circle the data values in your ordered list that are to the right of the segment. The median of these values is the **upper quartile**.

a. Find and record the lower quartile. 15

b. Find and record the upper quartile. 22.5

Use Labsheet 3B for Questions 27–29.

27 [Step 5] Graph the median, the extremes, and the quartiles below a number line. Then draw the box and whiskers.

Follow the directions for *Comparing Sugar Contents* to make a box-and-whisker plot for the numbers of grams of sugar in the desserts.

28 Compare the numbers of grams of sugar in candy bars with the numbers of grams of sugar in desserts by comparing the medians for the two data sets. Which appear to have more sugar, *candy bars* or *desserts*? Explain.

29 **Discussion** Which contains more sugar, a *slice of pie* or a *candy bar*? Explain.

28. candy bars; Half of the candy bars listed have a sugar content greater than 26 g, while half of the desserts listed have a sugar content greater than 19 g.

29. It depends on the kind of pie and the kind of candy bar; A piece of pumpkin pie contains 18 g of sugar, less than any of the candy bars listed. A piece of pecan pie contains 45 g of sugar, more than 75% of the candy bars listed.

HOMEWORK EXERCISES ▶ See Exs. 20–22 on pp. 496–497.

Key Concepts

Customary Units of Capacity (pp. 486–487)

Customary units of capacity include fluid ounce (fl oz), tablespoon (tbsp), cup (c), pint (pt), quart (qt), and gallon (gal). The table shows the relationships among customary units of capacity.

Customary Units of Capacity
1 tbsp = 0.5 fl oz
1 c = 8 fl oz
1 pt = 2 c = 16 fl oz
1 qt = 2 pt = 4 c = 32 fl oz
1 gal = 4 qt = 16 c = 128 fl oz

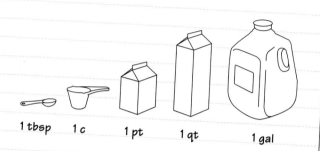

1 tbsp   1 c   1 pt   1 qt   1 gal

fluid ounce (fl oz)

tablespoon (tbsp)

cup (c)

pint (pt)

quart (qt)

gallon (gal)

Solving Inequalities (pp. 488–490)

When you solve problems that ask for a minimum or maximum amount, you might want to use an inequality.

Example $12x + 4 \geq 10$

$12x + 4 - 4 \geq 10 - 4$ ◀ Subtract **4** from each side.

$12x \geq 6$

$\dfrac{12x}{12} \geq \dfrac{6}{12}$ ◀ Divide both sides of the inequality by **12**.

$x \geq \dfrac{1}{2}$

Key Concepts Questions

30 The label on a full carton of buttermilk states that it contains $\frac{1}{2}$ pt. You pour out $\frac{3}{4}$ c and 2 tbsp of buttermilk. How much buttermilk remains in the carton?   **1 fl oz**

31 Solve each inequality.

   a. $3x > 18$ *x > 6*   **b.** $x - 5 < 12$ *x < 17*   **c.** $8 + x \leq 20$ *x ≤ 12*

Continued on the next page

CLOSURE QUESTION

Describe the relationships between tablespoons, fluid ounces, cups, pints, quarts, and gallons. Then state five values that can be read from a box-and-whisker plot.

Sample Response:
2 tblsp = 1 fl oz, 8 fl oz = 1 c, 2 c = 1 pt, 2 pt = 1 qt, 4 qt = 1 gal; You can read the median, upper and lower extremes, and the upper and lower quartile values from a box-and-whisker plot.

Section ③

Key Concepts

Box-and-Whisker Plots (pp. 491–492)

Box-and-whisker plots show the median and how spread out the data values are. They are useful for comparing sets of data.

Example

Amount of Calcium in Some Foods (mg)

lower extreme

upper extreme

lower quartile

upper quartile

32 Key Concepts Question The amounts of calcium in 20 vegetables were included in the box-and-whisker plot in the Example above. How many vegetables are represented by each whisker? by the box? *about 5 vegetables; about 10 vegetables*

Section ③

Practice & Application Exercises

YOU WILL NEED

For Exs. 20–21:
◆ graph paper

For Ex. 34
◆ Labsheet 3C

Replace each __?__ with the number that makes each a true statement.

1. 2 c = __?__ tbsp 32

2. 12 fl oz = __?__ pt $\frac{3}{4}$

3. $\frac{1}{2}$ gal = __?__ c 8

4. $\frac{3}{4}$ c = __?__ fl oz 6

5. 1 qt = __?__ fl oz 32

6. __?__ pt = $1\frac{1}{2}$ gal 12

7. **Health** Many health experts recommend that everyone needs 8 to 10 glasses of water each day, or about $2\frac{1}{2}$ qt. Use these facts to find the capacity of a glass. 8 to 10 fl oz

8. The directions on a 16 fl oz can of concentrated orange juice say to add 3 cans of cold water.

a. How many cups of water should be added? **6 c**

b. About how many quarts of orange juice will one can make? About how many gallons? **2 qt, $\frac{1}{2}$ gal**

9. Rachel has some crackers labeled "low fat" for an afternoon snack. One serving of the crackers has 2 g of fat and 60 Calories.

a. Each gram of fat contains 9 Cal. How many of the Calories in one serving of crackers come from fat?
18 Cal

b. What percent of the Calories in one serving of crackers comes from fat? **30%**

c. If less than 30% of the Calories from a food item come from fat, the food is considered to be *low fat*. Are Rachel's crackers actually *low fat*? Explain.
No; Exactly 30%, not less than 30%, of the Calories come from fat.

10. Look back at your work in Exercise 9.

a. Write an equation that can be used to find what percent of the Calories in a food item are from fat.

10. a. Let p = the percent Calories from fat, g = the number of grams of fat and C = the number of Calories in 1 serving of the food. Then, $\frac{9g}{C} \cdot 100 = p$.

b. Write an inequality that must be true for an item to be considered *low fat*. **Let g = the number of grams of fat and C = the number of Calories in 1 serving of the food. Then, $\frac{9g}{C} < 0.3$.**

c. A cupcake provides 129 Cal and 4.5 g of fat. What percent of the Calories in the cupcake comes from fat? Is the cupcake *low fat*? **31.4%; No.**

d. A container of fruit yogurt contains 225 Cal. About 10.4% of the Calories are from fat. About how many Calories are from fat? Round to the nearest Calorie. **23 Cal**

11. Beverages are said to be *very low sodium* if there is less than 35 mg of sodium in 8 fl oz.

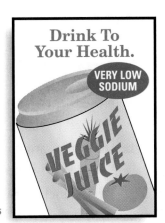

Drink To Your Health.

VERY LOW SODIUM

a. What is the most sodium that is allowed in a 12 fl oz can of *very low sodium* beverage? **52.5 mg**

b. Write an inequality to describe the amount of sodium allowed in a 12 fl oz can of *very low sodium* beverage. **Let s = the number of milligrams of sodium in 12 fl oz. Then, $s < 52.5$.**

▲ People with high blood pressure need to limit their intake of sodium.

13. b. No, 16 fl oz has to contain less than 280 mg; No, 15.5 fl oz has to contain less than 271 mg; Yes, 20 fl oz has to contain less than 350 mg and more than 87.5 mg.

12. The amounts of sodium in 12 fl oz cans of three types of soft drinks are listed below. Choose the letters of the soft drinks that can be labeled *very low sodium* as defined in Exercise 11 on page 495. A, C

   A. orange—35 mg   B. root beer—55 mg   C. cola—50 mg

13. A beverage is considered *low sodium* if 8 fl oz contains more than 35 mg of sodium but less than 140 mg of sodium.

   a. Write an inequality to show the amount of sodium allowed in 8 fl oz of a *low sodium* drink. Let s = the number of milligrams of sodium in 8 fl oz. Then, $35 < s < 140$

   b. Tell whether each drink below is a *low sodium* beverage. Explain your reasoning.

   • 16 fl oz of citrus punch containing 380 mg of sodium

   • 15.5 fl oz of chocolate drink containing 329 mg of sodium

   • 20 fl oz of citrus sports drink containing 275 mg of sodium

Solve each inequality.

14. $5x \le 100$ $x \le 20$ 15. $-2 + x \ge 6$ $x \ge 8$ 16. $4 < 7 + x$ $x > -3$

17. $\frac{1}{2}x < 14$ $x < 28$ 18. $3x + 1 \ge 4$ $x \ge 1$ 19. $2 \ge -4 + 6x$ $x \le 1$

20. Use the data in the table to make a box-and-whisker plot.

Average March Water Temperature at Eight Beaches (°F)			
Newport, RI	37	Oceanside, CA	58
Ocean City, MD	42	Seattle, WA	46
Key West, FL	75	Honolulu, HI	76
Freeport, TX	62	Juneau, AK	37

   a. Order the data. 37, 37, 42, 46, 58, 62, 75, 76   b. Find the extremes. 37, 76

   c. Find the median. 52   d. Find the quartiles. 39.5, 68.5

   e. Graph the median, the extremes, and the quartiles below a number line. Then draw the box and the whiskers.

20. e.

0 10 20 30 40 50 60 70 80

21. Answers will vary. Check students' work.

21. a. **Research** Find and record the numbers of grams of fat in 10 regular single-serving frozen entrees and in 10 reduced-Calorie or low-fat single-serving frozen entrees.

   b. Using the same number line, make a box-and-whisker plot for each data set in part (a).

   c. What conclusions can you draw from your graph? Explain.

Reflecting ◀▶ on the Section

Be prepared to report on the following topic in class.

22. Why do you think nutrition labels state the serving size in both customary and metric units, but the amounts of fat, protein, and carbohydrate in metric units only? Sample Response: There is no familiar and easy-to-use customary unit for very small weights.

Oral Report

Exercise 22 checks that you understand customary units.

Spiral ◀▶ Review

Find each percent. (Module 7, p. 479)

23. 30 is what percent of 12? 250%   24. 15 is what percent of 5? 300%

25. 86 is what percent of 44?   26. 6 is what percent of 5? 120%
    195.45%

Find each square root. (Module 6, p. 404)

27. $\sqrt{16}$ 4   28. $\sqrt{36}$ 6   29. $\sqrt{100}$ 10

Find each amount. (Module 5, p. 352)

30. 15% of 28 4.2   31. 40% of 32 12.8   32. 80% of 155 124

Extension ▶▶

Outliers

One candy bar in the box-and-whisker plot has 47 g of sugar. Another has 40 g of sugar.

Amounts of Sugar in 26 Candy Bars (g)

33. a. Where are these two candy bars located on the box-and-whisker plot? They are within the right whisker.

    b. How do the numbers of grams of sugar in these two candy bars compare with those in the other candy bars?
       They have more sugar than at least 75% of the other candy bars.

Data values that are much greater or much smaller than the other data values are *outliers*.

34. **Use Labsheet 3C.** Follow the steps in *Determining Outliers* to decide if the candy bars with 40 g and 47 g of sugar are outliers.

34. a. 9
    b. 50%
    c. 13.5
    d. 43.5
    e. 7.5
    f. 47 is an outlier.
    g.
       Amounts of Sugar in 26 Candy Bars (g)

Section ③
Extra Skill Practice

Replace each _?_ with the number that makes each a true statement.

1. 3 fl oz = _?_ tbsp 6

2. 16 fl oz = _?_ pt 1

3. $\frac{3}{4}$ gal = _?_ qt 3

4. $\frac{1}{2}$ qt = _?_ fl oz 16

5. 2 pt = _?_ fl oz 32

6. $2\frac{3}{4}$ gal = _?_ pt 22

Solve each inequality.

7. $4x \le 88$ $x \le 22$

8. $-3 + x \ge 9$ $x \ge 12$

9. $3 < 8 + x$ $x > -5$

10. $\frac{3}{4}x < 52$ $x < 69\frac{1}{3}$

11. $5x \ge 7$ $x \ge 1\frac{2}{5}$

12. $5 \ge 10 + x$ $x \le -5$

13. Make a box-and-whisker plot for the data in the table.

Food	Protein per serving (g)
bread	3
cereal	2
margarine	0
oatmeal	6
peanut butter	4
spaghetti	7
yogurt	8

Protein per Serving in 7 Foods (g)

0 1 2 3 4 5 6 7 8

Standardized Testing ◀▶ Multiple Choice

For each measure, choose the letter of the greater measure.

1. 16 pt B

   Ⓐ 2 gal   Ⓑ 10 qt   Ⓒ 30 c   Ⓓ 1 gal 2 qt

2. 1 pt 1 c D

   Ⓐ $1\frac{1}{2}$ pt   Ⓑ 3 c   Ⓒ 2 c 6 fl oz   Ⓓ 30 fl oz

Section 4

Circle Graphs, and Choosing a Graph

IN THIS SECTION

EXPLORATION 1
◆ Circle Graphs

EXPLORATION 2
◆ Choosing a Graph

GETTING YOUR

ZZzᶻᶻz

Setting the Stage ▸▹▸▹▸▹▸▹▸▹▸▹▸▹▸▹▸▹▸▹▸▹▸▹▸▹▸▹

Some studies show that many teens do not get enough sleep during the school week. In this section you'll examine how much sleep you and your classmates get. Then you'll compare this data with a survey of over 800,000 adults at least 29 years old.

The survey asked people how long they sleep each night. The results are shown in the graph at the right.

Adult Sleep Survey

8–8.9 hours

less than 7 hours

9 hours or more

7–7.9 hours

Think About It

1 Use the graph above. The percents of adults who fall into each sleep category are shown by the relative sizes of the circles.

  a. The greatest percent of people sleep how many hours? **8–8.9 h**

  b. The least percent of people sleep how many hours? **9 h or more**

2 **Try This as a Class** About 45% of the adults surveyed sleep between 8 h and 8.9 h each night. About what percent of the adults surveyed sleep less than 7 h? Was it difficult to estimate the percent? Explain. **about 15%; Sample Response: Yes; I had to compare the areas of the two circles.**

▾▾▾▾ **WARM-UP EXERCISES**

Solve each proportion.

  1. $\frac{3}{5} = \frac{x}{10}$ 6

  2. $\frac{12}{20} = \frac{8}{y}$ $13\frac{1}{3}$

  3. Find 25% of 100.   25
  4. Find 16% of 360.   57.6

Write each fraction as a decimal and a percent.

  5. $\frac{45}{80}$ 0.5625, 56.25%

  6. $\frac{381}{635}$ 0.6, 60%

GOAL

LEARN HOW TO...
◆ make a circle
  graph

AS YOU...
◆ conduct a survey
  on sleep habits

KEY TERMS
◆ circle graph
◆ central angle
◆ sector

Exploration 1

Circle GRAPHS

SET UP *You will need:* • *compass* • *protractor*

▶ Different kinds of graphs can be used to describe the same data.
A *circle graph* can be used to show the percent of adults in each sleep
category of the survey discussed in the *Setting the Stage* on page 499.
In a **circle graph**, the entire circle represents the whole, or 100%.

About 45% of the adults surveyed said
they sleep between 8 h and 8.9 h
each night. On a circle graph this is
shown with a *central angle* of 162°,
since 45% of 360° is 162°.

162°

A **central angle** is an
angle that has its vertex
at the center of a circle.

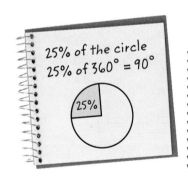
25% of the circle
25% of 360° = 90°
25%

3 Discussion Why is 360° used to find the central angle?
The number of degrees in a circle is 360°.

4 a. On a circle graph, what is the measure of a central angle that
represents 25%? 10%? 20%? 90°; 36°; 72°

b. Sketch a circle graph to show each percent in part (a). Clearly
label each percent. See below.

4. b.

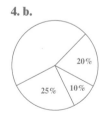
20%
25% 10%

▶ The complete circle graph for the
survey is shown at the right. Each
sector represents the data in a
different sleep category.

A **sector** is a wedge-shaped
region bounded by two radii
and an arc of a circle.

Adult Sleep Survey

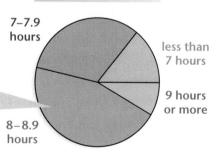
7–7.9
hours
less than
7 hours
9 hours
or more
8–8.9
hours

Use the completed circle graph on page 500 to answer Questions 5 and 6.

5 a. Estimate the percent of adults who sleep 7 h–7.9 h each night. *about* $33\frac{1}{3}\%$

b. Use a protractor to find how many degrees represent the sleep category 7 h–7.9 h. What percent of 360° is this? *115°; about 32%*

c. How does your estimate in part (a) compare with your answer in part (b)? *Sample Response: It is very close.*

6 Discussion Compare the circle graph on page 500 with the graph on page 499. Which graph do you think shows the survey results more clearly? Explain. *Sample Response: the graph on page 500; It is easier to estimate parts of a whole than to estimate relative areas.*

▶ **You have seen how much adults sleep each night. How do you think your sleeping habits and those of your classmates compare with those of adults?**

7 Try This as a Class Your teacher will announce each sleep category aloud to the class. Raise your hand when the sleep category that describes your own sleeping habit is announced. *Check students' work.*

a. Record the number of students in each sleep category in a table like the one shown.

Class Sleeping Habits

Sleep category	Number of students	Percent of class
less than 7 h	?	?
7 h–7.9 h	?	?
8 h–8.9 h	?	?
9 h or more	?	?

b. Find the percent of students in each sleep category. Round each answer to the nearest tenth of a percent.

▶ **To show your sleep data on a circle graph, you need to find the measure of the central angle that represents the percent in each sleep category.**

EXAMPLE

Suppose 58.1% of students said they slept 8 h–8.9 h each night. Find the measure of a central angle on a circle graph that represents this percent.

SAMPLE RESPONSE

Using a Proportion

$$\frac{58.1}{100} = \frac{x}{360} \quad \begin{matrix} \longleftarrow \text{part} \\ \longleftarrow \text{whole} \end{matrix}$$

$$100x = 58.1 \cdot 360$$

$$x = 209.16$$

Using an Equation

58.1% of 360 is what number?

$$\frac{58.1}{100} \cdot 360 = x$$

$$209.16 = x$$

Write the percent in fraction or decimal form.

Rounding to the nearest degree gives a central angle of 209°.

---

8 Suppose 22.4% of the students in one class said they slept 7 h–7.9 h every night. Find the measure of a central angle that represents 22.4%. Round your answer to the nearest degree. 81°

✔ QUESTION 9

...checks that you can make a circle graph.

9 ✔ CHECKPOINT Use your class data from Question 7.

Check students' work.

a. Find the measure of a central angle for each sleep category.

b. Use a compass and a protractor to make a circle graph of the results of your class sleep survey. Make sure your graph is clearly labeled.

10 Discussion Compare the circle graph showing your class results with the circle graph on page 500.

a. How do the sleeping habits of students in your class compare with those of the adults surveyed? Check students' work.

b. What are some other ways you might represent the sleep survey results? Sample Response: on a bar graph, in a table

11 Discussion Scientific studies show that teenagers need more sleep than children or adults.

a. Why do you think teenagers need more sleep?
Sample Response: Teenagers are more active.

b. Many teenagers need more than 9 h of sleep each night. What percent of your class is getting this much sleep? Check students' work.

HOMEWORK EXERCISES ▶ See Exs. 1–11 on pp. 507–508.

Choosing a GRAPH

SET UP *Work with a partner. You will need:*
• *protractor* • *compass* • *ruler* • *stopwatch*

▶ **How important is getting enough rest? Can even small amounts of rest make a difference? You'll answer these questions after completing an activity. The class will be divided into two groups—students who rest between trials and those who do not.**

12 Try This as a Class With your partner, decide which of you will rest between trials. This person is in Group A. The other person is in Group B. Students in both groups should complete three trials of the experiment. **Check students' work.**

Students in Group A should rest 30 seconds between each trial. Students in Group B should not rest between trials.

As you open and close your hand, be sure your fingertips touch the desk and your palm.

First

Place the arm you use for writing flat on your desk with your hand open, the palm up, and your fingers together.

Then

After your teacher gives a signal, close and open your hand as many times as you can in 30 seconds.

Have your partner count and record how many times your fingers hit the desk.

a. Record the results of each trial.

b. Record the class results of the third trial for Groups A and B in a table like the one shown.

c. How do the results for students who rested between trials compare with the results for those who did not?

Class Results of Third Trial	
Group A	Group B
?	?
?	?
?	?

▶ **Comparing Representations** To compare data values or sets of data, you can display the data using a graph. You have already learned several ways to represent a set of data. Some of those include:

FOR ◀ HELP
with *stem-and-leaf plots*, see
MODULE 5, p. 320.

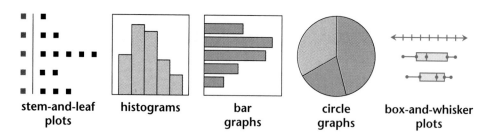

stem-and-leaf plots   histograms   bar graphs   circle graphs   box-and-whisker plots

13 Use your class results from Question 12. With your partner, make each graph below to compare the results of Groups A and B.
Check students' work.

a. Make two box-and-whisker plots comparing the results of Group A with those of Group B.

b. Make two circle graphs. You may need to divide each data set into intervals.

c. Display the class results in either a stem-and-leaf plot, a bar graph, or a line plot.

14 Work with your partner to answer each question in parts (a)–(e). Tell which graph from Question 13 you chose to find each answer, and explain your choices. Check students' work.

a. What was the range of data for Group A? for Group B?

b. How many students could close their hands more than 25 times in Group A? in Group B?

c. How many times could the greatest number of students in Group B close their hands? in Group A?

d. How do the fastest 25% of the students in Group A compare with the fastest 25% of the students in Group B?

e. Are there any gaps or clusters in the data for each group? If so, where?

15 Discussion Examine the graphs you made in Question 13.
Answers will vary. Check students' work.

a. Which graph do you think is most effective in showing the importance of rest? Explain.

b. Do you think small amounts of rest make a difference in performance? Explain.

HOMEWORK EXERCISES ▶ See Exs. 12–16 on pp. 508–509.

Section 4
Key Concepts ►►►►►►►►►►►►►►►►►►►►►►►►►

Circle Graphs (pp. 500–502)

A circle graph can be used to compare parts of a data set with the whole, or to display percent data.

circle graph

Example 1011 adults in the United States were surveyed about their sleeping habits. The circle graph below shows how they responded.

Question:
Do you think you get more
or less sleep than you need?

Number of people	Response
167	more
541	less
282	just right
21	don't know

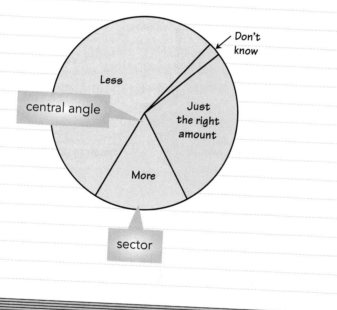

central angle

sector

16 Key Concepts Question Use the circle graph in the Example above.

a. Estimate the percent of adults who gave each response shown on the circle graph. more: about 15%; less: about 50%; just right: about 30%; don't know: about 5%

b. Measure the central angle for each sector to the nearest degree. Then find the actual percents. How close were your estimates? more: 59°, 16%; less: 193°, 54%; just right: 100°, 28%; don't know: 8°, 2%; Sample Response: My estimates were close.

Continued on the next page

Choosing a Graph (pp. 503–504)

The graph you choose to represent a data set depends on what message you want to communicate.

Box-and-whisker plots are good for comparing two sets of data.

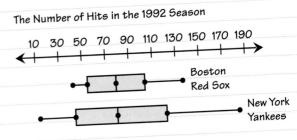

The Number of Hits in the 1992 Season

10 30 50 70 90 110 130 150 170 190

Boston Red Sox

New York Yankees

Bar graphs or **histograms** can be used to compare values in a data set.

Participation in Soccer, 1994	
Age in years	Number of participants
7–11	5494
12–17	3536
18–24	1394
25–34	1023

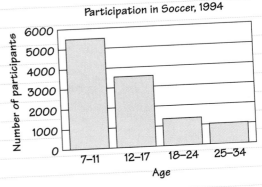

Participation in Soccer, 1994

A frequency table is helpful when you have a large set of data to organize.

Stem-and-leaf plots display individual data values. These plots can help you organize data and see gaps and clusters in the data.

Number of Bushels of Wheat Harvested per Acre for Selected States (1990)

```
2 | 8
3 | 1 2 4 5
4 | 0 8 8
5 |
6 | 1
7 | 3        6 | 1 represents 61 bushels.
```

CLOSURE QUESTION

Tell when a circle graph is a good representation for a set of data values.

Sample Response: When you are comparing parts of a whole.

17. Sample Response: Since you tallied the number of students in each sleep category and don't have individual sleep times, a stem-and-leaf plot and a box-and-whisker plot are inappropriate. Since the intervals over which the data are distributed are not equal, a histogram is inappropriate.

17 **Key Concepts Question** Which types of graphs described above would *not* be appropriate to use to represent the results of your class sleep survey? Explain your choices.

Section 4

Practice & Application Exercises ▶▶▶▶▶▶

YOU WILL NEED

For Ex. 10:
◆ compass
◆ protractor

For Exs. 12–14:
◆ Labsheet 4A
◆ compass
◆ protractor

Estimation For Exercises 1–3, use the circle graph to estimate each percent.

1. the percent of 1994 sports and compact cars that were red, green, or white about 50%

2. the percent of 1994 sports and compact cars that were blue about 20%

3. the percent of 1994 sports and compact cars that were black about 10%

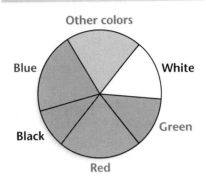

Colors of New Sports Cars and Compact Cars, 1994 Model Year

For Exercises 4–9, find the measure of the central angle for each sector of the circle. Round each measure to the nearest degree.

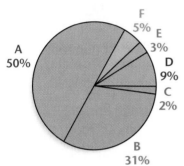

4. A 180°   5. B 112°

6. C 7°   7. D 32°

8. E 11°   9. F 18°

10. c.

less productive other 5% don't know
less alert 8% 9%
10%
crankiness 20% loss of energy 48%

10. **Sleep Survey** A thousand people were asked to identify the main consequence of not getting enough sleep. Their responses are summarized in the table.

   a. Write each number as a percent. See table.

   b. Find the measures of the central angles that represent the six responses on a circle graph. See table.

   c. Make a circle graph to show the results of the survey. Make sure your graph is clearly labeled. See above.

Main Consequence of Too Little Sleep		
Response	Number of people	
loss of energy	483	48.3%; 174°
crankiness	200	20.0%; 72°
less alert	103	10.3%; 37°
less productive	76	7.6%; 27°
other	48	4.8%; 17°
do not know/ no response	90	9.0%; 32°

11. C; Graph C is the only graph that shows a section greater than $\frac{1}{2}$ the circle to represent 60% and that has other fractional parts that correspond to the data.

11. Surveys People in France were asked how interesting they thought their lives were. Of those surveyed, 14% rated their lives as very interesting, 60% as fairly interesting, 22% as fairly dull, 3% as very dull, and 1% did not know. Choose the letter of the circle graph that shows these results. Explain your choice.

A.   B.   C.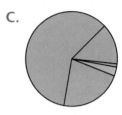

Use Labsheet 4A for Exercises 12–14.

12. Vacation Days *The Vacation Days Table* compares the number of vacation days per year for different jobs in various world cities. Make a graph that compares the vacation days for two of the jobs. See Additional Answers.

13. Write three conclusions you can draw based on the graph you made in Exercise 12.

13. Sample Response: The median number of days off is highest for plant managers. About 25% of the bus drivers, 75% of the auto mechanics, and 50% of the secretaries have 20 or fewer days off.

14. Several surveys have been done to find out the average time people go to sleep and wake up each day. The *Sleep Time Survey* results show the bedtimes and wake-up times of 11–15 year old girls and boys. Do teenagers get less sleep as they get older? Make a graph to support your answer. See Additional Answers.

15. Sample Response: No; The greatest percent appears to occupy the least area.

15. Radio Listening A radio station reports that of the total radio listening audience in the United States, 36% listen to the radio at work, 32% listen at home, and 30% listen in the car. Terri decides to show these results with a graph. Do you think her graph is accurate and effective? Explain.

Reflecting ▶on the Section

16. **Sleep Research** Scientists have divided sleep into stages. A group of sleepers were monitored to find out how much time they spent in each stage. The average percent of the total sleep period spent in each stage is shown in the graph. Each percent is represented by the height of a rectangular prism. **See below.**

Exercise 16 checks that you can analyze the effectiveness of a visual representation.

   a. About what percent of sleep time is spent in Stage 2? Is it possible for someone to incorrectly read the graph? Explain.

   b. Suppose you want to show that the total amount of time people spend in Stages 1, 3, and 4 is about the same as the time spent in REM sleep. Does this graph show this? Explain.

   c. Explain how you could represent the same results with a different type of graph.

   Sleep stages are defined by ▶ brain wave (EEG) patterns. There are two basic types of sleep— REM and non-REM, or NREM. The colorful, visual dreams that people are most likely to remember occur during REM, or rapid eye movement, sleep.

16. a. Accept reasonable estimates. Sample Response: about 50%; Yes. Someone could mistakenly compare the top edge of the front of a prism to the horizontal grid lines rather than comparing the top edge of the back of the prism to those grid lines.
b. Yes; The lengths of the 3 bars have to be added.
c. Sample Response: Use the same data on a 2–dimensional bar graph or find the percent spent in each stage and construct a circle graph.

Spiral ◀▶Review

Replace each ? with the number that makes each a true statement.
(Mod 7, p. 493)

17. 6 tbsp = ___?___ fl oz   3

18. 12 fl oz = ___?___ qt $\frac{3}{8}$

19. $\frac{3}{4}$ qt = ___?___ gal $\frac{3}{16}$

20. $\frac{1}{2}$ gal = ___?___ fl oz   64

Evaluate each expression. (Module 4, p. 284)

21. $\frac{1}{4}(-10) - 1$ $-3\frac{1}{2}$

22. $3.7 \div 2 + -8$ -6.15

23. $-12 \cdot \frac{5}{8} + 7$ -0.5

Find the area of each figure. (Module 6, p. 388)

24.
64 yd³

25.
6 cm²

26.
900 ft²

Working on the Module Project

The Picture of Health

Analyzing Data Before making a graph, you should decide what message you want the graph to convey. Begin by looking at your data.

The table lists the results of a survey conducted in the United States in 1993.

VIGOROUS EXERCISE

Participation in Exercise Activities			
Grade	Vigorous exercise	Stretching exercises	Strengthening exercises
9th	74.5%	64.3%	60.9%
10th	69.5%	57.4%	55.0%
11th	62.5%	50.9%	48.5%
12th	57.8%	46.9%	44.6%

 4 What message could you convey with this data? Here are some ideas to think about. **See Additional Answers.**

  ◆ Which type of exercise is the most popular?

  ◆ Is there a dramatic difference in participation among the different grade levels?

  ◆ Are there any surprising results in this data?

  ◆ Why is the total participation at each grade level greater than 100%?

 5 Make a graph that illustrates your ideas about participation in exercise activities by students in grades 9–12.
See Additional Answers.

STRETCHING EXERCISES

STRENGTHENING EXERCISES

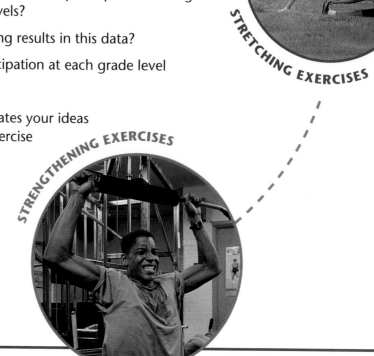

For each sector of the circle graph, find the measure of the central angle. Round each measure to the nearest degree.

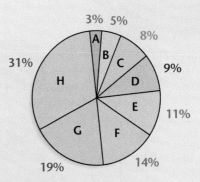

1. A 11°   2. B 18°   3. C 29°

4. D 32°   5. E 40°   6. F 50°

7. G 68°   8. H 112°

9. See Additional Answers.

9. a. Choose the best kind of graph to compare the average daily household television viewing during the months of February and July for the years listed in the table.

   b. Draw the graph you have chosen.

   c. Write three conclusions you can draw based on your graph.

Average Daily Household Television Viewing (minutes)		
Year	February	July
1988–1989	452	387
1989–1990	436	384
1990–1991	450	386
1991–1992	452	399
1992–1993	461	407

Standardized Testing ◀▶ Performance Task

Complete Exercises 1 and 2 for each type of graph named. **See Additional Answers.**

   a. bar graph   b. stem-and-leaf-plot   c. circle graph

   d. box-and-whisker plot   e. scatter plot   f. histogram

1. Tell what information about a data set can be read from each type of graph, and explain how each type of information is displayed.

2. Tell whether it is possible to make each type of graph misleading, and if it is possible, describe one way to do so.

Section ⑤ Quadrilaterals

IN THIS SECTION

EXPLORATION 1
♦ Classifying Quadrilaterals

EXPLORATION 2
♦ Area of a Trapezoid

WARM-UP EXERCISES

Sketch each polygon.
Sample responses are given.

1. parallelogram

2. square

3. rectangle

4. quadrilateral

Find the area of the figure.

5.
17.1 in.

22.8 in.

194.94 in.^{2}

6.
2 cm

8 cm

16 cm^2

A THOUSAND WORDS

◄--- *Setting the Stage*

Have you ever heard the expression, "A picture is worth a thousand words"? Pictures and graphs have long been used to present ideas. The United States Department of Agriculture (USDA) uses graphs to educate people about the importance of nutrition. The graph below is the USDA's Food Guide Pyramid.

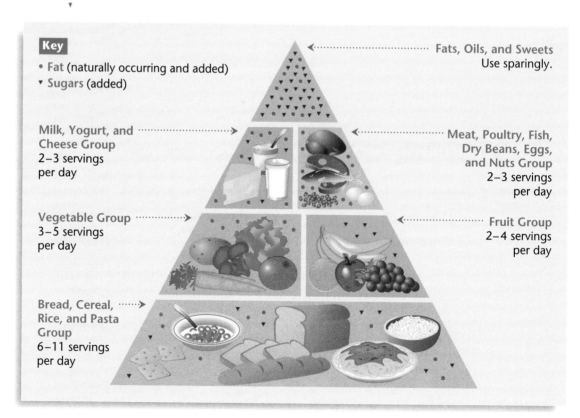

Key
• Fat (naturally occurring and added)
▾ Sugars (added)

Fats, Oils, and Sweets
Use sparingly.

Milk, Yogurt, and Cheese Group
2–3 servings per day

Meat, Poultry, Fish, Dry Beans, Eggs, and Nuts Group
2–3 servings per day

Vegetable Group
3–5 servings per day

Fruit Group
2–4 servings per day

Bread, Cereal, Rice, and Pasta Group
6–11 servings per day

Think About It ▸▸▸▹▸▹▸▹▸▹▸▹▸▹▸▹▸▹▸▹▸▹▸▹▸▹▸▹▸▹▸▹▸▹▸▹

1 The key for the Food Guide Pyramid shows symbols for fat and sugar. Where do these symbols appear in the pyramid? They appear throughout the pyramid, but especially concentrated at the top.

2 Why do you think there are sugar symbols in the *Milk, Yogurt, and Cheese Group*? These foods contain sugar.

3 Which food group of the pyramid shows no fats? the Fruit Group

4 The USDA chose polygons to represent each food group of the pyramid. How many different types of polygons were used? 2

5 Are any of these polygons congruent? If so, which ones? Yes; those in the second row

---

Exploration 1 ▸▹▸▹▸▹▸▹▸▹▸▹▸▹▸▹▸▹▸▹▸▹▸▹▸▹▸▹▸▹

CLASSIFYING Quadrilaterals

SET UP *Work in a group of three. You will need:*
• *Labsheets 5A–5C* • *scissors*

The USDA surveyed people to determine the effectiveness of different graphs. Those surveyed generally felt that the pyramid was more visually appealing than other representations, such as a bar graph or a circle graph.

6 Look at the Food Guide Pyramid. Describe the shapes of the food group polygons. The figure in the top row is a triangle. The rest are quadrilaterals.

▶ Except for the *Fats, Oils, and Sweets Group*, the parts of the Food Guide Pyramid are all *trapezoids*.

7 **Discussion** These polygons are all trapezoids. List two properties common to all the trapezoids. 4 sides, exactly 1 pair of parallel sides

The arrowheads show that segments are parallel.

GOAL

LEARN HOW TO...
◆ identify trapezoids and rhombuses
◆ classify quadrilaterals

AS YOU...
◆ play the game *Quadrilateral Sets*

KEY TERMS
◆ trapezoid
◆ bases of a trapezoid
◆ rhombus

Section 5 Quadrilaterals **513**

▶ A **trapezoid** is a quadrilateral that has only one pair of opposite sides which are parallel.

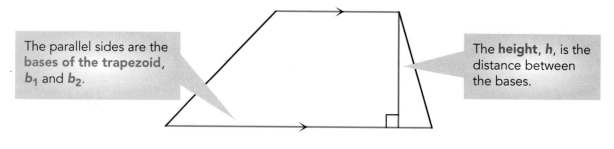

The parallel sides are the **bases of the trapezoid,** b_1 and b_2.

The **height**, h, is the distance between the bases.

Meat, Poultry, Fish, Dry Beans, Eggs, Nuts
2–3 servings

Milk, Yogurt, Cheese
2–3 servings

Vegetables
3–5 servings

Bread, Cereal, Rice, Pasta
6–11 servings

Fruit
2–4 servings

Fats, Oils, Sweets *Use sparingly.*

▶ The graph at the left was not one used by the USDA, but it makes use of some of their ideas.

For example, the areas of the polygons are proportional to the average number of servings you should have every day.

8. a. all: quadrilaterals; milk: parallelogram, rectangle; meat: parallelogram, rectangle, rhombus, square; vegetables: parallelogram; bread: trapezoid; fruit: parallelogram, rhombus; fats: trapezoid

8 Try This as a Class Use the graph above.

a. Give as many names as you can for each polygon in the graph.

b. The polygon for the *Fruit Group* is a *rhombus*. A **rhombus** is a parallelogram that has four congruent sides. The quadrilaterals for which other food groups in the graph are rhombuses?

Meat, Poultry, Fish, Dry Beans, Eggs, Nuts

▶ In the game *Quadrilateral Sets*, you'll match a picture of a quadrilateral with the quadrilateral's name and one of its *attributes*, or properties.

Each set must contain one quadrilateral card, one name card, and one attribute card.

Quadrilateral Card

Name Card

Square

Attribute Card

All angles are right angles.

9 Try This as a Class Suppose you received the cards below in the game *Quadrilateral Sets*. Can you make two complete sets? Explain.

No; Neither quadrilateral card can be matched with the 1st attribute card.

Quadrilateral Card

Name Card

Parallelogram

Attribute Card

Only one pair of opposite sides is parallel.

Quadrilateral Card

Name Card

Rhombus

Attribute Card

All sides are congruent.

10 Use Labsheets 5A–5C. Cut out the *Quadrilateral Sets Game Cards*. Read the directions below and play the game twice.

Check students' work.

QUADRILATERAL SETS

SET UP

- Cut out the cards on Labsheets 5A–5C. Shuffle the cards and deal six cards face down to each of the three players. Any remaining cards should be placed face down in the middle of the table. This is the draw deck.

- Turn over the top card. This is the start of the discard pile.

PLAY

- Play begins with the player to the dealer's left and continues clockwise.

- On your turn, you may pick up the top card from either the discard pile or the draw deck. Use your cards to try to make two sets, each one containing one name, one attribute, and one quadrilateral card that go together.

- Then discard one card. Your turn is now over.

WINNING

When you have two complete sets of cards, show them to the other players. If the sets are complete and correct, you win!

CHALLENGE

You may challenge another player's set by showing that one of the cards does not belong. If the sets are not complete or accurate, the cards are picked up and the game continues.

11 Discussion What strategies did you use in the game? Were some cards better to keep than others? Why? Sample Response: I discarded trapezoid cards since so few attribute cards applied to them.

HOMEWORK EXERCISES ▶ See Exs. 1–9 on p. 519.

Exploration 2

AREA OF A Trapezoid

SET UP *Work in a group. You will need:* • *Labsheet 5D* • *scissors* • *metric ruler* • *tracing paper*

In designing the Food Guide Pyramid, the USDA considered the relative sizes of the parts. For instance, the *Bread Group*, with 6–11 servings, should be larger than the *Milk Group*, with 2–3 servings. You can explore the relative sizes of the food groups by comparing their areas.

FOR◄HELP

with *area of a parallelogram*, see **MODULE 6, p. 388**

▶ You can use what you know about the area of a parallelogram to determine the area of a trapezoid.

Parallelogram

Trapezoid

Area = base length • height

Area = **?**

12. a. Trapezoid 1: about 22 cm², Trapezoid 2: about 22 cm², Trapezoid 3: about 26 cm², Trapezoid 4: about 15 cm²
c. Trapezoid 1: 45 cm², Trapezoid 2: 44 cm², Trapezoid 3: 52 cm², Trapezoid 4: 30 cm²; Sample Response: I used the formula $A = bh$.
d. Trapezoid 1: 22.5 cm², Trapezoid 2: 22 cm², Trapezoid 3: 26 cm², Trapezoid 4: 15 cm²; I divided the area of the parallelogram by 2.

12 Use Labsheet 5D.

a. Cut out one of the *Trapezoids*. (Each member of your group should work with a different trapezoid.) Estimate the area of your trapezoid in square centimeters.

b. Trace your trapezoid from part (a) and cut it out. The two trapezoids are congruent. Form a parallelogram with the trapezoids. Check students' work.

c. Find the area of the parallelogram in square centimeters. Explain how you found the area.

d. What is the area of the original trapezoid? Explain how you found the area.

e. How close was your estimate in part (a) to your answer in part (d)?

Sample Response: very close

13 **Try This as a Class** In Question 12, you used two trapezoids to form a parallelogram.

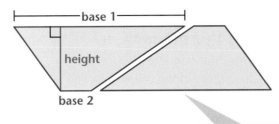

This side has the same length as **base 1**.

a. Use the diagram above to write an expression for the area of the parallelogram. If b_1 = the length of base 1 and b_2 = the length of base 2, then $A = (b_1 + b_2)h$.

b. The area of one trapezoid is half the area of the parallelogram. Write a formula for the area of a trapezoid.

$$A = \frac{1}{2}(b_1 + b_2)h.$$

14 Use your trapezoid from Question 12.

a. Calculate the area of your trapezoid using your formula from Question 13(b). Trapezoid 1: 22.5 cm², Trapezoid 2: 22 cm², Trapezoid 3: 26 cm², Trapezoid 4: 15 cm²

b. Compare your answer in part (a) with your answer in Question 12(d). Sample Response: They are the same.

15 ✔ **CHECKPOINT** Use the *Bread Group* and *Milk Group* polygons from the Food Guide Pyramid on page 512.

a. Find the area of each polygon. 3.8 cm², 19.4 cm²

b. About how many times as many servings should you have of the *Bread Group* as of the *Milk Group*? Do you think the relative areas of the parts of the Food Guide Pyramid show this? Explain. 2 to $5\frac{1}{2}$ times; Yes; The area of the *Bread Group* polygon is about 5 times that of the *Milk Group* polygon.

HOMEWORK EXERCISES ▸ See Exs. 10–20 on pp. 519–520.

✔ **QUESTION 15**

...checks that you can find the area of a trapezoid.

Section 5

Key Concepts

Key Terms

trapezoid

bases of a trapezoid

rhombus

Trapezoids and Rhombuses (pp. 513–515)

A trapezoid is a quadrilateral that has exactly one pair of parallel sides. The sides that are parallel are the bases of the trapezoid.

A rhombus is a parallelogram that has four congruent sides (as indicated by the tick marks).

Area of a Trapezoid (pp. 516–517)

The area of a trapezoid can be calculated using the formula

$$A = \frac{1}{2}(b_1 + b_2)h$$

where A is the area, h is the height, and b_1 and b_2 are the base lengths.

Example Find the area of the trapezoid shown.

$$A = \frac{1}{2}(3 + 4.5)2 = \frac{1}{2}(7.5)2 = \left(\frac{7.5}{2}\right)2 = 7.5$$

The area is 7.5 m².

16. a. parallelogram
b. rectangle
c. square
d. rhombus
e. trapezoid

CLOSURE QUESTION

State the formula for the area of a trapezoid. How is it like the formula for the area of other quadrilaterals? How is it different?

Sample Response:
$A = \frac{1}{2}(b_1 + b_2)h$;

Both this formula and the formula for the area of any type of parallelogram ($A = bh$) use multiplication of base length and height to find area. However, since a trapezoid has two bases of different lengths, the average of these lengths is used. The formula for a trapezoid could also be used for a parallelogram; since the bases are congruent,

$A = \frac{1}{2}(b + b)h = bh$.

Key Concepts Questions

16 Copy the Venn diagram below and then fill in the missing quadrilateral names.

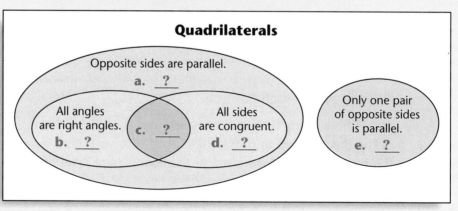

17 Find the area of a trapezoid with base lengths 3 cm and 5 cm and height 4 cm. **16 cm²**

Section 5
Practice & Application Exercises

YOU WILL NEED

For Ex. 6:
◆ graph paper

For Exs. 18 and 19:
◆ Labsheet 5D
◆ metric ruler

Choose the letters of all the figures of each type.

1. trapezoid B, F

2. parallelogram that is not a rhombus A, E

3. rhombus C, D

A.

B.

C.

D.

E.

F.

4. Suppose you have a parallelogram card in your hand during a game of *Quadrilateral Sets*. Which attribute cards can go with it?
Both pairs of opposite sides are parallel; Both pairs of opposite sides are congruent.

5. Suppose you have the attribute card "All sides are congruent." in a game of *Quadrilateral Sets*. Which quadrilateral cards can go with it? rhombus, square

6. Open-ended Draw a trapezoid, a rhombus, a square, a parallelogram, and a rectangle on graph paper.

6. Sample Response:

Find the area of each rhombus.

7.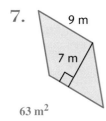
9 m
7 m
63 m²

8.
2 cm
4 cm²

9.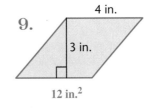
4 in.
3 in.
12 in.²

10. Urban Gardening A corner plot of an urban garden is set aside for the Rodriguez family, as shown. What *percent* of the garden will be used by the Rodriguez family? 17.5%

25 ft
15 ft
10 ft
30 ft
50 ft

Find the area of each trapezoid with the given measurements.

11. b_1 = 4 in., b_2 = 2 in., h = 6 in. 18 in.^{2}

12. b_1 = 4.3 m, b_2 = 5.1 m, h = 2.7 m 12.69 m^2

13. b_1 = $4\frac{1}{4}$ in., b_2 = $7\frac{1}{2}$ in., h = $3\frac{1}{2}$ in. $20\frac{9}{16}$ in.^{2}, or 20.5625 in.^{2}

14. b_1 = 6.75 cm, b_2 = 5.64 cm, h = 3.2 cm 19.824 cm^2

For each trapezoid, find the unknown dimension or the area.

15.
2 cm
A = ?
5 cm
9 cm
27.5 cm^2

16.
13 in.
A = ?
9 in.
15 in.
165 in.^{2}

17.
⊢ 8 cm ⊣
h = ?
A = 35 cm^2
6 cm
5 cm

Use Labsheet 5D for Exercises 18 and 19.

18. a–b. Measurements may vary. Sample Response:

3.0 cm
≈ 1.8 cm^2
8.1 cm^2
≈ 5.0 cm^2
2.7 cm
1.3 cm   3.0 cm   3.7 cm

Area: about 14.9 cm^2

18. In Exploration 2, you found the area of a trapezoid by forming a parallelogram from two congruent trapezoids. Another way to find the area is to think of the trapezoid as a *composite figure*— one made from a combination of other shapes.

   a. Draw segments to separate the *Trapezoid* into other shapes.

   b. Find the area of the *Trapezoid* by finding the area of these smaller shapes. Measure to the nearest tenth of a centimeter.

   c. Is this method easier to use than the other methods you learned in Exploration 2? Why or why not?
   Sample Response: No; This method requires more measurement and calculations.

19. **Open-ended** Separate the *Polygon* into quadrilaterals and triangles. Find the area of the *Polygon* in square centimeters.
   Check students' work. Area is about 12 cm^2 or 13 cm^2.

Visual THINKING

Exercise 20 checks that you understand what a trapezoid is and how to find its area.

Reflecting ▶ on the Section

20. Suppose the area of a trapezoid is 8 cm^2 and its height is 2 cm. Draw two trapezoids that fit this description. See below.

20. Sample Response:

2 cm
2 cm
6 cm

2 cm
3 cm   5 cm

Spiral ◀▶ Review

For each sector of the circle graph, find the measure of the central angle. Round to the nearest degree.
(Module 7, p. 505)

21. A 22°   22. B 32°   23. C 47°

24. D 65°   25. E 76°   26. F 119°

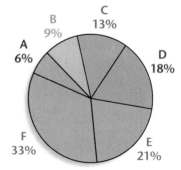

C 13%
B 9%
A 6%
D 18%
F 33%
E 21%

For Exercises 27 and 28, write an expression that models each situation. (Module 2, p. 124)

27. Danny's Aunt Judy is twice as old as Danny. Danny is *x* years old. How old is Danny's aunt? $2x$

28. Marisa studied 20 minutes more than Burt did. If Marisa studied for *t* min, how long did Burt study? $t - 20$

29. Draw a tree diagram to represent all the possible outcomes when you toss a coin twice. (*Hint:* The outcomes are *heads* (H) and *tails* (T).) How many outcomes are there? (Module 3, p. 171)

29. 1st Toss 2nd Toss

4 outcomes

Career ▪ Connection

Research Geologist: Martha Withjack

Geology is the study of the earth and its rocks. Martha Withjack uses her knowledge of geology to help locate underground deposits of oil and natural gas. To find these deposits, she needs to understand how the rocks that hold the oil and natural gas have moved through time.

Rocks can be pulled apart, or *extended*. When the stressed rock layer breaks, part of it collapses, forming a hole. Since the rock layer has only changed shape and no rock has been removed or destroyed, the amount of rock that left the gap is the same as the amount of rock in the extended part of the layer.

▲ Martha Withjack constructs scaled laboratory models to understand how rocks change through time.

30. a. Find the area of the side view of the hole in the rock layer. 10 km^2

   b. Use your answer from part (a) to find *HG*, the amount of extension. 2 km

Area of trapezoid **ABCD** = Area of rectangle **EFGH**

The amount of extension is the distance the rock has moved.

Original Rock Formation

Extended Rock Formation

Section ⑤

Extra Skill Practice

Choose the letters of all the figures of each type.

1. trapezoid C, E

2. parallelogram that is not a rhombus A, D, F

3. rhombus B

A.

B.

C.

D.

E.

F.

Find the area of each trapezoid.

4.

4 cm
14 cm
16 cm   140 cm²

5.

24 in.
12 in.
27 in.
468 in.²

6.

4.5 m
9 m
12 m
74.25 m²

For each quadrilateral, find each unknown dimension or the area.

7. Trapezoid 21 ft

9 ft
15 ft
$b_2 = ?$
$A = 225$ ft²

8. Parallelogram 96 mm²

6 mm
16 mm
$A = ?$

9. Trapezoid 18 m

24 m
36 m
$h = ?$
$A = 540$ m²

Standardized Testing ◀▶ Free Response

The trapezoid shown was formed by putting together a square and two triangles. The area of the smaller triangle is $\frac{1}{2}$ the area of the larger triangle and $\frac{1}{4}$ the area of the square. Find the areas of the square, the two triangles, and the trapezoid formed by the square and the two triangles.

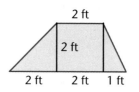

2 ft
2 ft
2 ft   2 ft   1 ft

area of square = 4 ft²   area of small △ = 1 ft²
area of large △ = 2 ft²   area of trapezoid = 7 ft²

The Picture of Health

Choosing a Data Display In this module, you have seen several examples of how data can be presented, and you have made a graph using data that you were given. Now you are ready to make your own graph, using data you have selected. To convey information *and* get the reader's attention, you may want to use photos, drawings, and colors to make your graph stand out. **Check students' work.**

6 Examine the data you have selected for your project. What message would you like to convey with these data? Write a paragraph about the data that explains your conclusions.

7 a. What types of graphs could you use to display the data?

   b. Decide which type of graph you think will best represent the data. Then make a graph of the data.

8 Does the graph tell your message clearly? Could it be considered misleading? Is it easy to understand? How could you change your graph to better represent the data?

9 Create an eye-catching poster or brochure that includes your graph and your paragraph from Project Question 6. Think of ways you might make your graphic design more interesting for the reader.

Review and Assessment

You will need: • *compass* (Ex. 24) • *protractor* (Ex. 24)

Find the volume of each cylinder. Use 3.14 for π. (Sec. 1, Explor. 1)

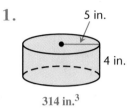

1. 5 in. / 4 in.

314 in.³

2. 7 cm / 12 cm

461.58 cm³

3. 3 cm / 6 cm

42.39 cm³

Find the slope of a line with each rise and run. (Sec. 1, Explor. 2)

4. rise 2
   run 4 $\frac{1}{2}$

5. rise 9
   run 9   1

6. rise 8
   run 2   4

7. rise 0
   run 3   0

For Exercises 8–11, use the bar graph.
(Sec. 1, Explor. 3)

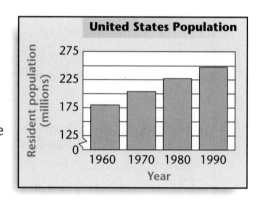

8. Without looking at the scale, compare the data values visually. See below.

9. Use the scale to estimate the data values. See below.

10. Based on your estimates of the data values, were your visual comparisons in Exercise 8 accurate? No.

11. How can you redraw the graph so that it is less misleading? Eliminate the gap in the vertical scale.

Find each percent. Round each answer to the nearest whole percent.
(Sec. 2, Explor. 1)

12. 72 is what percent of 45? 160%

13. 126 is what percent of 84? 150%

14. 175 is what percent of 20? 875%

15. 83 is what percent of 17? 488%

For Exercises 16–17, find each percent of change. (Sec. 2, Explor. 2)

16. Yesterday's price: $28.00
    Today's price: $24.80 about an 11.4% decrease

17. First-year enrollment: 180
    Second-year enrollment: 240 $33\frac{1}{3}$% increase

18. The cost to send a child to a daycare center for a week increased by 10% from 1993 to 1996. The cost per week was $150 in 1993. What was the cost in 1996? (Sec. 2, Explor. 2) $165

Replace each _?_ with the number that makes each a true statement.
(Sec. 3, Explor. 1)

19. 5 pt = _?_ c 10

20. 7 c = _?_ qt $1\frac{3}{4}$

21. $\frac{1}{2}$ gal = _?_ fl oz 64

8. Sample Response: The values appear to increase rapidly with the greatest value about twice the least value.
9. Accept reasonable estimates: about 175 million, about 200 million, about 225 million, about 250 million.

22. Suppose a test has two types of questions: multiple-choice, worth 3 points each, and short-answer, worth 5 points each. A student gets *m* multiple-choice questions and *n* short-answer questions correct. Write an inequality that models the relationship among *m*, *n*, and the maximum score of 100. (Sec. 3, Explor. 2) $3m + 5n \leq 100$

23. Estimate the median, the upper and lower extremes, and the upper and lower quartiles in the box-and-whisker plot. (Sec. 3, Explor. 3) lower extreme: about 1, lower quartile: about 9, median: about 15, upper quartile: about 31, upper extreme: about 80

Amount of Vitamin C in Some Foods (mg)

Some common fruits

24. Make a circle graph for the data in the table below. (Sec. 4, Explor. 1)

School enrollments

Public School Enrollment in the U.S., October 1992 (thousands)			
Grade	pre-school	1–8	9–12	college
Enrollment	4605	27,054	12,158	11,065

Because of rounding, the percents add up to 100.1% rather than 100%.

25. **Choosing a Data Display** To display the ages of all the members of the U.S. Congress, would you draw a *box-and-whisker plot*, a *stem-and-leaf plot*, or a *histogram*? Explain. (Sec. 4, Explor. 2)

a histogram; The number of people with a given age can be read from the height of the bars. You wouldn't use a stem-and-leaf plot because there are over 500 data points. A box-and-whisker plot does not show individual data points.

26. **Writing** Suppose in a phone call to a friend you have to explain what a parallelogram is. How would you describe the relationship between opposite sides? opposite angles? (Sec. 5, Explor. 1)

Both pairs of opposite sides are congruent; Both pairs of opposite angles are congruent.

Find the area of each trapezoid. (Sec. 5, Explor. 2)

27. 8 mm
7 mm
16 mm

84 mm²

28. 6 m
1.5 m
6 m

22.5 m²

29. 9 ft
4 ft
8 ft

34 ft²

Reflecting ▶ on the Module

30. **Research** Find a variety of graphs in newspapers or magazines. Analyze them based on what you have learned in this module.
Check students' work.

HEART
OF THE CITY

1 Counting Problems

As you find travel routes between and within cities:

◆ Find all the different ways to order a group of items
◆ Use tree diagrams and the counting principle

2 Drawing Views and Finding Volumes

As you build models of skyscrapers:

◆ Draw front, back, and side views of space figures
◆ Find volumes of pyramids

3 Permutations and Combinations

As you find the shortest paths through a grid of city streets:

◆ Find permutations with repeated items
◆ Select items to create combinations when order is not important

4 Tessellations and Volumes of Cones

As you explore how art is used to brighten up the urban landscape:

◆ Create tessellations with triangles and quadrilaterals
◆ Find volumes of cones

The Module Project

Traffic Flow

Have you ever been caught in a traffic jam? You'll use your problem solving, measurement, and estimation skills to analyze and develop a plan to improve the movement of foot traffic through a busy hallway in your school.

More on the Module Project
See pp. 538, 561, and 577.

INTERNET
To learn more about the theme:
http://www.mlmath.com

527

Section ① Counting Problems

IN THIS SECTION

EXPLORATION 1
• Introduction to Permutations

EXPLORATION 2
• The Counting Principle

Take a Trip

WARM-UP EXERCISES

1. Assuming you eat one fruit at a time, in how many orders could you eat a banana and a pear?
   2

2. Suppose you also eat an apple. List the different orders in which you could eat these three fruits.
   p-b-a, p-a-b, b-a-p, b-p-a, a-p-b, a-b-p

3. How many of the orders in Question 2 have the pear first?
   2

4. How many of the orders in Question 2 do not have the apple last?
   4

1. Sample Response:
The beat may refer to the rhythm of a crowd of walking people and the stream may refer to the crowd itself.

‹‹‹ **Setting the Stage**

In *City in All Directions*, urban poet Arnold Adoff describes the constant motion of life in New York City.

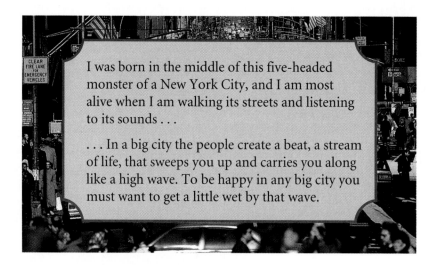

I was born in the middle of this five-headed monster of a New York City, and I am most alive when I am walking its streets and listening to its sounds . . .

. . . In a big city the people create a beat, a stream of life, that sweeps you up and carries you along like a high wave. To be happy in any big city you must want to get a little wet by that wave.

Think About It

1 What do you think the poet means when he says that people in a city create a "beat" and a "stream of life"❓

2 Name some things that make a city interesting or exciting for you.
Sample Response: the variety of people, stores, and buildings

Perhaps you have had the chance to experience the rhythm and energy of a big city yourself. Did you know that mathematics plays a very important role in making this "stream of life" flow smoothly❓

Managing traffic, planning routes, constructing skyscrapers, and designing plazas all depend on mathematics. In this module, you'll see how many aspects of city life are organized using mathematics.

INTRODUCTION TO
Permutations

GOAL

LEARN HOW TO...
- find all possible arrangements of items

AS YOU...
- plan routes for a trip

KEY TERM
- permutation

SET UP *Work in a group of five.*

There are many guidebooks that rank cities in the United States according to aspects such as weather and recreation. Suppose it is up to you to rank the ten United States cities shown below.

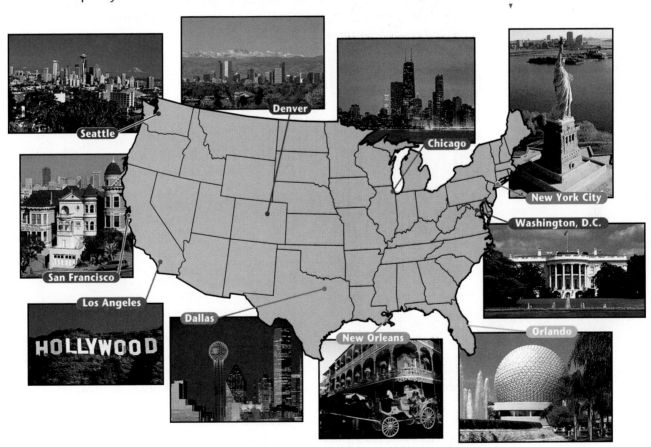

Seattle · Denver · Chicago · New York City · San Francisco · Washington, D.C. · Los Angeles · Dallas · New Orleans · Orlando

3. Answers will vary. Check students' work.

3 **a.** Work independently. Rank the cities in order from the one you most want to visit (1) to the one you least want to visit (10).

b. Give some reasons why you ranked the cities the way you did.

4 Discussion Suppose your group is going on a tour together and can visit only five of the cities on page 529.

a. How can your group use each person's individual rankings to decide on the five cities your group would most like to visit?

b. Together choose the top five cities for your group to visit.

c. Is the order in which your group selected or listed the cities in part (b) important? Why or why not?

5 a. List the five cities your group selected in the order you would prefer to visit them. Why did you choose this order?

b. Discussion Compare your list with those of the other members in your group. How many different orders did your group find?

▶ **Permutations** An arrangement of a group of items in which the order is important is called a **permutation**. The notebook below shows the six possible orders in which a group visiting Washington, D.C., can visit the Washington Monument, the Lincoln Memorial, and the Jefferson Memorial.

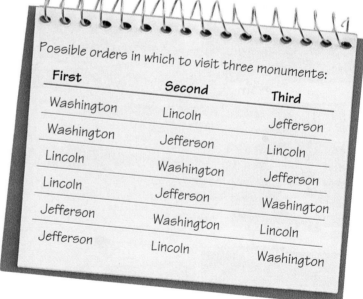

Possible orders in which to visit three monuments:

First	Second	Third
Washington	Lincoln	Jefferson
Washington	Jefferson	Lincoln
Lincoln	Washington	Jefferson
Lincoln	Jefferson	Washington
Jefferson	Washington	Lincoln
Jefferson	Lincoln	Washington

6 Discussion Suppose your group will visit only two of the monuments shown. How will this affect the list of possible orders?

✔ QUESTION 7

...checks that you can use an organized list to find permutations.

7 ✔ CHECKPOINT List all the possible orders in which your group could visit two of these four monuments: the Washington Monument, the Lincoln Memorial, the Jefferson Memorial, and the FDR Memorial. Washington–Lincoln, Washington–Jefferson, Washington–FDR, Lincoln–Washington, Lincoln–Jefferson, Lincoln–FDR, Jefferson–Washington, Jefferson–Lincoln, Jefferson–FDR, FDR–Washington, FDR–Lincoln, FDR–Jefferson

HOMEWORK EXERCISES ▶ See Exs. 1–6 on p. 535.

Exploration 2

The Counting Principle

GOAL

LEARN HOW TO...
- apply tree diagrams to counting problems
- use the counting principle

AS YOU...
- find the number of routes between cities

KEY TERM
- counting principle

SET UP *You will need Labsheet 1A.*

To find the best routes between cities, travel agents and managers of shipping or trucking companies may need to identify and compare all the possible orders of travel. One way to solve this type of problem is to start by solving a simpler one.

Use the *Table of Orders* on Labsheet 1A to record the results of Questions 8 and 9.

8 To find all the possible orders to travel among five cities, begin with the top two cities that your group chose in Question 4.

   a. In how many orders can you visit the two cities? Use the abbreviations to record the orders in the *Table of Orders*. For example, write the order New York City to Orlando as NY-O.
      2; Answers will vary.

   b. With two cities, how many cities can you choose from to visit first? 2

   c. After you have chosen the city to visit first, how many cities are left to choose from for the next city on the trip? 1

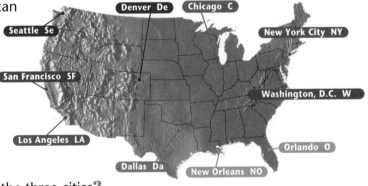

9 Now consider the top three cities your group chose in Question 4.

   a. In how many orders can you visit the three cities? Use the abbreviations to record the orders. For example, write the order Los Angeles to Denver to New York City as LA-De-NY.
      6; Answers will vary.

   b. With three cities, how many cities can you choose from to visit first? 3

   c. After you have chosen the city to visit first, how many cities are left to choose from to visit second? 2

   d. After you have chosen the first two cities to visit, how many cities are left to choose from for the third city? 1

▶ **Using Tree Diagrams** A tree diagram is a useful tool for finding permutations. This tree diagram shows all the possible orders for traveling among Los Angeles, New York City, and New Orleans.

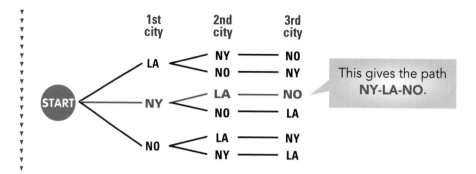

This gives the path **NY-LA-NO**.

▶ Here is part of another tree diagram. It shows all the possible orders for traveling among Los Angeles, New York City, New Orleans, and Chicago when Los Angeles is the first city you visit.

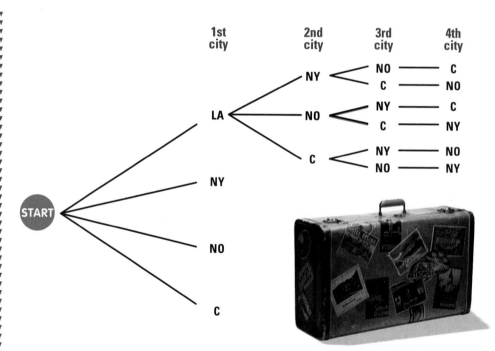

10 Refer to the tree diagram above. In how many different orders can you visit the four cities if you visit Los Angeles first and New York City second? if you visit Los Angeles first and either New Orleans or Chicago second? 2, 4

Use Labsheet 1A for Questions 11–13.

11 Use the top four cities chosen by your group in Question 4. Make a *Tree Diagram for Four Cities* on Labsheet 1A to show all the possible orders in which you can visit the four cities.
Check students' work.

12 Use your *Tree Diagram for Four Cities* to complete the last row of the *Table of Orders* with your answers to these questions.

    a. How many choices are there for the first city you would visit? 4

    b. After leaving the first city, how many choices are there for the second city you would visit? 3

    c. After leaving the second city, how many choices are there for the third city you would visit? 2

    d. After leaving the third city, how many choices are there for the fourth city you would visit? 1

    e. In how many different orders can you visit the four cities? 24

13 **Try This as a Class** Look for a pattern in your *Table of Orders*. Explain how the total number of orders in which you can visit the cities is related to the number of choices for each stop on the trip.

    total number of choices = number of choices for 1st city · number of choices for 2nd city · number of choices for 3rd city · number of choices for 4th city

▶ The pattern you explored in Question 13 is called the **counting principle**. The example below shows how to apply this principle to find the total number of permutations.

EXAMPLE

You can use the counting principle to find the number of possible orders in which a group can visit the Washington Monument, the Lincoln Memorial, and the Jefferson Memorial.

Number of choices for the 1st monument		Number of choices remaining for the 2nd monument		Number of choices remaining for the 3rd monument		Total possible orders for visiting all three monuments
3	·	2	·	1	=	6

Multiply the number of choices at each stop on the tour.

There are six possible orders in which to visit the monuments.

---

14 ✔ **CHECKPOINT** Use the counting principle to calculate the number of different orders in which you can visit the five cities your group chose in Question 4. 120 orders

HOMEWORK EXERCISES ▶ See Exs. 7–18 on p. 536.

✔ **QUESTION 14**

…checks that you can calculate the total number of permutations.

permutation

Permutations (pp. 529–530)

The possible arrangements of a group of items in which order is important are called permutations. An organized list can help you find permutations.

Example Reta, Amy, Trinja, and Jennifer are being considered for the lead role and a supporting role in a play. Here are the possible ways in which the roles can be assigned.

Lead role	Supporting role	Lead role	Supporting role
Reta	Amy	Trinja	Reta
Reta	Trinja	Trinja	Amy
Reta	Jennifer	Trinja	Jennifer
Amy	Reta	Jennifer	Reta
Amy	Trinja	Jennifer	Amy
Amy	Jennifer	Jennifer	Trinja

counting principle

Tree Diagrams and the Counting Principle (pp. 531–533)

A tree diagram can also be used to list permutations. However, if you want to know only the *number* of permutations, you can simply multiply together the number of options at each point where you make a choice. This fact is called the counting principle.

Example You can use the counting principle to find the number of ways in which the roles can be assigned.

Number of choices for the lead		Number of choices remaining for the supporting role		Total possible ways in which the roles can be assigned
4	•	3	=	12

CLOSURE QUESTION

When would you want to use the Counting Principle to find the number of permutations instead of listing the possibilities or making a tree diagram?

Sample Response: when you only need to know the number of permutations or if the number of permutations are too many to list

15 **Key Concepts Question** Suppose there is a fifth person named Julie in the Examples above. Use the counting principle to find the number of ways in which the roles can be assigned. Check the result by making a tree diagram. 20; Check students' diagrams.

Section 1

Practice & Application Exercises ▸ ▸ ▸ ▸ ▸ ▸ ▸ ▸

YOU WILL NEED

For Ex. 12–15:
♦ calculator

List all the permutations for each situation.

1. Two out of four plants, an azalea, an ivy, a fern, and a cactus, must be arranged side by side.

2. A person marks his or her first and second choices out of five movies labeled A, B, C, D, and E.

3. The High School marching band, Boy Scouts, Girl Scouts, and Fire Department will all march in the Memorial Day parade. See below

4. **Sports** The Ironman Triathlon is held annually on the Saturday in October closest to the full moon, in Kailua-Kona, Hawaii. The men and women who compete in this triathalon do a 2.4 mile ocean swim, followed by a 112 mile bicycle race, followed by a 26.2 mile run. List all the *other* possible orders for these three events.

swim–run–bike, run–swim–bike, run–bike–swim, bike–swim–run, bike–run–swim

5. **Area Codes** The first three digits of a long distance telephone number are called the *area code*. In the United States, every state has a different area code and some states with large urban areas have more than one area code.

  a. Suppose you remember that the numbers in the Montana area code are 6, 4, and 0, but you have forgotten the order of these digits. List all the possible orders of these three digits.
  640; 604; 460; 406; 064; 046

  b. If the number 0 (used to call the operator) cannot be used as the first digit, how many orders are possible? 4

6. Beth, Carol, and Danielle are finalists in a figure skating competition. The order of their performances in the final event will be determined by a random drawing.

  a. List all possible orders in which they might skate in the final event.
  See below
  b. **Probability Connection** What is the probability that Beth will skate first? that Danielle will not skate last?

  c. **Writing** Do you think the order in which skaters skate in a competition matters? Why or why not?
  Sample Response; Yes; A skater might become more nervous going last.

1. azalea–ivy, azalea–fern, azalea–cactus, ivy–azalea, ivy–fern, ivy–cactus, fern–azalea, fern–ivy, fern–cactus, cactus–azalea, cactus–ivy, cactus–fern

2. A–B, A–C, A–D, A–E, B–A, B–C, B–D, B–E, C–A, C–B, C–D, C–E, D–A, D–B, D–C, D–E, E–A, E–B, E–C, E–D

3. band–BS–GS–FD, band–BS–FD–GS, band–GS–BS–FD, band–GS–FD–BS, band–FD–BS–GS, band–FD–GS–BS, BS–band–GS–FD, BS–band–FD–GS, BS–GS–band–FD, BS–GS–FD–band, BS–FD–band–GS, BS–FD–GS–band, GS–band–BS–FD, GS–band–FD–BS, GS–BS–band–FD, GS–BS–FD–band, GS–FD–band–BS, GS–FD–BS–band, FD–band–BS–GS, FD–band–GS–BS, FD–BS–band–GS, FD–BS–GS–band, FD–GS–band–BS, FD–GS–BS–band

6. b. $\frac{2}{6}$, or $\frac{1}{3}$; $\frac{4}{6}$, or $\frac{2}{3}$

6. a. Beth–Carol–Danielle, Beth–Danielle–Carol, Carol–Beth–Danielle, Carol–Danielle–Beth, Danielle–Beth–Carol, Danielle–Carol–Beth

Find how many permutations are possible for each situation.

7. four runners on a relay team
   24

8. nine batters in a batting order
   362,880

9. the first three finishers in an eight-swimmer race 336

10. the top 2 candidates out of 100 applicants for a job 9900

11. A school cafeteria has organized its serving line so that students can choose chicken or roast beef at the first station, rice, potatoes, or bread at the second station, and soup or salad at the third station.

    a. Suppose one item is chosen at each station. Draw a tree diagram to show all the possible meals that could be chosen.

    b. How many different meals are possible? 12

    c. Suppose a fourth station is added that serves milk or juice. How does this affect the number of possible meals?
       The number of possible meals is doubled.

11. a.

1st Station	2nd	3rd
	Rice	Soup / Salad
Chicken	Potatoes	Soup / Salad
	Bread	Soup / Salad
	Rice	Soup / Salad
Roast Beef	Potatoes	Soup / Salad
	Bread	Soup / Salad

Calculator The value of 6!, read "six factorial," is the product $6 \cdot 5 \cdot 4 \cdot 3 \cdot 2 \cdot 1 = 720$. Use the factorial key [x!] on a calculator to find the total number of permutations for each set of items. Tell whether your answer is approximate or exact. Explain.

12. 4 musical notes 24 ;exact

13. 13 songs on a CD 6,227,020,800 ;exact

14. 20 poems in a book
    2.43×10^{18}; approximate

15. 52 cards in a deck
    8.07×10^{67}; approximate

16. **ZIP Codes** In 1963, the United States Postal Service first introduced the ZIP Code to reorganize the routing of mail to different cities and also to different areas within a city.

    a. How many different 5-digit ZIP Codes can the Postal Service create using the digits 1, 2, 3, 4, and 5, if each digit is used only once? 120

    b. How many different 5-digit ZIP Codes can be created using the digits 0 through 9, if each digit can be repeated? 100,000

17. **Challenge** Suppose you are designing a door lock. To open the door, you have to press each of a set of colored buttons in a particular order. For better security, you want to have at least 5000 possible orders. How many buttons must the lock have?
    at least 7 buttons

Reflecting ▶on the Section

Be prepared to report on the following topic in class.

18. Permutations and tree diagrams are mathematical ideas that can be applied in many situations. Describe how each of these two ideas can be applied to situations related to a city. Sample Responses: in assigning ID numbers to city employees, in designing alternate traffic routes

Find the area of each trapezoid. (Module 7, p. 518)

19.
6 in.

4 in.

8 in.   28 in.²

20.
7.5 cm

4.5 cm

6 cm   36 cm²

Solve each equation. Check each solution. (Module 4, p. 300)

21. $5 - 2n = 9$ –2

22. $2x + 4 = 20$ 8

23. $11 = 3c - 4$ 5

24. $-6y + 7 = -5$ 2

25. $\frac{b}{2} + 3 = 5$ 4

26. $a - \frac{2}{3} = \frac{4}{3}$ 2

Find the surface area of a right rectangular prism with the given dimensions. (Module 6, p. 404)

27. 4 ft, 5 ft, 7 ft   166 ft²

28. 3.5 m, 2.5 m, 6 m   89.5 m²

29. $2\frac{1}{2}$ yd, $2\frac{1}{2}$ yd, 8 yd $92\frac{1}{2}$ yd²

30. 3 cm, 6 mm, 2 mm   504 mm²

Career ◀ Connection

Computer Hardware Engineer: Omar Green

At Xionics, Omar Green helps to design computer chips to perform certain tasks. When he tests the computer chips, he creates permutation charts to list the possible orders in which the tasks can be performed.

Suppose the following tasks can be performed in any order: rotate an image 90°, make a color image black and white, and change the size of an image.

31. In how many orders can these three tasks be performed? List all the possibilities.   6; rotate–color/bw–size, rotate–size–color/bw, color/bw–rotate–size, color/bw–size–rotate, size–rotate–color/bw, size–color/bw–rotate

32. In how many orders can any two of these three tasks be performed? List all the possibilities.
6; rotate–color/bw, rotate–size, color/bw–rotate, color/bw–size, size–rotate, size–color/bw

Beginning the Module Project

Traffic Flow

Imagine walking to the lunchroom. Suddenly, the student in front of you stops. You swerve and bump into someone else. Looking for a clear path, you slow your pace. There seem to be hundreds of students ahead of you, all heading in the same direction!

For this project, you'll work in a group. Using the techniques of traffic engineers, your group will develop a plan to improve the traffic flow in your school.

SET UP

Work in a group. You will need:

- *tape measure*

Estimating and Measuring Lengths You'll estimate and measure the length and width of a section of hallway where there is a traffic problem.

Answers will vary. Check students' work.

1 Identify a hallway in your school that has a traffic problem.

2 a. Use estimation to mark off a 25 ft long section of the hallway. Measure to check your estimate.

　 b. Estimate the width of the hallway. Measure to check your estimate.

3 Describe any places where students gather and any obstacles, such as drinking fountains, that could interfere with traffic flow.

Scale Drawings In order to study the section of hallway you selected, you'll make a scale drawing of it.

4 a. Make a scale drawing of the section of hallway that you measured. Be sure to label the width and the length, and include the scale. Label all obstacles and gathering places.

　 b. Find the area of the chosen section of the hallway.

5 One way to solve the traffic problem is to widen the hallway.

　 a. If the width of the chosen section of the hallway were doubled, what would happen to the area of that section?
The area would be doubled.

　 b. If the width *and* length were doubled, what would happen to the area?
The area would be multiplied by 4.

For Exercises 1 and 2, list all the permutations for each situation.

1. Four singers, Alma, Mei, Dyani, and Luz, must line up for a photo.

2. Two out of three instruments, a trumpet, a saxophone, and a flute, must be hung side by side in a display case.
T–S, T–F, S–T, S–F, F–T, F–S

3. Your seven-digit phone number consists of an *exchange* (the first three digits) and your individual number (the last four digits).

   a. Suppose only the digits 1, 2, 3, and 4 can be used for the individual number and no digit can be repeated. Use a tree diagram to list all the possible phone numbers with the exchange 555. How many phone numbers are possible?
   Check students' diagrams; 24 numbers

   b. Suppose any digits can be used for the individual number and the digits can be repeated. Use the counting principle to determine how many phone numbers there can be with the exchange 555. 10,000 phone numbers

4. How many permutations are possible when 6 movies are to be shown in 6 different theaters? 720

5. How many permutations are possible when 4 out of 20 students are called on to give oral reports? 116,280

6. Suppose Norma has a seven-period school day. Her main subjects are mathematics, English, science, and social studies. She also has electives in French and art, and she plays trumpet in the band. In how many different orders can Norma's classes meet? Explain.

1. Alma, Mei, Dyani, Luz;
Alma, Mei, Luz, Dyani;
Alma, Dyani, Mei, Luz;
Alma, Dyani, Luz, Mei;
Alma, Luz, Mei, Dyani;
Alma, Luz, Dyani, Mei;
Mei, Alma, Dyani, Luz;
Mei, Alma, Luz, Dyani;
Mei, Dyani, Alma, Luz;
Mei, Dyani, Luz, Alma;
Mei, Luz, Alma, Dyani;
Mei, Luz, Dyani, Alma;
Dyani, Alma, Mei, Luz;
Dyani, Alma, Luz, Mei;
Dyani, Mei, Alma, Luz;
Dyani, Mei, Luz, Alma;
Dyani, Luz, Alma, Mei;
Dyani, Luz, Mei, Alma;
Luz, Alma, Mei, Dyani;
Luz, Alma, Dyani, Mei;
Luz, Mei, Alma, Dyani;
Luz, Mei, Dyani, Alma;
Luz, Dyani, Alma, Mei;
Luz, Dyani, Mei, Alma

6. 5040 ways; Once a class is scheduled for the 1st period, there are 6 classes remaining that could be scheduled for the 2nd period. Then, 5 classes remain that could be scheduled for the 3rd period, and so on. So, the number of different orders = 7!.

Study Skills ▷ Teaching Another Person

Teaching another person requires that you know the material extremely well, so teaching can help you find out whether there are any ideas or topics that you do not fully understand. 1–2. Answers will vary.

1. Look back at the ideas presented in this section. Choose a topic that you feel you understand well. Teach it to another student.

2. Describe what happened when you taught another student. Could you explain the material clearly? Did the other student have difficulty understanding your explanations? Did you discover any ideas that were unclear to you?

A Tower of Power

‹‹‹ *Setting the Stage*

SET UP *You will need 20 centimeter cubes.*

As cities have become more populated, and the land available for constructing new buildings has decreased, many have expanded in the only direction remaining—straight up! The tallest skyscraper, the Petronas Towers in Kuala Lumpur, Malaysia, now soars 1,483 ft into the air.

> "There's no limit to the height you can build if you have a place big enough to put it."
> Leslie Robertson, structural engineer

▲
Petronas Towers in Kuala Lumpur, Malaysia

WARM-UP EXERCISES

Find the volume and surface area of a right rectangular prism with the given dimensions.

1. 1 cm by 1 cm by 10 cm
   10 cm^3; 42 cm^2
2. 2 cm by 5 cm by 1 cm
   10 cm^3; 34 cm^2
3. 4.3 ft by 12.4 ft by 6.2 ft
   330.6 ft^3; 313.7 ft^2
4. 8.6 ft by 6.2 ft by 6.2 ft
   330.6 ft^3; 290.2 ft^2

Think About It

1 **a.** What is the maximum height a skyscraper could reach, according to structural engineer Leslie Robertson? Given enough space, there is no limit.

b. Why do you think a taller building requires more ground space? Sample Response: The weight of the tower can be spread over a greater area.

2 Use centimeter cubes for parts (a)–(d).

a. Explain why the volume of a single cube is 1 cubic centimeter. volume = length × width × height = 1 cm × 1 cm × 1 cm = 1 cm³

b. Start with a single centimeter cube and stack as many cubes as possible above it to build the highest tower that you can. What is the volume of the tower you built? Answers will vary. Check students' work.

c. What do you think causes the tower to topple when it becomes too high? Sample Response: The base area is not big enough to support the weight of the tower.

d. The space figure you built in part (b) is an example of a *rectangular prism*. Give dimensions for 3 different rectangular prisms that all have the same volume as one another.
Sample Response: 3 cm × 4 cm × 1 cm, 2 cm × 3 cm × 2 cm, 12 cm × 1 cm × 1 cm

Exploration 1

VIEWS OF A SPACE FIGURE

SET UP *You will need 20 centimeter cubes.*

▶ In order to design and construct buildings, architects, engineers, and construction workers must be able to visualize shapes from various views. Several different views of a building are shown below.

front   right

 front view

 right-side view

top view

▲
Rowes Wharf,
Boston, Massachusetts

▶ A building plan includes a *base plan*. You can think of a base plan as a view looking directly down on a building, with the height of each section of the base indicated by numbers. A base plan for the building above is shown.

3 a. Use centimeter cubes to create a model of the building shown above. Check students' work.

b. Look at the building from the top, the front, and the right side to check each of the drawings above. Which view—the *top*, the *front*, or the *right-side*—is used in the base plan? the top

c. Draw the back and the left-side views of the building.

d. How do the front and the back views compare? They are the same.

e. How do the right-side and the left-side views compare? They are the same.

f. Do you think the answers to parts (d) and (e) are true for all buildings? Experiment by building other structures with your centimeter cubes. No; Check students' work.

3. c.

✔ **QUESTION 4**

...checks that you can draw different views of a space figure.

4. b.

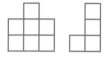

4 ✔ **CHECKPOINT** Use centimeter cubes.

a. Build the model building shown. Begin with the partial base plan. Check students' work.

b. Draw the front and right-side views of the model building.

c. Copy and complete the base plan for the model building.

2	3	2
1	1	1

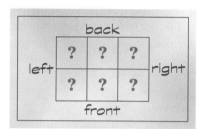

5 Look at the model building shown at the right. Its front and right-side views and its base plan are given below.

front view   right-side view

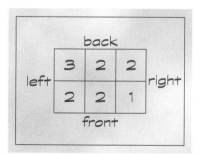

a. Use centimeter cubes to build the model building. Check students' work.

b. What is the volume of the model building? 12 cm³

c. By moving only one cube, change the building into a rectangular prism.
Move the cube in the 3rd layer into the space in the 2nd layer.

d. Draw the base plan for the rectangular prism you built in part (c).

2	2	2
2	2	2

e. How can you find the volume of the rectangular prism in part (c) without counting the cubes? Sample Response: Add the numbers of cubes in the base plan.

f. Does moving a cube to a different position in the building change the volume of the building? Why or why not? No; The number of cubes remains the same.

6 a. Use centimeter cubes to build a model building with the base plan shown. Then find the volume. *Check students' work; 9 cm³*

b. Draw the front and right-side views of the model building.

c. Suppose you want to paint the outside of your model building, including the base. How many cube faces will you need to paint? Recall that this number represents the *surface area* of the building in square centimeters.
34 faces

d. By moving exactly 3 cubes, change the building into a rectangular prism. Then draw the base plan for the rectangular prism.

e. Find the volume and the surface area of the new rectangular prism. Compare them to the original volume and surface area.
9 cm³; 30 cm²; The volumes are the same; The surface area of the rectangular prism is less.

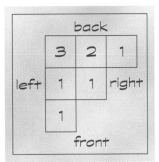

back

	3	2	1
left	1	1	right
	1		

front

6. b.

FOR ◄ HELP
with *surface area*, see
MODULE 6, p. 404

6. d. Possible answers:

1	1	1
1	1	1
1	1	1

3	3	3

7 Suppose the base plan for the model building shown is 3 units long by 2 units wide. Use 14 centimeter cubes to build the model building.

Sample Response:

6	2	2
2	1	1

a. Rearrange the cubes to form a model building that has a larger surface area than the original model building but the same base. Then draw the base plan of the structure you built.

9	1	1
1	1	1

b. Rearrange the cubes to form a model building that has the largest possible surface area but the same base. Then draw the base plan of the structure you built.

c. Explain why you think the structure you built in part (b) has the largest possible surface area. *The number of cubes with 4 faces exposed is at a maximum.*

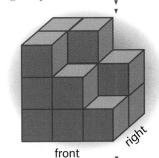

front

right

8. b. Yes; Sample Response: Some, or all, of the empty sections in the base plan could be filled in. Example:

4	2	4
2	2	1
1	1	1

8 The front and right-side views of a building are shown below.

Sample Response:

4	2	4
	2	
	1	

a. Copy and complete the base plan for the building, using the front and right-side views.

b. Discussion Is there a different base plan that would produce the same front and right-side views? Explain.
See above.

front view   right-side view

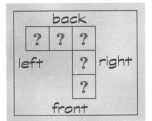

back

?	?	?
left		?	right
	?	

front

HOMEWORK EXERCISES ▶ See Exs. 1–6 on pp. 548–549.

GOAL

LEARN HOW TO...
- recognize a pyramid
- find the volume of a pyramid

AS YOU...
- build rectangular prisms using pyramid blocks

KEY TERM
- pyramid

Exploration 2

VOLUME
OF A PYRAMID

SET UP   *You will need:* • *Labsheet 2A* • *scissors* • *tape* • *metric ruler*

▶ A city skyline usually contains many different types of space figures. To organize the space of a building efficiently, architects need to consider the amount of space or volume a building will enclose. In this exploration you'll see how the volume of a **pyramid** relates to the volume of a rectangular prism. Several types of pyramids are shown below.

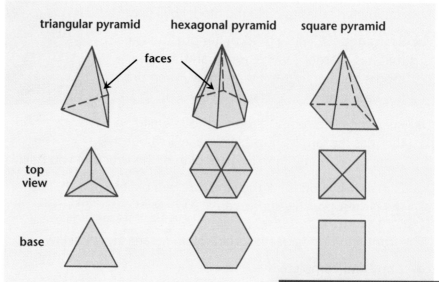

▲ The Transamerica Building in San Francisco, California, incorporates a square pyramid.

The *height* is the perpendicular distance from the base to the vertex opposite it.

9. The faces, not including the base, are triangles that meet in a point; The shapes of the triangles and of the bases are different.

9 How are the three pyramids above alike? How are they different?

10 **Use Labsheet 2A.**
Cut out the *Pyramid Nets.* Crease each net along the dashed lines. Then fold each net and tape the edges together to form two pyramids.
Check students' work.

For Questions 11–17, use the pyramids you made in Question 10.

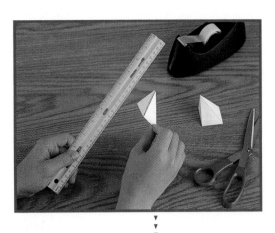

11 The two pyramids you made are identical. Look at one of the pyramids.

   a. What type of pyramid did you form? a square pyramid

   b. Not including the base, how many faces does the pyramid have? 4

   c. Which faces of the pyramid are congruent? Explain. See below.

11. c. the 2 largest triangular faces and the 2 smallest triangular faces; They have the same size and shape.

12 Measure the height of one of your pyramids to the nearest centimeter. 4 cm

height

13 The dashed lines below represent folds.

   a. Use your two pyramids to make a figure with the views shown. Check students' work.

front view   top view   right-side view

   b. Use your two pyramids to make a figure with the front and back views shown. Then draw the top view of the figure.

front view   back view

14 Work with a partner.

   a. Make a cube by putting three of your pyramids together. Check students' work.

   b. Write an expression to represent the volume of the cube. Use *B* for the area of the base of the cube and *h* for the height of the cube. *Bh*

   c. Compare the area of the base and the height of a single pyramid with the area of the base and the height of the cube you formed. The areas of the bases and the heights are the same.

   d. Suppose you know the volume of a cube formed by putting together three identical pyramids as in part (a). How can you find the volume of each pyramid? Divide the volume of the cube by 3.

   e. Use your answers to parts (b)–(d) to write an expression for the volume of a pyramid with height *h* and base area *B*. $\frac{1}{3}Bh$

15 Work as a group. Think of the pyramids you made in Question 10 as "pyramid blocks."

a. Build a square pyramid using four pyramid blocks. Check students' work.

b. Add pyramid blocks to the square pyramid you made in part (a) until it forms a rectangular prism with the same height and base as the square pyramid. How many pyramid blocks does it take to form the rectangular prism? 12

c. The volume of the rectangular prism you made in part (b) is given by $B \cdot h$ where B is the area of the prism's base and h is the height. Write an expression for the volume of the square pyramid you made in part (a). $\frac{1}{3}Bh$

▶ The volume V for any pyramid is given by the formula $V = \frac{1}{3}Bh$ where B is the area of its base, and h is its height.

EXAMPLE

Find the volume of a pyramid that has a base area of 12 cm^2 and a height of 4 cm.

$$V = \frac{1}{3}Bh$$

$$= \frac{1}{3}(12)(4)$$

$$= 16$$

height = 4 cm

base area = 12 cm^2

The pyramid has a volume of 16 cm^3.

---

16 Measure the height and the dimensions of the base of a single pyramid block from Question 10 to the nearest centimeter. Then find its volume to the nearest cubic centimeter. 4 cm, 4 cm × 4 cm; 21 cm^3

17 a. Use your answer from Question 16 to find the volume of the square pyramid you constructed in Question 15(a). 84 cm^3

b. Measure the height and a side of the base of the square pyramid to the nearest centimeter. Use the formula for the volume of a pyramid to find its volume to the nearest cubic centimeter. Compare this answer with the result in part (a). 4 cm, 8 cm ; 85 cm^3; They are about the same.

✔ **QUESTION 18**

...checks that you can find the volume of a pyramid.

18 ✔ **CHECKPOINT** The Transamerica Pyramid shown on page 544 is 853 ft tall and has a base area of 21,025 ft^2. Find its volume. Round your answer to the nearest cubic foot. 5,978,108 ft^3

HOMEWORK EXERCISES ▶ See Exs. 7–17 on pp. 549–550.

Section 2

Key Concepts

Key Term

Views of Space Figures (pp. 541–543)

Space figures with the same volume can have different surface areas.

Volume = 5 cm³
Surface area = 20 cm²

Volume = 5 cm³
Surface area = 22 cm²

front view   right-side   top view
              view

front view   right-side   top view
              view

Volume of a Pyramid (pp. 544–546)

A pyramid is a space figure that has one base. All the other faces are triangles that meet at a single vertex. The height is the perpendicular distance from the base to the vertex opposite it.

vertex

height

face

base

hexagonal pyramid

pyramid

The volume V of a pyramid is given by the formula $V = \frac{1}{3}Bh$, where B is the area of its base, and h is its height.

A pyramid is named for the shape of its base.

Example Suppose a hexagonal pyramid has a base area of 36 cm² and a height of 7 cm. Find its volume.

$$V = \frac{1}{3}Bh = \frac{1}{3}(36)(7) = 84$$

The volume of the pyramid is 84 cm³.

CLOSURE QUESTION

State the formulas for the volume of a prism and the volume of a pyramid. How does the volume of a pyramid compare to the volume of a prism with the same base area and height?

Answer: Prism: $V = Bh$; Pyramid: $V = \frac{1}{3}Bh$; The volume of the pyramid is $\frac{1}{3}$ the volume of the prism.

19 Key Concepts Question A pyramid has a height of 12 ft and a volume of 351 ft³. What is the area of the base of the pyramid?

$87\frac{3}{4}$ ft²

◄◄◄◄◄◄◄◄◄◄

YOU WILL NEED

For Ex. 1:
- ◆ Labsheet 2B
- ◆ scissors
- ◆ tape

1. a. **Use Labsheet 2B.** Follow the directions on Labsheet 2B to make four cubes using the *Cube Nets*.   Check students' work.

   b. Form three different buildings by putting together all the cubes. Check students' work.

   c. For each building in part (b), sketch front and right-side views, and a base plan.

   d. Does every building you made in part (b) have the same volume? the same surface area? Explain.   Yes, No; The same number of cubes is used; The number of exposed cube faces is not the same.

1. c. Sample Response:

front   right-side

front   right-side

front   right-side

base plan

2.

3. Sample Response:

For Exercises 2 and 3, use the front and right-side views of a building that are shown below.

front view   right-side view

2. Draw a base plan that will create a building with the greatest possible volume, using the given front and right-side views.

3. Draw a base plan that will create a building with the least possible volume, using the given front and right-side views. Each cube must share a face with at least one other cube.

4. **Challenge** The front of the Reception Building in the Olympic Port of Barcelona is shown in the photograph. Tell whether each view is the *right-side*, *left-side*, or *back view* of the building.

   a. back view   b. right-side   c. left-side

5. The cube-shaped Reception Building has edges that are 12.5 m long. What are the volume and the surface area of such a cube?

$V = 1953.125 \text{ m}^3;$
$SA = 937.5 \text{ m}^2$

6. **Industrial Design** An industrial designer strives to design products that are easy to use and that can be produced at a reasonable cost. Industrial designers describe their designs with drawings of different views. For each view shown, tell whether it is the *front*, *top*, or *side view* of the product shown.

front

a. front

b. side

c. top

For Exercises 7–9, use the pyramid at the right. Use the letters of the vertices to name each of the following.

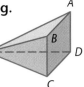

7. the base *ABCD*

8. the other faces

$\triangle ADE$, $\triangle BCE$, $\triangle CDE$, $\triangle ABE$ *E*

9. the vertex opposite the base *E*

Mental Math The base of each figure is a rectangle. Use mental math to estimate the volume of each figure. Then find each volume. Round decimal answers to the nearest tenth.

10.

about 40,000 ft³; 41,097 ft³

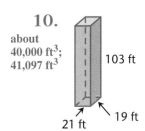

103 ft

19 ft

21 ft

11.

about 6 cm³; 6.3 cm³

3.09 cm

2.48 cm

2.48 cm

12.

28 m

5 m

59 m

19 m

about 18,000 m³; 16,067.7 m³

Determine whether each net can be folded to create a pyramid. If so, identify the type of pyramid it will form.

13.

Yes; triangular pyramid

14.

No.

15.

Yes; hexagonal pyramid

16. **Rainforest Pyramid**
The *Rainforest Pyramid* in Galveston Island, Texas, is 100 ft high. Its base is a square that is 200 ft on a side. What is the volume of the Rainforest Pyramid?

$1{,}333{,}333\frac{1}{3}$ ft³

◄ The Rainforest Pyramid is home to a wide variety of tropical plants and other wildlife, including over 2000 butterflies.

Reflecting ▶ **on the Section**

Write your response to Exercise 17 in your journal.

17. a. Draw sketches to show how the faces of prisms and pyramids can be different types of geometric figures.

b. Suppose you are sketching the top view of a pyramid or a prism that is sitting on its base. How many different geometric figures are possible? Explain your reasoning.

Spiral ◀▶ **Review**

Find how many permutations are possible for each situation. (Module 8, p. 534)

18. 7 charms on a bracelet 5040   19. 11 hats on 11 heads 39,916,800

Tell whether each set of side lengths can or cannot form a triangle. If they can, tell whether the triangle is *isosceles*, *equilateral*, or *scalene*. (Module 3, p. 223)

20. 2 m, 3 m, 4 m
can; scalene

21. 4 in., 4 in., 7 in.
can; isosceles

22. 3 cm, 5 cm, 8 cm
cannot

Sketch an example of each shape. Mark parallel sides. (Module 7, p. 518)

23. trapezoid

24. quadrilateral

25. rhombus

---

17. Sample Response:

a. rectangular pyramid

face   base   top view

triangular prism

face   base   top view

b. an unlimited number; The base can be any polygon.

Extension ▶ ▶

Three-Dimensional Views

Three-dimensional views of model buildings made from centimeter cubes, like the ones shown in Exercises 1–3 at the top of page 551, show depth as well as length and width.

26. Draw a three-dimensional view of a model building that has the two-dimensional views shown.

front view   right-side view   left-side view

Sample Response:

27. Draw a three-dimensional view of another model building with the same front, right, and left views as in Exercise 26, but a different number of centimeter cubes.

Sample Response:

Section 2

Choose the letter from A to I of the front view and the right-side view for each model building.

1.
B, D

front   right

2.
I, F

front   right

3.
A, G

front   right

A.

B.

C.

D.

E.

F.

G.

H.

I.

Find the volume of each pyramid with the given base area *B* and height *h*. Round decimal answers to the nearest tenth.

4. $B = 22$ cm^2
$h = 6$ cm
44 cm^3

5. $B = 48$ in.^{2}
$h = 7$ in.
112 in.^{3}

6. $B = 19$ ft^2
$h = 12$ ft
76 ft^3

7. $B = 32$ mm^2
$h = 10$ mm
106.7 mm^3

Standardized Testing ▶ **Open-ended**

Suppose you have eight centimeter cubes.   Sample responses are given.

1. Draw a space figure consisting of eight cubes.

2. Draw the right, left, and front views of your space figure, and the base plan.

3. Find the volume and the surface area of your space figure.

1.

2.

right view   left view   front view

2	1
4	1

base plan

3. 8 cm^3; 30 cm^2

Section ③ Permutations and Combinations

IN THIS SECTION

EXPLORATION 1
◆ Permutations

EXPLORATION 2
◆ Combinations

WARM-UP EXERCISES

List the permutations for each situation.

1. Arrangements of the letters in the word BOO.

   BOO; OBO; OOB

2. Sam, Freda, and Alix coming through a doorway.

   SFA, SAF, FAS, FSA, AFS, ASF

How many permutations are possible for each situation?

3. Five coats on five different colored hangers.

   120

4. President and Vice-President chosen from a group of 5 people.

   20

👉 Escape to Central Park

◀◀▶ *Setting the Stage*

SET UP *You will need Labsheet 3A.*

The Horses of Central Park, by Michael Slade, is the story of a boy named Wendell who communicates with horses. He learns that the horses that pull carriages in New York City's Central Park are unhappy. Wendell comes up with an idea to raise their spirits. In the passage below Wendell explains his idea to his friend Judith.

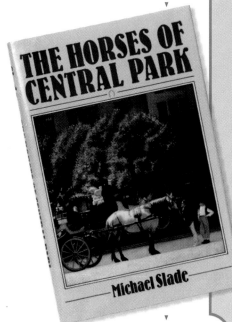

> Wendell looked around to make sure no one was near. Then he looked Judith dead in the eye and very softly and sincerely said, "I'm going to set them free."
>
> Judith could feel herself smiling on the inside as well as the outside. She might not be able to hear the horses, but Judith knew that she was very good at planning things. "Where are the stables?" she asked.
>
> "West Forty-sixth Street," said Wendell, a little nervously. "Very West Forty-sixth Street. Almost to the river. Between Eleventh and Twelfth avenues."
>
> The Hudson River was as west as you could go in Manhattan. It's what separates New York from New Jersey.
>
> The smile vanished from Judith's face. Somehow, she had just assumed that the horses lived somewhere right by the park. West Forty-sixth Street between Eleventh and Twelfth avenues was quite a walk from the park. They were going to have to find a way to get the horses from Forty-sixth Street to Central Park without anybody seeing them. "Let's go have a look," said Judith, very seriously.

Think About It ▸▸▸▸▸▸ ▸▸▸▸ ▸▸▸▸ ▸▸▸▸ ▸▸▸▸ ▸▸▸▸ ▸▸▸▸ ▸▸▸

Use Labsheet 3A for Questions 1 and 2.

1. Check students' work.

1 a. Find the Hudson River on the *Map of New York City*.

   b. Label the general location of the horse stables.

   c. Label the location of the entrance to Central Park nearest
      the horse stables.

2 Judith's and Wendell's initial plan is to free the horses from the
   stable and lead them in ones and twos to the nearest Central Park
   entrance, by the shortest possible route. To avoid suspicion,
   they want to take each group of horses by a *different* route.

   a. Explain how it is possible for two different routes to be the
      same distance.

   b. Trace three different routes the horses could take, using the
      shortest distance possible.   Check students' work.

   c. Discussion Compare your answers in part (b) with those of
      other classmates. Estimate how many possible shortest routes
      the horses could take. Then discuss how you could find all the
      possible shortest routes.   Check students' work.

2. a. Sample Response:
Think of two opposite
corners of a rectangle.
The distance along the
top and down one side is
the same as the distance
along the bottom and up
the other side.

Exploration 1

PERM⋃TATIONS

SET UP   *You will need Labsheet 3B.*

▶ To find all the possible shortest routes that the horses could take on their journey from the stables to the entrance of Central Park, you could first solve a simpler problem. Think about the possible shortest routes from the intersection marked "X" to the intersection marked "Y."

This route can be labeled S-E-E for "one block south then two blocks east."

3 **a.** What are all the possible shortest routes from intersection X to intersection Y? Make a list of the routes using letters to show the direction taken at each intersection. S–E–E, E–E–S, E–S–E

b. Suppose you are given the letters for one shortest route. How can you find all the possible shortest routes without the map?

Find all permutations of the letters.

4 **a.** Find all the possible shortest routes between two intersections if you know that one shortest route is given by the directions S-W-W-S. S–W–W–S, W–S–S–W, S–W–S–W, W–S–W–S, S–S–W–W, W–W–S–S

b. How did you make sure you had found all of the routes?

Sample Response: I compared these results with those obtained using a map.

c. Could S-W-W-W be a shortest route? How do you know?

No, not for this problem; The shortest route contains 2 S's and only 2 W's.

▶ In the street diagram below, three of the possible shortest paths from X to Y are S-S-E-E-E, S-E-S-E-E, and S-E-E-S-E.

The route shown is written "S-E-S-E-E."

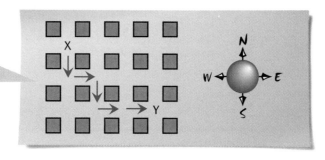

5 Use the street diagram at the bottom of page 554.

    a. How many possible shortest paths from X to Y do you think there are? *Sample Response: 10*

    b. Describe a strategy you can use to find all the possible shortest paths from X to Y. (*Hint:* Look for a pattern in the three given paths).

    c. Find all the possible shortest paths from X to Y. How many are there?

    d. Discussion Compare your answers in part (c) with those of other classmates. Compare the methods used to find all the routes. Decide which method you think worked best.
                                             Check students' work.

Use the *Street Diagram* on Labsheet 3B for Questions 6 and 7.

6 Follow the directions on Labsheet 3B to fill in the circles on the *Street Diagram.*

7 Suppose the variables *p*, *s*, and *t* represent the total number of shortest paths from intersection X on the street diagram below. Use your results from Question 6 to write an equation that shows the relationship between the variables *p*, *s*, and *t*. $p + t = s$

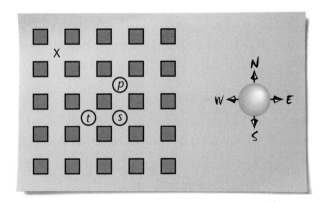

8 ✔ **CHECKPOINT** Use the *Escape Route Map* on Labsheet 3B.

    a. Assume that all the horses must start at the intersection of 11th Avenue and West 46th Street. How many possible shortest routes are there to the Columbus Circle entrance of Central Park? Explain how you found your answer.

    b. How does your answer in part (a) compare with your original estimate in Question 2? *Answers will vary.*

HOMEWORK EXERCISES ▸ See Exs. 1–7 on p. 559.

---

5. b. Sample Response:
Find all permutations of the letters S, S, E, E, and E.

c.
S–S–E–E–E,
S–E–E–S–E,
S–E–E–E–S,
S–E–S–E–E,
E–S–S–E–E,
E–S–E–S–E,
E–S–E–E–S,
E–E–S–S–E,
E–E–S–E–S,
E–E–E–S–S;
10

6.

X	1	1	1	1
1	2	3	4	5
1	3	6	10	15
1	4	10	20	35

8. a. 455; Use the number patterns found in the Street Diagram on Labsheet 3B to record a number at each intersection in the rectangle bounded by 11th Ave., 8th Ave., West 46th St. and West 58th St. The number recorded at the intersection of West 58th St. and 8th Ave. is the number of possible shortest routes.

✔ **QUESTION 8**

...checks that you can find all the possible permutations when items repeat.

GOAL

LEARN HOW TO...
- list and find all the possible combinations
- distinguish a combination from a permutation

AS YOU...
- consider ways to group horses

KEY TERM
- combination

Combinations

Wendell and Judith plan to free ten horses: Elmer, Winston, Molly, Archibald, Quentin, Angelina, Samantha, Cromwell, Chloe, and Old Barnaby. Each name can be represented by its first two letters: El, Wi, Mo, Ar, Qu, An, Sa, Cr, Ch, and Ol.

9 a. Which of the following selections represents the same group of ten horses listed above? Selection 1

Selection 1:	Wi, Mo, Qu, An, Ol, Ch, Cr, Sa, El, Ar
Selection 2:	Mo, Qu, An, Sa, Cr, Ch, Ol, Ch, Mo, Ar
Selection 3:	Sa, Ch, Ol, Ar, Mo, El, Qu, Wi, Cr

b. Does changing the order of the horses change the group itself? No.

▶ A selection of items in which order is not important is called a **combination**. One way to find all possible combinations in a situation is to first list all the possible permutations.

10 The diagram shows all the ways Wendell and Judith could have paired up the mares Molly (Mo), Angelina (An), Samantha (Sa), and Chloe (Ch).

a. How many permutations of two of these four mares are there? 12

b. Discussion Why are some of the permutations crossed out? The ones crossed out are pairs of horses already listed, just in a different order.

c. How many different combinations are possible in this situation? 6

11 Try This as a Class How is a combination different from a permutation?
Sample Response: In a combination, order is not important.

▶ Sometimes it is not practical to list all the possible permutations and then cross out repeats to find the combinations. Instead, you can make an organized list just of the combinations.

12 Suppose Judith and Wendell want to divide all ten horses into groups of two and lead each group on a different route to the Park. Copy and extend the table as you answer the questions.

First horse picked	Possible second horses to pick	Combinations of two horses	Number of combinations
El	Wi Mo Ar Qu An Sa Cr Ch Ol	El, Wi El, Mo El, Ar El, Qu El, An El, Sa El, Cr El, Ch El, Ol	9
Wi	?	?	?

12. b. Molly, Archibald, Quentin, Angelina, Samantha, Cromwell, Chloe, Old Barnaby

c.

Wi	Mo	Wi, Mo	8
	Ar	Wi, Ar	
	Qu	Wi, Qu	
	An	Wi, An	
	Sa	Wi, Sa	
	Cr	Wi, Cr	
	Ch	Wi, Ch	
	Ol	Wi, Ol	

a. With which horse is Winston already grouped in the table? **Elmer**

b. Which horses remain to be grouped with Winston?

c. Use your answers to parts (a) and (b) to complete Winston's row of the table.

d. Extend the table to include all the possible combinations for this situation. What pattern do you notice?
See Additional Answers.

e. How many different groups of two horses could Judith and Wendell form? **45**

13 ✔ **CHECKPOINT** Suppose six horses are entered in a race. First, second, and third place results are recorded.

a. How many results are possible for the first three places? **120 results**

b. Suppose the first three horses are recorded in no particular order. How many results are possible? **20 results**

c. Which question in parts (a) and (b) is a permutation question? Which is a combination question? Explain your answers. **a, b; Order is significant; Order doesn't matter.**

✔ **QUESTION 13**

…checks that you understand the difference between a permutation and a combination.

HOMEWORK EXERCISES ▶ See Exs. 8–16 on pp. 559–560.

Permutations with Repeated Items (pp. 554–555)

The number of permutations of 4 different items is $4 \cdot 3 \cdot 2 \cdot 1 = 24$. When items repeat, the number of permutations is reduced.

Example Suppose the letters N and E stand for the map directions north and east. The permutations of the letters N, E, E, and N give the 6 possible shortest routes from intersection A to intersection B below.

Route 1: N-E-E-N
Route 2: N-E-N-E
Route 3: N-N-E-E
Route 4: E-N-E-N
Route 5: E-N-N-E
Route 6: E-E-N-N

combination

Combinations (pp. 556–557)

A combination is a selection of objects in which order is not important.

Example An organized list can help you find combinations. This list shows the 10 possible groups of 3 out of the 5 options A, B, C, D, and E.

1st option picked	2nd option picked	Possible 3rd option	Combinations	Number of combinations
A	B	C	ABC	3
		D	ABD	
		E	ABE	
A	C	D	ACD	2
		E	ACE	
A	D	E	ADE	1
B	C	D	BCD	2
		E	BCE	
B	D	E	BDE	1
C	D	E	CDE	1

CLOSURE QUESTION

Describe one situation in which you would want to use a permutation and one in which you would want to use a combination.

Sample Response: You could use a permutation to find the number of ways to line up 5 different books on a shelf. You could use a combination to find the number of ways to choose 3 people from a group of 20 to be on a committee.

14 **Key Concepts Question** Is the following list a correct list for the situation in the second Example above?

EDC, EDB, EDA, ECB, ECA, EBA, DCB, DCA, DBA, CBA

Why or why not? Yes; The same sets of three are listed and order is not important.

Section 3

Practice & Application Exercises ▸▸▸▸▸▸▸

List all the permutations of the letters in each word.

1. EAT   2. FREE   3. NOON   4. PUPPY   5. DEEDED

1. EAT, ETA, AET, ATE, TEA, TAE

6. Find the number of permutations of four letters in each case.

  a. All four letters are the same. 1

  b. Three of the letters are the same. 4

  c. Two of the letters are the same. 12

  d. The four letters are different. 24

7. **Challenge** The numbers below have been arranged in a
   right triangle shape. **a.** The 1st number is multiplied by the number of numbers
   in the column, *n*. The next number is multiplied by *n* – 1, the next by *n* – 2, and so on.
   a. Explain the multiplication pattern in each column shown,
      as you move from the top to the bottom of the column.

  b. Copy the triangle and use the pattern you found in part (a)
     to add three more columns to the triangle.

  c. How are the numbers in the triangle related to
     your answers to Exercise 6?

  d. Suppose you have eight letters and
     exactly three of them are the same.
     Use the triangle to find the
     number of possible
     permutations
     of the letters.
     Explain your
     method.

							?
						?	?
					?	?	?
			1	?	?	?	
		1	5	?	?	?	
	1	4	20	?	?	?	
1	3	12	60	?	?	?	
1	2	6	24	120	?	?	?

8. Suppose there are seven police officers who patrol in a certain
   city precinct. They are assigned to work in groups of two per
   patrol car. How many different groups of two officers can be
   assigned to a patrol car? Explain how you solved the problem.

9. **Geometry Connection** Draw all possible segments connecting
   five different points on a circle. How many segments are there?
   (*Hint:* Only one segment can be drawn between two points.)

2. FREE, FERE, FEER,
   RFEE, REFE, REEF,
   EERF, EEFR, ERFE,
   EFRE, EREF, EFER

3. NOON, ONON, OONN,
   ONNO, NNOO, NONO

4. PUPPY, PUPYP,
   PUYPP, PYPUP, PYPUP,
   PYPPU, PPUPY, PPUYP,
   PPYUP, PPYPU, PPPUY,
   PPPYU, UPPPY, UYPPP,
   UPYPP, UPPYP, YUPPP,
   YPUPP, YPPPU, YPPUP

5. DEEDED, DEEDDE,
   DEDEDE, DEDEED
   DEDDEE, DEEEDD,
   DDEEED, DDEEDE,
   DDEDEE, DDDEEE,
   EDEDED, EDEDDE,
   EDEEDD, EDDEED,
   EDDEDE, EDDDEE,
   EEDDDE, EEDEDD,
   EEDDED, EEEDDD

7. **b.**

		1
	1	8
1	7	56
6	42	336
30	210	1680
120	840	6720
360	2520	20,160
720	5040	40,320

c. Reading from the
bottom up, the numbers
in the 4th column give the
number of permutations
of 4 letters if none are the
same, 2 are the same, 3
are the same, and all are
the same.

d. 6720; Read the 8th
column from the bottom
up. The number of
permutations of 8 cards if
none are the same is
40,320, if 2 are the same
is 20,160, and if 3 are the
same is 6720.

8. 21; Since there are 7
choices for the 1st
partner and 6 for the
second, there are 7 · 6, or
42 possible groups of 2.
But since the group
Bob–Tom is the same as
the group Tom–Bob,
divide 42 by 2 to
eliminate duplication.

9.

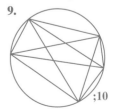

;10

For Exercises 10–12, tell whether each is a *permutation* or a *combination*.

10. Ten planes are lining up to take off on a runway. **permutation**

11. Two players from a team of twelve are chosen for an all-star team.
combination

12. Three out of a group of eight paintings are hung in a row. **permutation**

13. **a.** Suppose you are choosing four out of these five pieces of fruit: an apple, a banana, a kiwi, an orange, and a pear. List all of the possible combinations. **See Additional Answers.**

    b. Repeat part (a) for three out of five, two out of five, and one out of five pieces of fruit. **See Additional Answers.**

14. **a. Sample Response:**
The numbers in the outside diagonals are all 1's. Each number in an inside diagonal is the sum of the 2 numbers above it. The numbers in the 3rd diagonal row follow the pattern 1, 1 + 2, 1 + 2 + 3, 1 + 2 + 3 + 4, and so on.

c. Disregard the 1's on the triangle. To find the number of combinations of 3 things from a group of 6, for example, locate the row that begins with 6. Count over 3 numbers. The number of combinations is 20.

14. The triangle of numbers below is sometimes referred to as *Pascal's triangle*.

    a. Describe three number patterns you can see in the triangle.

    b. Copy the triangle and use the patterns you found in part (a) to add the next three rows. **See Additional Answers.**

    c. **Challenge** Explain how to use the triangle to find the number of possible combinations for a situation.

```
              1
            1   1
          1   2   1
        1   3   3   1
      1   4   6   4   1
    1   5  10  10   5   1
  1   6  15  20  15   6   1
```

15. **Elections** In order to count the possible outcomes of an election, sometimes you need to use permutations and sometimes you need to use combinations.

    a. Suppose eight candidates are running for two openings on a school council. How many different pairs of candidates can be elected? **28**

    b. Suppose an eight-member council chooses a chairperson and a secretary. How many results are possible? **56**

    c. Which question in parts (a) and (b) is a permutation question? Which is a combination question? Explain your answers.
    b, a; Order is important; Order is not important.

R e f l e c t i n g ▶ on the Section

Journal

Exercise 16 checks that you recognize situations involving permutations and combinations.

Write your response to Exercise 16 in your journal.

16. Give an example of a situation that can be described using a combination. Then identify a situation that can be described using a permutation. How are the two concepts different? **Answers will vary.**

Find the volume of a pyramid with the given base area and height.
(Module 8, p. 547)

17. Area of base = 30 cm²
Height = 12.5 cm 125 cm³

18. Area of base = 12 ft²
Height = 25 ft 100 ft³

Find each sum or difference. (Module 3, p. 183)

19. $3\frac{5}{6} - 1\frac{2}{3}$ $2\frac{1}{6}$ **20.** $1\frac{3}{5} + 3\frac{1}{12}$ $4\frac{41}{60}$ **21.** $6\frac{1}{2} - 4\frac{6}{7}$ $1\frac{9}{14}$ **22.** $7\frac{3}{5} + 9\frac{3}{4}$ $17\frac{7}{20}$

23. The measures of three angles in a quadrilateral are 45°, 85°, and 100°. Find the measure of the fourth angle. (Module 6, p. 429) 130°

Traffic Flow

Estimation Traffic engineers need to estimate the amount of traffic during peak travel times.   **6–8. Answers will vary.**

 6 Identify two peak travel times for the section of hallway you chose.

 7 Suppose that for one instant during each peak travel time, you could magically stop everyone walking in the hallway. Brainstorm with your group to determine a method you could use to estimate the number of students in the chosen section of hallway at any instant during peak travel times.

 8 a. During both peak travel times, estimate the number of students in that section of hallway at any instant.

b. Use your estimate in part (a) to determine the number of square feet of hallway per walker during each peak travel time.

c. Did your answers to part (b) vary greatly for the two peak travel times you identified in Project Question 6? Explain.

List all the permutations of the letters in each word.

1. ERR   2. LULL   3. DADDY   4. LLAMA

5. Find the number of permutations of three letters in each case.

   a. All three letters are different. 6

   b. Two of the letters are the same. 3

   c. All three letters are the same. 1

For Exercises 6–8, tell whether each is a _permutation_ or a _combination_.

6. Students in a class of 24 are organized into groups of 3. combination

7. Three photos out of a group of ten are chosen to be used in a magazine article. combination

8. Twenty people are forming a line to buy movie tickets.   permutation

9. List all the ways four tennis players, Sue, Flora, Hiroko, and Yuki, can be matched up for the semifinal round of a singles tennis tournament. **See Additional Answers.**

10. How many different groups of three students can be formed from a group of four students? Did you find the answer using the idea of a combination or a permutation? Explain. 4; **Sample Response: I used Pascal's Triangle. combination; Order is not important.**

1. ERR, RER, RRE

2. LULL, LLUL, LLLU, ULLL

3. DADDY, DADYD, DAYDD, DYDAD, DYDDA, DYADD, DDAYD, DDADY, DDYAD, DDYDA, DDDAY, DDDYA, ADDDY, ADYDD, ADDYD, AYDDD, YADDD, YDADD, YDDAD, YDDDA

4. LLAMA, LLMAA, LLAAM, LAMAL, LAMLA, LALAM, LAAML, LAALM, LALMA, LMLAA, LMAAL, LMALA, ALALM, ALAML, ALMAL, ALMLA, ALLMA, ALLAM, AMALL, AMLAL, AMLLA, AALLM, AALML, AAMLL, MLLAA, MLALA, MLAAL, MALLA, MAALL, MALAL

Tell whether each situation is a _permutation_, a _combination_, _neither_, or _both_. Explain your answer.

1. Maria is catering a party. She will serve five appetizers. The host wants her to serve the stuffed mushrooms first and the shrimp last. In how many orders can Maria serve the appetizers? **permutation; Order is important.**

2. Four people are in line for theater tickets. There are only five tickets left. If only one ticket is required to get into the theater, how many people can get into the theater? **neither**

3. Suppose you want to buy five different pens, but only have enough money for four pens. How many different groups of pens can you buy? **combination; Order is not important.**

Wrap It Up

SET UP *You will need:* • *paper bag* • *scissors* • *tape or glue* • *ruler*
See the Resource Book for a detailed discussion of this Extended Exploration.

The Situation

Many of the products we buy in stores come in boxes. The shapes of boxes are chosen for various reasons, such as shelf size or ease of handling. Package designers must also think about the amount of material used to create them. Reducing the total area of the outside surface of the box is a major factor in any package design.

The Problem

What is the biggest box that can be wrapped using a paper bag?

Something to Think About   Check students' work.

• What kind of space figure is a box?

• How can making a net help you solve the problem?

• What measure(s) do you need to maximize in order to produce the biggest box?

• Is there any other information you need to obtain before you can begin working on this problem? If so, what is it?

Present Your Results

Give an oral report describing how you created your box design. Include the volume and the surface area of the box. Be sure to display your net and the box it forms.

Section ④ Tessellations and Volumes of Cones

IN THIS SECTION

EXPLORATION 1
◆ Tessellations

EXPLORATION 2
◆ Volume of a Cone

Art **IN THE** City

◄◄◄ *Setting the Stage*

SET UP Work with a partner. You will need $\frac{1}{2}$ bucket of pattern blocks.

Plazas are one place in a city where people can gather for entertainment, food, and conversation while also enjoying the outdoors. Plazas like the one shown provide a place for festivals, street performers, and public forums.

► The photo shows how Stockholm, Sweden, brought color and art to a plaza.

Think About It

1 Use your pattern blocks to create a colorful, artistic walkway for a plaza. Do not leave gaps between your pattern blocks or lay one pattern block on top of another. (Save your walkway tiling to use in Question 4.) **Check students' work.**

2 **a.** Which polygons did you use? Why?
   Sample Response: triangles and squares; They fit together with no gaps or overlaps.
   b. What types of polygons do you think could be used to cover a walkway? **Sample Response: triangles, squares, hexagons.**

essellations

GOAL

LEARN HOW TO...
◆ create a tessellation

USING...
◆ triangles and quadrilaterals

KEY TERMS
◆ tessellation
◆ vertex of a tessellation

SET UP *Work with a partner. You will need:* • *pattern blocks* • *protractor* • *index card* • *ruler* • *scissors* • *graph paper*

▶ **A tiling that uses congruent polygons in a repeating pattern to cover a plane with no gaps or overlaps is a tessellation. Designers often use tessellations to bring beauty and color to a plaza.**

3 The **vertices of a tessellation** are the points where the corners of the polygons touch. One **vertex** is marked in the tessellation shown.

a. What polygons surround each vertex?
squares and other rhombuses

b. Use your pattern blocks to form one vertex of this tessellation.
Check students' work.

c. Measure the angle of each pattern block that forms the vertex.   90°, 60°, 90°, 120°

d. What is the sum of the angle measures at the vertex?   360°

e. What group of polygons form the repeating pattern?
2 squares and 2 other rhombuses

4 **Discussion** Look at your tiling from Question 1. Is there a group of polygons that repeat in a pattern? Did you cover a portion of the plane with no gaps or overlaps? Is your tiling a tessellation?
Answers will vary.

▶ **In Question 1 you had no restrictions on your tiling. You could have used one type of pattern block or many different ones. Many tessellations are created using a single shape repeatedly to form a pattern.**

5 **Discussion** Look at the pattern in the tiling shown on page 564.

a. What types of polygons were used to create the pattern?
equilateral triangles

b. Do you think there are other types of triangles that can be used to create a tessellation? Explain.
Yes; Any 2 congruent triangles can be put together to form a parallelogram that tessellates.

6 a. Use a ruler to draw a triangle on an index card and cut it out.
Check students' work.

b. Trace around your triangle to create a tessellation. Be sure to line up the corresponding sides.
Check students' work.

7 Discussion The tessellation below was created by tracing around a triangle. Why are six triangles needed at the vertex rather than five or seven?

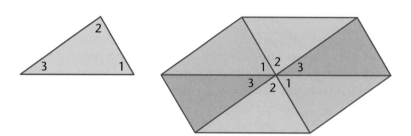

8 Look at your tessellation from Question 6.

a. Describe the triangle you used in your tessellation. Was it *right*, *obtuse*, or *acute*? Was it *scalene*, *isosceles*, or *equilateral*?
Answers will vary.

b. Will any triangle tessellate? Explain.
Yes; Any 2 congruent triangles can be put together to form a parallelogram that tessellates.

9 Parallelograms can also be used to create a tessellation.

a. On graph paper, create a tessellation using a parallelogram. Be sure every parallelogram is congruent to the first one you drew. Check students' work.

b. Is there a larger similar parallelogram in your tessellation? If so, outline it. Check students' work.

10 ✔ CHECKPOINT Use a ruler to draw a quadrilateral on an index card. Cut out your quadrilateral. Then trace around your quadrilateral to create a tessellation. Be sure to match up the corresponding sides. Check students' work.

11 Discussion Look at your tessellation from Question 10.

a. Was your quadrilateral in Question 10 concave or convex?
Answers will vary.

b. Will any convex quadrilateral tessellate? Explain. See above.

c. Will any concave quadrilateral tessellate? Explain. See above.

FOR◄HELP
with the *sum of the angles of a triangle*, see
MODULE 6, p. 429

7. Since the sum of the measures of the angles of a triangle is 180°, it takes 2 sets of these angles to fill in the 360° around 1 vertex of the tessellation.

11. b. Yes; Since the sum of the measures of the 4 angles of a convex quadrilateral is 360°, the angles will fill the space around a vertex without gaps or overlaps.

c. Yes; Since the sum of the measures of the 4 angles of a concave quadrilateral is 360°, the angles will fill the space around a vertex without gaps or overlaps.

✔ QUESTION 10
...checks that you can create a tessellation.

FOR◄HELP
with *concave* and *convex* polygons, see
MODULE 6, p. 388

HOMEWORK EXERCISES ▶ See Exs. 1–6 on pp. 572–573.

You can also use computer drawing software to create a tessellation, as in Questions 6, 9, and 10 on page 566.

Step 1 Use the polygon tool to draw a triangle or another shape. Then duplicate the polygon a number of times.

Step 2 Flip or rotate the copies and move them together to form a pattern.

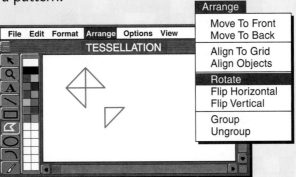

Step 3 Group the polygons in the pattern together to form one object. This new object can be duplicated and moved as one piece to create a tessellation.

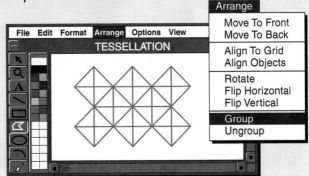

GOAL

LEARN HOW TO...
◆ find the volume of a cone

AS YOU...
◆ examine sculptures

KEY TERM
◆ cone

Exploration 2

Volume of a Cone

SET UP *Work with a partner. You will need:* • *Labsheets 4A and 4B* • *scissors* • *tape* • *rice*

Museums bring art to the city in different ways. Museums themselves are sometimes considered works of art. The Spiral Building, a museum in Tokyo, uses light, shadow, and shapes to create an interesting and complex exterior. What shapes and tessellations do you notice?

12 Discussion On the upper right side of the building is a steel circular *cone.* Why do you think the architects decided to use a circular cone instead of a circular cylinder or a rectangular prism? Sample Response: The cone is a more unusual and interesting shape.

▶ **All the cones and cylinders in this section have circular bases. You can refer to them as cones and cylinders rather than *circular cones* and *circular cylinders.***

A space figure with a circular base and a vertex is a circular **cone.**

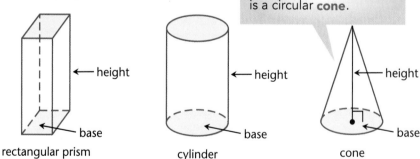

rectangular prism   cylinder   cone

13 Suppose each figure above is the same height and the areas of the bases are equal. Which figure do you think has the least volume? Why? Sample Response: the cone; There is a great deal of empty space between the base of the cone and its tip.

▶ **When a cone and a cylinder have the same height and the areas of their bases are equal, their volumes are related.**

14 **Use Labsheet 4A.** Follow the directions on Labsheet 4A to investigate the relationship between the volumes of cones and cylinders using the *Cone and Cylinder Nets.* Check student's work.

15 **Try This as a Class** The graph shows the volumes of several cones that have a height of 1 m.

   a. Suppose you want to estimate the volume of a cone with a radius of 3 m. How would you connect the points in the graph? Would you use segments or a curve? a curve

   b. Copy the graph. Use segments to estimate the volume of a cone with a radius of 3 m. Then use a curve to estimate the volume. about 15 m³; about 10 m³

   c. The volume of a cone with a radius of 3 m is about 9.5 m³. Which method in part (b) gave the best estimate of the volume of the cone? using a curve

Use Labsheet 4B for Questions 16 and 17.

16 Follow the directions on Labsheet 4B to complete the *Comparing Volumes of Cones and Cylinders* table and graph.
See Additional Answers.

17 Look at your completed graph from Question 16.

   a. A cylinder with a radius of 5 m and a height of 1 m has a volume of about 78.5 m³. Estimate the volume of a cone with the same radius and height. about 26 m³

   b. A cone with a radius of 7 m and a height of 1 m has a volume of about 51.3 m³. Estimate the volume of a cylinder with the same radius and height. about 153.9 m³

   c. How many times greater is the volume of a cylinder compared to the volume of a cone when both have the same radius and height? How does the graph show this? about 3 times; For any given radius, the volume of the cone is about $\frac{1}{3}$ that of the cylinder.

18 **Discussion** The volume of a cylinder can be found using the equation $V = Bh$.

   a. What do V, B, and h represent in the equation? volume, area of the base, height

   b. Based on your work in Questions 14, 16, and 17, what equation can you use to find the volume of a cone? $V = \frac{1}{3}Bh$

FOR◀HELP
with *volume of a cylinder*, see
MODULE 7, p. 464

EXAMPLE

Find the volume of a cone with a radius of 1.5 m and a height of 0.7 m.

SAMPLE RESPONSE

$$V = \frac{1}{3}Bh \quad \blacktriangleleft \quad B = \text{area of base}$$

$$V = \frac{1}{3} \cdot \pi r^2 \cdot h$$

$$\approx \frac{1}{3} \cdot 3.14 \cdot (1.5)^2 \cdot 0.7 \quad \blacktriangleleft \quad \text{Remember, } \pi \approx 3.14.$$

$$\approx 1.6485$$

The volume of the cone is about 1.6 m³.

For answers throughout the rest of the book, 3.14 is used. Answers may vary slightly if the π key is used.

19 a. In the Example, what does *r* represent? What is the value of *r*?
    the radius of the base, 1.5 m

   b. What is the area of the base? about 7.065 m²

   c. How can you use the diameter of the base instead of the radius to find the volume of a cone? Divide the diameter by 2.

20 The diameter of a cone is 12 ft. The height is 3.5 ft. Find the volume.
    about 131.88 ft³

21 ✔ CHECKPOINT The cone on the Spiral Building has a radius of 2.5 m and a height of 7.5 m. What is the volume of a cone with these dimensions? about 49.1 m³

✔ QUESTION 21

...checks that you can find the volume of a cone.

22 The Spiral Building's cone is made of steel. Steel has a mass of 7860 kg for every cubic meter (m³).

   a. Find the mass of a steel cone with a radius of 2.5 m and a height of 7.5 m. about 385,631 kg

   b. An African bull elephant has a mass between 5400 kg and 7200 kg. About how many elephants are equivalent to the mass of the steel cone in part (a)?
    about 60 elephants

23 Discussion The floor under the steel cone on the Spiral Building can support no more than 5900 kg. How do you think the architects reduced the mass of the steel cone?
    Sample Response: by making the cone hollow

HOMEWORK EXERCISES ▶ See Exs. 7–13 on pp. 573–574.

Section 4
Key Concepts

Tessellations (pp. 565–566)

A tessellation is a tiling that uses congruent polygons in a repeating pattern to cover a plane with no gaps or overlaps. All triangles and quadrilaterals tessellate.

The sum of the angle measures around a vertex is 360°.

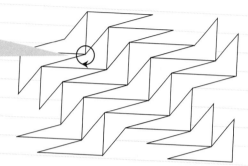

Volume of a Cone (pp. 568–570)

The volume of any cone is given by the formula $V = \frac{1}{3}Bh$ where B equals the area of its base and h equals its height.

height

base

Example

The height of a cone is 4 ft and the base has an area of 12 ft². Find the volume.

$$V = \frac{1}{3}(12)(4) = 16$$

The volume of the cone is 16 ft³.

CLOSURE QUESTION

How are the formulas for the volumes of a pyramid and a cone alike? How are they different?

Sample Response: Both formulas are given by $V = \frac{1}{3}Bh$, where B is the area of the base and h is the height. The area of the base of a pyramid is the area of whatever polygon forms the base, while the area of the base of a cone is always the area of a circle and can be found by using $A = \pi r^2$ where r is the radius of the base.

Key Concepts Questions

24 In the tessellation above, three of the angles at a vertex have measures of 90°, 38°, and 18°. What is the measure of the fourth angle? 214°

25 How would the volume of the cone in the Example change if it were twice as high? if the radius were doubled but the height did not change? The volume would double; The volume would be 4 times as great.

Section 4

YOU WILL NEED

For Ex. 4:
- Labsheet 4C

For Ex. 5:
- index card
- scissors
- tape

For Ex. 16:
- graph paper

For Ex. 17:
- $\frac{1}{2}$ bucket of pattern blocks

Trace each polygon below and then create a tessellation with it. Be sure to match up the corresponding sides.

1.

2.

3.

1–3. Check students' work.

4. **Use Labsheet 4C.** A polygon is called a *repeated tile*, or *rep-tile*, if congruent polygons can be arranged to form a larger similar polygon. The equilateral triangle pattern block is a rep-tile. For each other pattern block that is a rep-tile, make a sketch to show how four of the blocks can be made into a larger similar polygon.

See Additional Answers.

5. **Create Your Own** Maurits Cornelius Escher, the Dutch artist known as M. C. Escher, used tessellations, rotations, and translations to create many fascinating tilings like the one shown. Check students' work.

a. Follow Steps 1–3 below to create your own tiling.

b. **Research** Look up another of Escher's tilings. Describe the transformations he used.

Step 1

Draw a parallelogram on an index card and cut it out.

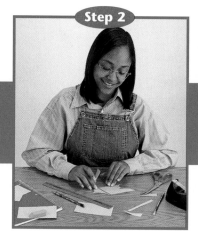

Step 2

Draw a design along one side of the parallelogram. Cut it out and translate it to the opposite side. Tape on the translated piece.

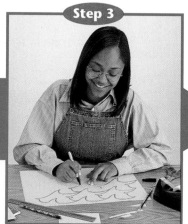

Step 3

Repeat the last step on the other sides, if you wish. Then use your shape to create a tiling. Personalize it by adding color and other details.

6. In a *regular tessellation*, one regular polygon is used to create the tessellation. Four regular polygons are shown.

  a. What is the measure of an interior angle of each polygon? (*Hint:* Draw diagonals to form triangles.) 60°, 108°, 120°, 90°

  b. How can you use the measure of the interior angle to determine if a regular polygon will tessellate?
  If the measure of the angle is a factor of 360°, the polygon will tessellate.
  c. Which of these four regular polygons will tessellate?
  triangle, hexagon, square

Use the approximate dimensions given to estimate the volume of each cone. Round decimal answers to the nearest tenth.

7.

h≈4.4 in.
r≈0.9 in.

about 3.7 in.³

8.

h≈11.2 in.
r≈2.6 in.

about 79.2 in.³

9.

h≈46.8 cm
r≈118.6 cm

about 689,007.0 cm³

10. A cone and a cylinder both have volumes of 12π cm³.

  a. Give a set of possible dimensions for the cylinder. Then sketch a model.

  b. If the cone and the cylinder have congruent bases, what is the relationship between their heights?
  The height of the cone is 3 times that of the cylinder.

11. Suppose a cone and a cylinder have congruent bases and equal heights. A pyramid and a prism also have congruent bases and equal heights. Write a proportion to relate the volumes of all four solids.

$$\frac{\text{volume of ?}}{\text{volume of ?}} = \frac{\text{volume of ?}}{\text{volume of ?}}$$

Sample Response: $\dfrac{\text{volume of cone}}{\text{volume of cylinder}} = \dfrac{\text{volume of pyramid}}{\text{volume of prism}}$

10. a. Sample Response:
$r = 2$ cm, $h = 3$ cm

2 cm

3 cm

12. Challenge The cone on the Spiral Building is hollow and the walls are 6 mm thick. To find the volume of the walls of the hollow cone you can think of it as a cone inside a cone, as shown in the drawing below. Use the information below to find the volume of the walls of the hollow cone.

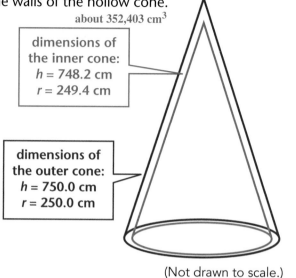

about 352,403 cm³

dimensions of the inner cone:
$h = 748.2$ cm
$r = 249.4$ cm

dimensions of the outer cone:
$h = 750.0$ cm
$r = 250.0$ cm

(Not drawn to scale.)

Discussion

Exercise 13 checks that you can find and compare volumes of cones.

Reflecting ‹▸on the Section

Be prepared to discuss your response to Exercise 13 in class.

13. The table and graph show the volumes of cones that all have a height of 10 in.

10-Inch-Tall Cones	
Radius (in.)	Volume (in.³)
0.5	2.62
1.5	23.55
2.5	65.42
3.5	128.22
4.5	211.95
5.5	316.62

a. How many times greater is the volume of a cone with a radius of 4.5 in. compared to a cone with a radius of 1.5 in.? 9 times

b. How many times greater is the volume of a cone with a radius of 5 in. compared to a cone with a radius of 2.5 in.? 4 times

c. In general, how does a change in the radius change the volume? How does the graph show this?

If the radius is increased x times, the volume is increased x^2 times.

Tell whether each is a *permutation* or a *combination*. (Module 8, p. 558)

14. the number of ways to arrange 6 books on a shelf permutation

15. the number of ways to select 3 books from a choice of 7 books
 combination

16. **a.** Plot and label each point in a coordinate plane. Then draw segments connecting *A* to *B*, *B* to *C*, and so on up to *E* to *F*. Finally, connect *F* to *A*. (Module 2, p. 95)

A(1, 3)	*B*(2, 2)	*C*(–1, –1)
D(–3, 1)	*E*(–2, 2)	*F*(–1, 1)

b. Use coordinates to describe a transformation that will result in an image similar to the polygon you plotted in part (a). Then draw the image after your transformation. (Module 4, p. 299)

16. a.

b. Sample Response: $(x + 2, y - 1)$

Extension ▶ ▶

Semi-Regular Tessellations

In Exercise 6 on page 573, you saw that one regular polygon can be used to create a tessellation. You can also create tessellations using more than one regular polygon. For example, an equilateral triangle and a regular hexagon were used to create the tessellation below.

17. **a.** Which pattern blocks are regular polygons?
 triangles, squares, hexagons
 b. Create two or three different tessellations that include more than one type of the pattern blocks you identified in part (a).
 Check students' work.

A *semi-regular tessellation* uses more than one kind of regular polygon, and has the same arrangement of polygons at every vertex. The tessellation shown above is an example of a semi-regular tessellation.

18. Two different arrangements of regular polygons appear in the tessellation below, so it is not a semi-regular tessellation.

 a. Identify which of your tessellations from Exercise 17(b) are semi-regular tessellations.
 Answers will vary.
 b. Is the tessellation shown on page 565 a semi-regular tessellation? Explain.
 No; The polygons are not all regular.

Trace each polygon below and then create a tessellation with it.
Be sure to match up the corresponding sides.   Check students' work.

1.   2.   3.

Use the figures below for Exercises 4 and 5.

A.   B.   C.   D.

4. Which of the figures tessellate?   B, C, D

5. Which two figures can combine to tessellate?   B and D

Find the volume of each cone. Round decimal answers to the nearest tenth.

6.
261.7 cm³   10 cm   5 cm

7. 1674.7 mm³   8 mm   25 mm

8.
301.4 in.³   8 in.   12 in.

Standardized Testing ◀▶ Multiple Choice

1. Use these heights and base radii of cones to answer the question.

   I. $h = 9$ cm   II. $h = 2$ cm   III. $h = 1$ cm   IV. $h = 4$ cm
      $r = 2$ cm $r = 4$ cm $r = 6$ cm $r = 3$ cm

   Which dimensions produce cones with the same volume? ($\pi \approx 3.14$)   D

   Ⓐ None   Ⓑ I and III only   Ⓒ III and IV only   Ⓓ I, III, and IV only

2. Which figure does not always tessellate?   B

   Ⓐ triangle   Ⓑ pentagon   Ⓒ convex quadrilateral   Ⓓ concave quadrilateral

Completing the Module Project

Traffic Flow

You determined the traffic flow through a section of hallway in your school that has a traffic problem. Now you'll develop a plan for improving the flow of traffic through that section of hallway.

Traffic engineers have found that there are no limits on walking speed when each walker has at least 40 ft^2 of floorspace. Then, as a walkway becomes more crowded, it becomes harder to walk at certain speeds.

The engineers' findings are summarized in this table. *Maximum capacity flow* is the greatest number of walkers that a walkway can hold.

Effect of Overcrowding on Walking Speed				
No speeds restricted	Few speeds restricted	Some speeds restricted	All speeds restricted	Maximum capacity flow
40 ft^2/walker	24–40 ft^2/walker	15–24 ft^2/walker	6–15 ft^2/walker	6 ft^2/walker

9–13. Check students' work.

9 How would you classify the traffic flow in your section of the hallway during each peak travel time you identified in Project Question 6?

10 Is the traffic in your hallway over the maximum capacity? If not, how many more students can use the hallway?

11 Suppose you want to alter your section of hallway so students can walk at any speed. Give dimensions for the least width that would allow this during peak travel times. Would it be practical to build a hallway this wide?

12 Think about how obstacles or gathering places cause traffic jams in the hallway.

   a. Describe any changes you think should be made.

   b. If no changes are needed, estimate how much enrollment would have to increase to create a traffic problem.

13 Make a presentation of your findings and recommendations. Use graphs and traffic flow data to support your views.

You will need: • *graph paper* (Ex. 23)

List all the permutations for each situation. (Sec. 1, Explor. 1)

1. A band and an orchestra will perform separately at a concert.
   band–orchestra, orchestra–band

2. A family will visit three vacation sites: Sequoia National Park, Joshua Tree National Park, and Mono Lake. See Additional Answers.

3. A student will do homework for Spanish, art, and social studies.
   See Additional Answers.

4. Two out of four colored blankets will be layered on a bed. The colors are beige, pink, yellow, and green. beige–pink, beige–yellow, beige–green, pink-beige, pink–yellow, pink–green, yellow-beige, yellow-pink, yellow–green, green-beige, green-pink, green-yellow.

Find how many permutations are possible for each situation. (Sec. 1, Explor. 2)

5. five bicycles being put in a bicycle rack 120

6. eight songs to be sung in a concert 40,320

7. the first three batters on a softball team with ten players 720

8. the first two finishers in a race among 50 runners 2450

For Exercises 9–12, use the base plan below. (Sec. 2, Explor. 1)

9. Draw the front and right-side views of the building.

10. What is the volume of the building?
    10 cubic units

11. What is the surface area of the building? 42 square units

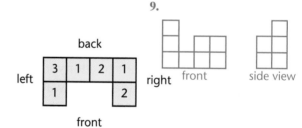

9.

back

left | 3 | 1 | 2 | 1 |

| 1 | | | 2 |

right front   side view

front

12. Suppose a building has the shape of a rectangular prism that is 5 cubes long, 2 cubes wide, and 1 cube high. Compare the volume and the surface area of this building to the volume and the surface area of the building in Exercises 9–11.
    The volumes are the same; the surface area is less because fewer faces are exposed.

Find the volume of each pyramid with the given base area B and height h. (Sec. 2, Explor. 2)

13. $B = 15$ cm²
    $h = 5$ cm 25 cm³

14. $B = 21$ ft²
    $h = 8$ ft 56 ft³

15. $B = 40$ m²
    $h = 12$ m 160 m³

Use the street diagram. Find all of the shortest routes between the given intersections. (Sec. 3, Explor. 1)

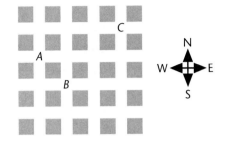

16. from A to B E-S, S-E

17. from B to C N-N-E-E, E-E-N-N, N-E-N-E, E-N-E-N, N-E-E-N, E-N-N-E

18. from C to A
W-W-W-S, W-W-S-W, W-S-W-W, S-W-W-W

List all the permutations of the letters in each word. (Sec. 3, Explor. 1)

19. BOOT   20. BELLE   21. NANNY

19–21. See Additional Answers.

22. Freddi has five dogs: Bubba, Taffy, Radar, Dexter, and Lucky. Suppose she takes them for walks in groups of two or more. (Sec. 3, Explor. 2)

   a. How many different groups of three dogs can she take? 10 groups

   b. How many different groups of two dogs can she take? 10 groups

   c. How are your answers to parts (a) and (b) related? Explain. See Additional Answers.

   d. Is this situation a *permutation* or a *combination*? Explain.
      Combination; Order is not significant.

23. Draw a trapezoid on graph paper. Then create a tessellation with it. Explain why any trapezoid will tessellate. (Sec. 4, Explor. 1)   Check students' work; Since the sum of the measures of the angles of a trapezoid is 360°, the angles will fill the space around a vertex without gaps or overlaps.

Find the volume of each cone. Round decimal answers to the nearest tenth. (Sec. 4, Explor. 2)

24.

10 m   6 m

376.8 m³

25.

3 cm   1.2 cm

4.5 cm³

26.
12 in.

⊢— 15 in. —⊣ 706.5 in.³

R e f l e c t i n g ◀▶ on the Module

27. Suppose the following four measurements can be either the height or the radius of a cone: 2 m, 5 m, 6 m, and 12 m.

   a. How many different cones can be formed with these measurements?

   b. Which dimensions will make the cone with the least volume? the greatest volume? Explain.

27. a. 12, since the same measurement cannot be used for both the height and the radius
b. $r = 2$, $h = 5$ and $r = 12$, $h = 6$; Since the radius is squared, it should be the smallest number for the least volume and the greatest number for the greatest volume. The height should be the next lowest or highest number.

CONTENTS

STUDENT RESOURCES

STUDENT RESOURCES

TOOLBOX

Adding and Subtracting Decimals

When you add or subtract decimals, line up the decimal places and use the same rules as for adding and subtracting whole numbers.

EXAMPLE

$7.75 + 6.61 \longrightarrow$

$$\begin{array}{r} 1 \\ 7.75 \\ + \ 6.61 \\ \hline 14.36 \end{array}$$

$4.6 - 2.25 \longrightarrow$

$$\begin{array}{r} 5\ 10 \\ 4.\cancel{6}0 \\ - \ 2.25 \\ \hline 2.35 \end{array}$$

Write a zero so that both numbers have the same number of decimal places.

You may find it helpful to use mental math skills to add and subtract decimals.

EXAMPLE

Find 32 + 19.8.

Trade a whole number for 19.8: 19.8 + **0.2** = **20**

SOLUTION

$32 + \mathbf{20} = 52$
$52 - \mathbf{0.2} = 51.8$
$32 + 19.8 = 51.8$

Take off the extra **0.2** that you added.

EXAMPLE

Find 2.8 + 3.6 + 2.2 + 5.4.

SOLUTION Pair up numbers that are compatible and can be added easily.

$\mathbf{2.8 + 3.6 + 2.2 + 5.4} = 5 + 9 = 14$

Find each sum or difference. Use mental math when possible.

1. 7.2 + 14 21.2
2. 38.9 – 16 22.9
3. 5.25 + 8.75 14
4. 13.3 + 24.16 37.46
5. 8.5 – 3.1 5.4
6. 4.4 – 1.7 2.7
7. 6.75 – 3.5 3.25
8. 8.3 – 6.15 2.15
9. 0.42 + 3.7 4.12
10. 4.08 + 0.6 4.68
11. 9 – 5.1 3.9
12. 32.5 + 8.7 41.2
13. 14.9 – 6.03 8.87
14. 6.85 + 2.8 9.65
15. 20.97 + 3.58 24.55
16. 18.4 – 9.68 8.72
17. 11.7 + 9.3 + 4 25
18. 44.8 + 7.5 + 23.2 75.5
19. 48.5 + 2.4 + 3.6 + 11.5 66

Divisibility by 2, 5, and 10

A number is divisible by two if its last digit is 0, 2, 4, 6, or 8.

A number is divisible by five if its last digit is 0 or 5.

A number is divisible by ten if its last digit is 0.

EXAMPLE

376 is divisible by 2 because its last digit is 6.

12,040 is divisible by 2, 5, and 10 because its last digit is 0.

81 is not divisible by 2, 5, or 10 because its last digit is 1.

Tell whether each number is divisible by 2, 5, and 10.

1. 48 2
2. 26 2
3. 125 5
4. 10,273 none
5. 1065 5
6. 390 2, 5, 10
7. 862 2
8. 39,407 none
9. 3270 2, 5, 10
10. 76,195 5

Estimation

You can estimate an answer if you do not need it to be exact. One way to estimate a sum or difference is to round each number first.

EXAMPLE

Round each addend to the nearest hundred. Then use mental math to add.

1213		1200
468	→	500
+ 96		+ 100
		1800

Round each number to the nearest whole number. Then use mental math to subtract.

43.45 − 8.7 ⟶ 43 − 9 = 34

1–13. Answers may vary. Sample responses are given.

Use rounding to estimate each sum or difference.

1. 509 + 384 about 900
2. 176 − 93 about 100
3. 20.8 + 5.7 about 27
4. 87.2 − 49.6 about 40
5. 1226 − 479 about 700
6. 58.8 − 40.36 about 20
7. 64.6 + 35.4 about 100
8. 4841 + 7385 about 12,000
9. 3.85 + 11.2 about 15
10. 61,432 − 13,951 about 47,000
11. 9132 + 342 + 188 about 9600
12. 18,970 + 1,304 + 978 about 21,000
13. $14.95 + $1.25 + $.99 + $2.05 about $19

Another way to estimate an answer is to first look at the front-end digits and then use the other digits to adjust.

EXAMPLE

$$\begin{array}{r} 2372 \\ + \ 3027 \end{array}\Big\}\ \text{about } 370 + 30, \text{ or } 400$$

$$5000 + 400$$

The sum is about 5400.

$$\begin{array}{r} 1.21 \\ 7.89 \end{array}\Big\}\ \text{about } 1$$

$$\begin{array}{r} 2.56 \\ + \ 8.44 \end{array}\Big\}\ \text{about } 1$$

$$18 + 2$$

The sum is about 20.

You can use rounding to multiply whole numbers. You can use compatible numbers to divide whole numbers. Compatible numbers have sums, products, or quotients that are easy to compute.

EXAMPLE

$$602 \cdot 17 \longrightarrow 600 \cdot 20 = 12{,}000$$

Round each factor to the greatest decimal place.

The product 602 · 17 is about 12,000.

EXAMPLE

$$382 \div 23 \longrightarrow 400 \div 25 = 16$$

Round the dividend to the greatest decimal place or places.

Change the divisor to the closest convenient factor of the new dividend.

The quotient 382 ÷ 23 is about 16.

14–22. Answers may vary. Sample responses are given.

Estimate each sum by adjusting the sum of the front-end digits.

14. 595 + 308 about 900

15. 83.1 + 47.4 about 130

16. 3.126 + 5.283 about 8.4

17. 9783 + 10,215 about 20,000

18. 264.8 + 41.6 about 300

19. 14,898 + 875.2 about 16,000

20. 497 + 228 + 561 about 1300

21. 38.15 + 11.25 + 9.65 about 59

22. 2520 + 3214 + 1387 about 7000

Use rounding or compatible numbers to estimate each product or quotient. 23-30. Answers may vary. Sample responses are given.

23. 19 · 69 about 1400

24. 24 · 48 about 1250

25. 692 ÷ 12 about 70

26. 783 ÷ 39 about 20

27. 485 · 18 about 10,000

28. 9125 ÷ 307 about 30

29. 586 · 712 about 420,000

30. 1621 ÷ 78 about 20

Finding a Fraction

A fraction compares a part to a whole. The numerator represents the part, and the denominator represents the whole.

EXAMPLE

There are six circles in the whole set. Five of the six parts are shaded.

$$\text{part} \rightarrow \frac{5}{6} \leftarrow \text{numerator}$$
$$\text{whole} \rightarrow \phantom{\frac{5}{6}} \leftarrow \text{denominator}$$

You can use a diagram or mental math to help you find a fraction of a number.

EXAMPLE

To find $\frac{3}{4}$ of 12, first find $\frac{1}{4}$ of 12.

The denominator tells you to divide the 12 dots into four groups with the same number of dots in each group.

$\frac{1}{4}$ of 12 is **3**.

$\frac{3}{4}$ of 12 is **9**.

EXAMPLE

To find $\frac{2}{3}$ of 12, think: $\frac{1}{3}$ of 12 is 4, so $\frac{2}{3}$ of 12 is **2** • 4 = 8.

$\frac{2}{3}$ of 12 is **8**.

Write a fraction to represent each shaded region or part of a set.

1. $\frac{7}{8}$

2. $\frac{3}{4}$

3. $\frac{3}{5}$

4. $\frac{4}{9}$

Find each value.

5. $\frac{1}{3}$ of 6 2

6. $\frac{1}{2}$ of 10 5

7. $\frac{2}{7}$ of 14 4

8. $\frac{4}{5}$ of 15 12

9. $\frac{3}{4}$ of 16 12

10. $\frac{5}{6}$ of 18 15

11. $\frac{2}{3}$ of 21 14

12. $\frac{7}{10}$ of 30 21

13. $\frac{7}{8}$ of 40 35

14. $\frac{5}{9}$ of 63 35

15. $\frac{15}{16}$ of 80 75

16. $\frac{11}{12}$ of 120 110

Finding Equivalent Fractions

Equivalent fractions are fractions that name the same part of a whole.

EXAMPLE

$\dfrac{1}{2}$ $\longrightarrow$

$\dfrac{4}{8}$ $\longrightarrow$

There are 4 times as many parts, but each part is one fourth of its original size.

$\dfrac{1}{2}$ and $\dfrac{4}{8}$ are equivalent fractions.

You can multiply or divide the numerator and the denominator of a fraction by the same whole number other than zero to find an equivalent fraction.

EXAMPLE

Find the missing number to complete each pair of equivalent fractions.

SOLUTION

$\dfrac{24}{30} = \dfrac{?}{5}$ — What number do you divide 30 by to get 5?

$\dfrac{24}{30} = \dfrac{24 \div 6}{30 \div 6}$

$\dfrac{24}{30} = \dfrac{4}{5}$

$\dfrac{1}{3} = \dfrac{?}{21}$ — What number do you multiply 3 by to get 21?

$\dfrac{1}{3} = \dfrac{1 \cdot 7}{3 \cdot 7}$

$\dfrac{1}{3} = \dfrac{7}{21}$

Complete each pair of equivalent fractions.

1. $\dfrac{8}{12} = \dfrac{?}{3}$ 2

2. $\dfrac{1}{2} = \dfrac{?}{48}$ 24

3. $\dfrac{4}{5} = \dfrac{?}{15}$ 12

4. $\dfrac{15}{20} = \dfrac{3}{?}$ 4

5. $\dfrac{12}{16} = \dfrac{3}{?}$ 4

6. $\dfrac{15}{27} = \dfrac{?}{9}$ 5

7. $\dfrac{2}{3} = \dfrac{14}{?}$ 21

8. $\dfrac{5}{8} = \dfrac{30}{?}$ 48

Write three equivalent fractions for each fraction. 9–16. Answers will vary. Sample responses are given.

9. $\dfrac{1}{3}$ $\dfrac{2}{6}, \dfrac{3}{9}, \dfrac{4}{12}$

10. $\dfrac{3}{4}$ $\dfrac{6}{8}, \dfrac{9}{12}, \dfrac{12}{16}$

11. $\dfrac{12}{60}$ $\dfrac{6}{30}, \dfrac{3}{15}, \dfrac{4}{20}$

12. $\dfrac{18}{54}$ $\dfrac{9}{27}, \dfrac{3}{9}, \dfrac{1}{3}$

13. $\dfrac{35}{140}$ $\dfrac{7}{28}, \dfrac{1}{4}, \dfrac{2}{8}$

14. $\dfrac{60}{150}$ $\dfrac{30}{75}, \dfrac{6}{15}, \dfrac{12}{30}$

15. $\dfrac{80}{96}$ $\dfrac{40}{48}, \dfrac{20}{24}, \dfrac{10}{12}$

16. $\dfrac{36}{63}$ $\dfrac{4}{7}, \dfrac{8}{14}, \dfrac{12}{21}$

Comparing Fractions

To find out if a fraction is greater or less than another fraction, you can use a diagram or equivalent fractions.

EXAMPLE

Compare $\frac{5}{12}$ and $\frac{1}{2}$.

SOLUTION Use fraction strips that are the same length.

Shade $\frac{5}{12}$ of one strip.

Shade $\frac{1}{2}$ of the other strip.

Compare the shaded parts. $\frac{5}{12} < \frac{1}{2}$

EXAMPLE

Replace the _?_ with >, <, or =: $\frac{1}{2}$ _?_ $\frac{7}{12}$

SOLUTION Write a fraction equivalent to $\frac{1}{2}$ with denominator 12.

$$\frac{1}{2} = \frac{?}{12}$$

$$\frac{1}{2} = \frac{1 \cdot 6}{2 \cdot 6} = \frac{6}{12}$$

$$\frac{6}{12} < \frac{7}{12}, \text{ so } \frac{1}{2} < \frac{7}{12}$$

Replace each _?_ with >, <, or =.

1. $\frac{5}{7}$ _?_ $\frac{6}{7}$ <

2. $\frac{16}{24}$ _?_ $\frac{3}{4}$ <

3. $\frac{2}{3}$ _?_ $\frac{11}{15}$ <

4. $\frac{5}{6}$ _?_ $\frac{15}{18}$ =

5. $\frac{1}{2}$ _?_ $\frac{7}{16}$ >

6. $\frac{16}{48}$ _?_ $\frac{3}{8}$ <

7. $\frac{25}{35}$ _?_ $\frac{4}{5}$ <

8. $\frac{1}{4}$ _?_ $\frac{7}{28}$ =

9. $\frac{4}{9}$ _?_ $\frac{12}{36}$ >

10. $\frac{11}{33}$ _?_ $\frac{1}{3}$ =

11. $\frac{6}{40}$ _?_ $\frac{3}{20}$ =

12. $\frac{7}{20}$ _?_ $\frac{2}{5}$ <

Adding and Subtracting Fractions

To add or subtract fractions with the same denominator, add or subtract the numerators of the fractions.

EXAMPLE

$$\frac{2}{8} + \frac{3}{8} = \frac{2+3}{8}$$ ◄ Add the numerators.

$$= \frac{5}{8}$$

EXAMPLE

$$\frac{11}{12} - \frac{4}{12} = \frac{11-4}{12}$$ ◄ Subtract the numerators.

$$= \frac{7}{12}$$

You can use mental math skills to add and subtract mixed numbers.

EXAMPLE

Add the **whole numbers**.
Add the **fractions**.

$$\begin{array}{r} 6\frac{2}{5} \\ + 3\frac{1}{5} \\ \hline 9\frac{3}{5} \end{array}$$

$$6\frac{2}{5} + 3\frac{1}{5} = 9\frac{3}{5}$$

Subtract the **whole numbers**.
Subtract the **fractions**.

$$\begin{array}{r} 6\frac{2}{5} \\ - 3\frac{1}{5} \\ \hline 3\frac{1}{5} \end{array}$$

$$6\frac{2}{5} - 3\frac{1}{5} = 3\frac{1}{5}$$

Find each sum or difference.

1. $\frac{3}{10} + \frac{4}{10}$ $\frac{7}{10}$

2. $\frac{4}{5} - \frac{1}{5}$ $\frac{3}{5}$

3. $\frac{2}{7} + \frac{4}{7}$ $\frac{6}{7}$

4. $\frac{7}{9} - \frac{3}{9}$ $\frac{4}{9}$

5. $\frac{8}{15} - \frac{4}{15}$ $\frac{4}{15}$

6. $\frac{9}{11} - \frac{5}{11}$ $\frac{4}{11}$

7. $\frac{3}{14} + \frac{5}{14} + \frac{1}{14}$ $\frac{9}{14}$

8. $\frac{3}{10} + \frac{3}{10} + \frac{3}{10}$ $\frac{9}{10}$

9. $\frac{8}{12} + \frac{6}{12} - \frac{3}{12}$ $\frac{11}{12}$

10. $4\frac{1}{3} + 2\frac{1}{3}$ $6\frac{2}{3}$

11. $5\frac{6}{7} - 2\frac{1}{7}$ $3\frac{5}{7}$

12. $7\frac{3}{5} - 4\frac{2}{5}$ $3\frac{1}{5}$

13. $3\frac{5}{9} + 8\frac{2}{9}$ $11\frac{7}{9}$

14. $5\frac{1}{10} + 4\frac{1}{10} + 6\frac{7}{10}$ $15\frac{9}{10}$

15. $\frac{6}{12} - \frac{2}{12} + \frac{1}{12}$ $\frac{5}{12}$

Modeling Percent

Percent means "per hundred" or "out of 100." You can use a 100-square grid to model a percent.

EXAMPLE

To model 39 percent shade 39 out of the 100 squares on the grid.

$\frac{39}{100}$ of the grid is shaded.

0.39 of the grid is shaded.

39% of the grid is shaded.

% is the symbol for percent.

Tell what percent each 100-square grid represents.

1.

67%

2.

83%

3.

6%

4.

11%

5.

25%

6.

72%

Sketch a 100-square grid to represent each percent. 7–14. See Toolbox Answers.

7. 95%   8. 78%   9. 8%   10. 50%

11. 22%   12. 49%   13. 18%   14. 61%

Modeling Integers

The integers are the numbers … –3, –2, –1, 0, 1, 2, 3, … . You can model integers with integer chips.

EXAMPLE

1   –1   –2   0   0

You read this as "negative two."

These two chips form a zero pair.

To add with integer chips, model each number and count the total number of chips.

EXAMPLE

$$3 + 4 = 7 \qquad -2 + (-3) = -5$$

EXAMPLE

$$5 + (-3) = 0 + 2 = 2$$

Tell what number each group of integer chips models.

1. 3

2. –3

3. 0

4. –4

5. 0

6. 5

Find each sum.

7. 4 + (–2) 2

8. –3 + 1 –2

9. 4 + (–3) 1

10. –5 + 5 0

11. –5 + 2 –3

12. 2 + (–2) 0

13. 3 + (–1) 2

14. –4 + 4 0

15. 2 + (–7) –5

16. 2 + (–6) –4

17. –6 + 4 –2

18. 3 + (–5) –2

To subtract with integer chips, model the first number, then remove the chips that represent the second number.

EXAMPLE

To find –5 – (–3):

Remove three negative chips. Two negative chips remain.

–5 – (–3) = –2

EXAMPLE

To find –3 – 2:

Model the first number. –3

To subtract two positive chips, add two zero pairs. –3 + 0

Five negative chips remain.

Remove two positive chips. –3 + 0 – 2 = –5

–3 – 2 = –5

EXAMPLE

To find –1 – (–4):

Model the first number. –1

Add zero pairs until there are four negative chips to subtract. –1 + 0

Three positive chips remain.

Remove four negative chips. –1 + 0 – (–4) = 3

–1 – (–4) = 3

Find each sum or difference.

19. 4 + (–2) 2
20. 3 – 5 –2
21. –3 – (–3) 0
22. 5 – 3 2
23. –3 + (–5) –8
24. –2 – 4 –6
25. –1 + 6 5
26. 4 – (–3) 7
27. –2 – (–5) 3
28. 6 – (–6) 12
29. –1 + 4 3
30. 2 – 8 –6
31. 5 + (–2) 3
32. –1 + 2 1
33. 6 – 7 –1
34. 1 – (–4) 5
35. –7 + 7 0
36. –5 + (–1) –6

Perimeter and Using a Ruler

The perimeter, *P*, of a figure is the sum of the lengths of its sides.

4 in. 5 in.

7 in.

$4 + 5 + 7 = 16$

$P = 16$ in.

7 cm

3 cm   3 cm

7 cm

$3 + 7 + 3 + 7 = 20$

$P = 20$ cm

You can use a ruler to measure the length of a segment. A United States customary ruler shows measurements in inches.

Measure the segment to the nearest $\frac{1}{16}$ of an inch.

The other end of the segment is between $1\frac{9}{16}$ in. and $1\frac{5}{8}$ in., closer to $1\frac{9}{16}$ in.

Line up one end of the segment with the 0 mark on the ruler.

in.   1   2

The segment is about $1\frac{9}{16}$ in. long.

Find the perimeter of each figure.

1.
8 m
8 m   8 m
8 m   32 m

2.
32 in.
20 in.   20 in.
72 in.

3.
14 cm
12 cm   12 cm
14 cm   52 cm

Measure the length of each segment to the nearest $\frac{1}{16}$ of an inch.

4. ———————————————— about $2\frac{7}{16}$ in.

5. ——————— about $\frac{15}{16}$ in.

Use a ruler to find the perimeter of each figure. Measure to the nearest $\frac{1}{16}$ of an inch.

6. about $2\frac{13}{16}$ in.

7. about $3\frac{3}{16}$ in.

8. about $3\frac{3}{4}$ in.

Converting Measurements

To change from a larger unit of measure to a smaller one, multiply.
Use the Table of Measures on page 597.

EXAMPLE

4 mi = __?__ ft

There are **5280 ft**
in 1 mi, so multiply
by **5280**.

$4 \cdot 5280 = 21{,}120$

4 mi = 21,120 ft

EXAMPLE

3 lb 8 oz = __?__ oz

There are 16 oz in 1 lb, so
3 lb = 3 · 16 oz = 48 oz.

$48 + 8 = 56$

3 lb 8 oz = 56 oz

To change from a smaller unit of measure to a larger one, divide.

EXAMPLE

67 in. = __?__ ft

There are **12 in.** in
1 ft, so divide by **12.**

$67 \div 12 = 5\frac{7}{12}$

67 in. $= 5\frac{7}{12}$ ft, or 5 ft 7 in.

Replace each __?__ with the correct number. Use the Table of Measures
on page 597.

1. 21 ft = __?__ in. 252

2. 83 oz = __?__ lb $5\frac{3}{16}$

3. 50 yd = __?__ ft 150

4. 6000 lb = __?__ tons 3

5. 2 mi = __?__ ft 10,560

6. 77 in. = __?__ yd $2\frac{5}{36}$

7. 3 lb = __?__ oz 48

8. 5280 yd = __?__ mi 3

9. 171 oz = __?__ lb $10\frac{11}{16}$

10. 5 yd = __?__ in. 180

11. 4 tons = __?__ lb 8000

12. 95,040 ft = __?__ mi 18

13. 156 in. = __?__ ft 13

14. 28 ft = __?__ yd $9\frac{1}{3}$

15. 10 mi = __?__ yd 17,600

16. 10 ft 6 in. = __?__ in. 126

17. 8 tons 60 lb = __?__ lb 16,060

18. 22 lb 13 oz = __?__ oz 365

19. 26 mi 385 yd = __?__ yd 46,145

20. 75 in. = __?__ yd __?__ in. 2; 3

21. 6000 ft = __?__ mi __?__ ft 1; 720

22. 35 oz = __?__ lb __?__ oz 2; 3

23. 4500 lb = __?__ tons __?__ lb 2; 500

24. 65 in. = __?__ ft __?__ in. 5; 5

25. 100 ft = __?__ yd __?__ ft 33; 1

Perimeter and Area of a Rectangle

The perimeter, *P*, of a rectangle is the sum of the lengths of its sides. You can use the formula at the right, where *l* represents the length and *w* represents the width, to find the perimeter of a rectangle.

$$P = l + l + w + w$$
$$P = 2 \cdot l + 2 \cdot w$$

EXAMPLE

3 in.
5 in.

$$P = 2 \cdot l + 2 \cdot w$$
$$= 2 \cdot 5 + 2 \cdot 3$$
$$= 10 + 6$$
$$= 16$$

The perimeter of the rectangle is 16 in.

The area, *A*, of a rectangle is the amount of surface that the rectangle covers. Area is measured in square units.

EXAMPLE

3 in.
5 in.

The rectangle can be divided into 3 rows with 5 square inches in each row.

$$A = 3 \cdot 5$$
$$= 15$$

The area of the rectangle is 15 square inches, or 15 in.^{2}.

Find the perimeter and the area of each rectangle.

1.

   8 in.

   5 in.   *P* = 26 in.; *A* = 40 in.^{2}

2. 6 ft

   6 ft   *P* = 24 ft; *A* = 36 ft^2

3. 4 yd

   12 yd
   P = 32 yd; *A* = 48 yd^2

4. a rectangle with length 16 ft and width 8 ft   *P* = 48 ft; *A* = 128 ft^2

5. a square with sides of length 7 in.   *P* = 28 in.; *A* = 49 in.^{2}

6. a rectangle with length 3 yd and width 4 ft   *P* = 26 ft; *A* = 36 ft^2

Making a Bar Graph

You can use a bar graph to display data that are in categories, such as the national park data shown in this table.

National Park	Approximate area (mi²)	Number of months open	Miles of hiking trails
Glacier (MT)	1580	5	700
Isle Royale (MI)	850	7	165
Mt. Rainier (WA)	378	6	240
Shenandoah (VA)	310	12	500

EXAMPLE

Follow the steps below to make a bar graph to display the hiking trail data for the national parks.

Step 1 Draw and **label** the axes.

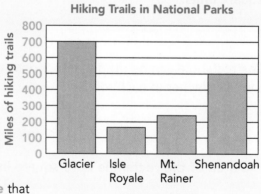

Step 3 Include a **title** for the graph.

Step 4 Draw a **bar** for each category.

Step 2 Mark a "nice" **scale** that goes slightly beyond the greatest data value. Divide the scale evenly.

Use the data in the table above. Make a bar graph for each set of data. 1–2. See Toolbox Answers.

1. the areas of the national parks

2. the number of months the national parks are open

Making a Line Graph

Use a line graph to show how data change over time.

Average temperature (°F)						
City	Jan/Feb	Mar/Apr	May/Jun	Jul/Aug	Sep/Oct	Nov/Dec
Indianapolis, IN	28	46	68	74	61	37
Duluth, MN	9	31	55	64	49	21
Phoenix, AZ	54	65	82	91	79	57

EXAMPLE

Follow the steps below to make a line graph to display the temperature data for Indianapolis.

Step 1 Draw and **label** the axes.

Step 2 Mark "nice" **scales**. Divide each scale evenly.

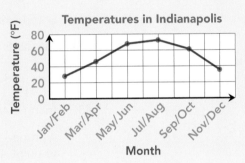

Step 3 Include a **title** for the graph.

Step 4 Graph each data item as a **point**. Connect the points.

Make a line graph for each set of data.   1–2. See Toolbox Answers.

1. the temperature data for Duluth

2. the temperature data for Phoenix

Finding the Mean

To find the mean of a data set, find the sum of all the data items.
Then divide the sum by the number of data items.

EXAMPLE

To find the mean of this data set, add the numbers and divide by 8:

6, 8, 5, 9, 7, 11, 4, 6

$$\text{mean} = \frac{6 + 8 + 5 + 9 + 7 + 11 + 4 + 6}{8} = \frac{56}{8} = 7$$

There are **8** data items.

The mean is 7.

Find the mean of each set of data.

1. 8, 4, 6, 10, 7 7
2. 24, 33, 27, 32, 24, 28 28
3. 120, 110, 110, 132, 160, 100 122

TABLE OF SYMBOLS

SYMBOL		Page
%	percent	**3**
=	equals	**11**
...	and so on	**14**
·	times	**15**
−	minus	**15**
3^4	3 to the 4th power	**17**
$\frac{1}{2}$	1 part of 2 equal parts	**24**
$P(A)$	probability of event A	**32**
+	plus	**37**
1.2	decimal point	**37**
$\overline{)}$	divided into	**46**
÷	divided by	**57**
( )	parentheses—grouping symbol	**61**
[ ]	brackets—grouping symbol	**61**
$\overrightarrow{AB}$	ray AB	**77**
$\angle A$	angle A	**78**
°	degree(s)	**78**
$m\angle A$	measure of angle A	**78**
⌐	right angle	**83**
−1	negative 1	**89**
>	is greater than	**90**
<	is less than	**90**
−3	the opposite of 3	**91**
|−4|	the absolute value of −4	**91**
(1, −2)	ordered pair of numbers	**93**

SYMBOL		Page
10^{-2}	$\frac{1}{10^2}$	**195**
×	times	**206**
$\overline{CD}$	segment CD	**218**
π	pi, a number approximately equal to 3.14	**234**
≥	is greater than or equal to	**241**
≈	is approximately equal to	**248**
$0.\overline{54}$	the digits 5 and 4 repeat	**253**
$\frac{6}{11}$	6 divided by 11	**253**
$\triangle ABC$	triangle ABC	**266**
A'	A prime—point A goes to point A' after a transformation	**267**
1 : 2	ratio of 1 to 2	**359**
≤	is less than or equal to	**381**
$\sqrt{}$	positive square root	**396**
~	is similar to	**413**
≅	is congruent to	**413**
AB	length of $\overline{AB}$	**415**
$\overleftrightarrow{AB}$	line AB	**425**
6!	6 factorial	**536**

TABLE OF MEASURES

Time

60 seconds (s) = 1 minute (min)	
60 minutes = 1 hour (h)	
24 hours = 1 day	
7 days = 1 week	
4 weeks (approx.) = 1 month	

$$\left.\begin{array}{l} 365 \text{ days} \\ 52 \text{ weeks (approx.)} \\ 12 \text{ months} \end{array}\right\} = 1 \text{ year}$$

10 years = 1 decade
100 years = 1 century

METRIC

Length

10 millimeters (mm) = 1 centimeter (cm)

$$\left.\begin{array}{l} 100 \text{ cm} \\ 1000 \text{ mm} \end{array}\right\} = 1 \text{ meter (m)}$$

1000 m = 1 kilometer (km)

Area

100 square millimeters = 1 square centimeter
(mm^2)   (cm^2)

10,000 cm^2 = 1 square meter (m^2)

10,000 m^2 = 1 hectare (ha)

Volume

1000 cubic millimeters = 1 cubic centimeter
(mm^3)   (cm^3)

1,000,000 cm^3 = 1 cubic meter (m^3)

Liquid Capacity

1000 milliliters (mL) = 1 liter (L)

1000 L = 1 kiloliter (kL)

Mass

1000 milligrams (mg) = 1 gram (g)

1000 g = 1 kilogram (kg)

1000 kg = 1 metric ton (t)

Temperature — Degrees Celsius (°C)

0°C = freezing point of water

37°C = normal body temperature

100°C = boiling point of water

UNITED STATES CUSTOMARY

Length

12 inches (in.) = 1 foot (ft)

$$\left.\begin{array}{l} 36 \text{ in.} \\ 3 \text{ ft} \end{array}\right\} = 1 \text{ yard (yd)}$$

$$\left.\begin{array}{l} 5280 \text{ ft} \\ 1760 \text{ yd} \end{array}\right\} = 1 \text{ mile (mi)}$$

Area

144 square inches (in.^{2}) = 1 square foot (ft^2)

9 ft^2 = 1 square yard (yd^2)

$$\left.\begin{array}{l} 43{,}560 \text{ ft}^2 \\ 4840 \text{ yd}^2 \end{array}\right\} = 1 \text{ acre (A)}$$

Volume

1728 cubic inches (in.^{3}) = 1 cubic foot (ft^3)

27 ft^3 = 1 cubic yard (yd^3)

Liquid Capacity

8 fluid ounces (fl oz) = 1 cup (c)

2 c = 1 pint (pt)

2 pt = 1 quart (qt)

4 qt = 1 gallon (gal)

Weight

16 ounces (oz) = 1 pound (lb)

2000 lb = 1 ton (t)

Temperature — Degrees Fahrenheit (°F)

32°F = freezing point of water

98.6°F = normal body temperature

212°F = boiling point of water

TABLE OF FORMULAS

RECTANGLE

Area:
$A = \text{length} \times \text{width}$
$A = lw$

Perimeter:
$P = 2l + 2w$

PARALLELOGRAM

Area:
$A = \text{base} \times \text{height}$
$A = bh$

TRIANGLE

Area:
$A = \frac{1}{2} \times \text{base} \times \text{height}$

$A = \frac{1}{2}bh$

CIRCLE

Area:
$A = \pi r^2$

Circumference:
$C = 2\pi r$ or $C = \pi d$

TRAPEZOID

Area:
$A = \frac{1}{2} \times (\text{sum of bases}) \times \text{height}$

$A = \frac{1}{2}(b_1 + b_2)h$

PRISM

Volume:
$V = (\text{area of base}) \times \text{height}$
$V = Bh$

Surface Area:
$S.A. = \text{sum of areas of faces}$

CYLINDER

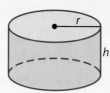

Volume:
$V = (\text{area of base}) \times \text{height}$
$V = Bh = \pi r^2 h$

PYRAMID

Volume:
$V = \frac{1}{3} \times (\text{area of base}) \times \text{height}$

$V = \frac{1}{3}Bh$

CONE

Volume:
$V = \frac{1}{3} \times (\text{area of base}) \times \text{height}$

$V = \frac{1}{3}Bh = \frac{1}{3}\pi r^2 h$

PRE-COURSE TEST

Decimals and Whole Numbers (Toolbox, pp. 581–583)

Find each sum or difference. Use mental math when possible.

1. $3.8 + 4.2$ 8
2. $12.09 + 7.98$ 20.07
3. $15.75 - 2.25$ 13.5
4. $20.06 - 18.78$ 1.28

Tell whether each number is divisible by 2, 5, and 10.

5. 504 2
6. 67,995 5
7. 2550 2, 5, 10
8. 34,235 5

Estimate each sum, difference, product, or quotient.

9. $702 + 895$ about 1600
10. $229 - 57$ about 170
11. $8120 \div 92$ about 90
12. 589×38 about 24,000
13. $25.6 - 17.9$ about 8
14. $15.83 + 65.16$ about 81

Fraction Concepts (Toolbox, pp. 584–587)

Find each value.

15. $\frac{4}{7}$ of 49 28
16. $\frac{2}{3}$ of 24 16
17. $\frac{5}{12}$ of 60 25

Replace each ? with >, <, or =.

18. $\frac{1}{3}$ __?__ $\frac{4}{15}$ >
19. $\frac{19}{36}$ __?__ $\frac{10}{18}$ <
20. $\frac{27}{42}$ __?__ $\frac{9}{14}$ =

Find each sum or difference.

21. $\frac{3}{6} + \frac{2}{6}$ $\frac{5}{6}$
22. $\frac{11}{12} - \frac{4}{12}$ $\frac{7}{12}$
23. $8\frac{1}{7} + 2\frac{3}{7}$ $10\frac{4}{7}$

Modeling Percents and Integers (Toolbox, pp. 588–589)

Sketch a 100-square grid to represent each percent. 24–26. See Additional Answers.

24. 26%
25. 83%
26. 12%

Find each sum or difference.

27. $5 + (-14)$ −9
28. $8 - (-3)$ 11
29. $-7 - 7$ −14

GEOMETRY AND MEASUREMENT

Using and Converting Measurements (Toolbox, pp. 591–592)

Find the perimeter of each figure.

30.

20 cm

4 cm

4 cm

5 cm

7 cm

31.

23 in.

8 in.

5 in.

10 in.

Replace each ? with the correct number. Use the Table of Measures on page 597.

32. 48 oz = _?_ lb **3** 33. 5 ft = _?_ in. **60** 34. 10,560 ft = _?_ mi **2** 35. 18 yd = _?_ in. **648**

Perimeter and Area of a Rectangle (Toolbox, p. 593)

Find the perimeter and the area of each rectangle.

36. a rectangle with length 9 in. and width 2 in. **P = 22 in.; A = 18 in.²**

37. a rectangle with length 7 m and width 5 m **P = 24 m; A = 35 m²**

DATA ANALYSIS AND DISPLAYS

Making Bar Graphs and Line Graphs (Toolbox, pp. 594–595)

38. Make a bar graph of the data below. **38–39. See Additional Answers.**

Day	Mon	Tues	Wed	Thurs	Fri
Minutes of exercise	30	50	45	20	30

39. Make a line graph of the data below.

Minutes of exercise	0	5	10	15
Heart rate (beats per minute)	72	90	124	130

Finding the Mean (Toolbox, p. 595)

Find the mean of the data.

40. 20, 24, 43, 32, 35, 16, 18, 36 **28**

41. 250, 175, 205, 270, 300, 180 **230**

TEST-TAKING SKILLS

◄◄◄◄◄◄◄◄◄◄◄◄◄◄ REReading AND SOLVING WORD PROBLEMS

Reading a Word Problem

Before you can solve a word problem, you have to understand the information being given and the question being asked.

- Read quickly through the problem once to get a general sense of what the problem is about.

- Read carefully through the problem a second time, focusing on those things that relate to solving the problem.

Problem

Maggie wants to tile the kitchen wall behind her stove with 2 rows of tiles. The portion of the wall behind the stove is 3 feet across. She has already tiled the first row with 6-in. by 6-in. tiles. She can use either 5-in. by 5-in. tiles or 4-in. by 4-in. tiles to do the second row. If Maggie does not want to cut any of the tiles, should she use the 5-in. by 5-in. or 4-in. by 4-in. tiles?

Solving a Word Problem

- Underline, jot down, and/or make a quick sketch of any information that can be used to solve the problem.

Tiles in the second row are 5 in. by 5 in. or 4 in. by 4 in.

Tiles cannot be cut.

- Decide which math topic(s) relate to the problem. Think of procedures, formulas, and definitions related to that topic that can be used to solve the problem.

- Solve the problem, making sure that the question answered is the question asked.

Conversion: 1 foot = 12 inches

Divisibility: Does 5 or 4 divide the length evenly?

Convert: 1 foot = 12 inches
$\qquad$ 3 feet = 36 inches

Divide: 36 ÷ 5 = 7 R1
$\qquad$ 36 ÷ 4 = 9

Maggie should use 4 in. by 4 in. tiles.

- Check your work.

6 • 6 in. = 36 in.

36 in. ÷ 4 = 9 tiles

TEST-TAKING TIPS FOR STUDENTS

Keep up with the course.

Ask questions about things you don't understand. Take advantage of extra-help sessions. If you get a problem wrong on a test or on your homework, try to figure out why you got it wrong. If you are absent, find out what material you missed and make up the work.

Become familiar with the test.

Make sure you know the answers to the following questions before you take the test:

- How much time do I have to complete the test?

- How many points are assigned to each type of question?

- About how much time should I spend answering a multiple choice question? a short response question? an extended reponse question?

- If I can't answer a multiple choice question, is it better to guess, or to leave a blank?

- Am I better off answering the easy, or the more difficult questions first, or should I just answer the questions as they come?

- Is paper provided for scrap work, or should it be done in the white space of the test booklet?

- On which, if any, parts of the test may I use a calculator?

During the Test

- As soon as the test begins, jot down on scrap paper or in the white space of the test booklet any formulas or procedures you're afraid you'll forget.

- Quickly scan the entire test to get an idea of which problems will probably take you the most time to do. Some people prefer to do those problems first. Others do them last.

- Skip over any question you are stuck on. Make a mark next to the question in your test booklet so that you can go back to it later if you have time. Be sure to leave a blank on your answer sheet for the answer to the question.

- Read an entire problem carefully before you start to answer it. Don't assume you know the question that will be asked.

- When answering a multiple choice question, don't assume your answer is correct because it is one of the choices. Always double check your work.

- If you think you can't do a multiple choice question, try substituting each choice back into the problem to see if it is the correct choice.

- If you must guess on a multiple choice question, first try to eliminate any choices that are obviously wrong because they have the wrong units or sign, for example.

- As you write the answer to an extended or short response question, imagine that you are writing an explanation for a fellow student who doesn't know how to solve the problem.

- If you can do part, but not all, of an extended or short response question, write down what you can do. Something written may receive partial credit. Nothing written definitely receives no credit.

BUILDING TEST-TAKING SKILLS (For use after Module 2.)

Strategies for Answering

Multiple Choice Questions

You can use the 4-step approach to solving problems on page 44 to solve any problem. If you have difficulty solving a problem involving multiple choice, you may be able to use one of the strategies below to choose the correct answer. You may also be able to use these strategies and others to check whether your answer to a multiple choice question is reasonable.

Strategy: Estimate the Answer

Problem 1

At a bakery, bagels cost $.89 each and muffins cost $2.05. ●----- You need to add the cost of buying 3 bagels and the cost of buying 2 muffins.
How much will it cost to buy 3 bagels and 2 muffins?

A. $2.94

B. $5.17

C. $6.77

D. $8.24 ●----- Estimate: $3(0.89) + 2(2.05) \approx 3(1) + 2(2) = 7$, so the correct answer is C.

Strategy: Use Visual Clues

Problem 2

The line graph shows the amount ●--- of money in Jerome's bank account over several weeks. Between which two weeks did Jerome deposit the greatest amount of money?

Look for the steepest segment connecting two consecutive points.

F. week 0 and week 1

G. week 3 and week 4

H. week 5 and week 6 ●---The steepest segment occurs between week 5 and week 6, so the correct answer is H.

I. week 9 and week 10

Jerome's Bank Account

Strategy: Use Number Sense

Problem 3

What value of x would make the expression ●------ $6 \cdot (2 + x)$ equal to 0?

Use the fact that the product of 0 and any number is 0. Multiplying 6 by 0 would equal 0, so think of what value of x would make $2 + x$ equal to 0.

A. −2 ●------ $2 + (−2) = 0$ and $6 \cdot 0 = 0$, so the correct answer is A.

B. 0

C. 1

D. 2

Eliminating Unreasonable Choices

The strategies used to find the correct answers for Problems 1–3 can also be used to eliminate answer choices that are unreasonable or obviously incorrect.

Strategy: Eliminate Choices

Problem 4

The length of a tablecloth is 110 centimeters. ●---- The width is 40 centimeters less than the length. What is the area?

Read the problem carefully. The width of the tablecloth is $110 - 40 = 70$ cm, not 40 cm. Use the formula $A = lw$ to find the area.

F. 4400 cm² ●----- *Not the correct answer:* $110 \cdot 70 \approx 100 \cdot 70 = 7000$.

G. 6800 cm² ●----- *Not the correct answer:* In the estimate above, 110 is rounded down, so the actual area should be greater than 7000 cm².

H. 7500 cm ●----- *Not the correct answer:* area is measured in *square* units.

I. 7700 cm² ●---- $110 \cdot 70 = 7700$, so I is the correct answer.

Watch Out! Some answers may appear correct at first glance, but they may be incorrect answers you would find by making common errors.

TRY THIS *Sample Response:* Width is not measured in square units.

Explain why the highlighted answer choice is unreasonable.

1. An in-ground pool has a length of 20 feet and a perimeter of 64 feet. What is the width of the pool?

   A. 5 ft   ✗ B. 10 ft²   C. 12 ft   D. 14 ft

2. What is the difference $7.062 - 5.163$? *Sample Response:* 12.225 is the sum of the numbers.

   F. 1.899   G. 2.101   H. 2.899   ✗ I. 12.225

3. The data below show the number of minutes Beth spent talking on the phone each day for 2 weeks. What is the mean number of minutes?

   24, 30, 10, 0, 52, 12, 35, 4, 20, 7, 14, 5, 0, 25

   Sample Response: 60 is greater than every number in the data set, so it cannot be the mean.

   A. 15   B. 17   C. 25   ✗ D. 60

Multiple Choice

1. Predict the 10th term in the following sequence. **D**

$$3, 7, 11, 15, \ldots .$$

   A. 11   **B.** 19   **C.** 35   **D.** 39

2. What is the value of the expression $5x - y$ when $x = 7$ and $y = 4$? **G**

   F. 13   **G.** 31   **H.** 35   **I.** 39

3. The dimensions of a family room are shown below. If carpeting costs $2.90 per square foot, how much will it cost to carpet the family room? **D**

   9 ft

   15 ft

   A. $47.93   **B.** $69.60

   C. $135.00   **D.** $391.50

4. What is the value of $5.17 + 0.94 + 2.08$? **G**

   F. 3.19   **G.** 8.19

   H. 12.74   **I.** 16.65

5. The table gives the number of yards gained or lost during each of the first 5 plays of a football game. What was the total number of yards gained or lost? **C**

Play	Yards gained or lost
1	5
2	−3
3	7
4	2
5	−6

   A. −5   **B.** 0   **C.** 5   **D.** 10

6. The bar graph shows the prices of different passes to a theme park. About how many times more does a childs one-week pass cost than a childs day pass? **I**

   F. 2 times more   **G.** 3 times more

   H. 4 times more   **I.** 6 times more

7. The ages of 8 people in a family are listed below. What is the median age? **A**

   $$77, 52, 22, 10, 75, 50, 16, 20$$

   A. 36   **B.** 38   **C.** 50   **D.** 70

8. Which of the following statements is *not* true about the angles shown below? **G**

   F. The angles are complementary.

   G. The angles are supplementary.

   H. The sum of the angle measures is 90°.

   I. Both angles are acute.

Strategies for Answering

Short Response Questions

Scoring Rubric

FULL CREDIT
- answer is correct, *and*
- work or reasoning is included

PARTIAL CREDIT
- answer is correct, but reasoning is incorrect, *or*
- answer is incorrect, but reasoning is correct

NO CREDIT
- no answer is given, *or*
- answer makes no sense

A *short response* question should take about five minutes to answer. A solution should always include the work or reasoning that leads to a correct answer. The three ways a solution can be scored are listed above.

Problem

It takes about $2\frac{1}{2}$ minutes to wash a car and about $4\frac{1}{4}$ minutes to wax it. How many can can be washed and waxed in $5\frac{1}{2}$ hours?

FULL CREDIT SOLUTION

The number of cars equals the total number of minutes for the car wash, 330, divided by the sum of the time it takes to wash a car and the time it takes to wax a car.

● ----- This reasoning is the key to choosing the operations you need.

$$\text{Cars} = \text{Total time} \div (\text{Wash time} + \text{Wax time})$$

● ----- The steps of the solution are clearly written.

$$= 330 \div (2\frac{1}{2} + 4\frac{1}{4}) = 330 \div 6\frac{3}{4} = 330 \times \frac{4}{27} = \frac{440}{9} = 48\frac{8}{9}$$

Because there is not enough time for 49 cars, the team can wash and wax 48 cars.

● ---- The question asked is answered correctly.

PARTIAL CREDIT SOLUTION

Divide the total amount of time, 330 minutes, by the time needed for each car, $6\frac{3}{4}$ minutes.

● ------- The reasoning and calculations are correct.

$$\text{Cars} = 330 \div \frac{27}{4} = 330 \times \frac{4}{27} = \frac{440}{9} = 48\frac{8}{9}$$

The team can wash $48\frac{8}{9}$ cars. ●

● ---- The answer makes no sense. You cannot have a fractional number of cars.

The total amount time it takes to wash and wax each car is about 7 minutes. ●--- The problem does not call for an estimated answer.

The team can wash 48 cars. ●-------------------- The answer is correct, but there is no evidence of work or calculations.

NO CREDIT SOLUTION

$5\frac{1}{2} \div (2\frac{1}{2} + 4\frac{1}{4}) = 5\frac{1}{2} \div 6\frac{3}{4}$ ●-------------- The units are not equivalent. Hours should be converted to minutes.

$= \frac{11}{2} \times \frac{27}{4} = \frac{297}{8} = 37\frac{1}{8}$ ●---- The student did not multiply by the reciprocal.

The team can wash 37 cars. ●----------------- The answer is incorrect.

TRY THIS

Score each solution to the short response question below as *full credit*, *partial credit*, or *no credit*. Explain your reasoning.

Watch Out!
Remember to think about positive and negative numbers when working with depth.

Problem

A submarine containing 3 marine biologists dives 1250 feet below the surface of the water. The submarine rises 720 feet to observe some marine life, and then dives 300 feet. How many feet below the surface of the water is the submarine?

1. $-1250 - 720 + 300 = -1670$. The submarine is 1670 feet below the surface of the water.

   No credit; the answer is incorrect, nothing is explained and the incorrect operations were performed.

2. $-1250 + 720 = -530$; $-530 - 300 = -830$. After rising 720 feet, the submarine was 530 feet below the surface of the water. Diving another 300 feet makes the submarine 830 feet below the surface of the water.

   Full credit; the reasoning is correct, the steps are clearly written, and the question is answered correctly.

3. The submarine started at 300 feet below the surface of the water and then went another 1250 feet, putting it at 1550 feet below the surface. Rising 720 feet brought the submarine to 830 feet below the surface of the water.

   Partial credit; the solution is correct, but the explanation is mixed up as to the order of the depths of the submarine.

Short Response Exercises 1–9. See Additional Answers for explanations.

1. Your school is holding a talent competition. Each talent act is allowed $2\frac{1}{2}$ minutes to perform. The judges are given $1\frac{1}{4}$ minutes to score each talent act. How many acts can perform if the talent competition is $1\frac{1}{3}$ hours long? Show your work. **21 acts**

2. Darcy is packaging bath products to sell at a fair. She has 64 small bottles of shampoo and 96 small bars of soap. If the packages are identical and there are no leftovers, what is the greatest number of packages that Darcy can put together? How many bottles of shampoo and bars of soap would be in each package? **16 packages; 4 bottles of shampoo and 6 bars of soap**

3. The tables below show the wins and losses for the basketball teams at Valley Middle School. (There were no ties.) Did the girls' team or the boys' team win the greater fraction of the games? Explain. **the girls' team**

Girls' Team	
Won	Lost
6	4

Boys' Team	
Won	Lost
7	5

4. Darren is starting an exercise program. His goal is to run a total of 8 miles in four days. In the next four days Darren runs 1 mile, $1\frac{3}{4}$ miles, $2\frac{1}{4}$ miles, and $2\frac{1}{2}$ miles. Did Darren meet his goal? Explain your reasoning. **No**

5. On Saturday, 18 volunteers showed up to work at the senior center. Of these volunteers, $\frac{1}{3}$ painted the walls of the recreation room. Of the remaining volunteers, $\frac{3}{4}$ raked leaves. The remaining volunteers served lunch. How many volunteers served lunch? Explain your reasoning. **3 volunteers**

6. The integers 5, 9, –10, 13, –18, and –7 are temperature readings in degrees Celsius. Graph the integers on a number line and find the median temperature. **–1°C**

7. A bowling alley's pricing information is shown below. Let x = the number of games bowled. Write an equation for the total cost of bowling for a person who needs to rent shoes. Hanna rented shoes and bowled several games. If Hanna paid a total of $22.25, how many games did she bowl? Show your work. **Let c = the total cost. $c = 4x + 2.25$; 5 games**

Shoe rental	$2.25
Cost per game bowled	$4.00

8. An embroidery hoop has a diameter of 23 inches. Another embroidery hoop has a diameter of 18 inches. What is the difference in the circumferences of the hoops? Show your work. **5π in., or approximately 15.7 in.**

9. Can a triangle be formed by the three segments shown below? Explain why or why not. **Yes**

3.5 cm

1.8 cm

2.1 cm

Context-Based Multiple Choice Questions

Some of the information you need to solve a context-based multiple choice question may appear in a table, a diagram, or a graph.

Problem 1

A canoe rental company charges by the hour. How much would it cost to rent a canoe from 9 A.M. to 4 P.M.?

Hours	Cost
1	$5.50
2	$11.00
3	$16.50
4	$22.00

A. $27.50   **B.** $33.00

C. $38.50   **D.** $44.00

Solution

1) **Look for a pattern in the table. You can use the pattern to write a function that models the cost of renting a canoe.**

   ●--- Read the problem carefully. Decide what information you are given and how you can use it to solve the problem.

   Compare the rental cost to the number of hours for each row of the table.

   $$\frac{\$5.50}{1 \text{ hour}} \qquad \frac{\$5.50}{\cancel{\$11.00}} \qquad \frac{\$5.50}{\cancel{\$16.50}} \qquad \frac{\$5.50}{\cancel{\$22.00}}$$
   $$\qquad\qquad \frac{}{\cancel{2 \text{ hours}}} \qquad \frac{}{\cancel{3 \text{ hours}}} \qquad \frac{}{\cancel{4 \text{ hours}}}$$
   $$1 \qquad\qquad 1 \qquad\qquad 1$$

   In each case, you get the same unit rate, $5.50 per hour.

2) **The cost y of renting a canoe for x hours is given by the function y = 5.5x.**

   ●---- Write the function.

3) **The cost of renting a canoe from 9 a.m. to 4 p.m. is the value of the function when x = 7. Substitute 7 for x in the function rule.**

   ●-------- There are 7 hours between 9 A.M. to 4 P.M.

   $$y = 5.5x = 5.5(7) = 38.50$$

   The cost is $38.50. The correct answer is C.

4) **As a check, extend the table. For each additional hour, the cost increases by $5.50. The cost for 7 hours is $38.50. The correct answer is C .**

   ●------- Check to see that your answer is reasonable.

Hours	Cost
5	$27.50
6	$33.00
7	$38.50

Problem 2

An object is randomly dropped and lands in the square shown. What is the probability that the object lands in the shaded target?

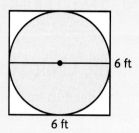

6 ft

6 ft

F. 7.85%   G. 28.26%

H. 36%   I. 78.5%

Solution

1) The area of the circular target = π(3)² = 9π ≈ 28.26 ft². ●--- Use the formula for the area of a circle, $A = \pi r^2$.

2) The area of the square landing area = 6² = 36 ft². ●-------- Use the formula for the area of a square $A = s^2$.

3) Find the probability that the object lands in the ●---------- Write the ratio as a target area by finding the ratio of the target area to the total landing area:

percent, since that is the form in which the answer choices are given.

$$\text{Probability} = \frac{28.26 \text{ ft}^2}{36 \text{ ft}^2} = 0.785 = 78.5\%$$

The probability that the object lands in the target area is 78.5%, so the correct answer is I .

TRY THIS

1. In Problem 2, what is the probability that the object does not land in the shaded circle? B

   A. 11.5%   B. 21.5%   C. 36%   D. 78.5%

2. What is the unknown angle measure in the triangle? F

   F. 40°   G. 44°

   H. 50°   I. 54°

3. A scale drawing of a rug is shown at the right. The actual rug is 4.5 meters long. How wide is the actual rug? B

   2.1 cm

   4.2 cm

   A. 2.25 cm   B. 2.25 m

   C. 9 cm   D. 9 m

Context-Based Multiple Choice

1. A scale drawing of a school banner is shown. If the width of the actual banner is 3 feet, what is the length of the actual banner? **D**

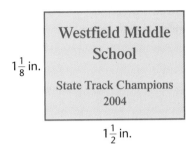

$1\frac{1}{8}$ in.

Westfield Middle School

State Track Champions
2004

$1\frac{1}{2}$ in.

A. $2\frac{1}{4}$ ft

B. $3\frac{3}{8}$ ft

C. $3\frac{1}{2}$ ft

D. 4 ft

2. A personal trainer charges $50 for one training session. The discounts the trainer offers for buying more than one training session are listed in the table. How many training sessions can you buy for $500? **G**

Sessions	2	3	4	5
Discount	$5	$10	$15	$20

F. 10 **G.** 11 **H.** 12 **I.** 13

3. The stem-and-leaf plot shows the ages of children at a daycare center. What is the median age of the children? **B**

```
0 | 5 7 7
1 | 1 4
2 | 2 2 5 6 6 9
3 | 1 2 3 3 7 8 8
4 | 0 0 3
```

Key: 3 | 1 = 31

A. 21 months **B.** 22 months

C. 23 months **D.** 26.6 months

4. In the diagram below, lines *m* and *n* are parallel. What is the measure of ∠1? **I**

F. 5° **G.** 18° **H.** 28° **I.** 108°

5. What is the unknown angle measure in the quadrilateral? **C**

A. 55° **B.** 75°

C. 135° **D.** 145°

6. The table shows how Carey used the $300 she earned last summer. How much more did Carey spend on clothing than on movies? **G**

Summer Spending	
Savings	40%
Clothing	30%
Movies	15%
Food	10%
Other	5%

F. $15 **G.** $45 **H.** $90 **I.** $135

7. The volume of the prism at the right is 2500 cm³. Which measurements are not possible for the length and width? **D**

25 cm

A. 25 cm and 4 cm

B. 10 cm and 10 cm

C. 20 cm and 5 cm

D. 15 cm and 6 cm

BUILDING TEST-TAKING SKILLS (For use after Module 8.)

Strategies for Answering

Extended Response Questions

Scoring Rubric

FULL CREDIT
- answer is correct, *and*
- work or reasoning is included

PARTIAL CREDIT
- answer is correct, but reasoning is incorrect, *or*
- answer is incorrect, but reasoning is correct

NO CREDIT
- no answer is given, *or*
- answer makes no sense

Problem

A company packs cans of tuna in a box that is 34 centimeters long, 26 centimeters wide, and 17 centimeters high. If the tuna cans all have the same orientation, what is the greatest number of cans that can be packed in a box? Explain your reasoning.

FULL CREDIT SOLUTION

The cans could be flat or on their sides. I found the number of cans that fit in one layer of the box by dividing the length and width of the box by the dimension of the can.

The method for finding the number of cans that fit in one layer of the box is explained.

Cans packed flat

12 cans in one layer

Cans packed on sides

27 cans in one layer

The diagrams support the answer.

To find the number of layers that could fit in the box, I divided the height of the box by the appropriate dimension of the can.

Cans packed flat: 17 cm ÷ 3.6 cm ≈ 4.7, so 4 layers can fit in the box. 12 cans × 4 layers = 48 cans.

Cans packed on sides: 17 cm ÷ 8.5 cm = 2, so 2 layers can fit in the box. 27 cans × 2 layers = 54 cans.

The greatest number of tuna cans fit in the box when the cans are packed on their sides. Packed this way, 54 tuna cans fit in the box.

The answer is correct. The explanation is clear, complete, and reflects correct mathematical thinking.

I calculated the number of tuna cans that could fit on ●---- The reasoning is correct.
their sides in one layer of the box by dividing the box's
length by 3.6 centimeters and dividing the box's width
by 8.6 centimeters.

8.5 cm

25.5 cm

3.6 cm

32.4 cm

27 cans in one layer

●-------------------- It is correctly determined
that 27 cans fit in one layer.
The diagram supports this
calculation.

A total of 27 cans fit in the first layer of the box. ●-------- The height of the box was
To find the number of layers that fit in the box, divide   divided by the wrong
the height of the box by 3.6 centimeters.   dimension of the can.

   17 cm ÷ 3.6 ≈ 4.7, so 4 layers can fit in the box.

   27 cans × 4 layers = 108 cans.

The greatest number of cans that can be packed in ●------- The answer is incorrect.
the box is 108.

TRY THIS

1. A student's answer to the problem on page 612 is given
   below. Score the solution as *full credit*, *partial credit*, or
   no credit. Explain your choice. If you choose *partial credit*
   or *no credit*, explain how you would change the answer
   to earn a score of *full credit*. **See Additional Answers.**

> **Watch Out!**
> Scoring is often based
> on how clearly you
> explain your reasoning.

Because 34 ÷ 8.5 = 4, 4 cans fit along the length of
the box.

Because 26 ÷ 8.5 ≈ 3.1, 3 cans fit along the width of
the box.

Because 17 ÷ 3.6 ≈ 4.7, 4 cans can fit stacked along
the height of the box.

Since 4 × 3 × 4 = 48, the greatest number of cans
that can be packed in the box is 48.

8.5 cm

25.5 cm

8.5 cm

34 cm

Extended Response Exercises 1–6. See Additional Answers for explanations.

1. At a movie theater, you can buy a small box of popcorn for $3.75 or a large cylindrical tub of popcorn for $5.25. Which size of popcorn is the better buy? Explain. **the large tub of popcorn**

Popcorn 8 in.
6 in. 3 in.

8 in.
Popcorn 5 in.

2. An insulated beverage container is cylindrical in shape. The height of the container is 8.9 inches and the diameter is 2.9 inches. Find the volume of the container. About how many cups of water will fit in the container? Use the fact that 1 cubic inch equals about 0.554 fluid ounces. Show your work. **about 58.79 in.³; about 4 cups**

3. A clothing store is having a clearance sale and displays the sign below. Which item is marked down by the greatest percent? Show your work. **slippers**

Item	Original price	Sale price
T-shirts	$15	$8.50
Sweatshirts	$29	$15
Slippers	$19.99	$8.99

Item	Original price	Sale price
Jeans	$42.50	$29.99
Sweaters	$49.95	$24
Sweatpants	$21.50	$12.50

4. The circle graph at the right shows the results of a survey in which 350 students were asked to name the European country they want to visit. Find the percent of students who gave each of the responses shown. The "Other" sector includes 35 students who named Spain as the European country they want to visit. Explain how you could redraw the circle graph to include a sector for Spain.

European Country Students Want to Visit

Other 42
Italy 105
Ireland 49
Germany 56
France 98

5. Three of the 5 students on the math team are being chosen to take part in a math competition. How many different combinations of 3 students are possible? In how many different orders can the 3 students finish the competition (first, second, and third)? Explain your method. **10 combinations; 6 orders**

6. The data below are the ages of people at a family reunion. Make a box-and-whisker plot of the data. About what percent of the people are between the ages of 11 and 58? Explain how you can tell from the box-and-whisker plot. **about 50%**

7, 10, 12, 32, 65, 70, 41, 35, 2, 56, 23, 60, 18

GLOSSARY

A ▸▸▸▸▸▸▸▸▸▸▸▸▸▸▸▸▸▸▸▸▸▸▸▸

absolute value (p. 91) The distance from a number to zero on a number line.

acute angle (p. 83) An angle whose measure is greater than 0° but less than 90°. *See also* angle.

acute triangle (p. 415) A triangle with three acute angles.

alternate exterior angles (p. 425) A pair of angles outside two lines intersected by a transversal and on different sides of the transversal.

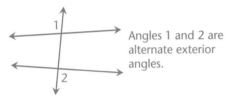

Angles 1 and 2 are alternate exterior angles.

alternate interior angles (p. 424) A pair of angles between two lines intersected by a transversal and on different sides of the transversal.

Angles 1 and 2 are alternate interior angles.

angle (p. 78) A figure formed by two rays with a common endpoint, called the *vertex*.

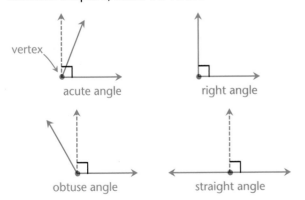

acute angle   right angle

obtuse angle   straight angle

arc (p. 218) A part of a circle.

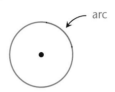

arc

arc of a network (p. 442) A curve or segment connecting vertices of a network. *See also* network.

associative property of addition (p. 105) Changing the grouping of numbers in an addition problem does not affect the sum.

associative property of multiplication (p. 281) Changing the grouping of factors in a multiplication problem does not affect the product.

axis (plural: axes) (p. 3) *See* coordinate plane.

B ▸▸▸▸▸▸▸▸▸▸▸▸▸▸▸▸▸▸▸▸▸▸▸▸▸

bar graph (p. 3) A visual display of data that fall into distinct categories.

base (p. 17) *See* exponential form.

base of a polygon (pp. 383, 388, 514) *See* parallelogram *and* trapezoid.

base of a space figure (pp. 398, 457, 547, 568) *See* prism, cylinder, pyramid, *and* cone.

benchmark (p. 208) An item whose measure you know that can be used to estimate other measures.

box-and-whisker plot (pp. 334, 492) A diagram that shows the median, the other quartiles, and the extremes for a numerical set of data. The *box* contains about 50% of the data values. The two *whiskers* each contain about 25% of the data values.

Average January Temperature in 50 U.S. Cities

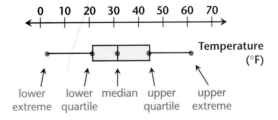

lower extreme   lower quartile   median   upper quartile   upper extreme

capacity (p. 440) The amount of fluid a container can hold.

center (p. 218) *See* circle.

central angle (p. 500) An angle with its vertex at the center of a circle.

certain event (p. 33) An event that has a probability of 1.

chord (p. 218) A segment whose endpoints are both on a given circle. *See also* circle.

circle (p. 218) The set of all points in a plane that are the same distance from a given point.

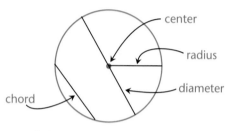

center
radius
diameter
chord

circle graph (p. 500) A graph in which the entire circle represents the whole, or 100%.

circumference (p. 233) The distance around a circle.

combination (p. 556) A selection of items in which order is not important.

commutative property of addition (p. 105) Changing the order of numbers in an addition problem does not affect the sum.

commutative property of multiplication (p. 281) Changing the order of the factors in a multiplication problem does not affect the product.

compatible numbers (p. 583) Numbers which have sums, differences, products, or quotients that are easy to compute.

complementary angles (p. 82) Two angles whose measures have a sum of 90°.

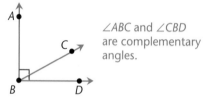

∠ABC and ∠CBD are complementary angles.

complementary events (p. 386) Two events where one or the other must occur, but they cannot both happen at the same time.

composite number (p. 150) A whole number greater than 1 that has more than two factors.

concave (p. 382) A polygon that is not convex is concave. *See also* polygon.

cone (p. 568) A space figure with one curved base and a vertex.

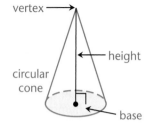

vertex
height
circular cone
base

congruent (pp. 217, 267) Two figures that have the same shape and the same size are congruent.

construction (p. 219) A figure drawn using only a straightedge and compass.

convex (p. 382) A polygon is convex when all of its diagonals lie in the interior of the polygon. *See also* polygon.

coordinate (p. 93) A number in an ordered pair that gives a point's location left or right of zero, or up or down from zero. *See also* coordinate plane.

coordinate plane (p. 93) A grid with a horizontal axis and a vertical axis that intersect at a point.

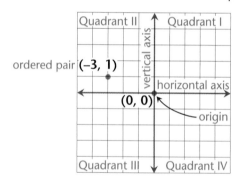

Quadrant II
Quadrant I
vertical axis
ordered pair (–3, 1)
horizontal axis
(0, 0)
origin
Quadrant III
Quadrant IV

corresponding angles (p. 424) Angles in the same position with respect to two lines and a transversal.

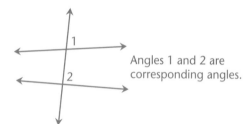

Angles 1 and 2 are corresponding angles.

corresponding parts (p. 412) When two figures are similar, for each angle or side of one figure there is a similar angle or side on the other figure.

counting principle (p. 533) To find the number of permutations, you can multiply together the number of options at each point where you make a choice.

cross products (p. 329) Products formed from a pair of ratios by multiplying the numerator of each fraction by the denominator of the other fraction.

cube (p. 18) A closed space figure with six square surfaces.

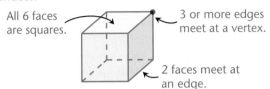

All 6 faces are squares.

3 or more edges meet at a vertex.

2 faces meet at an edge.

cylinder (p. 457) A space figure that has a curved surface and two parallel, congruent bases.

circular cylinder

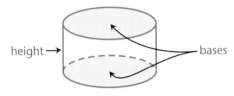

height → ← bases

D ▶▶▶▶▶▶▶▶▶▶▶▶▶▶▶▶▶▶▶▶▶▶▶▶▶▶▶▶▶

decimal places (p. 191) The positions of the digits in a number which determine their values.

degree (p. 78) A unit of measurement of an angle that is $\frac{1}{360}$ of a complete turn.

diagonal (p. 428) A segment that connects two nonconsecutive vertices of a polygon.

diameter (p. 218) Any chord that passes through the center of a circle. The length of a diameter is called *the* diameter. *See also* circle.

distributive property (p. 237) Each addend inside a set of parentheses can be multiplied by a factor outside the parentheses. For example,

$$5\left(2 + \frac{3}{5}\right) = (5 \cdot 2) + \left(5 \cdot \frac{3}{5}\right).$$

divisible (p. 150) When a number can be divided evenly by another number, it is divisible by that number.

E ▶▶▶▶▶▶▶▶▶▶▶▶▶▶▶▶▶▶▶▶▶▶▶▶▶▶▶▶▶

edge (pp. 19, 398) A segment where two faces of a space figure are joined. *See also* cube *and* prism.

equally likely (p. 30) When the probability of two or more outcomes is the same, the outcomes are equally likely.

equation (p. 16) A mathematical sentence stating that two quantities or expressions are equal.

equilateral triangle (p. 217) A triangle with three congruent sides.

equivalent fractions (p. 163) Fractions that represent the same amount.

evaluate (pp. 61, 119) To carry out mathematical operations in the correct order or to substitute a value for a variable and perform the operations in the correct order. *See also* order of operations.

event (p. 28) A set of outcomes of an experiment.

experiment (p. 28) An activity whose results can be observed and recorded.

experimental probability (p. 28) A probability determined by repeating an experiment a number of times and observing the results. To calculate an experimental probability, you can divide the number of times an outcome occurs by the number of times the experiment is done.

exponent (pp. 17, 20) A raised number that tells the power of the base. *See also* exponential form.

exponential form (p. 17) A way of writing a number using exponents. A number that can be written using an exponent and a base is a power of the base.

8 is a power of 2.

standard form $8 = 2 \cdot 2 \cdot 2 = 2^3$ exponential form

exponent

base

expression (p. 60) A mathematical phrase that can be formed using numbers, variables, and operation symbols.

exterior angle (p. 424) An angle that is outside two lines intersected by a transversal.

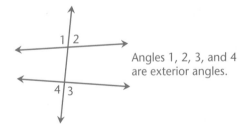

Angles 1, 2, 3, and 4 are exterior angles.

F ▶▶▶▶▶▶▶▶▶▶▶▶▶▶▶▶▶▶▶▶▶▶▶▶▶▶▶▶▶

face (pp. 19, 398) A flat surface of a space figure. *See also* cube *and* prism.

factor (p. 150) When one whole number divides another whole number with no remainder, the first number is a factor of the second.

fitted line (p. 332) A line drawn on a scatter plot to identify the trend in the data. Roughly half the points fall above the line and half the points fall below it. *See also* scatter plot.

frequency (p. 5) The number of times a data item occurs.

frequency table (pp. 5, 7) A table which shows how often each data item occurs.

function (p. 119) A relationship between input and output. For each input there is exactly one output. Output depends on input.

G

geometric probability (p. 387) A probability that is based on length, area, or volume.

greatest common factor (p. 154) The greatest number that is a factor of each of two or more numbers.

H

height of a polygon (pp. 383, 388, 514) *See* parallelogram *and* trapezoid.

height of a space figure (pp. 398, 457, 547, 568) *See* prism, cylinder, pyramid, and cone.

histogram (p. 318) A special type of bar graph that displays the frequencies of data in given intervals of equal width. Each bar touches the next.

horizontal axis (p. 3) A horizontal line on a graph that is labeled with the categories or with the scale. *See also* coordinate plane.

I

image (p. 264) The figure resulting from a transformation.

impossible event (p. 33) An event that has a probability of 0.

inequality (pp. 90, 380) A mathematical sentence stating that one quantity or expression is greater than or less than another.

integer (p. 89) A whole number or the opposite of a whole number, which is any number in the set of numbers ..., –3, –2, –1, 0, 1, 2, 3, ...

interior angle (p. 424) An angle that is between two lines intersected by a transversal.

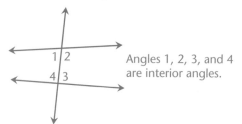

Angles 1, 2, 3, and 4 are interior angles.

intersect (p. 92) When two geometric figures share at least one point, they intersect.

interval (p. 4) The step between grid lines on a scale.

inverse operations (p. 135) Operations which "undo" each other like addition and subtraction or multiplication and division.

isosceles triangle (p. 217) A triangle with at least two congruent sides.

L

least common denominator (p. 165) The least common multiple of the denominators of two or more fractions.

least common multiple (p. 155) The least number that is a multiple of each of two or more numbers.

line graph (p. 4) A graph on which plotted points are connected with line segments. It can be used to show change in data over time.

line symmetry (p. 268) If one half of a figure is a reflection of the other half, the figure has line symmetry.

line of symmetry

lower extreme (p. 492) The least data value in a set of data. *See also* box-and-whisker plot.

lower quartile (p. 492) The median of the data values that are less than the median of the total data set. *See also* box-and-whisker plot.

lowest terms (p. 163) A fraction is in lowest terms when the greatest common factor of the numerator and denominator is 1.

M ▸

mass (p. 440) The amount of matter in an object.

mean (p. 595) In a numerical data set, the sum of all the data divided by the number of data items.

median (p. 315) The middle item in a data set ordered from least to greatest. If there is no single middle item, the number halfway between the two data items closest to the middle.

mixed number (p. 178) The sum of a nonzero whole number and a fraction between 0 and 1.

mode (p. 315) The item or items that appear most often in a data set. There can be no mode.

multiple (p. 154) The multiple of a whole number is the product of that number and any nonzero whole number.

multistage experiment (p. 365) A situation that involves two or more events happening one after another.

N ▸

negative (p. 89) Less than zero.

net (p. 399) A flat pattern that can be cut out and folded to form a space figure without any gaps or overlaps.

network (p. 442) Vertices connected by arcs.

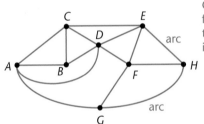

One path from vertex E to vertex G is E-H-G.

numerator (p. 584) The top number in a fraction that tells how many parts of the whole to consider.

O ▸

obtuse angle (p. 83) An angle whose measure is greater than 90°. *See also* angle.

obtuse triangle (p. 415)
A triangle with one obtuse angle.

opposites (p. 91) Two numbers that are the same distance from 0 but on opposite sides of 0 on a number line. The opposite of 3 is −3.

order of operations (p. 61) The correct order in which to perform the mathematical operations in an expression: operations inside grouping symbols first, exponents next, then multiplication and division in order from left to right, and finally addition and subtraction in order from left to right.

ordered pair (p. 93) A pair of numbers used to identify and plot points in a coordinate plane. *See also* coordinate plane.

origin (p. 93) *See* coordinate plane.

outcome (p. 28) The result of an experiment.

P ▸

parallel (p. 92) In a plane, two lines that do not intersect are parallel.

parallelogram (p. 383) A four-sided polygon in which both pairs of opposite sides are parallel.

The perpendicular distance between bases of a parallelogram is the height.

bases

percent (p. 3) Percent means "per hundred" or "out of 100."

percent of change (p. 475) The percent by which an amount increases or decreases from its original amount.

permutation (p. 530) A possible arrangement of a group of items in which order is important.

perpendicular (p. 92) Two lines that intersect at 90° angles are perpendicular.

plane (p. 92) A flat surface that goes on forever.

polygon (p. 382) A closed figure made from segments that are drawn on a flat surface and do not cross.

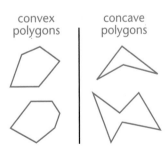

convex polygons | concave polygons

A polygon can have 3 or more sides. Some types of polygons are:

pentagon (5 sides)
hexagon (6 sides)
octagon (8 sides)
decagon (10 sides)

positive (p. 89) Greater than zero.

power (p. 17) *See* exponential form.

prime factorization (p. 151) The expression of a number written as the product of prime factors.

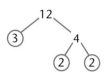

factor tree

The prime factorization of 12 is 2 • 2 • 3.

prime number (p. 150) A whole number greater than 1 that has exactly two factors, 1 and itself.

principal square root (p. 396) The positive square root. The symbol for it is √ .

prism (p. 398) A space figure with faces shaped like polygons. Two of the faces, the bases, are parallel and congruent. The other faces are parallelograms. In a *right* prism, the other faces are rectangles.

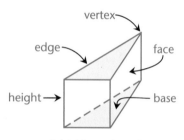

right triangular prism

probability (p. 28) A number from 0 to 1 that tells how likely an event is to happen.

proportion (p. 314) An equation stating that two ratios are equivalent.

pyramid (p. 547)
A space figure that has one polygon-shaped base. All the other faces are triangles that meet at a single vertex.

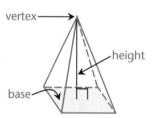

square pyramid

Q ▸▸▸▸▸▸▸▸▸▸▸▸▸▸▸▸▸▸▸▸▸▸▸▸▸▸▸▸▸▸▸▸

quadrilateral (p. 383) A four-sided polygon.

R ▸▸▸▸▸▸▸▸▸▸▸▸▸▸▸▸▸▸▸▸▸▸▸▸▸▸▸▸▸▸▸▸

radius (plural: radii) (p. 218) A segment whose endpoints are the center and any point on a given circle. The length of a radius is called *the* radius. *See also* circle.

range (p. 316) The difference between the greatest data value and the least data value in a data set.

rate (p. 313) A ratio that compares quantities measured in different units.

ratio (p. 313) A comparison of two quantities by division. The ratio of 6 and 8 can be expressed as 6 to 8, 6:8, or $\frac{6}{8}$.

ray (p. 77) A part of a line that starts at an endpoint and goes on forever in one direction.

endpoint ▸

reciprocals (p. 238) Two numbers whose product is 1.

reflection (p. 267) A flip of a figure across a line.

line of reflection

repeating decimal (p. 252) A decimal in which a digit or a sequence of digits keeps repeating.

rhombus (p. 514)
A parallelogram that has four congruent sides.

right angle (p. 83) An angle whose measure is 90°. *See also* angle.

right triangle (p. 415)
A triangle with one right angle.

rise (p. 461) *See* slope.

rotation (p. 264) A turn of a figure about a fixed point, the center of rotation, a certain number of degrees either clockwise or counterclockwise.

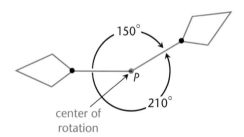

rotational symmetries (p. 265) The numbers of degrees less than 360° that a figure can be rotated and fit exactly on itself.

rotational symmetry (p. 265) When a figure can be rotated less than 360° about its center and fit exactly on itself, the figure has rotational symmetry.

run (p. 461) *See* slope.

S ▸▸▸▸▸▸▸▸▸▸▸▸▸▸▸▸▸▸▸▸▸▸▸▸▸

scale of a drawing (p. 413) The ratio of a length measurement on a drawing to the measurement of the corresponding part on the object represented.

scale on a graph (p. 4) The numbers written along an axis of a graph.

scalene triangle (p. 217) A triangle with no congruent sides.

scatter plot (p. 332) A graph of a set of data points in a coordinate plane that represents a relationship between two quantities.

Average Temperature in 50 U.S. Cities

scientific notation (p. 197) A number is in scientific notation when it is written as the product of a decimal greater than or equal to 1 and less than 10 and a power of 10. For example:

standard form → $5261 = 5.261 \cdot 10^3$ ← scientific notation

sector (p. 500) A wedge-shaped region in a circle bounded by two radii and an arc.

sector

sequence (p. 14) An ordered list of numbers or objects.

similar (pp. 295, 417) Figures are similar if they have the same shape, but not necessarily the same size. In similar polygons, the measures of the corresponding angles are equal, and the ratios of the lengths of the corresponding sides are equal.

slope (p. 461) The ratio of the vertical change to the horizontal change along a line.

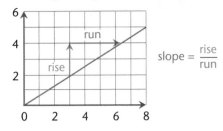

$slope = \dfrac{rise}{run}$

solution of an equation (p. 134) A value of a variable that makes an equation true.

solving an equation (p. 134) The process of finding a solution.

square root (p. 396) If $A = s^2$, then s is a square root of A. For example, 5 and –5 are square roots of 25. The symbol for a positive square root is $\sqrt{}$. The symbol for a negative square root is $-\sqrt{}$.

standard form (p. 17) *See* exponential form.

stem-and-leaf plot (p. 316) A display of data where each number is represented by a *stem* (the left-most digits) and a *leaf* (the right-most digits).

straight angle (p. 83) An angle whose measure is 180°. *See also* angle.

supplementary angles (p. 81) Two angles whose measures have a sum of 180°.

∠ABC and ∠CBD are supplementary angles.

surface area of a prism (p. 399) The sum of the areas of a prism's faces.

T ▸▸▸▸▸▸▸▸▸▸▸▸▸▸▸▸▸▸▸▸▸▸▸▸▸

term number (p. 14) A number indicating the position of a term in a sequence.

term of a sequence (p. 14) A number or object in a sequence.

terminating decimal (p. 253) A decimal in which the digits stop, or *terminate*.

tessellation (p. 565) A tiling that uses congruent polygons in a repeating pattern to cover a plane with no gaps or overlaps.

theoretical probability (p. 30) A probability that can be determined without actually doing an experiment. If the outcomes of an experiment are equally likely, you can calculate the theoretical probability by dividing the number of favorable outcomes by the number of possible outcomes.

transformation (p. 291) A change made to the shape, size, or position of a figure.

translation (p. 291) A transformation that slides each point of a figure the same distance in the same direction.

transversal (p. 423) A line that intersects two lines in a plane at separate points.

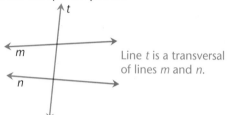

Line *t* is a transversal of lines *m* and *n*.

trapezoid (p. 514) A quadrilateral that has only one pair of opposite sides that are parallel.

base 2

height

base 1

traversable (p. 449) When a network can be drawn without lifting your pencil off the paper or drawing any arc more than once, the network is traversable.

tree diagram (p. 168) A display of the possible outcomes of an experiment.

triangle (p. 58) A three-sided polygon.

U ▸

unit rate (p. 313) A ratio that compares a quantity to one unit of another quantity.

upper extreme (p. 492) The greatest data value in a set of data. *See also* box-and-whisker plot.

upper quartile (p. 492) The median of the data values that are greater than the median of the total data set. *See also* box-and-whisker plot.

V ▸

variable (p. 16) A quantity, usually represented by a letter, that is unknown or that changes.

vertex of an angle (p. 78) The common endpoint of two rays that form an angle. *See also* angle.

vertex of a cube (plural: vertices) (p. 19) A point where three or more edges of a cube meet. *See also* cube.

vertex of a network (p. 442) A point in a network. *See also* network.

vertex of a prism (p. 398) A point where three or more edges of a prism meet. *See also* prism.

vertex of a tessellation (p. 565) A point where the corners of the polygons in a tessellation touch.

vertical angles (p. 424) Two angles whose sides form two pairs of opposite rays.

Angles 1 and 3 are vertical angles, and angles 2 and 4 are vertical angles.

vertical axis (p. 3) A vertical line on a graph that is labeled with the categories or with the scale. *See also* coordinate plane.

volume (p. 18) The amount of space inside a space figure. Volume is measured in cubic units.

W ▸

weighted network (p. 444) A network in which the arcs are labeled with numbers representing such things as distances and times.

X ▸

x-axis (p. 292) The horizontal number line in a coordinate plane. *See also* coordinate plane.

Y ▸

y-axis (p. 292) The vertical number line in a coordinate plane. *See also* coordinate plane.

INDEX

388–390, 393

and integers, 89–91, 94, 101–110, 115, 280

probability, 28

Number sense

fraction-decimal-percent relationships, 346, 588

See also Comparison, Estimation, Mental math, Modeling, *and* Pattern.

Number theory

absolute value, 91, 94, 97, 100

common factors, 154, 237, 241

composite number, 150, 156, 157

cube of a number, 21

divisibility, 150, 153–154, 156–159, 161, 582

greatest common factor, 154, 156, 158, 161

least common multiple, 155–156, 159, 161

multiples, 154–156

opposites, 91, 94, 97, 100

order of operations, 60–61, 65–66, 70, 282

Pascal's triangle, 560

perfect square, 396–397, 404

prime factorization, 151, 155–157, 161

prime number, 150, 156, 157

reciprocals, 238, 241–242, 244, 246

square of a number, 18, 21, 396

square root, 396–397, 404–406, 409

Numeration

comparing and ordering decimals, 192–193, 198, 200, 203

fractions, 163–165, 170, 172–173, 586

integers, 90, 94, 96–97, 100

exponential form, 17, 21, 23, 25, 194–195, 198, 200–201, 203

integers, 89–91, 94–97, 100, 589–590

place value, 190–193, 198–199

reading and writing decimal numbers, 191–192, 198–199

rounding, 234, 241, 253, 349, 582–583

scientific notation, 196–197, 199, 201, 203

standard form, 17, 21, 23, 25, 194, 196–198, 200–201, 203

O ▸ ▸ ▸ ▸ ▸ ▸ ▸ ▸ ▸ ▸ ▸ ▸ ▸ ▸ ▸ ▸ ▸

Obtuse angle, 79, 83–84, 87

Obtuse triangle, 415, 417, 419, 421

Open-ended problems, 8, 127, 138, 186, 200, 245, 261, 272, 287, 303, 340, 391, 419, 519, 520

See also Create Your Own, Extended Exploration, *and* Standardized testing, open-ended.

Opposites, 91, 94, 97, 100

sum of, 109

Oral Report, 46, 85, 174 , 407, 497, 536

Order of operations, 60–61, 65–66, 70, 282, 296

Ordered pair, 93

graphing, 15, 93, 95, 97–98, 100

Ordering

decimals, 192–193, 198, 200, 203, 253

fractions, 163–165, 170, 172–173

integers, 90, 94, 96–97, 100

See also Comparison.

Origin, 93, 95

Outcome(s), 28, 33

equally likely, 30, 33

tree diagrams and, 168–169, 171, 174–175, 363–365, 367, 370–372

Outlier, 497

Output value, 119

P ▸ ▸ ▸ ▸ ▸ ▸ ▸ ▸ ▸ ▸ ▸ ▸ ▸ ▸ ▸ ▸ ▸

Parallel

lines, 92, 94, 97, 98, 100, 423–425, 429–430, 434

segments, 513

Parallelogram, 383, 388

angles of, 430

area of, 383–384, 388, 391, 393, 516

Pascal's triangle, 560

Pattern(s)

and problem solving, 43, 52

recognizing and applying, 13–25, 53–54, 153, 202, 237, 239, 251, 281, 406, 439, 533, 555, 557, 559–560

See also Tessellation.

Percent(s), 3, 7

of change (increase or decrease), 475–483

and circle graphs, 500–502, 505, 507–508, 511

equations and, 474, 477, 479, 502

estimating with, 344–345, 347–348, 350–355, 357, 361–362, 473, 499, 501, 507

finding, 348–351, 353, 357, 473–474, 480, 483

fraction-decimal-percent relationships, 346, 588

greater than 100%, 473–474, 479–480, 483

modeling, 345–346, 348, 350, 352, 354, 355, 588

predicting with, 362, 366, 369, 371

proportions and, 348–352, 355, 474, 502

Perfect square, 396–397, 404

Perimeter, 186, 591, 593

Permutation, 530, 532–536, 539

when items repeat, 554–555, 558–560, 562

Perpendicular lines, 92, 94, 97, 98, 100

Pi (π), 234, 241

Pictograph, 244

Pint (pt), 487, 493

Place value, decimal, 190–193, 198–199

Plane(s), 92, 94, 98

See also Coordinate plane.

Point, 77

Point of intersection, 122

Polygon(s), 382, 388

angle sum, 432

area of, 383–384, 388, 391–393, 520

concave, 382

congruent, 295, 413, 417–418

convex, 382

diagonal of, 429

regular, 382

See also Space figure.

Portfolio, *See under* Assessment.

Positive integers, 89

Power(s), 17–21, 23, 25, 194, 198

multiplying and dividing, 201–202

of negative integers, 286

scientific notation and, 196–197, 199, 201, 203

zero as, 195, 198

Practice, *See* Extra Skill Practice *and* Spiral Review.

Pre-Course Test, 599–600

Prediction

using a fitted line, 332, 336, 339, 343

of measures, 597
as a problem-solving strategy,
52, 534, 557
of symbols, 596
of values, 15, 118–122,
124–129, 459–460
Tablespoon (tbsp), 486, 493
Technology, *See* Calculator *and*
Computer.
Temperature, 96, 100, 106,
133, 287
wind-chill, 106
Term of a sequence, 14, 20
Term number of a sequence,
14, 20
Terminating decimals, 253,
256, 258, 261
Tessellation, 565–567,
571–573, 575–576
regular, 573
semi-regular, 575
Test-Taking Skills
Building Test-Taking Skills,
603-604, 606-607, 609-610,
612-613
Practicing Test-Taking Skills,
605, 608, 611, 614
Reading and Problem Solving,
601
Test-Taking Tips, 602
Themes, module
The Art of Motion, 230–231
Flights of Fancy, 376–377
Health and Fitness, 454–455
Heart of the City, 526–527
Making Choices, xx–1
Recreation, 310–311
Search and Rescue, 74–75
A Universal Language, 146–147
Theoretical probability,
30–39, 169, 387
Tiling, *See* Tessellation.
Time, 148–152, 155, 158, 327
Transformations, 291, 299
image of, 264, 267, 270, 291,
297
reflections, 266–268, 270, 272,
276, 291, 302
rotations, 264–265, 270–272,
276, 291, 572
squashing and stretching,
294–295, 299, 301–302, 306
translations, 291–293,
299–301, 306, 572
Translation, 291–293, 299–301,
306, 572
Transversal, 423, 429

Trapezoid, 513–514, 518–519,
522
area of, 516–518, 520, 522
Tree diagram, 168–169, 171,
174–175, 363–365, 367,
370–372
and permutations, 532–534,
536, 539, 556
Triangle(s)
angle sum, 426–427, 429, 431,
434
area, 384, 388, 391–393
classification by angles, 415,
417, 419, 421
classification by side lengths,
217, 223–224, 226
constructing, 218–219,
223–224, 226
naming, 266
relationship between the
lengths of the sides, 219,
223, 224, 226
tessellating, 566, 571
vertex, 266
Turn, *See* Rotation.

U ▸ ▸ ▸ ▸ ▸ ▸ ▸ ▸ ▸ ▸ ▸ ▸ ▸ ▸ ▸ ▸ ▸

Unit rate, 313–314, 319, 321,
325
Upper extreme, 492, 494
Upper quartile, 492, 494

V ▸ ▸ ▸ ▸ ▸ ▸ ▸ ▸ ▸ ▸ ▸ ▸ ▸ ▸ ▸ ▸ ▸

Variable(s), 16, 20
Venn diagram, 518
Vertex (vertices)
of an angle, 77–78, 83
of a cone, 568
of a network, 442, 446
of a polygon, 266
of a prism, 19, 398, 404
of a pyramid, 544, 547
of a tessellation, 565, 571
of a triangle, 266
Vertical angles, 424–425, 429,
430, 434
Vertical axis, 3, 7, 93, 95, 292
Visual representations
factor tree, 151
fitted line, 332–333, 336,
338–339, 341, 343
flow chart, 164–165, 470
line plot, 334
locations on a coordinate plane,
15, 93, 95
map, 88, 97, 129, 326, 553
network, 440–442, 446,
448–450

of patterns, 14–15, 18
place value chart, 191
of percents, 345–346, 348, 350,
352, 354
of probability, 364, 367, 370
scatter plot, 332–333, 336,
338–339, 341, 343
self-assessment scales, 49, 51,
53–55, 60, 62–63, 65
stem-and-leaf plot, 316–317,
320, 322–325
tree diagram, 168–169, 171,
174–175, 363–365, 367,
370–372, 532–534, 536, 539,
556
Venn diagram, 518
See also Graph, Modeling,
Transformations, *and* Visual
thinking.
Visual thinking, 24, 56, 58, 98,
159, 172, 261, 274, 324, 341,
392, 406, 419, 431, 448, 509,
520
Vocabulary, *See* Key Concepts.
Volume, 18, 542–543, 547
of a cone, 568–571, 573–574,
576
of a cube, 18–19, 21, 23, 25,
540
of a cylinder, 457–458,
464–466, 470
estimating, 549, 569, 573
of a prism, 437–439, 445–447,
450, 457
of a pyramid, 545–547, 549,
551

W ▸ ▸ ▸ ▸ ▸ ▸ ▸ ▸ ▸ ▸ ▸ ▸ ▸ ▸ ▸ ▸ ▸

Weight, 184, 328–330, 332, 408
estimating, 130–131
Weighted network, 444, 446
Writing, 8, 23, 37, 45, 73, 84,
96, 97, 127, 140, 143, 145,
173, 212, 229, 244, 272, 273,
309, 322, 339, 370, 453, 467,
482, 525, 535
See also Extended Exploration;
Journal; Projects, module; *and*
Research.

Z ▸ ▸ ▸ ▸ ▸ ▸ ▸ ▸ ▸ ▸ ▸ ▸ ▸ ▸ ▸ ▸ ▸

Zero
and division, 254, 256
as an exponent, 195, 198
as a placeholder, 249, 251, 255,
581

CREDITS

ACKNOWLEDGMENTS

13 "Smart" poem from *Where the Sidewalk Ends* by Shel Silverstein. Copyright © 1974 by Evil Eye Music, Inc. **35** Excerpt from "There's a Moral Here, Cougar Fans" by Jerry Kirshenbaum. Copyright © 1983, Time Inc. Reprinted courtesy of *Sports Illustrated*, September 5, 1983. All rights reserved. **50** "Wed., August 13, 1980," from *Alesia* by Eloise Greenfield and Alesia Revis. Copyright © 1981 by Eloise Greenfield and Alesia Revis. Reprinted by permission of Scott Treimel, New York, for the author. **162** Diagrams from *Mathematisches Arbeitsbuch* by Walter Traeger and Karl-Heinz Unger. By permission of Verlag Moritz Diesterweg. **164** Diagram from *Matematnka 5. KAAC.* By permission of Prosveta Publishers. **166** Diagram from *Maths 8 2E* by Lynch, Parr, Picking, Keating. Reprinted by permission of Addison Wesley Longman Australia. **166** Diagram from *Hightop Shougaku 3-nen Suugaku* mathematics textbook. By permission of Obunsha Co., Ltd., Tokyo, Japan. **411** Excerpt from *Epic of Flight: Barnstormers & Speed Kings* by Paul O'Neil and the Editors of Time-Life Books, © 1981 Time-Life Books, Inc.

COVER PHOTOGRAPHY

Front (*clockwise*) Joe McBride/Tony Stone Images; Holway & Lobel Globus/The Stock Market; Fred Chase/Impact Visuals; Doug Milner/Uniphoto Picture Agency; RMIP/Richard Haynes; Per Eide/The Image Bank; Corbis (2002 ed.), Gianfranco Gorgoni/Contact Press Images (1999 ed.); David Young Wolff/Tony Stone Images. **Back** Photo of STEM pilot students: Sal Skog

PHOTOGRAPHY

iii RMIP/Richard Haynes; **iv** David Young Wolff/Tony Stone Images; **v** Per Eide/The Image Bank; **vi** Fred Chase/Impact Visuals; **vii** Holway & Lobel Globus/The Stock Market; **viii** Doug Milner/Uniphoto Picture Agency; **vix** Joe McBride/Tony Stone Images; **x** David Young Wolff/Tony Stone Images; **xi** Corbis (2002 ed.), Gianfranco Gorgoni/Contact Press Images (1999 ed.); **1** RMIP/Richard Haynes; **2** Nancie Battaglia; **5** Ian Shaw/Tony Stone Images; **8** National Baseball Hall of Fame; **9** Courtesy of the Vermont Youth Corps; **11** Jeff Greenberg/The Picture Cube; **15** RMIP/Richard Haynes; **24** Lawrence Migdale; **26** RMIP/Richard Haynes; **27** School Division, Houghton Mifflin Company; **28** School Division, Houghton Mifflin Company; **32** School Division, Houghton Mifflin Company; **34** Uniphoto (tl); Bachmann/Image Works (tr); David Wientraub/Stock Boston (bl); B.W. Hoffman/ Unicorn Stock Photo (br); **36** RMIP/Richard Haynes; **38** RMIP/Richard Haynes; **41** Randy Ory/The Stock Market; **43** RMIP/Richard Haynes; **45** Inga Spence/The Picture Cube; **46** School Division, Houghton Mifflin Company; **51** School Division, Houghton Mifflin Company; **56** RMIP/Richard Haynes; **57** RMIP/Richard Haynes; **59** Watterson/Universal Press Syndicate; **62** RMIP/Richard Haynes; **66** School Division, Houghton Mifflin Company; **68** Stanley Rowin/The Picture Cube; **69** RMIP/Richard Haynes; **71** RMIP/Richard Haynes; **74-75** Per Eide/The Image Bank; **76** David Lissy/The Picture Cube; **79** RMIP/Richard Haynes; **80** PhotoDisc, Inc.; **82** David Lissy/The Picture Cube; **85** PhotoDisc, Inc.; **88** Gayna Hoffman; **92** Emory Kristof/National Geographic Image Collection; **99** RMIP/Richard Haynes; **101** RMIP/Richard Haynes; **111** Sue McCartney/Photo Researchers; **112** Fred Hirschman/Tony Stone Images (tl); Art Wolfe/Tony Stone Images (tr); Larry Urlich/Tony Stone Images (bl); **114** RMIP/Richard Haynes; **116** RMIP/Richard Haynes; **117** Michael J. Howell/Stock Boston (l); Alese & Mort Pechter/The Stock Market (r); **121** Mug Shots/The Stock Market; **122** Jack Van Antwerp/The Stock Market; **125** Courtesy of the Institute of Texan Cultures; **126** Brown Brothers; **127** Julian Calverly/Uniphoto (t); Ken Lax/Photo Researchers (b); **128** Amy Etra; **130** RMIP/Richard Haynes; **134** RMIP/Richard Haynes; **138** UPI/Corbis-Bettman (tl); Dennis Brack/Black Star (r); Archive Photos (b); **139** Superstock; **143** RMIP/Richard Haynes; **146-147** Fred Chase/Impact Visuals; **148** Mark E. Gibson (t); Lawrence Migdale/Stock Boston (b); **151** School Division, Houghton Mifflin Company; **153** School Division, Houghton Mifflin Company; **155** Jose Azel/AURORA; **157** Michael Newman/ PhotoEdit; **160** Corbis-Bettmann; **162** School Division, Houghton Mifflin Company; **163** RMIP/Richard Haynes; **165** RMIP/Richard Haynes; **172** National Geographic Image Collection; **173** Lawrence Migdale/Stock Boston; **174** RMIP/Richard Haynes; **177** Courtesy of the Museum of the American Numismatic Assoication; **180** The Granger Collection; **184** James P. Rowan/DRK Photo (tr); Jeff Foott/Tom Stack & Associates (cl); Barbara Gerlach/DRK Photo (cr); Stephen J. Krasemann/ DRK Photo (bl); **185** Johnny Johnson/DRK Photo; **186** PhotoDisc, Inc.; **187** Donn Carl Harper; **189** Eric P. Newman Numismatic Education Society (t); RMIP/ Richard Haynes (b); **190** The Granger Collection; **193** RMIP/Richard Haynes; **196** School Division, Houghton Mifflin Company; **200** Red Morgan; **201** Ken Edward/Photo Researchers, Inc.; **204** RMIP/Richard Haynes; **206** Mark E. Gibson; **207** RMIP/Richard Haynes; **208** RMIP/Richard Haynes; **209** RMIP/Richard Haynes; **211** Mitsuaki Iwago/Minden Pictures; **218** RMIP/Richard Haynes; **225** RMIP/Richard Haynes; **227** RMIP/Richard Haynes; **230-231** Holway & Lobel Globus/The Stock Market; **232** School Division, Houghton Mifflin Company; **233** RMIP/Richard Haynes; **242** Gayna

Hoffman/Stock Boston; **243** Edward S. Curtis/San Diego Museum of Man (t); David Ball/The Stock Market (b); **245** A. Adducci; **247** S. Dalton/Animals Animals; **248** S. Dalton/Animals Animals; **250** The Harold E. Edgerton 1992 Trust, Courtesy of Palm Press, Inc.; **252** The Harold E. Edgerton 1992 Trust, Courtesy of Palm Press, Inc.; **260** RMIP/Richard Haynes; **263** RMIP/Richard Haynes; **265** Dr. E. R. Degginger/Color-Pic, Inc. (l); Index Stock Photography, Inc. (r); **266** RMIP/Richard Haynes; **268** David Scharf/Peter Arnold, Inc.; **272** James Solliday/Biological Photo Service; **273** Addison Doty; **275** RMIP/Richard Haynes; **277** RMIP/Richard Haynes; **279** RMIP/Richard Haynes; **282** RMIP/Richard Haynes; **285** Novastock/PhotoEdit; **305** Courtesy of Karen Kiser; **307** RMIP/Richard Haynes; **308** Index Stock Photography, Inc.; **310-311** Doug Milner/Uniphoto Picture Agency; **312** PhotoDisc, Inc.; **313** Spencer Grant/The Picture Cube; **318** Douglas Landrum; **321** Dan Campbell (t); Robert Houser (b); **322** Lee Snider; **327** Alan Baldwin (b); Courtesy of Ashrita Furman; **328** Dennis Kitchen/Tony Stone Images; **329** Library of Congress, Negative No. USZ62-063370; **331** RMIP/Richard Haynes; **332** RMIP/Richard Haynes; **334** Courtesy of John Kolar; **338** M.C. Chamberlain/ DRK Photo; **342** Michelle Bridwell/PhotoEdit; **344** David Young-Wolff/PhotoEdit; **350** Antonio Balducci/FPG International; **353** Laima Druskis/Stock Boston; **355** David Young-Wolff/Tony Stone Images; **356** RMIP/ Richard Haynes; **358** David Madison/Duomo (l); PhotoDisc, Inc. (r); **359** PhotoDisc, Inc.; **360** RMIP/ Richard Haynes; **361** Jim Cummins/FPG International (t); David Madison/Duomo (b); **365** David Madison/ Duomo; **368** Reuters/Gary A. Cameron/Archive Photos; **369** Steve Maines/Stock Boston; **371** Courtesy of the Mayo Clinic; **373** RMIP/Richard Haynes; **376-377** Joe McBride/Tony Stone Images; **378** The Smithsonian Institution; **379** RMIP/Richard Haynes; **381** Stephen Dalton/Animals Animals; **382** Johnny Johnson/Animals Animals; **383** RMIP/Richard Haynes; **385** Jean-Francois Causse/Tony Stone Images (r); RMIP/Richard Haynes (l); **386** RMIP/Richard Haynes; **390** UPI/Corbis-Bettmann (t); The Smithsonian Institution (b); **394** Glenn Randall (l); UPI/Corbis-Bettmann (r); **397** Chris Luneski/Image Cascade; **399** RMIP/Richard Haynes (t); School Division, Houghton Mifflin Company (b); **401** UPI/Corbis-Bettmann (r); Bob Harris (l); **407** Peter Essick/Aurora; **408** RMIP/Richard Haynes (l, c); School Division, Houghton Mifflin Company (r); **410** Digging It Up/University of North Florida (r); Culver Pictures (l); **411** RMIP/Richard Haynes; **414** RMIP/Richard Haynes; **418** Courtesy of the Boeing Company; **420** Anson Seale (t); *La Raspa* by Jesse Trevino, Collection of Elaine DeganBela and Richard Bela (b); **422** Brown Brothers; **425** RMIP/Richard Haynes; **427** RMIP/Richard Haynes; **430** Emmanuel Faure/Superstock; **433** RMIP/Richard Haynes; **436** Courtesy of United Parcel Service; **437** Aaron Strong/Liaison; **438** RMIP/Richard Haynes; **447** Courtesy of United Parcel Service; **451** RMIP/Richard Haynes; **454-455** David Young Wolff/Tony Stone Images; **456** Tony Freeman/PhotoEdit (l); Dennis MacDonald/Unicorn Stock Photo (cl); Gayna Hoffmann

(cr); Nancy Sheehan/The Picture Cube (r); **459** RMIP/ Richard Haynes; **460** RMIP/Richard Haynes; **461** Tony Freeman/PhotoEdit; **466** David Young-Wolff/PhotoEdit; **469** RMIP/Richard Haynes (r); School Division, Houghton Mifflin Company (l); **471** Don Mason/The Stock Market; **472** RMIP/Richard Haynes; **475** RMIP/ Richard Haynes; **476** RMIP/Richard Haynes; **480** Wayne Lynch/DRK Photo (tl); Doug Perrine/DRK Photo (bl); **480** Francois Gohier/Photo Researchers (tr); **480** Joe McDonald/ Animals, Animals (br); **482** Robert Brenner/ PhotoEdit; **485** Mary Kate Denny/PhotoEdit; **488** RMIP/ Richard Haynes; **490** RMIP/Richard Haynes; **491** School Division, Houghton Mifflin Company; **495** RMIP/ Richard Haynes; **496** Capece/Monkmeyer; **499** Roy Morsch/The Stock Market; **503** RMIP/Richard Haynes; **507** Corbis-Bettmann **508** RMIP/Richard Haynes; **510** Brooks Dodge/New England Stock Photo (t); Kindra Clineff/The Picture Cube (c); Richard Hutchings/ PhotoEdit (b); **515** RMIP/Richard Haynes; **516** RMIP/ Richard Haynes; **519** Joseph Schuyler/Stock Boston; **521** Don Tremain; **523** RMIP/Richard Haynes; **526-527** Corbis; **528** Ken Ross/FPG International; **529** (*clockwise*) Mark Segal/Tony Stone Images; Jerry Driendl/FPG International; Vladimir Pcholkin/FPG International; A & L Sinibaldi/Tony Stone Images; Tony Stone Images; Age Fotostock/FPG International; Andre Jenny/Photo 20-20; Wes Thompson/The Stock Market; Chromosohm/Sohm/ Photo Researchers, Inc.; Travelpix/FPG International; **530** Joachim Messerschmidt/FPG International (t); Jerry Driendl/FPG International (c); Telegraph Colour Library/ FPG International (b); **532** PhotoDisc, Inc.; **535** Lawrence Migdale/Tony Stone Images (t); PhotoEdit (b); **537** Donna Wright; **538** RMIP/Richard Haynes; **540** J. Apicella/CP&A; **541** M. Dwyer/Stock Boston; **542** RMIP/Richard Haynes; **544** Richard Bryant/Arcaid; **545** RMIP/Richard Haynes; **548** Luis Casals/Fotografia; **549** Courtesy of The Pyramids of Moody Gardens (b); School Division, Houghton Mifflin Company (t); **556** School Division, Houghton Mifflin Company; **557** Richard Laird/FPG International; **561** PhotoDisc, Inc.; **563** PhotoDisc, Inc. (background); RMIP/Richard Haynes (b); **564** PhotoDisc, Inc. (t); Ulf Sjostedt/FPG International (r); **568** Richard Bryant/ Arcaid; **570** Richard Bryant/Arcaid; **572** "Fish" (woodcut on textile) by M.C. Escher. © 1997 Cordon Art-Baarn-Holland. All rights reserved. (t); RMIP/Richard Haynes (b); **573** Elizabeth Simpson/FPG International (l); Michael Dwyer/Stock Boston (c); JPL/NASA (r); **574** Richard Bryant/Arcaid; **577** PhotoDisc, Inc. (t); Robin L. Sachs (b).

ILLUSTRATIONS
50 George Ford; **82, 84, 86, 88, 92, 99, 114** John Sanderson; **121, 122, 126** Ellen Kuzdro; **138** Dave Ballard; **194, 195, 395** Jeremy Spiegel; All other illustrations by School Division, Houghton Mifflin Company, or by McDougal Littell Design Group; **Electronic Technical Art** Network Graphics.

SELECTED ANSWERS

MODULE 1

Section 1, Practice and Application (p. 8)
1. about $1300 **3.** about $4500; I extended the graph.
7. less than **9.** more than **11.** less than **13.** Japan

17.

Pieces of mail received each day for a month	Tally	Frequency
5	IIII I	6
6	IIII II	7
7	IIII	5
8	IIII	5
9	III	3
10	I	1

19.

Sizes of sweatshirts for a softball team	Tally	Frequency
small	III	3
medium	IIII	5
large	IIII I	6
extra large	I	1

Spiral Review
22. 40 in.^{2} **23.** 54 yd^2 **24.** 20 ft^2 **25.** $\frac{3}{5}$ **26.** $\frac{4}{6}$ or $\frac{2}{3}$
27. $\frac{6}{8}$ or $\frac{3}{4}$ **28.** Sample Response:

29. Sample Response:

30. Sample Response:

Extra Skill Practice
1. about 2,200,000 **3.** Yes; The graph is of data that changes over time. **5.** less than **7.** more than

9.

Ages of students cleaning up a neighborhood playground	Tally	Frequency
10	II	2
11	III	3
12	IIII I	6
13	III	3
14	IIII	5
15	IIII	5

Study Skills, Taking Notes
1. a. Sample Response: ideas about the differences between line and bar graphs **b.** Sample Response: Use fewer words and more diagrams.

Section 2, Practice and Application (p. 21)
1. $1.88 **5.** $t = 6n$ **7.** $t = n + 5$

9.

Term number	1	2	3	4
Term	7	14	21	28

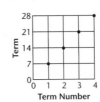

If t = the term and n = the term number, then $t = 7n$; 700

11. a. 1859 **b.** 153 **13.** 3^2 **15.** 25 **17.** 14,641
19. 1,000,000 **21.** 1 **23.** 200^3 **25.** 1331 ft^3
27. 15,625 in.^{3} **29.** 9

Spiral Review
33. about $\frac{150}{750}$ or $\frac{1}{5}$ **34.** Jordan **35.** Sample Response: $\frac{4}{8}$
36. Sample Response: $\frac{60}{75}$ **37.** Sample Response: $\frac{30}{70}$

Career Connection
39. after 22 m^3

Extra Skill Practice

1. $t = 8n$ **3.** $t = n - 5$

5.

Term number	1	2	3	4
Term	4	8	12	16

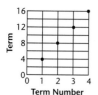

If t = the term and n = the term number, then $t = 4n$; 400

7.

Term number	1	2	3	4
Term	12	13	14	15

If t = the term and n = the term number, then $t = n + 11$; 111

9.

Term number	1	2	3	4
Term	$\frac{1}{2}$	1	$\frac{3}{2}$	2

If t = the term and n = the term number, then $t = \frac{1}{2}n$; 50

11. 5^2 **13.** 3^6 **15.** $3 \cdot 7^2$ **17.** 81 **19.** 32 **21.** 10,000
23. 0 **25.** 8 in.^{3} **27.** 3375 m^3 **29.** 1728 in.^{3}
31. 140,608 cm^3

Standardized Testing, Open-ended
1. Sample Response: 1, 4, 9, 16,...
2. Sample Response: $t = n^2$

Section 3, Practice and Application (p. 34)
1–3. Answers will vary from 0 to 1. **5. a.** $\frac{10}{26}$ or $\frac{5}{13}$
b. Sample Response: The spinner stops on a number less than 9; The spinner stops on a number greater than 10.
7. Sample Response: 6 and 3, 5 and 2, 4 and 1
9. Sample Response: 5 and 1, 4 and 2, 3 and 3
11. Sample Response: 6 and 1, 6 and 2, 6 and 3
13. a. $\frac{1}{2}$, $\frac{1}{2}$ **b.** They are about the same. **15.** 7, 8, 9, 10, 12; 6, 7, 8, 9, 10, 11; 6, 7, 8, 9, 10; 4, 5, 6, 7, 8, 9; 3, 4, 5, 6, 7, 8; 2, 3, 4, 5, 6, 7 **17.** $\frac{5}{36}$ **19.** $\frac{5}{36}$ **21.** $\frac{6}{36}$ or $\frac{1}{6}$
23. $\frac{18}{36}$ or $\frac{1}{2}$ **25. a.** 2, 4, 6, 8, 10, 12, 14, 16, 18, 20, 22, 24; 1, 3, 5, 7, 9, 11, 13, 15, 17, 19, 21, 23 **b.** $\frac{1}{2}$
27. a. green, blue **b.** No; Blue covers a larger area.

c. $\frac{1}{4}$, $\frac{3}{4}$; The area covered by blue is 3 times that covered by green.

Spiral Review
31.

Term number	1	2	3	4
Term	10	20	30	40

If t = the term and n = the term number, then $t = 10n$; 1000

32.

Term number	1	2	3	4
Term	16	17	18	19

If t = the term and n = the term number, then $t = n + 15$; 115

33. 37.63 **34.** 14.55 **35.** 5.017 **36.** 25 min

Extension
37. a. $P(\text{red}) = \frac{3}{6} = \frac{1}{2}$, $P(\text{green}) = \frac{2}{6} = \frac{1}{3}$, $P(\text{yellow}) = \frac{1}{6}$
b. 1 **c.** 4; Since 5 out of 10 cubes would be yellow, $P(\text{yellow}) = \frac{5}{10} = \frac{1}{2}$.

Extra Skill Practice
1. $\frac{40}{100} = \frac{2}{5}$ **3.** $\frac{28}{100} = \frac{7}{25}$ **5.** $\frac{60}{100} = \frac{3}{5}$ **7.** $\frac{88}{100} = \frac{22}{25}$
9. $\frac{80}{100} = \frac{4}{5}$ **11.** $\frac{2}{8} = \frac{1}{4}$ **13.** $\frac{2}{8} = \frac{1}{4}$ **15.** $\frac{4}{8} = \frac{1}{2}$ **17.** $\frac{0}{8} = 0$
19. 125; Sample Response: theoretical; Experimental probability can vary greatly for a small number of trials. As the number of trials increases, the experimental probabilities should begin to approach the theoretical probabilities. So when they can be calculated, it is better to use theoretical probabilities to make predictions.

Standardized Testing, Performance Task
1. $\frac{1}{8}$; One quarter out of 8 is dated 1975. **2.** $\frac{3}{7}$; There are 7 quarters left and 3 are dated 1985. **3.** 1; All the coins in the bank are quarters.

Section 4, Practice and Application (p. 45)
1. a. 12 min **b.** 240 min **c.** 561,600 min **d.** No; It takes almost 6 times as long to burn 2000 Cal jogging as it does stair-stepping. **3.** 3 dogs **5.** No; She would have to get a 120 on the next quiz.

Spiral Review
8. a. R, B, W **b.** $P(R) = \frac{3}{6}$ or $\frac{1}{2}$, $P(B) = \frac{2}{6}$ or $\frac{1}{3}$, $P(W) = \frac{1}{6}$
c. about 15 **9.** about 5 **10.** about 2 **11.** about 4

Extra Skill Practice
1. 5 h **3.** 36

Standardized Testing, Free Response
48 different orders

Section 5, Practice and Application (p. 56)
1. B, Sample Response:

Spiral Review
8. Eliminate 5, 19, and 47 because the sum of 6 odd integers is an even integer. Eliminate 56 because the highest possible score is 54 (9 · 6). A score of 32 is possible because 5 · 5 + 7 = 32. **9.** 540 **10.** 144 **11.** 3 **12.** 20 **13.** 80 **14.** 1 **15.** about 4800; 240 · 20 = 4800 **16.** about 30; 2700 ÷ 90 = 30 **17.** about 1070; 240 + 480 + 350 = 1090 **18.** about 1500; 1900 − 400 = 1500 **19.** about 6000; 50 · 120 = 6000 **20.** about 300; 100 + 90 + 110 = 300

Extra Skill Practice
1. a. 4 pennies, 4 dimes, and 3 quarters or 4 pennies, 9 dimes, and 1 quarter **b.** If there were one more of any of the coins, the change could be made. If, for example, there were 5 pennies, 4 dimes, and 3 quarters, the change would be 5 pennies, 3 quarters, and 2 dimes. If there were 4 pennies, 5 dimes, and 3 quarters, the change would be 5 dimes and 2 quarters. **2. a.** 37 **3. a.** Yes; If the average movie is 2.5 h long, this is about 436 movies or about 7 per year from age 12 on.

Standardized Testing, Free Response
a. Make an organized list of the 8 possible combinations and find the cost of each. Then use estimation or mental math to find the combination that would feed a whole number of friends at a total cost that comes closest to $12 without going over. Deluxe sandwich, apple, and water costs $3, so he can feed 4 people for exactly $12. **b.** Yes; Look at the table to see whether any meal costs exactly $3 or $4. **c.** Yes; Take the price of the combination he chooses and multiply by 4 or 5.

Section 6, Practice and Application (p. 66)
1. 6 **3.** 64 **5.** 81 **7.** 3 **9.** 2.25 **11.** (28 − 9) · 2 = 38 **13.** (6 + 6) ÷ 2 · (6 − 1) = 30 **17. a.** Draw a square. **b.** Both sets of instructions are correct. One is appropriate for someone who doesn't know what a square is and the other is not. **19.** 4000 **21.** Sample Response: There was a sharp increase in the number of Hispanic public officials between 1991 and 1992. Overall, the number of Hispanic public officials has increased over the years 1985–1994. **23.** Sample Response: 3; The first diagram would be clearer if brackets were used to show the top row is composed of 3 squares plus 4 squares.

Spiral Review
27. $\frac{20}{60}$ or $\frac{1}{3}$ **28.** $\frac{33}{60}$ or $\frac{11}{20}$ **29.** $\frac{7}{60}$ **30.** 2 red, 3 white, 1 blue; Using the experimental probabilities, 1 out of 3 or 2 out of 6 faces are red, about 1 out of 2 or 3 out of 6 are white, and the remaining face is blue.

Extra Skill Practice
1. 12 **3.** 12 **5.** 22 **7.** 2 **9.** 2 **11.** 38 **13.** (3 + 12) · 6 = 90 **15.** ($3^2 + 5^2$) ÷ 2 = 17

Standardized Testing, Multiple Choice
1. B **2.** B

Review and Assessment
1. $15 **2.** March 1 and June 1 **3.** March and April **4.** May **5.** about $47.50; The value of the stock is increasing at a rate of about $2.50/month.

6.

Amount of Money Withdrawn	Tally	Frequency
$10	I	1
$20	II	2
$30	III	3
$40	I	1
$50	II	2
$100	I	1

7. a. The number corresponds to the number of small triangles in the shape.
b.

Term number	1	2	3	4
Term	1	4	9	16

c.

Term number	1	2	3	4
Term	1	4	9	16
Exponential form of term	1^2	2^2	3^2	4^2

;

Each term is the term number squared. If t = the term and n = the term number, then $t = n^2$. **d.** 25, 5^2, 25 **e.** 2500

8.

Term number	1	2	3	4
Term	6	12	18	24

Term Number

If t = the term and n = the term number, then $t = 6n$; 600

9. 729 cm^3 **10.** P(red) = $\frac{14}{50}$ or $\frac{7}{25}$, P(blue) = $\frac{10}{50}$ or $\frac{1}{5}$, P(green) = $\frac{26}{50}$ or $\frac{13}{25}$ **11.** red, blue, green **12.** P(red) = $\frac{1}{4}$, P(blue) = $\frac{1}{4}$, P(green) = $\frac{1}{2}$ **13.** about 15 **14.** 26; There are 16 triangles which are 1 triangle high, 6 which are 2 triangles high, 3 which are 3 triangles high, and 1 which is 4 triangles high. **16.** 0 **17.** 162 **18.** 6 **19.** 10

MODULE 2

Section 1, Practice and Application (p. 84)

1. $\overrightarrow{CH}$ **3.** ∠BCH, ∠HCG, ∠HCF **5.** Possible answers: ∠BCH, 40°; ∠GCF, 45° **7.**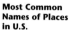
90° right angle **9.** 138° obtuse angle

11. 53° acute angle **13.** 100° obtuse angle **15.** About 135° **19.** ∠CBK and ∠KBH; ∠GBF and ∠FBD **21. a.** 165° **b.** 75°
23. a. 135° **b.** 45° **25. a.** 93° **b.** 3° **27. a.** 85°
b. not possible

Spiral Review

31. 44 **32.** 15 **33.** 22 **34.**
35. 14 ft **36.** 46 in.

Most Common Names of Places in U.S.

Extra Skill Practice

1. Sample Response: $\overrightarrow{TW}$, $\overrightarrow{VW}$ **3.** ∠VTQ, ∠STQ
5. 180° straight angle **7.** 65° acute angle **9.** ∠WTP, ∠PTS
11. a. 17° **b.** not possible **13. a.** 124° **b.** 34°

Section 2, Practice and Application (p. 95)

1. $25 **3.** –5 points **7.** > **9.** < **11.** > **13.** Sample Response: 60°F or 16°C **15.** –40°F **17.** 0°C **19.** 5°C
21. 0, –2, –4 **23.** –50, 0, 50 **25.** –6 **27.** 9 **29.** 24
31. 0 **33.** –4 **35.** 100 **37.** 8 **39.** 0 **41.** 62 **43.** 514
45. > **47.** > **49.** > **51.** Sample Response: Calle 13 and Calle 14 **53.** Sample Response: Calle Rufino Barrios and Calle 15 **55. a.** V(–2, 4), W(1, 3), X(4, 0), Y(2, –2), Z(–3, –4) **b.** V and Y, V and Z

Spiral Review

60. 47° **61.** 8° **62.** 64°
63.

Average Monthly Fahrenheit Temperature in Aswan, Egypt (°F)

64. $\frac{3}{5}$ **65.** $\frac{3}{4}$
66. $\frac{5}{9}$ **67.** $\frac{1}{6}$

Extra Skill Practice

1. –85 ft **3.** < **5.** > **7.** < **9.** < **11.** < **13.** > **15.** –8, 8
17. 16, 16 **19.** 2001, 2001 **21.** 93, 93 **23.** 72, 72
25. d, a **27.** a and b intersect at (–4, 1), b and c at (4, 3), c and a at (–1, –2), and d and a at (1, –4).

Standardized Testing, Open-ended

1. Sample Response: A man weighed 160 lb. He lost 5 lb and then gained 18 lb. How much did he then weigh? **2.** Sample Response: At the beginning of 1989, the population of a town was 5557. During the year, 206 people moved out of the town and 157 people moved in. What was the population of the town at the end of 1989? **3.** People would probably be wearing shorts or other summer clothing. They might be swimming or just sitting outside to stay cool. **4.** People would be wearing winter coats or jackets. They might be skiing or making a snowman. **5.** People would be wearing layers and layers of clothing trying to stay warm. The only people who would be involved in outdoor activities would be those who had to work outdoors (like a police officer directing traffic).

Section 3, Practice and Application (p. 110)

1. –6; –4 + (–2) = –6 **3.** –8; 0 – 8 = –8 **5. a.** –1
b. Start at 2. Face the positive direction. Move backward 3 units. **c.** Sample Response: Start at 2. Face the positive direction. Move forward 0 units.
7. –17 **9.** –21 **11.** –11 **13.** –9 **15.** 300 **17.** Mike; Danessa's score is 0, Jonah's is –900, and Mike's is 100.
19. –30,000 + 43,000 = 13,000; $13,000 gain **21.** –15
23. 8 **25.** –10 + 2 **27.** 9 + 17 **29.** About –17°F
31. –17 **33.** 6 **35.** 19 **37.** 1493 ft **39.** 25 **41.** 11
43. 13 **45.** No.

Spiral Review

48.

49. 3.34
50. 67.46
51. 6.57
52. 15, 11, 7
53. 81, 100, 121

Extension

55. –2, –1, 0, 1, 2, 3, 4, 5

Extra Skill Practice

1. –2 + 5 = 3 **3.** –1 – 3 = –4 **5.** –9 **7.** –3 **9.** 5
11. –100 **13.** –10 **15.** 0 **17.** 40 **19.** 0 **21.** –20 **23.** 6
25. 21 **27.** 16 **29.** –10 **31.** –30 **33.** 6 **35.** –9

Standardized Testing, Multiple Choice

1. B **2.** C

Section 4, Practice and Application (p. 125)

1. C **3.** p + 3 **5.** 120 **7.** 24 **9.** 21 **11.** 7 **13.** –12
15. 8 **17.** –4 **19.** 36 **21.** 12 **23.** 24

25. a.

Travel time (hours)	Distance covered by Covered Wagon (miles)	Distance covered by Stage Coach (miles)
0	0	0
1	2	5
2	4	10
3	6	15
4	8	20
5	10	25
6	12	30

Travel time (hours)	Distance covered by Pony Express (miles)	Distance covered by Railroad (miles)
0	0	0
1	10	22
2	20	44
3	30	66
4	40	88
5	50	110
6	60	132

b. Possible answers: for the covered wagon, $d = 2t$; for the stage coach, $d = 5t$; for the pony express, $d = 10t$; for the railroad, $d = 22t$

c–d. Possible answers:

Distance Traveled by Covered Wagon

Distance Traveled by Stage Coach

(4.5, 9)

(4.5, 22.5)

Distance Traveled by Railroad

(4.5, 99)

Distance Traveled by Pony Express

(4.5, 45)

27.

x	−10	−5	0	5	10
y	−25	−15	−5	5	15

29.

x	−1	0	1
y	2	3	4

31.

x	−1	0	1
y	3	2	1

35. a. Bowling Alley A: $y = 17x + 4$; Bowling Alley B: $y = 18.50x + 2$

b.

Bowling Costs

c. when the bowling time is more than 1 h 20 min

d. when the bowling time is 1 h 20 min

Spiral Review

37. −60 **38.** 7 **39.** −17 **40.** $\frac{1}{8}$ **41.** 0 **42.** $\frac{4}{8}$ or $\frac{1}{2}$

43. Place in sequence

Place in sequence p	1	2	3	4
Value v	6	7	8	9

; $v = p + 5$; 105

Extra Skill Practice

1. $n + 5$ (cm) **3.** 50 **5.** 0 **7.** 2 **9.** 36 **11.** 13 **13.** −11

15. Sample Response:

Nearby house number x	4	6	10
House number y	2	4	8

$y = x - 2$

17. Sample Response:

Number x	1	2	3
Number y	8	10	12

$y = 2x + 6$

19.

x	−1	0	1
y	0	1	2

21.

x	−1	0	1
y	3	4	5

Standardized Testing, Free Response

Sample Response: Because the road from Praitis to Mt. Boris was undergoing construction, the Kartanels had to travel slowly, at an average rate of 50 km/h. The ascent up Mt. Boris, which took them about half an hour, slowed them up even more. Their progress was further delayed when, between 1:30 P.M. and 2:00 P.M., they decided to have lunch at a restaurant they had passed about 10 km back. After lunch, they cautiously descended Mt. Boris on a narrow, twisting road at an average rate of 50 km/h. Once they hit the Flat Lands, they picked up speed and were able to cover the last 125 km of their journey in about 1 h.

Section 5, Practice and Application (p. 138)

1. $x + 4 = 8$ **5.** $x = 2$ **7.** $x = 8$ **9.** $y + 1973 = 1979$
11. a. $x + 150 = 180$ **b.** $180 - x = 150$ **13.** Let n represent the number of people in the dash who did not set a personal best. So, $n + 5 = 12$. **15.** Let n represent the number of prints Anna originally had. So, $n - 70 = 8$.
17. Let p represent the number of original subscribers. So, $p - 4 = 28$. **19.** 102 **21.** 72 **23.** 23 **25.** 40 **27.** 82
29. 0 **33.** Let d represent Darius's deposit. So, $1271.63 + d = 1453.95$; $182.32. **37–43.** Sample methods are given. **37.** mental math; 15 **39.** mental math; −10 **41.** mental math; 20.1 **43.** mental math; 5
45. a. $a + 37 = 90$ **b.** 53

Spiral Review

47. 1 **48.** −9 **49.** −59 **50.** 23 **51.** −26 **52.** −48

---

53. 12 h; Strategies will vary. **54.** 75 is divisible by 5.
55. 215 is divisible by 5. **56.** 253 is not divisible by 2, 5, or 10. **57.** 630 is divisible by 2, 5, and 10.

Extension

59. Remove one rectangular tile from each side of the equation and then remove two square tiles from each side. (The two steps can be reversed.) **61.** Remove three square tiles from each side of the equation and then remove one rectangular tile from each side. (The two steps can be reversed.) **63. a.** No; adding 35 to a number will never give the same result as adding 13 to the same number. **b.** Yes; any number increased by 4 is the same as 4 increased by the number. Every number is a solution.

Extra Skill Practice

1. $x + 5 = 6$ **3.** $6 = 1 + m$ **5.** Sample Response: Let b represent the number of apples Jill's brother picked. So, the equations are $53 + b = 85$ and $85 - b = 53$.
7. Sample Response: Let s represent the number of points Jenn has before she takes her last turn. So, the equations are $8 + s = 121$ and $121 - s = 8$. **9.** 50
11. −43 **13.** 56 **15.** −55 **17.** 72 **19.** 0 **21.** −5
23. 18

Standardized Testing, Performance Task

Sample Response: I don't agree with Sue. Heidi's goals to shots ratio was $\frac{3}{15}$, or $\frac{1}{5}$, Jen's was $\frac{4}{12}$, or $\frac{1}{3}$, and Sheila's was $\frac{3}{9}$, or $\frac{1}{3}$. Sue's reasoning seems to be that the person who had the highest goals to shots ratio during practice will be the person most likely to score during the game. Since Sheila and Jen had the same ratio, they are equally likely to be that person.

Review and Assessment

1. Possible answers: $\angle FCB$, $\angle BCE$, $\angle ACD$
2. Possible answers: $\angle ACB$, $\angle DCF$, $\angle DCE$
3. $\angle ACE$, $\angle DCB$ **4. a.** 45° **b.** $\angle BCF$ or $\angle ACD$, 45°; $\angle ACB$ or $\angle DCE$, 135° **5.** If 0 represents ground level, then negative integers represent meters below ground level, and positive integers represent meters above ground level. So, the stadium was built at −50 m.
6. −10, −5, −2, 0, 6, 8, 14 **7.** −5; 5 **8.** 1; 1 **9.** −72; 72
10. 303; 303 **11. a.** If a line were drawn through the jumper's upper body and another through the skis, the lines would not intersect. **b.** The skier would be standing up straight. **12–15.**

16. −4 **17.** −12
18. −4 **19.** −11
20. −3 **21.** 7
22. 3 **23.** −19
24. 30 **25.** 9
26. 3 **27.** −17
28. 15 **29.** 14

30. a.

Time (seconds)	Distance traveled (feet)	
	Recreational skier	Speed skier
10	220	2040
20	440	4080
30	660	6120
40	880	8160

b. Recreational skier, $d = 22t$; Speed skier, $d = 204t$.

c.

d. the speed skier; about 8000 ft

31. Let b represent the original number of baseball cards. So, $b + 45 = 315$.

32. 51 **33.** –8 **34.** –5 **35.** 6 **36.** –7 **37.** 21

MODULE 3

Section 1, Practice and Application (p. 157)

1. 1, 2, 3, 4, 6, 12 **3.** 1, 3, 5, 9, 15, 45 **5.** 1, 2, 4, 8, 16, 32, 64 **7.** 1, 2, 4, 5, 10, 20, 25, 50, 100 **9.** 1, 11, 121 **11.** 1, 2, 3, 5, 6, 10, 15, 25, 30, 50, 75, 150
13. Sample Response: 36, 49, 64, 81, 100; Perfect squares have an odd number of factors. **15.** composite
17. prime **19.** prime **21.** prime **23.** 2 • 2 • 7
25. 2 • 2 • 3 • 3 **27.** 2 • 5 • 5 **29.** 2 • 5 • 17
33. a. 30 m², 26 m **b.** 5 m by 6 m **c.** 2 m by 15 m, or 1 m by 30 m **35.** none **37.** 2, 4 **39.** 2, 3, 4, 5, 6, 10
41. 2, 3, 4, 5, 6, 10. **43.** If the number formed by the last 3 digits of the number is divisible by 8, the entire number is divisible by 8. Example: 9416 ÷ 8 = 1177
45. 3 **47.** 15 **49.** 1 **51.** 15 **53.** 13 **57.** 12 **59.** 40
61. 100 **63.** 36 **65.** Since the numbers listed are all multiples of 63, start with the lowest number and see if it is divisible by both 14 and 36. If it is, that is the LCM. If it isn't, repeat the process with the next larger number in the list. Continue until the LCM (252) is found.
67. a. No; If x is any common multiple of a set of numbers, then 2 • x is also a common multiple, and it is greater than x. So there is always a greater common multiple. **b.** Yes; Every whole number is divisible by 1, and 1 is the smallest whole number that can be a divisor, so 1 is the least common divisor of any set of whole numbers.

Extra Skill Practice
1. 1, 2, 3, 6, 9, 18 **3.** 1, 3, 17, 51 **5.** 1, 2, 3, 4, 6, 8, 9, 12, 18, 24, 36, 72 **7.** 1, 2, 3, 4, 6, 7, 12, 14, 21, 28, 42, 84 **9.** 1, 2, 3, 4, 6, 9, 12, 18, 27, 36, 54, 108
11. 1, 7, 13, 91 **13.** 2 • 2 • 2 • 3 **15.** 3 • 3 • 3 • 3
17. 2 • 3 • 3 • 5 **19.** 2 • 2 • 2 • 3 • 5 **21.** 2 • 3 • 3 • 3
23. 2 • 2 • 2 • 2 • 3 **25.** 2, 3, 6 **27.** 3 **29.** 2, 4
31. 2, 3, 4, 5, 6, 9, 10 **33.** 9 **35.** 5 **37.** 16 **39.** 7
41. 18 **43.** 45 **45.** 40 **47.** 60

Section 2, Practice and Application (p. 171)
1. $\frac{1}{5}$ **3.** $\frac{3}{4}$ **5.** $\frac{3}{7}$ **7.** $\frac{5}{13}$ **11.** $\frac{1}{4}$ **13. a.** Since $\frac{1}{14}$ of something is larger than $\frac{1}{16}$ of the same thing, $\frac{3}{14} > \frac{3}{16}$.
b. The fraction with the smaller denominator is greater.
c. Sample Response: $\frac{5}{21}$ **15. a.** greater than, less than, greater than **b.** Sample Response: Divide the denominator of the fraction by 2. If the numerator is less than the quotient, the fraction is less than $\frac{1}{2}$. If the numerator is more than the quotient, the fraction is more than $\frac{1}{2}$.
17. $\frac{1}{2}$ **19.** $\frac{1}{2}$ **21–27.** Sample methods are given.
21. mental math; > **23.** mental math; = **25.** estimation or paper and pencil; > **27.** mental math; <
29.

31. $\frac{11}{24}$ **33.** $\frac{1}{20}$ **35.** $\frac{7}{9}$ **37.** $\frac{1}{36}$ **39.** 2
43. Yes; $\frac{3}{4} + \frac{1}{20} + \frac{1}{5} = \frac{20}{20}$ **45. a.** The tree diagram shown uses an egg as the fourth item.

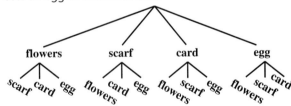

There are 12 possible outcomes. **b.** Sample Response: P(flowers, scarf) = $\frac{1}{12}$. P(flowers, not scarf) = $\frac{2}{12}$ or $\frac{1}{6}$.
47. a. $\frac{1}{12}$ **b.** $\frac{1}{12}$ **c.** $\frac{1}{6}$

Extra Skill Practice
1. $\frac{3}{4}$ **3.** $\frac{2}{3}$ **5.** $\frac{1}{9}$ **7.** $\frac{15}{31}$ **9.** $\frac{9}{13}$ **11.** > **13.** > **15.** < **17.** >

19. $\frac{15}{16}$ **21.** $\frac{5}{18}$ **23.** $\frac{2}{3}$ **25.** $\frac{23}{30}$ **27. a.** No; Each number represents a position on the relay team and is to be used only once. **b.** **c.** $\frac{1}{12}$

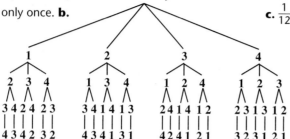

Standardized Testing, Performance Task
1. the yellow cake; the pineapple cake; Sample Response: I wrote each fraction as a decimal and compared the decimals. **2.** The first row represents the choices for server 1, the second row represents the choices for server 2, and so on, for the four servers. Let Y = yellow cake, C = chocolate cake, S = strawberry cake, and P = pineapple cake.

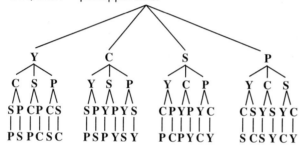

Sample Response: There would be more choices for each server to choose from, so the number of possible ways that they could share the cake would increase.

Section 3, Practice and Application (p. 184)
1. $4\frac{3}{5}$ **3.** $4\frac{1}{5}$ **5.** The fraction is not between 0 and 1; $2\frac{2}{3}$

7. The remainder was ignored; $15\frac{1}{2}$ **9.** $\frac{9}{8}$ **11.** $\frac{40}{9}$ **13.** $\frac{47}{5}$

15. $\frac{29}{2}$ **17.** $5\frac{1}{2}$ **19.** $\frac{27}{200}$ **21–25.** Sample methods are given. **21.** mental math; > **23.** mental math; <

25. paper and pencil; < **27.** $2\frac{3}{4}$ **29.** $1\frac{5}{8}$ **31.** $10\frac{2}{3}$

33. $3\frac{1}{12}$ **35.** $23\frac{1}{22}$ **37.** $8 = x + 5\frac{1}{3}$; $2\frac{2}{3}$

39. $18\frac{1}{2} = x + 15\frac{1}{2}$; 3 **41. a.** $11\frac{9}{16}$ in. **b.** $2\frac{1}{16}$ in.
c. so you know exactly how much wood is left

Spiral Review
44. $\frac{11}{12}$ **45.** $\frac{7}{18}$ **46.** $\frac{2}{3}$ **47.** $1\frac{7}{36}$ **48.** 2.055 **49.** 0.65
50. 2.9122 **51.** 90°; 45°

Extra Skill Practice
1. $1\frac{3}{5}$ **3.** $1\frac{3}{4}$ **5.** $7\frac{2}{3}$ **7.** $13\frac{1}{5}$ **9.** $4\frac{2}{7}$ **11.** $10\frac{1}{5}$ **13.** $\frac{14}{5}$
15. $\frac{66}{7}$ **17.** $\frac{33}{4}$ **19.** $\frac{121}{6}$ **21.** $\frac{154}{5}$ **23.** $\frac{193}{3}$ **25.** $4\frac{1}{12}$

27. $\frac{1}{4}$ **29.** $1\frac{8}{9}$ **31.** $11\frac{1}{5}$ **33.** $\frac{29}{35}$ **35.** $23\frac{1}{24}$

Standardized Testing, Multiple Choice
1. D **2.** A, D

Section 4, Practice and Application (p. 199)
1. two thousand five hundred twenty-three and twelve hundredths **3.** forty-three and sixty-five thousandths
5. $\frac{98}{100}$ or $\frac{49}{50}$ **7.** $\frac{208}{1000}$ or $\frac{26}{125}$ **9.** $1\frac{19}{10,000}$
11. $10\frac{85421}{1,000,000}$ **13.** easier to read; 6,400,000;

13,200,000 **15.** < **17.** > **19.** < **21.** C **23.** F **25.** H
27. G **29.** tenths, hundredths, thousandths **31.** 100
33. 10 **35.** 0.1 **37.** 0.0001 **39.** $\frac{1}{16}$ **41.** $\frac{1}{216}$ **43.** $\frac{1}{625}$
45. $\frac{1}{144}$ **47.** 10^6 **49.** 10^1 **51.** 10^{-6} **53.** 10^{-8} cm
55. 1,000,000,000,000,000,000,000 **57.** 0.01225
59. 130,240 **61.** 0.0000139 **63.** 0.0436 **65.** 5.437
67. 0.01205 **69.** $1.20684 \cdot 10^5$ **71.** $2.290098 \cdot 10^2$
73. $7.5 \cdot 10^{-5}$ **75.** 0.54 **77.** 2,000,000,000,000,000;
10,800,000,000,000,000; 19,100,000,000,000,000;
5,680,000,000,000,000; 38,200,000,000,000,000

Spiral Review
80. $2\frac{3}{8}$ **81.** $2\frac{5}{9}$ **82.** $1\frac{21}{40}$ **83.** $2\frac{7}{15}$ **84.** 125 in.^{3}
85. 1000 ft^3 **86.** 1 m^3 **87.** 125 cm^3 **88.** about 6 ft
89. about 75 in. **90.** about 25 yd

Extension
91. a. 10,000; 10^4 **b.** 256; 2^8 **c.** 64; 4^3 **d.** $\frac{1}{256}$; 2^{-8}
e. 0.001; 10^{-3} **f.** 9; 9^1 **g.** 100; 10^2 **h.** 4; 2^2 **i.** $\frac{1}{5}$; 5^{-1}
j. $\frac{1}{64}$; 4^{-3} **k.** $\frac{1}{10,000,000}$; 10^{-7} **l.** 59,049; 9^5
93. To multiply, add the exponents. To divide, subtract the exponents.

Extra Skill Practice
1. $\frac{1}{200}$ **3.** $12\frac{4}{5}$ **5.** < **7.** > **9.** > **11.** 1000 **13.** 1
15. 1,000,000 **17.** 100,000 **19.** 100,000,000 **21.** $\frac{1}{8}$
23. $\frac{1}{32}$ **25.** $\frac{1}{4096}$ **27.** $\frac{1}{81}$ **29.** $\frac{1}{1}$ **31.** 0.00245 **33.** 1.29723
35. 1.046 **37.** 305,908 **39.** 0.00312 **41.** $6.1 \cdot 10^{-3}$
43. $1.84536 \cdot 10^5$ **45.** $1.0177 \cdot 10^3$ **47.** $9.0533 \cdot 10^2$

Standardized Testing, Multiple Choice
1. D **2.** B

Section 5, Practice and Application (p. 211)
1. a. 3000 m; 5000 m; 10,000 m **b.** about 6000; about 10,000; about 20,000 **3.** 1800 **5.** 0.4 **7.** 0.06804
9. 600,000,000 **11.** = **13.** < **15.** < **17.** Sample Response: Change mm to m. **19.** Sample Response: Change mm to m. **31.** 90 mm **33.** 1.25 m
35. unreasonable; Sample Response: A doorknob comes about to my waist and the distance from the floor to my waist is about 1 m. **37.** unreasonable; Sample

Response: The length of our classroom is about 7 m, so the length of a room in a house would be about 5 m.
39. reasonable; Sample Response: Since two of my classrooms could probably fit along the edge of a pool and my classroom is about 7 m long, 15 m is reasonable.
40. a. the meter stick; yes, but the longer the measurement, the greater the error. **b.** kilometers to meters; Multiplying 8×1000 is easier than multiplying 5×1760.

Spiral Review
41. 10^3 **42.** 10^{-3} **43.** 10^1 **44.** 10^0 **45.** about 5 h, about 2 h **46.** about 7.5 mi, about 17.5 mi **47.** 25
48. 27 **49.** 46 **50.** 30 **51.** –12 **52.** 149

Extra Skill Practice
1. 48,200 **3.** 5,000,000 **5.** 0.032 **7.** 3,960,000
9. 0.5008 **11.** < **13.** = **15.** > **17.** < **19.** > **21.** 60.0
23. 14.5 **25.** 80

Section 6, Practice and Application (p. 224)
5. cannot **7.** can; scalene **9.** can; scalene **11.** 9
13. 18 **15.** 20 **17.** 400 **19.** $n = 3l$, where $n =$ the number of volunteers this year and $l =$ the number of volunteers last year; 36 volunteers **21.** $c = 5p$, where $c =$ the number of chickens and $p =$ the number of pigs; 30 chickens **23. a.** $t = 4l$, where $t =$ the number of pens sold this year and $l =$ the number of pens sold last year **b.** $l = \frac{t}{4}$, where $l =$ the number of pens sold last year and $t =$ the number of pens sold this year
c. 19 pens

Spiral Review
25. 3 **26.** 4600 **27.** 97.5 **28.** 0.0001084
29. a. $-43 + x = -34$ **b.** 9 **30.** 20 cm **31.** 40 in.
32. 70 m **33.** 11 ft

Extra Skill Practice
1. can; scalene **3.** cannot **5.** can; isosceles and equilateral **7.** can; scalene **9.** cannot **11.** 36 **13.** 10
15. 99 **17.** 15 **19.** 75 **21.** 14 **23.** $t = 2l$, where $t =$ the number of students in chorus this year and $l =$ the number of students in chorus last year; 78 students

Standardized Testing, Free Response
2. $f = 3s$, where $f =$ the length of the first banner and $s =$ the length of the second banner; $2\frac{5}{6}$ ft

Review and Assessment
1. $2 \cdot 2 \cdot 3$ **2.** $3 \cdot 7$ **3.** $2 \cdot 2 \cdot 2 \cdot 3$ **4.** $2 \cdot 3 \cdot 7$
5. $2 \cdot 2 \cdot 17$ **6.** 2, 24 **7.** 18; 180 **8.** 5; 150
9. 2; 840 **10.** < **11.** < **12.** > **13.** =

14. a.

b. $\frac{1}{2}$ **15.** $5\frac{7}{9}$ **16.** $\frac{17}{24}$
17. $3\frac{7}{10}$ **18.** $17\frac{12}{25}$ **19.** $\frac{3}{40}$
20. $12\frac{1}{4}$ **21.** $87\frac{17}{5000}$
22. $\frac{20,001}{200,000}$ **23.** $3\frac{33}{6250}$
24. Sample Response: 2.8151 and 2.81512
25. > **26.** < **27.** =
28. $\frac{1}{100,000}$ **29.** $\frac{1}{125}$
30. $\frac{1}{1}$ **31.** $\frac{1}{6}$ **32.** $\frac{1}{121}$
33. 2,532,000 **34.** 0.02532
35. 0.002532 **36.** 2532
37. $8.9 \cdot 10^9$
38. $3.42 \cdot 10^5$ **39.** $3.8 \cdot 10^{-4}$ **40.** $1.20056 \cdot 10^1$
41. 350 **42.** 300 **43.** 0.440 **44.** unreasonable; My waist is about 100 cm above the floor and the top of a desk is about 30 cm below my waist. **45.** reasonable; The length of a jump rope is about 2 m, or 0.002 km.
46. can; scalene **47.** cannot **48.** can; isosceles and equilateral **49.** 36 **50.** 28 **51.** 17 **52.** 132 **53. a.** Let $b =$ total area of black squares. Let $f =$ area of flag. $b = \frac{1}{2}f$
b. 30 in.^{2} **c.** 48 in.^{2}

MODULE 4

Section 1, Practice and Application (p. 242)
1. 59.66 ft or 59.69 ft **3.** 3.14 in. **5.** Sample Response: about 16 ft **7.** $3\frac{1}{2}$ **9.** $9\frac{1}{2}$ **11.** $2\frac{5}{8}$ **13.** $18\frac{3}{8}$ **15.** Rewrite the mixed numeral in the problem as the sum of a whole number and a fraction. Multiply each part of the sum by the other factor in the problem; 9, 10, 13
17. a little more than 4 **19.** a little more than 6
21. a. $2\frac{1}{4}$ **b.** 360 **c.** 400, 600 **23.** $\frac{7}{3}$ **25.** $\frac{8}{25}$ **29.** $3\frac{1}{2}$
31. $3\frac{1}{3}$ **33.** 48 **35.** $\frac{3}{22}$ **37.** $1\frac{1}{5}$ **39.** $2\frac{1}{4}$

Spiral Review
44. cannot **45.** can **46.** 9 **47.** 32 **48.** 40 **49.** 10^2
50. 10^{-2} **51.** 10^{-2} **52.** 10^{-3}

Extra Skill Practice
For 1–5, the first answer is found by using 3.14. The second is found by using π. **1.** 15.7 or 15.71 m
3. 75.36 or 75.40 ft **5.** 32.97 or 32.99 cm **7.** $\frac{3}{22}$ **9.** 20
11. 14 **13.** 6 **15.** 76 **17.** $8\frac{4}{7}$ **19.** $\frac{11}{8}$ **21.** $\frac{3}{13}$ **23.** 10
25. $1\frac{1}{2}$ **27.** 14 **29.** $3\frac{3}{7}$ **31.** $1\frac{14}{19}$ **33.** $2\frac{1}{7}$

Section 2, Practice and Application (p. 257)

1. 0.648 **3.** 3.11656 **5.** 253.302 **7.** 71.47 **9.** 0.819
11. Yes; Sample Response: 3 · $1.60 = $4.80; less than; 2.7 < 3 and $1.59 < $1.60 **13.** 292.5 **15.** 12.5
17. Problems 2 and 5 are incorrect; Since the divisors in both problems are less than 1, the quotients should be greater than the dividend. **19.** 8.5 **21.** 5.8 **23.** 0.725
25. a. smaller **b.** 4.16 cm **c.** 45 mm **27.** 0.315315
29. 0.027777 **31.** 0.78$\overline{3}$ **33.** 0.5$\overline{18}$ **35.** undefined
37. 0.6$\overline{3}$ **39.** 0.58 **41.** less than; The divisor is greater than 1. **43.** less than; The divisor is greater than 1.

Spiral Review

47. $\frac{3}{22}$ **48.** 10 **49.** 18 **50.** 4 **51.** $\frac{11}{12}$ **52.** 18
53. 7 blocks due west
54. **55.** **56.**

57.

174°
obtuse

Extra Skill Practice

1. 13.78 **3.** 5.4984 **5.** 0.15572 **7.** 2.6064 **9.** 4599.74
11. 1214.88 **13.** less than; 0 < 0.23 < 1 **15.** equal to; Any number multiplied by 1 is the number itself.
17. 0.003; 0.210 ÷ 70 = 0.003 **19.** 6.49; 10 ÷ 2 = 5
21. 6; 2 ÷ 0.5 = 4 **23.** 0.$\overline{1}$; 2 ÷ 20 = 0.1 **25.** 230; 17 ÷ 0.1 = 170 **27.** 0.98; 49 ÷ 49 = 1 **29.** greater than; 0 < 0.38 < 1 **31.** equal to; The divisor is 1.
33. less than; 3488 > 1 **35.** greater than; 0 < 0.8 < 1

Standardized Testing, Multiple Choice

1. A **2.** D

Section 3, Practice and Application (p. 271)

1. a. Sample Response: about 100° clockwise **b.** 105° clockwise **c.** 255° counterclockwise **3.** 30°; 72° **5.** 180°
7. 60°, 120°, 180°, 240°, and 300° **9.** 180° **11.** 120° and 240° **15.** No; The figures are not the same size.
17. Yes **19.** No **21.** Yes **23.** Yes; 180°.

Spiral Review

32. 2.128 **33.** 325.2 **34.** 119.14 **35.** 0.4$\overline{36}$
36. 0.00534 **37.** 96.5 **38. a.** $\frac{12}{40}$ or $\frac{3}{10}$, $\frac{15}{40}$ or $\frac{3}{8}$ **b.** 36, 45 **39.** −9 **40.** 39 **41.** 0 **42.** −33 **43.** −28 **44.** −46

Extension

45. a. Sample Response: about $\frac{1}{2}$ in. below the base of the shaded figure along a vertical line through the dot on the figure; about 120° **d.** The angles are right angles. **e.** The distances are about the same.
g. It is a little bit closer to the base of the shaded figure.
h. about 135°; It is a little greater than the estimate.

Extra Skill Practice

1. Sample Response: 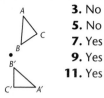 **3.** No
5. No
7. Yes
9. Yes
11. Yes

Standardized Testing, Free Response

1–3. Sample responses are given. **1.** a 90° rotation counterclockwise followed by a reflection **2.** a 180° rotation **3.** a 180° rotation followed by a reflection

Section 4, Practice and Application (p. 285)

1. −30 **3.** −42 **5.** 36 **7.** −36 **9.** −4 **11.** 5 **13.** 11
15. −50 **17.** −48 **19.** −72 **21.** 168 **23.** when all the factors are positive or when there are an even number of negative factors; when there are an odd number of negative factors **25. a.** −70 **b.** 9 **c.** −1 **27.** 19.5
29. −35 **31.** 4 **33.** −38 **35.** −32 **37.** 1.44 **39.** 4.88
41. 17 **43.** −7 **45.** 3$\frac{3}{4}$ **47.** 7$\frac{1}{2}$ **51.** about 23°C

Spiral Review

53. both **54.** line symmetry **55.** rotational symmetry
56. 7 **57.** 144 **58.** 9 **59.** 676
60. a–b. 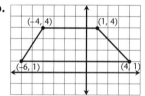 a trapezoid

Extension

61. 5x + 1 **63.** 3x + 9 **65.** 7x + 6

Extra Skill Practice

1. −28 **3.** 9 **5.** 48 **7.** 5 **9.** −14 **11.** −64 **13.** −71
15. 7.6 **17.** 15.5 **19.** 5$\frac{1}{4}$ **21.** 7$\frac{1}{2}$ **23.** 2.1 **25.** 13.6
27. 32 **29.** 24

Standardized Testing, Performance Task

Sample Response: Roger Jones incorrectly stated the discount as (23 − 2) · 16 = 336, or $3.36. This is his cost, and the discount is 2 · 16 = 32¢. The cashier incorrectly calculated the discount as (2 − 23) · 16 = −336, or −$3.36, which would mean Roger Jones owed him that amount. The cashier subtracted incorrectly by subtracting the cost from the discount instead of the discount from the cost.

Section 5, Practice and Application (p. 300)

1. No; The figure has been rotated. **3.** Yes **5.** (x, y − 5)
7. (x + 3, y) **9.** (x − 2, y − 4) **13.** The image of the rectangle should be 2 units to the left and 5 units below the original. **15.** A and C **17.** C **19.** B

21. a. $A(4, 5)$, $B(6, -1)$, $C(0, 2)$; $A'(-4, 5)$, $B'(-6, -1)$, $C'(0, 2)$ **b.** Multiply the y–coordinate by -1; Multiply the x–coordinate by -1. **c.** $(-3, 7)$, $(-4, 0)$, $(5, -8)$, $(-4, -9)$
23. 30 **25.** 2.3 **27.** $-1\frac{2}{3}$ **29.** $2\frac{1}{4}$ **31.** $2n + 7 = 31$; 12
33. $4 + 6n = 18$; $2\frac{1}{3}$

37. ⌊5⌋ ⌊+⌋ ⌊1⌋ ⌊2⌋ ⌊=⌋ ⌊×⌋ ⌊7⌋ ⌊=⌋; 119

Spiral Review
40. 59 **41.** -13 **42.** $-2\frac{1}{3}$ **43.** $31\frac{1}{4}$ **44.** 0.48 **45.** -88
46. 180 **47.** 1500 **48.** $1\frac{1}{2}$ **49.** < **50.** < **51.** >

Extra Skill Practice
1. No; The figure has been rotated or reflected.
3. No; The figure has been rotated or reflected.
5. $(x - 1, y + 5)$ **7.** The image of the rectangle will be 2 units to the left and 3 units above the original. **9.** No; There is only horizontal stretching. **11.** The sketch should be the same horizontal length and $\frac{1}{4}$ of the vertical length. **13.** 4 **15.** 2 **17.** 96 **19.** 135

Standardized Testing, Open-ended
The transformation is a horizontal stretch by a factor of 2 followed by a horizontal translation 2 units right, and a vertical squash by a factor of $\frac{3}{4}$.

Review and Assessment
1. 37.70 cm **2.** 25.13 ft **3.** 72.26 ft **4.** 1 **5.** $\frac{8}{5}$ **6.** $\frac{3}{4}$
7. $\frac{1}{9}$ **8.** $\frac{5}{18}$ **9.** $\frac{3}{4}$ **10.** $22\frac{1}{2}$ **11.** $1\frac{1}{3}$ **12.** $3\frac{3}{5}$ **13.** $12\frac{7}{15}$
14. $25\frac{5}{7}$ **15.** 2 **16.** 0.32, greater than, 0.288
17. 4, greater than, $3.\overline{5}$ **18.** 0.4, less than, 0.412
19. 4700, greater than, $4272.\overline{72}$ **20.** 0.3, less than, 0.3125 **21.** 10, greater than, 9.875 **22.** 2.8, greater than, 2.66 **23.** 100, less than, $120.\overline{6}$ **24.** 0.375
25. $0.8\overline{3}$ **26.** $0.\overline{2}$ **27.** 1.6 **28.** $\frac{3}{8}$ and $\frac{8}{5}$; $\frac{5}{6}$ and $\frac{2}{9}$
29. Yes; 20°; 40°; 60°; 80°; 100°; 120°; 140°; 160°; 180°; 200°; 220°; 240°; 260°; 280°; 300°; 320°; 340°
30. No; The distance from A to the line of symmetry is not the same as the distance from A' to the line of symmetry. **31.** -63 **32.** -7 **33.** 72 **34.** -6 **35.** 13
36. -26 **37.** -4 **38.** 420 **39.** 29.4 **40.** $\frac{15}{16}$ **41.** -4
42. a. $(x - 3, y - 1)$ **b.** Vertices are at $A'(-1, -2)$, $B'(1, 1)$, $C'(3, -2)$. **43. a.** I: The image will be twice as wide and half as high; II: The image will be twice as wide and twice as high; III: The image will be half as wide, but the same height. **b.** Vertices are: I: $A'\left(4, -\frac{1}{2}\right)$, $B'(8, 1)$,

$C'\left(12, -\frac{1}{2}\right)$; II: $A'(4, -2)$, $B'(8, 4)$, $C'(12, -2)$; III: $A'(1, -1)$, $B'(2, 2)$, $C'(3, -1)$; Only transformation II results in a similar triangle. **44.** 12 **45.** 12 **46.** 8

MODULE 5

Section 1, Practice and Application (p. 321)
1. 6.5 min/mi **3.** $5.50/lb **5.** 6¢/min **7.** 31.5
9. 4.8 mi/h **11. a.** 6, 60, 2400; 10 **b.** 40 h
13. a. 125 ft **c.** 125 ft; It is the same. **15. a.** 63 years
b. 28 years; 18 years and 25 years **c.** The median changes to 29. The mode is unaffected. **17. a.** 5 ages
b. 6 women **c.** From the histogram, we know only that the woman was between 55 and 59 years old.

Spiral Review
19. $8\frac{1}{4}$ **20.** 264 **21.** -48 **22.** about $2.00 **23.** about $7.50 **24.** about $2.00 **25.** $\frac{1}{3}$ **26.** $\frac{1}{5}$ **27.** $\frac{1}{2}$ **28.** $\frac{1}{5}$
29. $\frac{2}{5}$ **30.** $\frac{5}{6}$

Extra Skill Practice
1. $10.75/h **3.** 224 noodles/box **5.** 1.5 questions/min
7. greater than

Study Skills, Creating a Test
1. a. Sample Response: writing and simplifying ratios, rates, and proportions; interpreting and creating stem-and-leaf plots, frequency tables, and histograms; finding the mean, mode, median, and range of a set of data values

Section 2, Practice and Application (p. 337)
1. 20 lb **3.** 144 g **5.** 900 lb **7.** 4 **9.** 7 **11. a.** Yes
b. Ang simplified the left side of the proportion and then multiplied both sides by 5. **c.** Sample Response: $5 \times 4.8 \div 2$ **13. a.** about 90 stories
15. a–b.

c. Sample Response: about $400 **17.** C; The lowest data value, 12, and the highest data value, 63, are shown at the end of the whiskers in the stem-and-leaf plot in C.

Spiral Review
19. $7.25/h **20.** 9 min/mi **21.** $6.50/lb **22.** 5^2
23. 4^4 **24.** 3^5 **25.** 0.4 **26.** $0.\overline{3}$ **27.** 0.2

Extra Skill Practice

1. 18 **3.** 45

5.

7. about 3800 ft

9. about 8

Section 3, Practice and Application (p. 353)

1.

3. a. Sample Response: $\frac{1}{3}$ **b.** Sample Response: $33\frac{1}{3}$%

5. Sample Response: about 80% **7.** Sample Response: about 75% **9.** 33.3% **11.** 75% **13.** about 41%

15. a. about 175 million Americans **b.** about 83 million Americans **17.** 550 students; $\frac{68}{100} = \frac{374}{x}$ **19.** 40

21. 15.5 **23.** $16.00 **25. a.** Yes; The ratios Jo has set up are not equivalent. **b.** $\frac{34}{100} = \frac{x}{350}$; 119

Spiral Review

27. 9 **28.** 1 **29.** 10 **30.** 121 **31.** 43 **32.** 1 **33.** $\frac{5}{6}$
34. $\frac{2}{7}$ **35.** $\frac{1}{3}$

Extension

37. $504 **39. a.** $559.44 **b.** Answer to part (a) is greater.

Extra Skill Practice

1. about 55% **3.** about 22% **5.** 28% **7.** about 80%
9. 25% **11.** 66.7% **13.** 61.1% **15.** 70% **19.** 700
21. 10.8 **23.** 600

Standardized Testing, Performance Task

75; 6; 1	Sample conclusion:
59.3; 25.9; 14.8	Students liked the lunches
8; 13;16	better on Mon. through Wed.
25;12.5; 15; 62.5	than on Thurs. and Fri.
20; 10; 14; 70	

Section 4, Practice and Application (p. 368)

1. Holdsclaw: $\frac{6}{16}$, 0.375, 37.5%; Conklin: $\frac{5}{8}$, 0.625, 62.5%; Marciniak: $\frac{5}{13}$, 0.385, 38.5%; T. Johnson: $\frac{7}{10}$, 0.7, 70% **3.** 0.304 **5.** Kruk; Sample Response: Round the decimal forms of the ratios of *number of hits* to *times at bat* to the nearest ten-thousandth and compare the decimal numbers. **7.** 18% **9.** 10%
11. 62.5% **13.** 1.5 oz **17.** about 5 million
19. $\frac{3}{16}$ or 18.75% **21.** $\frac{3}{8}$ or 37.5%

23. a.

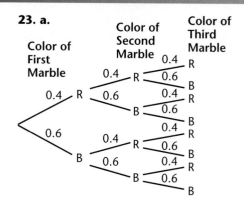

b. 0.064, 0.216, 0.144, 0.096, 0.288, 0.784

Spiral Review
26. 16 **27.** 75 **28.** 80 **29.** 50

Career Connection
31. a. 50 mg/mL **b.** $\frac{50\text{ mg}}{1\text{ mL}} = \frac{900\text{ mg}}{x\text{ mL}}$; 18 mL

Extra Skill Practice
1. $\frac{1}{3}$, 0.33$\overline{3}$, 33$\frac{1}{3}$% **3.** $\frac{4}{5}$, 0.8, 80% **5.** $\frac{2}{3}$, 0.66$\overline{7}$, 66$\frac{2}{3}$%
7. $\frac{9}{20}$, 0.45, 45% **9.** $\frac{7}{32}$, about 0.22, about 22%
11. 52% **13.** Sample Response: about 22%
15. Sample Response: about 75% **17.** about 19%
19. a. $\frac{2}{7}$ **b.** R = rain, N = no rain **c.** $\frac{25}{49} \approx$ 50%
d. $\frac{10}{49} \approx$ 20%

Standardized Testing, Multiple Choice
1. B, D **2.** D

Review and Assessment
1. about 8.6 min/mi **2.** $3.75/lb **3.** about 28.7 mi/gal
4. 15.625 km/L
5.

Areas of State Parks in 9 States		
0	9	7 | 5 represents 75,000 acres
1		
2	5	
3		
4	1 2 7	
5	0 7	
6	6	
7	5	

6. range: 66 thousand; mean: about 45.8 thousand; median: 47 thousand; mode: none **7.** I would have to add 27 more stems (8–34) and one more leaf. **8.** about 95 skaters **9.** No; Individual times are not indicated.
10. 4:00–4:59 and 8:00–8:59 **11.** 34 **12.** 13.5
13. 18 **14. a.** about 5.5 **b.** 2.5 mi **15. a.** about 150 m **b.** about 3.3 ft **16.** about 2:23; about 2:44 **17.** about 20% **18.** about 80% **19.** about 67% **20.** 40%
21. 50%, about 55%; $\frac{32}{58}$ **22.** 77.$\overline{7}$%, about 81%; $\frac{63}{78}$

23. 135.54 **24.** 1166.$\overline{6}$

25. a.

First marble   Second marble

$\frac{9}{25}$, 0.36, 36%

b. about 108 times

MODULE 6

Section 1, Practice and Application (p. 389)

1. $x < 8$

3. $5 < h \le 11$

5. If l = the hours of logged flight time, then $l \ge 500$.

7. from about 2.25 in. to about 8.5 in. **9.** If p = the percent of a hummingbird's body weight that is flight muscle, then $22 \le p \le 34$. **11.** Find which parts of the graphs overlap. **13.** square, rhombus, and rectangle; The kite has no pairs of opposite parallel sides and the trapezoid has only 1 such pair. A parallelogram has 2 pairs of opposite parallel sides. **17. a.** $\overline{EY}$; Neither of the others are segments perpendicular to $\overline{EF}$ and $\overline{HG}$.
b. 12 cm² **19.** $\frac{2}{5}$ **21.** $\frac{1}{2}$ **23.** 60 m² **25.** Board B; The probability of landing in the shaded area is greater for Board B (about 57%), than for Board A (about 42%) or Board C (50%).

Spiral Review
27. about 50% **28.** about $33\frac{1}{3}$% **29.** about 25%
30. about 20% **31.** $2 \cdot 2 \cdot 3$ **32.** $5 \cdot 5$
33. $2 \cdot 2 \cdot 2 \cdot 2 \cdot 3$ **34.** $2 \cdot 2 \cdot 5 \cdot 5$ **35.** 4 **36.** 25
37. 81 **38.** 100

Extra Skill Practice
1. $a > 8$

3. $4 < r < 7$

5. $6 < t \le 13$

7. No; The quadrilateral has only 1 pair of opposite parallel sides and a parallelogram has 2 such pairs.
9. Yes **11.** concave **13.** concave **15.** $\frac{1}{3}$, or $33\frac{1}{3}$%
17. $\frac{5}{9}$, or $55\frac{5}{9}$%

Section 2, Practice and Application (p. 405)
1. 9 ft × 9 ft **3.** −15 **5.** 1 and 2 **7.** about 14.3
9. about 23.4 **11. a.** 6 cm², 10 cm², 14 cm², 18 cm²
b. 42 cm²; Each time a cube is added, one face is lost and 5 are added for a total increase in area of 4 cm². Surface area = $6 + 4n$, where n is the number of added cubes.
13. a. Sample Response:

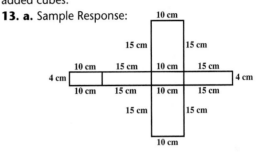

b. 150 cm², 150 cm², 40 cm², 40 cm², 60 cm², 60 cm²
c. 500 cm² **17.** 3660.25π m²; Possible answers: 11,493.19 m² or 11,499.02 m² **19.** about 8.46 ft
21. about 2.31 yd

Spiral Review
24. $t > 11$ **25.** $p \le 6$ **26.** 0.125 **27.** 0.400 **28.** about 0.609 **29.** about 0.677 **30.** $\frac{1}{2}$ **31.** $\frac{1}{4}$ **32.** $\frac{3}{5}$ **33.** $\frac{3}{8}$

Extra Skill Practice
1. 8 **3.** 7 **5.** about 8.9 **7.** about 5.5
9. a hexagonal prism
11. a. Sample Response:

b. 152 cm² **13.** 5.76π cm²; Possible answers: 18.09 cm² or 18.10 cm²

Standardized Testing, Multiple Choice
1. B **2.** C

Section 3, Practice and Application (p. 418)
1. congruent and similar ; $ABCD \cong PSRQ$ **3.** similar; $FGHKL \sim EABCD$ or $FGHKL \sim AEDCB$ **5.** about 70.8 m
7. about 64.8 m **9.** 180 mm **11.** acute **13.** acute
15. obtuse **17.** 120°, 23°, 127° **19.** 18 ft, 6 ft

22. 920 in.^{2} **23.** 17.18 cm^2 **24.** $\frac{7}{8}$ **25.** 1 **26.** 3
27. 108° **28.** 90° **29.** 68° **30.** 25°

Career Connection
31. a. about 87 ft 5 in. **b.** about 39 ft 7 in. high and
54 ft 5 in. across

Extra Skill Practice
1. $\overline{VT}, \overline{UV}$ **3.** 5 in., 2 in. **5.** acute **7.** obtuse **9.** right
11. 125°, 55°, 65°

Standardized Testing, Free Response
1. No; The ratios of corresponding sides may not be
equal. For example, two house-shaped pentagons could
have corresponding angles congruent, but one could
have all side lengths equal and one could have vertical
sides twice as long as the other sides. **2.** No; The measures of corresponding angles may not be equal. For
example, a house-shaped pentagon and a regular pentagon could have congruent sides but would have different angle measures.

Section 4, Practice and Application (p. 430)
1. ∠2, ∠3, ∠6, ∠7 **3.** ∠2 and ∠7, ∠3 and ∠6 **5.** ∠1
and ∠3, ∠2 and ∠4, ∠5 and ∠7, ∠6 and ∠8 **7.** $m\angle 6 =$
$m\angle 3 = m\angle 8 = 55°$, $m\angle 2 = m\angle 5 = m\angle 4 = m\angle 7 = 125°$

9. a. Sample Response: Since they form a straight angle,
$m\angle 4 + m\angle 5 = 180°$. Since ∠3 and ∠5 are corresponding
angles formed by 2 parallel lines and a transversal, $m\angle 3$
$= m\angle 5$. Substituting $m\angle 3$ for $m\angle 5$ in the first equation,
$m\angle 4 + m\angle 3 = 180°$. So, ∠3 and ∠4 are supplementary.
b. ∠1 and ∠2, ∠1 and ∠3, ∠1 and ∠5, ∠2 and ∠4, ∠2
and ∠6, ∠3 and ∠6, ∠4 and ∠5, ∠5 and ∠6 **c.** 360°
11. True; ∠7 and the 101° angle have the same measure since they are alternate interior angles, and ∠7 and
∠8 are supplementary angles, so $m\angle 8 = 180° - 101° =$
79°. **13.** False; ∠4 and the 105° angle are supplementary angles, so $m\angle 4 = 75°$. **15.** False; ∠10 and the 75°
angle are vertical angles, so $m\angle 10 = 75°$. ∠11 and ∠12
are supplementary and $m\angle 12 = 101°$ since it is a corresponding angle to a 101° angle. Therefore, $m\angle 11 =$
180° − 101° = 79° and $m\angle 10 \neq m\angle 11$. **17.** 35°
19. 95°, obtuse **21.** 55°, acute

Spiral Review
24. right **25.** obtuse **26.** acute **27.** $\frac{3}{2}$ **28.** 23 **29.** 30
30. 27 cm^3 **31.** 64 in.^{3} **32.** 1 ft^3 **29.** 1000 cm^3

Extension
35.

Polygon	Name of polygon	Number of sides	Number of triangles formed by the diagonals from 1 vertex	Sum of the measures of the angles
	triangle	3	1	180°
	quadrilateral	4	2	360°
	pentagon	5	3	540°
	hexagon	6	4	720°
	heptagon	7	5	900°
	octagon	8	6	1080°

Extra Skill Practice

1. ∠3, ∠4, ∠5, ∠6 **3.** ∠3 and ∠6, ∠4 and ∠5
5. Possible answers: ∠1 and ∠4, ∠2 and ∠3, ∠5 and
∠8, ∠6 and ∠7 **7.** 113° **9.** 67° **11.** 113° **13.** 52°;
acute **15.** 45°; right

Standardized Testing, Performance Task

Since $\overleftrightarrow{AF}$ and $\overleftrightarrow{BD}$ are transversals that intersect parallel
lines $\overleftrightarrow{AB}$ and $\overleftrightarrow{DF}$, ∠1 and ∠6 are alternate interior angles
and are congruent and ∠2 and ∠5 are alternate interior
angles and are congruent. ∠3 and ∠4 are vertical angles
and are also congruent.

Section 5, Practice and Application (p. 446)

1. 121.5 cm³ **3.** 180 cm³ **5.** 5 cm **7.** 91,000 **9.** 7.5
11. 2.7 **13.** 0.172 **17. a.** 7,953,628,000 cm³
b. 7,953,628 L **c.** 7,953,628 kg **19. a.** 1250 L
b. 1250 kg **21.** 3890 mi **23.** Los Angeles–Chicago–
New York

Spiral Review

26. 113° **27.** 19° **28.** 105° **29.** by the endpoint
of the right-hand whisker in the upper box plot
30. toothed whales: about 40,000 kg; baleen whales:
about 125,000 kg **31.** 19.625 cm² **32.** 50.24 in.²
33. 314 m² **34.** about 5.98 cm²

Extension

Sample responses **37.** **39.**
are given.

Extra Skill Practice

1. 5.2 in.³ **3.** 118.125 m³ **5.** 30 m³ **7.** 12,000 **9.** 47
11. 0.077 **13.** 1995 km

Review and Assessment

1. If s = salary in dollars, then $7514 \le s \le 11{,}627$.
2. If t = the hours worked each month, then $80 \le t < 85$.
3. 22 ft² **4.** $\frac{12}{22}$, or $\frac{6}{11}$ **5.** 11 **6.** 4.5 **7.** 13.2
8. Sample Response:
9. 79 cm²

10. 25π cm²; 78.5 cm² **11.** 100π mm²; 314 mm²
12. 3.0625π ft²; about 9.6 ft² **13. a.** 1 mm : 2 ft
b. about 64 ft **14.** $CD = 3.5$ cm, $EF = 2.4$ cm, $FG =$
5.2 cm; $m\angle ABC = 120°$, $m\angle FEH = 120°$, $m\angle EHG = 105°$,
$m\angle GFE = 67°$ **15.** $m\angle 1 = m\angle 3 = m\angle 7 = 127°$, $m\angle 2 =$
$m\angle 5 = m\angle 6 = m\angle 4 = 53°$ **16.** 90°, right **17.** 95°,
obtuse **18.** 85°, acute **19.** 3000 cm³ **20.** 3000 mL; 3 L
21. 2.345 **22.** 750 **23.** 0.004 **24.** Seattle, Walla Walla,
Boise **25.** 448 mi **26.** Portland-Walla Walla-Spokane

MODULE 7

Section 1, Practice and Application (p. 465)

1. 127.23 ft³ **3.** 69.12 cm³ **5.** 37.7 **7.** 16
9. a.

b	C
75	10.2
100	13.6
150	20.4
200	27.2

b.

**Calories Burned During
10 min of Studying**

c. 0.136

11. a. Sample Response: a horizontal scale from
75–200 lb for both graphs; vertical scales of 5–14 Cal
for sleeping, and 14–38 Cal for preparing food.
b. Sample Responses:

**Calories Burned During
10 min of Sleeping**

**Calories Burned During
10 min of Preparing Food**

13. $\frac{3}{2}$, or 1.5 **15.** 2 **17.** 2 **19.** 1 **21. a.** height
b. The heights of the graphs are in the same proportion
as the populations, but the areas are not.

c. Sample Response:

The Population of People, Cats, and Dogs in the United States (millions)

Spiral Review
23. 48 cm^3 **24.** 216 in.^{3} **25.** 2187 cm^3 **26.** $\frac{4}{8}$, or $\frac{1}{2}$
27. $\frac{2}{9}$ **28.** about 50 times, about 22 times **29.** 4%
30. 16% **31.** 65% **32.** 24%

Extension
33. a. 0, –2, undefined **b.** Since the slope = $\frac{rise}{run} = \frac{3}{0}$ and
division by 0 is undefined, the slope is undefined.
c. A line with a negative slope slants downward from left
to right, while one with a positive slope slants upward
from left to right.

Extra Skill Practice
1. 56.5 **3.** 1 **5.** $\frac{3}{4}$, or 0.75 **7.** 2 **9.** Yes; Different scales
are used on the vertical axes. Sample Response:

Calories Used in Reading for 10 min

Calories Used in Dancing for 10 min

Study Skills, Using Graphic Organizers
1. a. If the starting number is not divisible by 2, you add
1 to make it an even number. **b.** Since 9 is not divisible
by 2, you add 1 to generate 10.

Section 2, Practice and Application (p. 480)
1. 180% **3.** 12.5% **5.** 135% **7.** 200%
9. 162 beats per min **11.** 130, 25, 60, 90; 93%, 45%,
55%, 90% **13.** $33\frac{1}{3}$% decrease **15.** 275% increase
17. 60% decrease **19.** B; Since there are no parentheses
in A, the original amount, rather than the change in the

original amount, is divided by the original amount; The
expression in C has nothing to do with percent of
change. **21. a.** $42.49 **b.** 24%

Spiral Review
25. 1 **26.** $\frac{1}{2}$, or 0.5 **27.** $\frac{3}{2}$, or 1.5 **28.** $\frac{1}{4}$, or 0.25 **29.** $\frac{5}{8}$
30. $1\frac{13}{15}$ **31.** $5\frac{23}{24}$ **32.** Possible Answers: Let r = the
resting heart rate in beats per minute.
Canary: $500 \le r \le 800$

Mouse: $300 \le r \le 500$

Chicken: $300 \le r \le 350$

Cat: $120 \le r \le 140$

Dog: $70 \le r \le 120$

Person: $60 \le r \le 80$

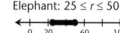

Lion: $40 \le r \le 50$ Elephant: $25 \le r \le 50$

Extra Skill Practice
1. 500% **3.** 300% **5.** 187.5% **7.** 100% **9.** $77.\overline{7}$%
increase **11.** 200% increase **13.** 102 beats/min
15. about a 16% decrease **17.** 20%; increase

Standardized Testing, Open-ended
Sample Response: If the base radii of the first and second
cylinders are 5 cm and 10 cm respectively, and the
height of both cylinders is 10 cm, then the percent
increase in the volume is $\frac{\text{Vol. of cyl. 2 – Vol. of cyl. 1}}{\text{Vol. of cyl. 1}} \cdot 100 =$
$\frac{1000\pi - 250\pi}{250\pi} \cdot 100 = 300\%$

Section 3, Practice and Application (p. 494)
1. 32 **3.** 8 **5.** 32 **7.** 8 to 10 oz **9. a.** 18 Calories
b. 30% **c.** No; Exactly 30%, not less than 30% of the
Calories come from fat. **11. a.** 52.5 mg **b.** Let s = the
mg of sodium in 12 fl oz. Then, $s < 52.5$.
13. a. Let s = the mg of sodium in 8 fl oz. Then,
$35 < s < 140$. **b.** No, 16 fl oz has to contain less than
280 mg; No, 15.5 oz has to contain less than 271 mg;
Yes, 20 fl oz has to contain less than 350 mg and more
than 87.5 mg. **15.** $x \ge 8$ **17.** $x < 28$ **19.** $x \le 1$

Spiral Review

23. 250% **24.** 300% **25.** 195.$\overline{45}$% **26.** 120% **27.** 4
28. 6 **29.** 10 **30.** 4.2 **31.** 12.8 **32.** 124

Extension

33. a. They are within the right whisker. **b.** They have more sugar than at least 75% of the other candy bars.

Extra Skill Practice

1. 6 **3.** 3 **5.** 32 **7.** $x \le 22$ **9.** $x > -5$ **11.** $x \ge 1\frac{2}{5}$

13.

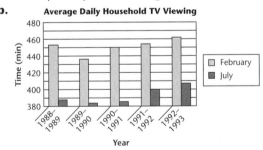

Protein per Serving
in 7 Foods (g)

Standardized Testing, Multiple Choice

1. B **2.** D

Section 4, Practice and Application (p. 507)

1. about 50% **3.** about 10% **5.** 112° **7.** 32° **9.** 18°
11. C; Graph C is the only graph that shows a section greater than $\frac{1}{2}$ the circle to represent 60% and that has other fractional parts that correspond to the data.
13. Sample Response: The median number of days off is highest for plant managers. About 25% of the bus drivers, 75% of the auto mechanics, and 50% of the secretaries have 20 or fewer days off. **15.** Sample Response: No; The greatest percent appears to occupy the least area.

Spiral Review

17. 3 **18.** $\frac{3}{8}$ **19.** $\frac{3}{16}$ **20.** 64 **21.** $-3\frac{1}{2}$ **22.** -6.15
23. -0.5 **24.** 64 yd³ **25.** 6 cm² **26.** 900 ft²

Extra Skill Practice

1. 11° **3.** 29° **5.** 40° **7.** 68°
9. a. Sample Response: a histogram
b.

Average Daily Household TV Viewing

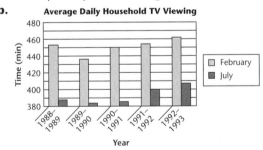

Year

c. Sample Response: Over the years, the trends for February and July were the same. The time spent watching TV in February was greater than that in July for all years. The time spent watching TV in February and in July declined in 1989–1990.

Standardized Testing, Performance Task

1. Sample responses are given. **a:** How different categories of values compare; data values are represented by height of bars in the graph. **b:** Extreme values, median, how the data values cluster; stem values

are listed vertically and leaves are listed horizontally beside the corresponding stem. **c:** The percent of the total that the data value represents; the values are drawn as areas in a circle. **d:** The minimum, lower quartile, median, upper quartile, maximum, any extreme values. The five values are calculated from the data and plotted above a number line. Then the box and whiskers are drawn. **e:** Specific data values and how they increase or decrease from one to the next; Data points are plotted on a two-dimensional grid. **f:** How different categories of values compare; Data intervals are made on the horizontal axis and the corresponding data values are shown as the heights of the bars. **2.** Sample responses are given. **a:** Yes; different vertical scales could be used and the bars could be made different widths. **b:** Yes; the stems chosen could be of various intervals. **c:** No. **d:** No. **e:** Yes; different horizontal and vertical scales could be used to display the data. **f:** Yes; different horizontal and vertical scales could be used and the bars could be made different widths.

Section 5, Practice and Application (p. 519)

1. B, F **3.** C, D **5.** rhombus, square **7.** 63 m²
9. 12 in.² **11.** 18 in.² **13.** $20\frac{9}{16}$, or 20.5625 in.²
15. 27.5 cm² **17.** 5 cm

Spiral Review

21. 22° **22.** 32° **23.** 47° **24.** 65° **25.** 76° **26.** 119°
27. $2x$ **28.** $t - 20$ **29.**

1st Toss   2nd Toss

H
H
T
H
T
T

4 outcomes

Extra Skill Practice

1. C, E **3.** B **5.** 468 in.² **7.** 21 ft **9.** 18 m

Standardized Testing, Free Response

area of square = 4 ft²; area of small △ = 1 ft²
area of large △ = 2 ft²; area of trapezoid = 7 ft²

Review and Assessment

1. 314 in.³ **2.** 461.58 cm³ **3.** 42.39 cm³ **4.** $\frac{1}{2}$ **5.** 1
6. 4 **7.** 0 **8.** Sample Response: The values appear to increase rapidly with the greatest value about twice the least value. **9.** about 175 million, about 200 million, about 225 million, about 250 million **10.** No.
11. Eliminate the gap in the vertical scale. **12.** 160%
13. 150% **14.** 875% **15.** 488% **16.** about an 11.4% decrease **17.** $33\frac{1}{3}$% increase **18.** \$165 **19.** 10 **20.** $1\frac{3}{4}$
21. 64 **22.** $3m + 5n \le 100$ **23.** lower extreme: about 1, lower quartile: about 9, median: about 15, upper quartile: about 31, upper extreme: about 80

24.

School enrollments

9–12 22.2%
college 20.2%
pre-school 8.4%
1–8 49.3%

25. a histogram; the number of people with a given age can be read from the height of the bars. You wouldn't use a stem-and-leaf plot because there are over 500 data points. A box-and-whisker plot does not show individual data points. **26.** Both pairs of opposite sides are congruent; Both pairs of opposite angles are congruent. **27.** 84 mm^2 **28.** 22.5 m^2 **29.** 34 ft^2

MODULE 8

Section 1, Practice and Application (p. 535)
1. azalea-ivy, azalea-fern, azalea-cactus, ivy-azalea, ivy-fern, ivy-cactus, fern-azalea, fern-ivy, fern-cactus, cactus-azalea, cactus-ivy, cactus-fern
3. band–BS–GS–FD, band–BS–FD–GS, band–GS–BS–FD, band–GS–FD–BS, band–FD–BS–GS, band–FD–GS–BS, BS–band–GS–FD, BS–band–FD–GS, BS–GS–band–FD, BS–GS–FD–band, BS–FD–band–GS, BS–FD–GS–band, GS–band–BS–FD, GS–band–FD–BS, GS–BS–band–FD, GS–BS–FD–band, GS–FD–band–BS, GS–FD–BS–band, FD–band–BS–GS, FD–band–GS–BS, FD–BS–band–GS, FD–BS–GS–band, FD–GS–band–BS, FD–GS–BS–band
5. a. 640; 604; 460; 406; 064; 046 **b.** 4 **7.** 24 **9.** 336
11. a.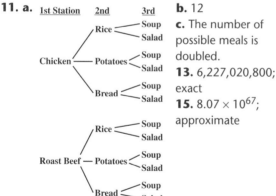

1st Station	2nd	3rd

Chicken — Rice — Soup / Salad; Potatoes — Soup / Salad; Bread — Soup / Salad
Roast Beef — Rice — Soup / Salad; Potatoes — Soup / Salad; Bread — Soup / Salad

b. 12 **c.** The number of possible meals is doubled. **13.** 6,227,020,800; exact **15.** 8.07×10^{67}; approximate

Spiral Review
19. 28 in.^{2} **20.** 36 cm^2 **21.** –2 **22.** 8 **23.** 5 **24.** 2 **25.** 4 **26.** 2 **27.** 166 ft^2 **28.** 89.5 m^2 **29.** $92\frac{1}{2}$ yd^2 **30.** 504 mm^2

Career Connection
31. 6; rotate–color/bw–size, rotate–size–color/bw, color/bw–rotate–size, color/bw–size–rotate, size–rotate–color/bw, size–color/bw–rotate

Extra Skill Practice
1. Alma, Mei, Dyani, Luz; Alma, Mei, Luz, Dyani; Alma, Dyani, Mei, Luz; Alma, Dyani, Luz, Mei; Alma, Luz, Mei, Dyani; Alma, Luz, Dyani, Mei; Mei, Alma, Dyani, Luz; Mei, Alma, Luz, Dyani; Mei, Dyani, Alma, Luz; Mei, Dyani, Luz, Alma; Mei, Luz, Alma, Dyani; Mei, Luz, Dyani, Alma; Dyani, Alma, Mei, Luz; Dyani, Alma, Luz, Mei; Dyani, Mei, Alma, Luz; Dyani, Mei, Luz, Alma; Dyani, Luz, Alma, Mei; Dyani, Luz, Mei, Alma; Luz, Alma, Mei, Dyani; Luz, Alma, Dyani, Mei; Luz, Mei, Alma, Dyani; Luz, Mei, Dyani, Alma; Luz, Dyani, Alma, Mei; Luz, Dyani, Mei, Alma **3. a.** Answers will vary; 24 numbers **b.** 10,000 phone numbers **5.** 116,280

Section 2, Practice and Application (p. 548)
1. d. Yes, No; The same number of cubes is used; the number of exposed cube faces is not the same.
3. Sample Response:

1	2	2
3		
1		

5. V = 1953.125 m^3; SA = 937.5 m^2
7. ABCD **9.** E

11. about 6 cm^3; 6.3 cm^3
13. Yes; triangular pyramid
15. Yes; hexagonal pyramid

Spiral Review
18. 5040 **19.** 39,916,800 **20.** can; scalene **21.** can; isosceles **22.** cannot **23.** **24.**
25.

Extension
27. Sample Response:

Extra Skill Practice
1. B, D **3.** A, G **5.** 112 in.^{3} **7.** 106.7 mm^3

Standardized Testing, Open-ended
1–3. Sample Responses are given.
1. **2.** **3.** 8 cm^3; 30 cm^2

right view   left view   front view   base plan

| 2 | 1 |
| 4 | 1 |

Section 3, Practice and Application (p. 559)
1. EAT, ETA, AET, ATE, TEA, TAE **3.** NOON, ONON, OONN, ONNO, NNOO, NONO **5.** DEEDED, DEEDDE, DEDEDE, DEDEED, DEDDEE, DEEEDD, DDEEED, DDEEDE, DDEDEE, DDDEEE, EDEDED, EDEDDE, EDEEDD, EDDEED, EDDEDE, EDDDEE, EEDDDE, EEDEDD, EEDDED, EEEDDD
9. ; 10 **11.** combination
13. a. apple-banana-kiwi-orange; apple-banana-kiwi-pear; apple-banana-orange-pear; apple-kiwi-orange-pear; banana-kiwi-orange-pear

b. 3 out of five: apple-banana-kiwi, apple-banana-orange, apple-banana-pear, apple-kiwi-orange, apple-kiwi-pear, apple-orange-pear, banana-kiwi-orange, banana-kiwi-pear, banana-orange-pear, kiwi-orange-pear; 2 out of five: apple-banana, apple-kiwi, apple-orange, apple-pear, banana-kiwi, banana-orange, banana-pear, kiwi-orange, kiwi-pear, orange-pear; 1 out of five: apple, banana, kiwi, orange, pear **15. a.** 28 **b.** 56 **c.** b, a; Order is important; Order is not important.

Spiral Review
17. 125 cm³ **18.** 100 ft³ **19.** $2\frac{1}{6}$ **20.** $4\frac{41}{60}$ **21.** $1\frac{9}{14}$
22. $17\frac{7}{20}$ **23.** 130°

Extra Skill Practice
1. ERR, RER, RRE **3.** DADDY, DADYD, DAYDD, DYDAD, DYDDA, DYADD, DDAYD, DDADY, DDYAD, DDYDA, DDDAY, DDDYA, ADDDY, ADYDD, ADDYD, AYDDD, YADDD, YDADD, YDDAD, YDDDA **5. a.** 6 **b.** 3 **c.** 1
7. combination **9.** Sue–Flora and Hiroko–Yuki, Sue–Hiroko and Flora–Yuki, Sue–Yuki and Flora–Hiroko

Standardized Testing, Free Response
1. permutation; Order is important. **2.** neither
3. combination; Order is not important.

Section 4, Practice and Application (p.572)
7. about 3.7 in.³ **9.** 689,007.0 cm³ **11.** Sample
Response: $\dfrac{\text{volume of cone}}{\text{volume of cylinder}} = \dfrac{\text{volume of pyramid}}{\text{volume of prism}}$

Spiral Review
14. permutation **15.** combination
16. a. **b.** Sample Response:
$(x + 2, y - 1)$

Extension
17. a. triangles, squares, hexagons **b.** Answers will vary.

Extra Skill Practice
5. B and D **7.** 1674.7 mm³

1. D **2.** B

Review and Assessment
1. band–orchestra, orchestra–band
2. Mono Lake–Joshua Tree–Sequoia, Mono Lake–Sequoia–Joshua Tree, Joshua Tree–Mono Lake–Sequoia, Joshua Tree–Sequoia–Mono Lake, Sequoia–Joshua Tree–Mono Lake, Sequoia–Mono Lake–Joshua Tree **3.** Spanish–art–social studies, Spanish–social studies–art, social studies–art–Spanish, social studies–Spanish–art, art–Spanish–social studies, art–social studies–Spanish **4.** beige-pink, beige-yellow, beige-green, pink-beige, pink-yellow, pink-green, yellow-beige, yellow-pink, yellow-green, green-beige, green-pink, green-yellow **5.** 120 **6.** 40,320 **7.** 720
8. 2450 **9.**

front view / right-side view

10. 10 cubic units
11. 42 square units
12. The volumes are the same; the surface area is less because fewer faces are exposed. **13.** 25 cm³
14. 56 ft³ **15.** 160 m³ **16.** E-S, S-E **17.** N–N–E–E, E–E–N–N, N-E-N-E, E–N–E–N, N-E-E-N, E-N-N-E
18. W-W-W-S, W-W-S-W, W–S–W–W, S-W-W-W
19. BOOT, BOTO, BTOO, TBOO, TOBO, TOOB, OOTB, OOBT, OTBO, OBTO, OTOB, OBOT **20.** BELLE, BEELL, BELEL, BLLEE, BLELE, BLEEL, LLEBE, LLBEE, LLEEB, LEBEL, LEBLE, LELBE, LELEB, LEEBL, LEELB, LBLEE, LBEEL, LBELE, ELELB, ELEBL, ELBEL, ELLEB, ELLBE, ELBLE, EBELL, EBLEL, EBLLE, EELLB, EELBL, EEBLL **21.** NANNY, NANYN, NAYNN, NYANN, NYNAN, NYNNA, NNANY, NNAYN, NNYAN, NNYNA, NNNAY, NNNYA, ANNNY, AYNNN, ANYNN, ANNYN, YANNN, YNANN, YNNAN, YNNNA
22. a. 10 groups **b.** 10 groups **c.** They are the same; To choose a group of 2 dogs from the 5 dogs, you can either choose the 2 that are in the group or you can choose the 2 that are not. So, the number of groups of 2 dogs is the same as the number of possible groups of 3 dogs. **d.** Combination; Order is not significant.
23. Sample Response: Since the sum of the measures of the angles of a trapezoid is 360°, the angles will fill the space around a vertex without gaps or overlaps.
24. 376.8 m³ **25.** 4.5 cm³ **26.** 706.5 in.³

TOOLBOX ANSWERS

NUMBERS AND OPERATIONS

Adding and Subtracting Decimals
1. 21.2 **2.** 22.9 **3.** 14 **4.** 37.46 **5.** 5.4 **6.** 2.7 **7.** 3.25
8. 2.15 **9.** 4.12 **10.** 4.68 **11.** 3.9 **12.** 41.2 **13.** 8.87
14. 9.65 **15.** 24.55 **16.** 8.72 **17.** 25 **18.** 75.5 **19.** 66

Divisibility by 2, 5, and 10
1. 2 **2.** 2 **3.** 5 **4.** none **5.** 5 **6.** 2, 5, 10 **7.** 2 **8.** none
9. 2, 5, 10 **10.** 5

Using Estimation
1–30. Answers may vary. Sample responses are given.
1. about 900 **2.** about 100 **3.** about 27 **4.** about 40
5. about 700 **6.** about 20 **7.** about 100
8. about 12,000 **9.** about 15 **10.** about 47,000
11. about 9,600 **12.** about 21,000 **13.** about $19
14. about 900 **15.** about 130 **16.** about 8.4
17. about 20,000 **18.** about 300 **19.** about 16,000
20. about 1300 **21.** about 59 **22.** about 7000
23. about 1400 **24.** about 1250 **25.** about 70
26. about 20 **27.** about 10,000 **28.** about 30
29. about 420,000 **30.** about 20

Finding a Fraction
1. $\frac{7}{8}$ **2.** $\frac{3}{4}$ **3.** $\frac{3}{5}$ **4.** $\frac{4}{9}$ **5.** 2 **6.** 5 **7.** 4 **8.** 12 **9.** 12
10. 15 **11.** 14 **12.** 21 **13.** 35 **14.** 35 **15.** 75 **16.** 110

Finding Equivalent Fractions
1. 2 **2.** 24 **3.** 12 **4.** 4 **5.** 4 **6.** 5 **7.** 21 **8.** 48
9–16. Answers will vary. Sample responses are given.
9. $\frac{2}{6}, \frac{3}{9}, \frac{4}{12}$ **10.** $\frac{6}{8}, \frac{9}{12}, \frac{12}{16}$ **11.** $\frac{6}{30}, \frac{3}{15}, \frac{4}{20}$ **12.** $\frac{9}{27}, \frac{3}{9}, \frac{1}{3}$
13. $\frac{7}{28}, \frac{1}{4}, \frac{2}{8}$ **14.** $\frac{30}{75}, \frac{6}{15}, \frac{12}{30}$ **15.** $\frac{40}{48}, \frac{20}{24}, \frac{10}{12}$ **16.** $\frac{4}{7}, \frac{8}{14}, \frac{12}{21}$

Comparing Fractions
1. < **2.** < **3.** < **4.** = **5.** > **6.** < **7.** < **8.** = **9.** > **10.** =
11. = **12.** <

Adding and Subtracting Fractions
1. $\frac{7}{10}$ **2.** $\frac{3}{5}$ **3.** $\frac{6}{7}$ **4.** $\frac{4}{9}$ **5.** $\frac{4}{15}$ **6.** $\frac{4}{11}$ **7.** $\frac{9}{14}$ **8.** $\frac{9}{10}$ **9.** $\frac{11}{12}$
10. $6\frac{2}{3}$ **11.** $3\frac{5}{7}$ **12.** $3\frac{1}{5}$ **13.** $11\frac{7}{9}$ **14.** $15\frac{9}{10}$ **15.** $\frac{5}{12}$

Modeling Percent
1. 67% **2.** 83% **3.** 6% **4.** 11% **5.** 25% **6.** 72%

7. **8.**

9. **10.**

11. **12.**

13. **14.**

Modeling Integers
1. 3 **2.** –3 **3.** 0 **4.** –4 **5.** 0 **6.** 5 **7.** 2 **8.** –2 **9.** 1
10. 0 **11.** –3 **12.** 0 **13.** 2 **14.** 0 **15.** –5 **16.** –4
17. –2 **18.** –2 **19.** 2 **20.** –2 **21.** 0 **22.** 2 **23.** –8
24. –6 **25.** 5 **26.** 7 **27.** 3 **28.** 12 **29.** 3 **30.** –6 **31.** 3
32. 1 **33.** –1 **34.** 5 **35.** 0 **36.** –6

GEOMETRY AND MEASUREMENT

Perimeter and Using a Ruler
1. 32 m **2.** 72 in. **3.** 52 cm **4.** about $2\frac{7}{16}$ in.
5. about $\frac{15}{16}$ in. **6.** about $2\frac{13}{16}$ in. **7.** about $3\frac{3}{16}$ in.
8. about $3\frac{3}{4}$ in.

Converting Measurements
1. 252 **2.** $5\frac{3}{16}$ **3.** 150 **4.** 3 **5.** 10,560 **6.** $2\frac{5}{36}$ **7.** 48
8. 3 **9.** $10\frac{11}{16}$ **10.** 180 **11.** 8,000 **12.** 18 **13.** 13
14. $9\frac{1}{3}$ **15.** 17,600 **16.** 126 **17.** 16,060 **18.** 365
19. 46,145 **20.** 2; 3 **21.** 1; 720 **22.** 2; 3 **23.** 2; 500

24. 5; 5 **25.** 33; 1

Perimeter and Area of a Rectangle

1. $P = 26$ in.; $A = 40$ in.^{2} **2.** $P = 24$ ft; $A = 36$ ft^2
3. $P = 32$ yd; $A = 48$ yd^2 **4.** $P = 48$ ft; $A = 128$ ft^2
5. $P = 28$ in.; $A = 49$ in.^{2} **6.** $P = 26$ ft; $A = 36$ ft^2

DATA ANALYSIS AND DISPLAYS

Making a Bar Graph

1.

2.

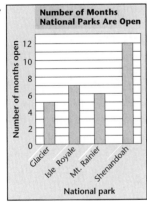

Making a Line Graph

1.

2.

Finding the Mean

1. 7 **2.** 28 **3.** 122

TEST-TAKING SKILLS SELECTED ANSWERS

Building Test-Taking Skills (p. 604)
1. Sample Response: Width is not measured in square units. **3.** Sample Response: 60 is greater than every number in the data set, so it cannot be the mean.

Practicing Test-Taking Skills (p. 605)
1. D **3.** D **5.** C **7.** A

Building Test-Taking Skills (p. 607)
1. No credit; the answer is incorrect, nothing is explained and the incorrect operations were performed. **3.** Partial credit; the solution is correct, but the explanation is mixed up as to the order of the depths of the submarine.

Practicing Test-Taking Skills (p. 608)
1. 21 acts; $80 \div (2\frac{1}{2} + 1\frac{1}{4}) = 80 \div 3\frac{3}{4} = 80 \cdot \frac{4}{15} = \frac{64}{3} = 21\frac{1}{3}$ **3.** the girls' team; You need to find the fraction of games that each team won. For each team, divide the number of games won by the total number of games played. Girls' team: $6 \div (6 + 4) = \frac{6}{10} = \frac{3}{5}$. Boys' team: $7 \div (7 + 5) = \frac{7}{12}$; $\frac{3}{5} = \frac{3 \cdot 12}{5 \cdot 12} = \frac{36}{60}$, $\frac{7 \cdot 5}{12 \cdot 5} = \frac{35}{60}$, so $\frac{3}{5} > \frac{7}{12}$.
5. 3 volunteers; $\frac{1}{3}$ of 18 volunteers, or 6, painted. That leaves $18 - 6 = 12$ volunteers. $\frac{3}{4}$ of 12 volunteers, or 9, raked leaves. That leaves $12 - 9 = 3$ volunteers who served lunch. **7.** Let c = the total cost. $c = 4x + 2.25$; 5 games; Substitute 22.25 for c. $22.25 = 4x + 2.25$, $22.25 - 2.25 = 4x$, $20 = 4x$, and $x = 5$. Hanna bowled 5 games. **9.** Yes; the sum of the lengths of the two shortest segments, 3.9 cm, is greater than the length of the longest segment, 3.5 cm.

Building Test-Taking Skills (p. 610)
1. B **3.** B

Practicing Test-Taking Skills (p. 611)
1. D **3.** B **5.** C **7.** D

Building Test-Taking Skills (p. 613)
1. Partial credit; the calculations for the number of cans that can be packed flat in the box are correct, but no reasoning is given. The greatest number of cans that can be packed is incorrect; the second orientation was not considered. To earn full credit, explain the reasoning behind the calculations. Do the calculations for the number of cans that can be packed on their sides, which makes packing 54 cans possible.

Practicing Test-Taking Skills (p. 614)
1. the large tub of popcorn; volume of box = $6 \cdot 3 \cdot 8 = 144$ in.^{3}; price per cubic inch of popcorn = $3.75 \div 144 \approx$ \$.026; volume of tub = $\pi(4)^2(5) \approx 251$ in.^{3}; price per cubic inch of popcorn = $5.25 \div 251 \approx$ \$.021; Since \$.021 < \$.026, the large tub of popcorn is the better buy. **3.** slippers; Find the percent of change for each item. T-shirts: $(15 - 8.5) \div 15 \approx 43\%$, sweatshirts: $(29 - 15) \div 29 \approx 48\%$, slippers: $(19.99 - 8.99) \div 19.99 \approx 55\%$, jeans: $(42.5 - 29.99) \div 42.5 \approx 29\%$, sweaters: $(49.95 - 24) \div 49.95 \approx 52\%$, sweatpants: $(21.5 - 12.5) \div 21.5 \approx 42\%$ **5.** 10 combinations; 6 orders; Sample Response: Number the students on the math team from 1 through 5 and make a list of the possible combinations of 3 students: 123, 124, 125, 134, 135, 145, 234, 235, 245, and 345; there are 3 choices for first, 2 choices for second, and 1 choice for third, so there are $3 \cdot 2 \cdot 1 = 6$ ways the students could finish.

ADDITIONAL ANSWERS

MODULE 1

Section 1, Practice and Application (p. 8)

17.

Pieces of mail received each day for a month	Tally	Frequency
5	ЖІ	6
6	ЖІІ	7
7	Ж	5
8	Ж	5
9	ІІІ	3
10	І	1

18.

Scores on a five-point quiz	Tally	Frequency
2	І	1
3	ІІІІ	4
4	ЖІІ	7
5	ІІІ	3

19.

Sizes of sweatshirts for a softball team	Tally	Frequency
small	ІІІ	3
medium	Ж	5
large	ЖІ	6
extra large	І	1

20.

Neighborhood pets	Tally	Frequency
none	ІІІІ	4
cat	Ж	5
dog	ЖІ	6
fish	ІІ	2
gerbil	І	1
horse	І	1
snake	І	1

Extra Skill Practice

8.

Number of daily phone calls on a month's bill	Tally	Frequency
0	І	1
1	Ж	5
2	ЖІІІІ	9
3	ЖІ	6
4	Ж	5
5	ІІІ	3
6	І	1

9.

Ages of students cleaning up a neighborhood playground	Tally	Frequency
10	ІІ	2
11	ІІІ	3
12	ЖІ	6
13	ІІІ	3
14	Ж	5
15	Ж	5

Section 2, Exploration 1

10. Pattern 1:

,   ;

Number of stories in the building	Total number of squares
1	3
2	6
3	9
4	12
5	15
10	30
90	270

Word Sentence: The total number of squares is the number of stories in the building times 3.

Pattern 2:

Number of squares in the tower	Total number of squares
1	4
2	5
3	6
4	7
5	8
10	13
90	93

Word Sentence: The total number of squares is the number of squares in the tower plus 3.

Pattern 3:

Number of stories in the building	Total number of squares
1	4
2	7
3	10
4	13
5	16
10	31
90	271

Word Sentence: The total number of squares is one more than 3 times the number of stories in the building.

Section 2, Practice and Application (p. 21)

9.

Term number	1	2	3	4
Term	7	14	21	28

If t = the term and n = the term number, then $t = 7n$.; 700

10.

Term number	1	2	3	4
Term	199	198	197	196

If t = the term and n = the term number, then $t = 200 - n$.; 100

38. c.

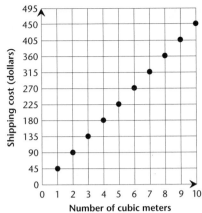

Number of cubic meters

Extra Skill Practice

5.

Term number	1	2	3	4
Term	4	8	12	16

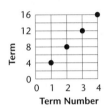

Term Number

If t = the term and n = the term number, then $t = 4n$; 400

6.

Term number	1	2	3	4
Term	999	998	997	996

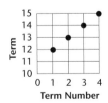

Term Number

If t = the term and n = the term number, then $t = 1000 - n$; 900

7.

Term number	1	2	3	4
Term	12	13	14	15

Term Number

If t = the term and n = the term number, then $t = n + 11$; 111

8.

Term number	1	2	3	4
Term	0	1	2	3

Term Number

If t = the term and n = the term number, then $t = n - 1$; 99

9.

Term number	1	2	3	4
Term	$\frac{1}{2}$	1	$\frac{3}{2}$	2

Term Number

If t = the term and n = the term number, then $t = \frac{1}{2}n$; 50

10.

Term number	1	2	3	4
Term	3	5	7	9

Term Number

If t = the term and n = the term number, then $t = 2n + 1$; 201

Section 3, Exploration 2 (p. 21)

16.   Difference Chart

Blue / Red	1	2	3	4	5	6
1	0	1	2	3	$\frac{(5-1)}{4}$	5
2	1	0	1	2	3	4
3	2	1	0	1	2	3
4	3	2	$\frac{(4-3)}{1}$	0	1	2
5	4	3	2	1	0	1
6	5	4	3	2	1	0

a. 1; 5 **b.** 36 **c.** $\frac{4}{36}$ or $\frac{1}{9}$ **d.** $\frac{4}{36}$ or $\frac{1}{9}$ **e.** $\frac{0}{36}$ **f.** 0

Spiral Review

31.

Term number	1	2	3	4
Term	10	20	30	40

If t = the term and n = the term number, then $t = 10n$; 1000

32.

Term number	1	2	3	4
Term	16	17	18	19

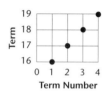

If t = the term and n = the term number, then $t = n + 15$; 115

Review and Assessment

6.

Amount on Money Withdrawn	Tally	Frequency
$10	I	1
$20	II	2
$30	III	3
$40	I	1
$50	II	2
$100	I	1

7. a. The number corresponds to the number of small triangles in the shape.

b.

Term number	1	2	3	4
Term	1	4	9	16

c.

Term number	1	2	3	4
Term	1	4	9	16
Exponential form of term	1^2	2^2	3^2	4^2

Each term is the term number squared. If t = the term and n = the term number, then $t = n^2$. **d.** 25, 5^2, 25 **e.** 2500

8.

Term number	1	2	3	4
Term	6	12	18	24

If t = the term and n = the term number, then $t = 6n$; 600

MODULE 2

Section 1, Exploration 2
20. a.

b.

c.

d.

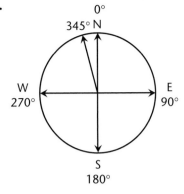

Section 4, Exploration 2

13.

Ambulance Location							
Travel Time (minutes)	0	4	8	12	16	20	24	t
Location (mile marker)	10	14	18	22	26	30	34	m

15., 17. c.

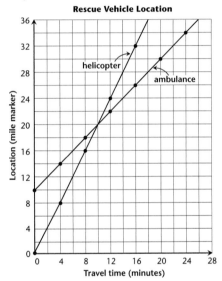

Section 4, Practice and Application (p. 125)
25. a.

Travel Time (hours)	Distance Covered by Covered Wagon (miles)	Distance Covered by Stage Coach (miles)
0	0	0
1	2	5
2	4	10
3	6	15
4	8	20
5	10	25
6	12	30

Travel Time (hours)	Distance Covered by Pony Express (miles)	Distance Covered by Railroad (miles)
0	0	0
1	10	22
2	20	44
3	30	66
4	40	88
5	50	110
6	60	132

25. b. For the covered wagon, $d = 2t$; for the stage coach, $d = 5t$; for the pony express, $d = 10t$; for the railroad, $d = 22t$

25. c–d.

29.

x	–1	0	1
y	2	3	4

30.

x	–1	0	1
y	–5	–4	–3

31.

x	–1	0	1
y	3	2	1

32. c.

Rider 1		Rider 2	
Travel Time (hours)	Distance Traveled (miles)	Travel Time (hours)	Distance Traveled (miles)
0	0	0	0
1	8	1	4
2	16	2	8
3	24	3	12
4	32	4	16

34. b.

35. a. For Bowling Alley A, $y = 17x + 4$ and for Bowling Alley B, $y = 18.5x + 2$

b.

c. when the bowling time is more than $1\frac{1}{3}$ h or

1 h, 20 min **d.** when the bowling time is $1\frac{1}{3}$ h or 1 h, 20 min

Extra Skill Practice

18.

x	–1	0	1
y	–1	0	1

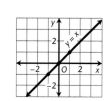

19.

x	–1	0	1
y	0	1	2

20.

x	–1	0	1
y	2	1	0

21.

x	–1	0	1
y	3	4	5

Standardized Testing, Free Response

Sample Response: Because the road from Praitis to Mt. Boris was undergoing construction, the Kartanels had to travel slowly, at an average rate of 50 km/h. The ascent up Mt. Boris, which took them about half an hour, slowed them up even more. Their progress was further delayed when, between 1:30 P.M. and 2:00 P.M., they decided to buy a carry-out lunch at a restaurant they had passed about 10 km back. After picking up lunch, they cautiously descended Mt. Boris on a narrow, twisting road at an average rate of 50 km/h. Once they hit the Flat Lands, they picked up speed and were able to cover the last 125 km of their journey in 1 h.

Review and Assessment

12–15.

MODULE 3

Section 1, Exploration 1
3. a. 3 dots

b.

Number of dots	Jump Size	Number of jumps
12	1	12
12	2	6
12	3	4
12	4	3
12	6	2
12	12	1
13	1	13
13	13	1
14	1	14
14	2	7
14	7	2
14	14	1
15	1	15
15	3	5
15	5	3
15	15	1

c. number of dots = jump size • number of jumps
d. No; There is no whole number that you can multiply by 7 to get 24.

Exploration 3
24. Multiples of 4: 4, 8, 12, 16, 20, 24, 28; Multiples of 5: 5, 10, 15, 20, 25, 30; Multiples of 6: 6, 12, 18, 24, 30; Multiples of 7: 7, 14, 21, 28; Multiples of 8: 8, 16, 24; Multiples of 9: 9, 18, 27; Multiples of 10: 10, 20, 30; Multiples of 11: 11, 22; Multiples of 12: 12, 24; Multiples of 13: 13, 26; Multiples of 14: 14, 28; Multiples of 15: 15, 30; Multiples of 16: 16; Multiples of 17: 17; Multiples of 18: 18; Multiples of 19: 19; Multiples of 20: 20; Multiples of 21: 21; Multiples of 22: 22; Multiples of 23: 23; Multiples of 24: 24; Multiples of 25: 25; Multiples of 26: 26; Multiples of 27: 27; Multiples of 28: 28; Multiples of 29: 29; Multiples of 30: 30; Multiples of 31: 31

Extra Skill Practice
1. 1, 2, 3, 6, 9, 18
2. 1, 2, 3, 4, 6, 8, 12, 24
3. 1, 3, 17, 51
4. 1, 2, 3, 4, 5, 6, 9, 10, 12, 15, 18, 20, 30, 36, 45, 60, 90, 180
5. 1, 2, 3, 4, 6, 8, 9, 12, 18, 24, 36, 72
6. 1, 13, 169
7. 1, 2, 3, 4, 6, 7, 12, 14, 21, 28, 42, 84
8. 1, 3, 5, 15, 25, 75
9. 1, 2, 3, 4, 6, 9, 12, 18, 27, 36, 54, 108
10. 1, 5, 25, 125
11. 1, 7, 13, 91
12. 1, 2, 4, 7, 8, 14, 28, 56
13. 2 • 2 • 2 • 3
14. 5 • 7
15. 3 • 3 • 3 • 3
16. 2 • 2 • 2 • 11
17. 2 • 3 • 3 • 5
18. 3 • 5 • 7
19. 2 • 2 • 2 • 3 • 5
20. 2 • 2 • 2 • 2 • 2 • 2 • 2
21. 2 • 3 • 3 • 3
22. 2 • 2 • 2 • 2 • 5
23. 2 • 2 • 2 • 2 • 3
24. 2 • 2 • 3 • 5

Section 2, Exploration 1
9. a. Sample Response: Do the fractions have the same denominator? **b.** Sample Response: The directions are not necessary; Change the fractions to equivalent fractions with the same denominators.
c. 15 is the least common multiple of 3 and 5, and each of the original fractions can be easily written as an equivalent fraction with 15 as a denominator.
d. the numerators; When comparing fractions with the same denominator, the fraction with the greater numerator is the greater fraction.
11. Sample Response:

Exploration 3
25. a.

Section 2, Practice and Application (p. 171)
14. a. The top row, in which 11 out of 12 segments are shaded, is longer than the bottom row, in which 7 out of 8 segments are shaded.
b.

c. The fraction with the greater denominator is greater.
d. Sample Response: $\frac{17}{18}, \frac{18}{19},$ and $\frac{19}{20}$

29.

30.

45. a. The tree diagram shown uses an egg as the fourth item.

There are 12 possible outcomes.
48. a.

$\frac{1}{2} = \frac{3}{6}$

$\frac{1}{3} = \frac{2}{6}$

b.

$\frac{1}{2} = \frac{3}{6}$
$\frac{1}{3} = +\frac{2}{6}$
$\frac{5}{6}$

c. Take 2 squares away from 3 squares.

Extra Skill Practice
27. a. No; Each number represents a position on the relay team and is to be used only once.
b.

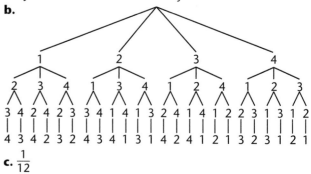

c. $\frac{1}{12}$

Standardized Testing, Performance Task
2. The first row represents the choices for server 1, the second row represents the choices for server 2, and so on, for the four servers. Let Y = yellow cake, C = chocolate cake, S = strawberry cake, and P = pineapple cake.

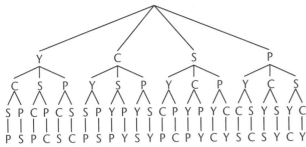

Sample Response: There would be more choices for each server to choose from, so the number of possible ways that they could share the cake would increase.

Section 3, Think About It

1. Sample Response: 7 dollars; Using shopping list #1, the change was 7 dollars $- 5\frac{7}{8}$ dollars $= 1\frac{1}{8}$ dollars. Using shopping list #2 and purchasing a song book for the teacher, the change was 7 dollars $- 6\frac{1}{8}$ dollars $= \frac{7}{8}$ dollar. Using shopping list #3 and purchasing a set of playing cards as a gift, the change was 7 dollars $- 5\frac{5}{8}$ dollars $= 1\frac{3}{8}$ dollars.

Section 4, Exploration 2

21. a. Change the exponent to any integer greater than 63; No; The exponent can always be increased to produce a greater positive number. **b.** Use negative exponents; No; The exponent can always be decreased to produce a smaller positive number.

Section 5, Exploration 2

18. Sample estimates are given. Check students' actual measurements. Width of chalkboard: 1 m, length of chalkboard: 4 m, height of classroom: 3 m, length of classroom: 7 m, width of classroom: 5 m, height of door: 2 m, width of door: 1 m

Working on the Module Project

7. Sample Response: Find what numbers occur most frequently; Look for double letters.

8., 10. a.

Code number	Code letter	Code letter's position in the alphabet	Decoded letter's position in the alphabet	Decoded letter
23	T	20	3	C
23	H	8	15	O
5	A	1	4	D
19	N	14	5	E
30	K	11	19	S
26	Y	25	1	A
33	O	15	18	R
26	U	21	5	E
26	T	20	6	F
29	H	8	21	U
15	A	1	14	N

9. a. code number, shift, decoded letter's position in the alphabet **b.** To find the shift for the third number on the list, look at the third letter in the message. Since that letter is A and A is the first letter in the alphabet, $s = 1$. **c.** E

Section 6, Exploration 1

3. Accept reasonable estimates. Sample responses are given. Philippines: 27 mm, 27 mm, 27 mm; Sudan: 27 mm, 23 mm, 23 mm; Tanzania: 20 mm, 29 mm, 35 mm; Equatorial Guinea: 27 mm, 17 mm, 17 mm; Bahamas: 27 mm, 23 mm, 23 mm; Trinidad and Tobago: 27 mm, 32 mm, 42 mm Group 1: Philippines; 27, 27, 27; All sides of the triangles are the same length. Group 2: Sudan, Bahamas, Equatorial Guinea; 27, 23, 23 and 27, 23, 23 and 27, 17, 17; Two sides of each triangle are the same length. Group 3: Tanzania, Trinidad and Tobago; 20, 29, 35 and 27, 32, 42; No sides of the triangles are the same length.

Review and Assessment

14. a.

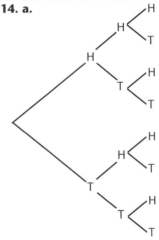

MODULE 4

Section 3, Exploration 2

15. a. It is the mirror image of $\triangle ABC$; It has the same size and shape as the triangle on the right side of the fold and it appears directly on top of it. **b.** Sample Response: The reflection will move closer to $\triangle ABC$; The reflection will move farther away from $\triangle ABC$.

20. a. Draw a segment connecting two corresponding points on the butterflies. Find the midpoint of the segment. Draw a line perpendicular to the connecting segment through its midpoint.

b.

Section 3, Extension

45. a. Sample Response: about $\frac{1}{2}$ in. below the base of the shaded figure along a vertical line through the dot on the figure; about 120° **b.** Check students' work. **c.** Check students' work. **d.** The angles are right angles. **e.** The distances are about the same. **f.** Check students' work. **g.** It is a little bit closer to the base of the shaded figure. **h.** about 135°; It is a little greater than the estimate.

Section 5, Practice and Application (p. 300)

16. a. Check students' work. **b.** Transformation A: The width will be 3 times that of the original figure; Transformation B: The image will be 2 units to the left of the original figure; Transformation C: The height will be $\frac{1}{4}$ that of the original figure; Transformation D: Both the width and the height will be 3 times that of the original figure. **c.** Check students' drawings. Vertices should be as follows: Transformation A: $W'(-3, 0)$, $X'(-3, 4)$, $Y'(3, 4)$, $Z'(3, 0)$; Transformation B: $W'(-3, 0)$, $X'(-3, 4)$, $Y'(-1, 4)$, $Z'(-1, 0)$; Transformation C: $W'(-1, 0)$, $X'(-1, 1)$, $Y'(1, 1)$, $Z'(1, 0)$; Transformation D: $W'(-3, 0)$, $X'(-3, 12)$, $Y'(3, 12)$, $Z'(3, 0)$; The images produced by transformations B and D are similar to *WXYZ* because both images have the same shape as *WXYZ*.

37.
119

Extra Skill Practice

11. Check students' work. The sketch should be the same horizontal length and $\frac{1}{4}$ of the vertical length.

Review and Assessment

47. Sample Response: All three produce images that are the same size as the original figure. The image may have the same shape or be the mirror image (the same shape but turned over). An image produced by a rotation or translation has the same orientation as the original figure. An image produced by a reflection has its orientation reversed. Check students' drawings.

MODULE 5

Section 2, Exploration 3
21.

Section 2, Practice and Application (p. 337)
14. a–b.

c. Sample Response: about 225 ft² to 250 ft²

15. a–b.

c. Sample Response: about $400

Section 3, Practice and Application (p. 353)
1.

```
0        3      6 7 8 9      12 commercials
├┼┼┼┼┼┼┼┼┼┼┼┼┼┤
0%      25%     50%↑66⅔%↑    100% percent
                  58%   75%
```

Working on the Module Project

6. Sample Response: My friends had a greater chance of being surveyed than other people did; Since all my friends are girls who play sports, neither girls who do not play sports nor boys were represented.

Standardized Testing, Performance Task

Sample Response: The table shows students' attitudes toward school lunches during one week. A survey of 20–28 students each day was asked to rate the lunches as Good, OK, or Not good. One conclusion is that students liked the lunches better on Monday to Wednesday than on Thursday and Friday.

Section 4, Exploration 1
4. a.

	Fraction	Decimal	%
Sheryl Swoopes	$\frac{27}{33}$	0.818	81.8%
Jennifer Azzi	$\frac{58}{64}$	0.906	90.6%
Nikki McCray	$\frac{28}{35}$	0.8	80%
Katy Steding	$\frac{50}{60}$	0.833	83.3%
Teresa Edwards	$\frac{13}{15}$	0.867	86.7%

b. Jennifer Azzi; Sample Response: the same **c.** decimals or percents

Exploration 3
21. a.

22. a.

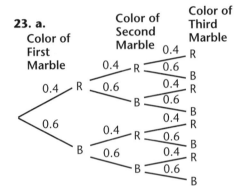

b. about 0.085; It is half as great; She now has only 1 chance, rather than 2 chances, to make exactly 1 free throw.

Section 4, Practice and Application (p. 368)
23. a.

Color of First Marble · Color of Second Marble · Color of Third Marble

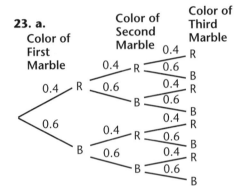

24. a.

Color of First Marble · Color of Second Marble · Color of Third Marble

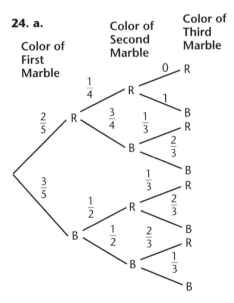

b. $P(R, R, R) = 0$; $P(B, B, B) = \frac{1}{10}$; $P(B, R, B) = \frac{1}{5}$; $P(R, R, B) = \frac{1}{10}$; $P(\text{exactly 2 R}) = \frac{3}{10}$; $P(\text{at least 1 R}) = \frac{9}{10}$

Review and Assessment
5.

Areas of State Parks in 9 States

```
0 | 9          7 | 5 represents 75,000 acres
1 |
2 | 5
3 |
4 | 1  2  7
5 | 0  7
6 | 6
7 | 5
```

15.

Some Notable Modern Bridges

MODULE 6

Section 2, Think About It
1. b.

Section 2, Key Concepts
32. a. Sample Response:

Section 2, Practice and Application (p. 405)
13. a. Sample Response:

Extra Skill Practice

11. a.

Section 4, Extension

35.

Polygon	Name of polygon	Number of sides	Number of triangles formed by the diagonals from 1 vertex	Sum of the measures of the angles
	triangle	3	1	180°
	quadrilateral	4	2	360°
	pentagon	5	3	540°
	hexagon	6	4	720°
	heptagon	7	5	900°
	octagon	8	6	1080°

Section 5, Exploration 1

8. a–b. Sample Response:

Length	Width	Height	Area of the base	Volume	Surface area of the prism
1 cm	18 cm	2 cm	18 cm²	36 cm³	112 cm²
2 cm	9 cm	2 cm	18 cm²	36 cm³	80 cm²
3 cm	6 cm	2 cm	18cm²	36 cm³	72 cm²
4 cm	9 cm	1 cm	36 cm²	36 cm³	98 cm²
6 cm	6 cm	1 cm	36 cm²	36 cm³	96 cm²
1 cm	1 cm	36 cm	1 cm²	36 cm³	146 cm²
1 cm	3 cm	12 cm	3 cm²	36 cm³	102 cm²
3 cm	4 cm	3 cm	12 cm²	36 cm³	66 cm²

11. d–e.

Number of layers	Area of base	Height	Volume
1	3 cm^2	1 cm	3 cm^3
2	3 cm^2	2 cm	6 cm^3
3	3 cm^2	3 cm	9 cm^3
4	3 cm^2	4 cm	12 cm^3
5	3 cm^2	5 cm	15 cm^3

Exploration 3

25. a.

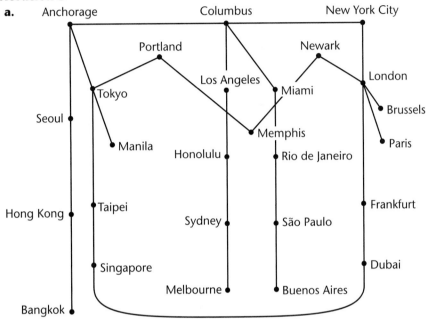

Extension 36.

Network	Number of odd vertices	Number of even vertices	Traversable? (*yes* or *no*)
	2	4	Yes
	2	4	Yes
	2	4	Yes
	0	9	Yes
	4	1	No
	2	1	Yes
	4	2	No

A network is transversable if it has at most 2 odd vertices; Check students' work; Check students' work.

Completing the Module Project

6. Sample Response:

	Exterior surface area	Weight	Sail loading
Wild Wing 1	0.15 ft²	0.17 oz	1.1 oz/ft²
Wild Wing 2	0.6 ft²	0.68 oz	1.1 oz/ft²

Review and Assessment

8. Sample Response:

MODULE 7

Section 1, Exploration 3

17. a. about half the original length; The line would appear to be steeper. **b.** The line would appear to be less steep.

c.

Sample Response: My predictions were correct.

Section 1, Practice and Application (p. 465)

9. a.

b	C
75	10.2
100	13.6
150	20.4
200	27.2

b.

c. 0.136 **d.** Answers will vary. Check students' work.

10. a. Sample Response: Use intervals of 10 s from 0 s to 60 s on the horizontal axis in order to include a fairly wide range of useful data on the graph. Use intervals of 6000 beats from 0 to 36,000 beats on the vertical axis since the frequencies of wing beats for 10 s intervals will be multiples of 6000.

b. Sample Response:

11. a. Answers will vary. Sample Response: a horizontal scale from 75–200 lb for both graphs; vertical scales of 5–14 Cal for sleeping, and 14–38 Cal for preparing food.

b. Sample responses are given.

Beginning the Module Project

2. a. Answers will vary. Sample responses are given. Bar graph: the heights of the bars show the number of people riding bicycles among the different age groups; pictograph: the number of symbols show the number of people riding bicycles among the different age groups. circle graph: the size of each sector and the percentages given allow you to compare the number of people riding bicycles among the different age groups.

b. Sample responses are given. Yes; bar graph: the

heights of the bars are about the same, although the height for the 12–17 year olds is slightly higher than the height for the 25–34 year olds; pictograph: the number of symbols used is about the same, although there are 4 full symbols for the 12–17 year olds and just more than $3\frac{1}{2}$ symbols for the 25–34 year olds; circle graph: the sizes of the sectors are about the same, although the percent of 12–17 year olds is 19%, while the percent of 25–34 year olds is only 17%.

Extra Skill Practice

9. Yes; Different scales are used on the vertical axes. Sample Response:

Calories Used in Reading for 10 min

Calories Used in Dancing for 10 min

Section 2, Spiral Review

32. Possible Answers: Let r = the resting heart rate in beats per minute.

Canary: $500 \le r \le 800$

Mouse: $300 \le r \le 500$

Chicken: $300 \le r \le 350$

Cat: $120 \le r \le 140$

Dog: $70 \le r \le 120$

Person: $60 \le r \le 80$

Lion: $40 \le r \le 50$

Elephant: $25 \le r \le 50$

Extended Exploration

Sample Response: If 97 is used as the additional number, the only winning set of numbers will be a 97 and a 3. If 1000 of each of those bottle cap numbers is issued, there is the possibility of 1000 people winning. The numbers of other bottle cap numbers issued doesn't matter; I started by adding 1 to the list, but realized there were then too many combinations of numbers that had a sum of 100. So, I started working from the other end of the list.

Section 4, Practice and Application, (p. 507)

12. Sample Response:

14. Yes; A sample graph is given using an unweighted average of the sleep times for school nights and weekend nights.

Sleep Time

Working on the Module Project

4. Sample Responses are given. Vigorous exercise is most popular at all grade levels. Yes; On average, 12th graders participate in exercise activities much less than 9th graders. Yes; Participation in exercise activities declines from 9th grade to 12th grade. Students participate in more than one type of exercise.

5. Sample Response:

Participation in Exercise Activities

Extra Skill Practice

9. a. Sample Response: a histogram

b.

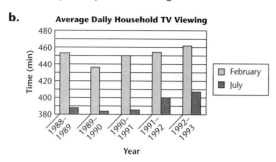

Average Daily Household TV Viewing

c. Sample Response: Over the years, the trends for February and July were the same. The time spent watching TV in February was greater than that in July for all years. The time spent watching TV in February and in July declined in 1989–1990.

Standardized Testing, Performance Task

1. Sample responses are given. **a:** How different categories of values compare; data values are represented by height of bars in the graph. **b:** Extreme values, median, how the data values cluster; stem values are listed vertically and leaves are listed horizontally beside the corresponding stem. **c:** The percent of the total that the data value represents; the values are drawn as areas in a circle. **d:** The minimum, lower quartile, median, upper quartile, maximum, any extreme values; The five values are calculated from the data and plotted above a number line. Then the box and whiskers are drawn. **e:** Specific data values and how they increase or decrease from one to the next; Data points are plotted on a two-dimensional grid. **f:** How different categories of values compare; Data intervals are made on the horizontal axis and the corresponding data values are shown as the heights of the bars.

2. Sample responses are given. **a:** Yes; different vertical scales could be used and the bars could be made different widths. **b:** Yes; the stems chosen could be of various intervals. **c:** No. **d:** No. **e:** Yes; different horizontal and vertical scales could be used to display the data. **f:** Yes; different horizontal and vertical scales could be used and the bars could be made different widths.

MODULE 8

Section 3, Exploration 2

12. d.

Mo	Ar Qu An Sa Cr Ch Ol	Mo, Ar Mo, Qu Mo, An Mo, Sa Mo, Cr Mo, Ch Mo, Ol	7
Ar	Qu An Sa Cr Ch Ol	Ar, Qu Ar, An Ar, Sa Ar, Cr Ar, Ch Ar, Ol	6
Qu	An Sa Cr Ch Ol	Qu, An Qu, Sa Qu, Cr Qu, Ch Qu, Ol	5
An	Sa Cr Ch Ol	An, Sa An, Cr An, Ch An, Ol	4
Sa	Cr Ch Ol	Sa, Cr Sa, Ch Sa, Ol	3
Cr	Ch Ol	Cr, Ch Cr, Ol	2
Ch	Ol	Ch, Ol	1

The number of combinations goes down by one each time.

Section 3, Practice and Application (p. 559)

13. a. apple–banana–kiwi–orange, apple–banana–kiwi–pear, apple–banana–orange–pear, apple–kiwi–orange–pear, banana–kiwi–orange–pear, **b.** 3 out of five: apple–banana–kiwi, apple–banana–orange, apple–banana–pear, apple–kiwi–orange, apple–kiwi–pear, apple–orange–pear, banana–kiwi–orange, banana–kiwi–pear, banana–orange–pear, kiwi–orange–pear; 2 out of five: apple–banana, apple–kiwi, apple–orange, apple–pear, banana–kiwi, banana–orange, banana–pear, kiwi–orange, kiwi–pear, orange–pear; 1 out of five: apple, banana, kiwi, orange, pear

14. b.

1	7	21	35	35	21	7	1	
1	8	28	56	70	56	28	8	1

1	9	36	84	126	126	84	36	9	1

Section 3, Extra Skill Practice

9. Sue–Flora and Hiroko–Yuki, Sue–Hiroko and Flora–Yuki, Sue–Yuki and Flora–Hiroko

Section 4, Exploration 2

16. 3.1 m³
12.6 m³
28.3 m³
50.3 m³
78.5 m³
113.1 m³
153.9 m³
201.1 m³
254.5 m³
314.2 m³

Volumes of Cylinders and Cones with a Height of 1 m

Section 4, Practice and Application (p. 572)

4.

Section 4, Review and Assessment

2. Mono Lake–Joshua Tree–Sequoia, Mono Lake–Sequoia–Joshua Tree, Joshua Tree–Mono Lake–Sequoia, Joshua Tree–Sequoia–Mono Lake, Sequoia–Joshua Tree–Mono Lake, Sequoia–Mono Lake–Joshua Tree

3. Spanish–art–social studies, Spanish–social studies–art, social studies–art–Spanish, social studies–Spanish–art, art–Spanish–social studies, art–social studies–Spanish

19. BOOT, BOTO, BTOO, TBOO, TOBO, TOOB, OOTB, OOBT, OTBO, OBTO, OTOB, OBOT

20. BELLE, BEELL, BELEL, BLLEE, BLELE, BLEEL, LLEBE, LLBEE, LLEEB, LEBEL, LEBLE, LELBE, LELEB, LEEBL, LEELB, LBLEE, LBEEL, LBELE, ELELB, ELEBL, ELBEL, ELLEB, ELLBE, ELBLE, EBELL, EBLEL, EBLLE, EELLB, EELBL, EEBLL

21. NANNY, NANYN, NAYNN, NYANN, NYNAN, NYNNA, NNANY, NNAYN, NNYAN, NNYNA, NNNAY, NNNYA, ANNNY, AYNNN, ANYNN, ANNYN, YANNN, YNANN, YNNAN, YNNNA

22. c. They are the same; To choose a group of two dogs from the 5 dogs, you can either choose the 2 that are in the group or you can choose the 2 that are not. So, the number of groups of 2 dogs is the same as the number of possible groups of 3 dogs.

Practicing Test-Taking Skills (p. 608)

1. 21 acts; $80 \div (2\frac{1}{2} + 1\frac{1}{4}) = 80 \div 3\frac{3}{4} = 80 \cdot \frac{4}{15} = \frac{64}{3} = 21\frac{1}{3}$ **2.** 16 packages; 4 bottles of shampoo and 6 bars of soap; Factors of 64 = 1, 2, 4, 8, 16, 32, 64. Factors 96 = 1, 2, 3, 4, 6, 16, 24, 32, 48, 96. The greatest number by which both 64 and 96 are divisible is 16, so 16 packages can be put together; $\frac{64}{16}$, or 4 bottles of shampoo and $\frac{96}{16}$, or 6 bars of soap should be in each package. **3.** the girls' team; You need to find the fraction of games that each team won. For each team, divide the number of games won by the total number of games played. Girls' team: $6 \div (6 + 4) = \frac{6}{10} = \frac{3}{5}$. Boys' team: $7 \div (7 + 5) = \frac{7}{12}$; $\frac{3}{5} = \frac{3 \cdot 12}{5 \cdot 12} = \frac{36}{60}$, $\frac{7 \cdot 5}{12 \cdot 5} = \frac{35}{60}$, so $\frac{3}{5} > \frac{7}{12}$. **4.** No; you need to add the four distances Darren ran, and see if the total is at least 8 miles; $1 + 1\frac{3}{4} + 2\frac{1}{4} + 2\frac{1}{2} = 7\frac{1}{2}$ mi. **5.** 3 volunteers; $\frac{1}{3}$ of 18 volunteers, or 6, painted. That leaves 18 − 6 = 12 volunteers. $\frac{3}{4}$ of 12 volunteers, or 9, raked leaves. That leaves 12 − 9 = 3 volunteers who served lunch.

6.

−1C°; If the readings are listed in increasing order, −18, −10, −7, 5, 9, 13, the two middle numbers are −7 and 5, so the median is $\frac{-7 + 5}{2} = \frac{-2}{2} = -1$.

7. Let c = the total cost. $c = 4x + 2.25$; 5 games; Substitute 22.25 for c. $22.25 = 4x + 2.25$, $22.25 - 2.25 = 4x$, $20 = 4x$, and $x = 5$. Hanna bowled 5 games. **8.** 5π in. or approximately 15.7 in.; Circumference of first hoop = 23π. Circumference of second hoop = 18π. $23\pi - 18\pi = 5\pi$ in. **9.** Yes; the sum of the lengths of the two shortest segments, 3.9 cm, is greater than the length of the longest segment, 3.5 cm.

Building Test-Taking Skills (p. 613)

1. Partial credit; the calculations for the number of cans that can be packed flat in the box are correct, but no reasoning is given. The greatest number of cans that can be packed is incorrect; the second orientation was not considered. To earn full credit, explain the reasoning behind the calculations. Do the calculations for the number of cans that can be packed on their sides, which makes packing 54 cans possible.

Practicing Test-Taking Skills (p. 614)

1. the large tub of popcorn; volume of box = $6 \cdot 3 \cdot 8 = 144$ in.³; price per cubic inch of popcorn = $3.75 \div 144 \approx$ \$.026; volume of tub = $\pi(4)^2(5) \approx 251$ in.³; price per cubic inch of popcorn = $5.25 \div 251 \approx$ \$.021; Since \$.021 < \$.026, the large tub of popcorn is the better buy. **2.** about 58.79 in.³; about 4 cups; $V = \pi(1.45)^2(8.9) \approx 58.79$ in.³; the number of fluid ounces = $58.79 \cdot 0.544 \approx 31.98$ fl oz; 1 c = 8 fl oz, so 31.98 fl $\approx$ 4 cups. **3.** slippers; Find the percent of change for each item. T-shirts: $(15 - 8.5) \div 15 \approx 43\%$, sweatshirts: $(29 - 15) \div 29 \approx 48\%$, slippers: $(19.99 - 8.99) \div 19.99 \approx 55\%$, jeans: $(42.5 - 29.99) \div 42.5 \approx 29\%$, sweaters:

$(49.95 - 24) \div 49.95 \approx 52\%$, sweatpants: $(21.5 - 12.5) \div 21.5 \approx 42\%$ **4.** Italy: 30%, France: 28%, Germany: 16%, Ireland: 14%, Other: 12%; 105 students out of 350 students responded *Italy*, so that percent is $\frac{105}{350} \approx 0.30 = 30\%$. 98 out of 350 students responded *France*, so that percent is $\frac{98}{350} \approx 0.28 = 28\%$. 56 out of 350, or $\frac{56}{350} \approx 0.16 = 16\%$ responded *Germany*. 49 out of 350, or $\frac{49}{350} \approx 0.14 = 14\%$ responded *Ireland* and $\frac{42}{350} \approx 0.12 = 12\%$ responded *Other*. To add a sector for Spain, find the percent of students who answered Spain: $35 \div 350 = 0.1 = 10\%$. Since 10% of 360 is 36, divide the "Other" sector into two sectors, one of which has an angle measure of 36°. Label the 36° sector "Spain" and the remaining sector "Other." **5.** 10 combinations; 6 orders; Sample Response: Number the students on the math team from 1 through 5 and make a list of the possible combinations of 3 students: 123, 124, 125, 134, 135, 145, 234, 235, 245, and 345; there are 3 choices for first, 2 choices for second, and 1 choice for third, so there are $3 \cdot 2 \cdot 1 = 6$ ways the students could finish.

Ages at a Family Reunion (Years)

6. 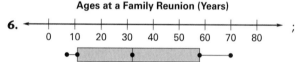 ;

about 50%; You can tell because the lower quartile, median, and upper quartile divide the data into four groups of approximately equal size. The data between the lower quartile, 11, and the upper quartile, 58, make up 2 of the 4 groups, or 50%.